The Evolution of Paleontological Art

edited by

Renee M. Clary
Department of Geosciences
Mississippi State University, Box 5448
Mississippi State, Mississippi 39762, USA

Gary D. Rosenberg
Geology Department, Milwaukee Public Museum
800 West Wells Street
Milwaukee, Wisconsin 53233, USA
and Earth Sciences Department
Indiana University–Purdue University
Indianapolis 46202, USA

Dallas C. Evans
Purdue Extension Marion County
Discovery Hall, Suite 201, 1202 East 38th Street
Indianapolis, Indiana 46205, USA

THE
GEOLOGICAL
SOCIETY
OF AMERICA®

Memoir 218

3300 Penrose Place, P.O. Box 9140 ▪ Boulder, Colorado 80301-9140, USA

2022

Published by The Geological Society of America, Inc.
3300 Penrose Place, P.O. Box 9140, Boulder, Colorado 80301-9140, USA
www.geosociety.org

Printed in U.S.A.

GSA Books Science Editors: Joan Florsheim, Christian Koeberl, and Nancy Riggs

Library of Congress Cataloging-in-Publication Data
Names: Clary, R. M. (Renee M.), editor. | Rosenberg, Gary D., editor. | Evans, Dallas C., editor.
Title: The evolution of paleontological art / edited by Renee M. Clary, Department of Geosciences, Mississippi State University, Box 5448, Mississippi State, Mississippi 39762, USA, Gary D. Rosenberg, Geology Dept., Milwaukee Public Museum, Wisconsin, 53202, Dallas C. Evans, The Children's Museum of Indianapolis, 3000 North Meridian Street, Indianapolis, Indiana, 46208, USA.
Description: Boulder, Colorado : The Geological Society of America, 2022. | Series: Memoir ; 218 | Includes bibliographical references. | Summary: "This volume samples the history of art about fossils—and the visual conceptualization of their significance—starting with biblical and mythological depictions, extending to renditions of ancient life in long-vanished habitats, and on to a modern understanding that paleoart conveys lessons for the betterment of the human condition. Twenty-nine chapters illustrate how art about fossils has come to be a significant teaching tool not only about evolution of past life, but also about conservation of our planet for the benefit of future generations"— Provided by publisher.
Identifiers: LCCN 2021048980 (print) | LCCN 2021048981 (ebook) | ISBN 9780813712185 (hardcover) | ISBN 9780813782188 (ebook)
Subjects: LCSH: Paleoart—History.
Classification: LCC QE714.2 .E96 2021 (print) | LCC QE714.2 (ebook) | DDC 560.22/2—dc23/eng/20211109
LC record available at https://lccn.loc.gov/2021048980
LC ebook record available at https://lccn.loc.gov/2021048981

Cover: *Cretaceous Life of New Jersey* by Benjamin Waterhouse Hawkins. 1877. Oil on canvas, 81 × 221.6 cm (31 7/8 in. × 87 ¼ in). Princeton University, Department of Geosciences, Guyot Hall, PP336. Credit: Princeton University Art Museum / Art Resource, NY.

We dedicate
GSA Memoir 218
to the artist in all scientists
and the scientist in all artists,
for you draw everyone
into the wonders and joys
of paleontology.

Contents

Preface and acknowledgments

The Evolution of Paleontological Art is the extension of a topical session convened during the 2018 annual meeting of the Geological Society of America (GSA) in Indianapolis, Indiana. We solicited additional submissions from the United States and beyond, and are delighted to include contributions from Eastern as well as Western Europe and from as far away as India and Australia.

The inspiration for the original topical session came from our conference location: The Children's Museum of Indianapolis is the repository for the Lazendorf collection, the world's largest collection of paleontological art. Beyond its illustrative value, the history of paleontological art demonstrates the progression of paleontological knowledge and artistic advancements, from canvas to computer graphics. It encompasses the history and philosophy of geology, identity, classification, and conceptualization of fossils and their life habitats, art, and graphic design, and acknowledges the pedagogical value of erroneous as well as correct interpretations of fossils throughout the history of our science. Importantly, paleoart, in its multiple venues and variations in quality, demonstrates that science is an endeavor in which everyone can participate.

The topical session was sponsored by the GSA History and Philosophy of Geology Division, History of Earth Sciences Society, Paleontological Society, Cushman Foundation, Paleontological Research Institution, and National Earth Science Teachers Association. The GSA History and Philosophy of Geology Division generously provided financial assistance for our keynote speaker.

A generous contribution to underwrite the publication of color images in this volume was made by the GSA History and Philosophy of Geology Division from the Mary C. Rabbitt Bequest. Additional donations came from Mississippi State University, Department of Geosciences, and from the History of Geology Group (HOGG) of the Geological Society of London. Several of our authors and/or their associated professional institutions also contributed toward color image reproduction and page costs of the volume.

We thank our many colleagues who served as reviewers of the submitted manuscripts. April Leo, managing editor for GSA Books; Jon Raessler, GSA circulation specialist; and Christian Koeberl, GSA Books science editor, provided guidance and assistance as we navigated this memoir from its conceptualization to its final publication. We are especially indebted to the tireless efforts and substantial assistance of April Leo.

We are saddened by the untimely loss of authors Dr. Matthew Parkes and Dr. Patrick Getty before publication of this volume and before we could celebrate the realization of their important contributions.

Renee M. Clary, Gary D. Rosenberg, and Dallas C. Evans, *Volume Editors*

The Geological Society of America
Memoir 218

Drawing things *together* with paleontological art*

Renee M. Clary
Department of Geosciences, Mississippi State University, Box 5448, Mississippi State, Mississippi 39762, USA

Gary D. Rosenberg
Geology Department, Milwaukee Public Museum, 800 W. Wells Street, Milwaukee, Wisconsin 53233, USA, and *Earth Sciences Department, Indiana University–Purdue University, Indianapolis 46202, USA*

Dallas C. Evans
Purdue Extension Marion County, Discovery Hall, Suite 201, 1202 East 38th Street, Indianapolis, Indiana 46205, USA

THE SIGNIFICANCE OF PALEONTOLOGICAL ART

A scientific discipline cannot exist without a written and *visual* language; therefore, if we "want to understand what draws *things* together," we must investigate "what *draws* things *together*" (Latour, 1990, p. 60). The visual language of geology—and its subdiscipline, paleontology—helped establish an optical consistency, or standardized visual representation, for the science (Rudwick, 1976, 1992).

Paleontological art (or in its abbreviated form, paleoart) is significant because it brings ancient life and lost worlds to light. Fossils and their representative paleoart also communicate critical paleontological concepts, including geologic time, biodiversity, evolution, and extinction. When paleoart is viewed as a historical progression, it documents the evolving science of paleontology (Clary and Wandersee, 2011). Once paleoartists depict any extinct organism beyond its direct fossil evidence, creativity and artistic license become important variables. Hence, the final artwork can represent the synergistic tension between the artist and supervising scientist, and in some modern paleoart interpretations, the tension between the artist and society.

PALEONTOLOGICAL ART AS PALEONTOLOGICAL PROXY

From the late eighteenth through early nineteenth centuries, early modern geological visualizations were pictorial, documenting objects as proxies of the actual specimens (Clary and Wandersee, 2015). Although intended by the artist to record objects and landscapes in a similar fashion as a modern traveler's photographs (Hineline, 1993), the images were not always accurate representations. Fossil illustrations could be unreliable because of "fossil preservation, artistic ability, scientific understanding, or the politics of publication" (Monaghan, 2001, p. 90). However, proxies allowed fossils to be visually shared; people could examine fossil images when they did not have access to the physical specimens. In one of the early scientific studies of fossils, paleontologist (and apothecary surgeon) James Parkinson (1755–1824) produced three volumes of beautifully illustrated fossil organisms (Lewis, Chapter 3). (Parkinson is best recognized as the surgeon who researched and described the shaking palsy that bears his name.) Parkinson's paleontology books remained popular 25 years after he died owing to Samuel Springsguth's (1769–184?) exceptional illustrations, even though the volumes' text had been rendered archaic after subsequent research by others (Lewis, Chapter 3).

Paleoart is not constrained within a two-dimensional 'flatland,' and can enter the realm of three-dimensional sculptures or models. Ward's Natural Science Establishment of Rochester, New York, pioneered three-dimensional reconstructions of exceptional fossil specimens for sale to museums and classroom use in the 1860s; these identical models provided standardized views of the organisms for students (Brice, Chapter 15).

Larger three-dimensional sculptures, life-sized interpretations of extinct organisms intended for public display, attracted a wider audience to experience the wonders of paleontology in person. Benjamin Waterhouse Hawkins (1807–1894) created the first models of dinosaurs and other extinct organisms for the

*Citations in this introduction are to papers in this Memoir unless stated otherwise.

Clary, R.M., Rosenberg, G.D., and Evans, D.C., 2021, *Drawing* things *together* with paleontological art, *in* Clary, R.M., Rosenberg, G.D., and Evans, D.C., eds., The Evolution of Paleontological Art: Geological Society of America Memoir 218, p. 1–8, https://doi.org/10.1130/2021.1218(01).

Crystal Palace in London, officially unveiled in 1854 (Peck and Rowland, Chapter 17). The models were immensely popular, attracting 40,000 to the opening ceremony alone.

PUBLIC FASCINATION WITH PALEONTOLOGICAL ART

Famous paleoartist Charles R. Knight (1874–1953) asserted that the impetus for paleontological art arose when scientists "have at last come to realize that what they had to offer in the way of information and interest must not be confined to conversations among themselves or hidden away in bulky volumes. On the contrary, they now see that it should be brought out, dusted off, as it were, and spread before the fascinated gaze of a hitherto totally uninformed public" (Knight, 1935, p. vii). Indeed, as he predicted, the public was fascinated with extinct organisms—both in fossil displays and interpreted paleoart—and the popular interest and demand fueled public displays of fossils as well as of their paleoartistic reconstructions.

The style of paleoart that emerged was varied, however. Victorian natural science museums appropriated a medieval metaphorical "Book of Nature" design through which visitors could experience exhibits of the natural world to understand God's creation. These museums' architectural designs functioned as the binding and layout of the book, and decorative paintings and sculptures served as the 'visual foreword,' guiding visitors as to how they should 'read' the objects on display (Jovanovic-Kruspel and Harzhauser, Chapter 13). The Natural History Museum Vienna in Austria utilized the book metaphor when construction began in 1871, but exhibits would be within a scientifically based historicity of nature. Rudolf Weyr sculpted 24 mythological figures to show the evolution of life forms through geologic time, from a figure draped in algae through those holding extinct Cenozoic mammal skulls. Weyr's artistic interpretation is most evident in the Mesozoic sculptures, where mythical figures struggle to control a living Mesozoic pterosaur and ichthyosaur, represented with varying degrees of scientific accuracy. The result is that the hall's sculptures—the dominating artistic element—merged the mythical with the scientific for a "science fiction" paleoart presentation (Jovanovic-Kruspel and Harzhauser, Chapter 13).

Dinosaur paleoart remained popular in books and museums and progressed to representations within other media for entertainment—eventually including television and movies. In 1874, Benjamin Waterhouse Hawkins began painting a series of prehistoric scenes for the College of New Jersey, later to become Princeton University. Our cover art (cover design by Amy Moe-Hoffman), features part of Hawkins' 1877 *Cretaceous Life of New Jersey* (Fig. 1). The cover image focuses upon a line of hadrosaurs, marching toward the lake to escape attacking tyrannosaurids.

Before Hawkins painted this picture, hadrosaurs had been restored as advanced iguanodontids—terrestrial herbivores. But because hadrosaurs lacked armor, fangs, or claws, Edward Drinker Cope (1840–1897) proposed them as large, slow-moving targets that would need to seek an aqueous refuge to avoid predators. Hawkins' painting was an early illustration of what would become the default, but incorrect, assumption for hadrosaurs. The large Jurassic sauropods were relegated to the same fate, and commonly reconstructed as helpless out of water. Hawkins may have envisioned the tyrannosaurid group correctly, though. Recent research indicated that tyrannosaurids might have hunted cooperatively in packs, in contrast to earlier hypotheses of solitary hunting or even scavenging behavior (Titus et al., 2021).

Through the 1960s, dinosaurs were illustrated as large, ponderous reptiles, but John Ostrom's and Robert Bakker's reconstructions of *Deinonychus* as an active predator catalyzed the reinterpretation of dinosaurs and led to a "dinosaur renaissance" (Allmon, Chapter 23). Bakker further challenged the notion that sauropods were uncomfortable out of water. The paleoart that ensued was further inspired by new fossil finds in China, including feathered dinosaurs that documented the close relationship between extinct theropod dinosaurs and their avian descendants. Scientists later found preserved melanosomes in fossil feathers that enabled them to interpret color patterns from extinct organisms (Vinther et al., 2008). Paleoartists followed advances in understanding dinosaur anatomy and reconstructed agile, feathered dinosaurs—and creatively experimented with color, skin patterns, textures, and feathers to produce "extreme dinosaur" proxies (Allmon, Chapter 23). The standardized visual representation of dinosaur paleoart had shifted.

PALEONTOLOGICAL ART REFLECTS AN EVOLVING SCIENCE

A historical progression of dinosaur and other fossil paleoart documents the evolution of the scientific discipline as data accumulated. With additional fossil discoveries, new scientific interpretations—whether correct or incorrect—guide the artistic product (Sendino, Chapter 10; Krzywiec and Arndt, Chapter 11; Goldstein and Getty, Chapter 16; Allmon, Chapter 23). The earliest fossil drawings of invertebrates—the first fossils ever artistically depicted—recorded a general shape, but with advancing knowledge and technologies, living positions of the fossil organisms became the standard visual representation, and organisms' important taxonomic details were added (Sendino, Chapter 10).

Not all early interpretations were scientific. Mythological interpretations were initially invoked for dinosaur tracks, such as sauropod tracks interpreted as being formed by a giant mule that carried the Virgin Mary up a hill (Goldstein and Getty, Chapter 16). Even when scientists recognized the affiliation of a dinosaur trackmaker, only 'relevant' information was included in the artistic rendition of it; what is considered 'relevant' has changed over time. Therefore, the paleoart information and details record the perceived utility of fossil objects, whether they were imagined to have been interesting novelties with a supernatural origin—such as bones from giant humans and shells of marine animals that perished in a Noachian deluge (Rosenberg and Coorough Burke, Chapter 29)—or data-rich objects of science, whose accurate details were important for strati-

Figure 1. Benjamin Waterhouse Hawkins painted *Cretaceous Life of New Jersey* in 1877. (Oil on canvas, 81 × 221.6 cm [31 7/8 in. × 87 ¼ in.] The original resides in Princeton University.) Image PP336, courtesy of Princeton University Art Museum, Princeton University, Department of Geosciences, Guyot Hall.

graphic correlation across England (Wigley, Chapter 4). From 'curiosities' to scientific specimens useful for stratigraphic correlation, paleoart documents a pioneering era of paleontology when modern geology was established in Poland (Krzywiec and Arndt, Chapter 11).

When viewed within its historical progression, paleoart demonstrates how the interpretation of fossils has evolved, how scientific advancements influence paleontological illustration, and how the scientific utility of fossils has advanced. Consequently, paleoart illustrates the nature of science, including that science is a human endeavor and way of knowing, based on empirical evidence and ever subject to revision in light of new observations and new data (National Research Council, 2012).

PALEONTOLOGICAL ART DOCUMENTS A SYNERGISTIC TENSION

Some scientists were gifted artists and illustrators who could create their own paleoart based on their fossil discoveries (Wigley, Chapter 4; Sharpe and Clary, Chapter 6; Şengör, Chapter 9; Wannier, Chapter 24). More commonly, the scientists supervised artists and engravers who produced the paleoart illustrations that accompanied a scientific text or a paleontological museum exhibit. Charles R. Knight, the premier paleontological artist of the early twentieth century, grudgingly acquiesced when Field Museum scientists stipulated that he revise his 'completed' murals according to their conceptions; Knight felt he was the more knowledgeable authority to reconstruct an extinct beast and its ecosystem since he had conducted extensive research with modern animals and landscapes (Clary, Chapter 18). While other artist-scientist relationships do not approach the acrid intensity that Knight had with Field Museum scientists, there remain issues to resolve for an accurate but artistic paleoart interpretation. Some creativity in color and extinct beasts' expressions may belong in the artists' realm, but anatomy and accurate morphological representation belong to the supervising scientists (Allmon, Chapter 23; Rowan, Funderburk, and Clary, Chapter 27). The final paleoart usually represents a compromise between the artist and the scientist. And as scientific knowledge evolves, the artistic leeway in reconstructing fossil finds becomes more constrained, as exemplified by scientists' more recent understanding of fossilized pigments.

Modern paleoart may reflect social mores. Artist Giles Ford personally questioned the role that art should take to visualize, educate, and prevent climate change disasters. Originally begun as an investigation into his late father's micropaleontological thin sections, Ford's Fossilarium series probed the role of industry, fossil fuels, and climate change ramifications for society (Ford, Chapter 28). Through repeating images, rhythms, and refrains, Ford investigated ethical consequences of the production of non-biodegradable plastics from fossil fuels and the Anthropocentric effects of *any* industry.

Paleoart reflects the human condition, and some modern paleoartists critique the human role in extinction and environmental degradation (Rosenberg and Coorough Burke, Chapter 29). Knowingly or unknowingly, value judgments inherent in culture influence both the sciences and the arts, and this is especially demonstrable in the science of paleontology. Fossils were once thought to be the remains of fierce beasts that guarded gold deposits along ancient trade routes, large vertebrate remains were presented as giant humans drowned in the biblical deluge, even more modest fossils were held to be evidence of the favor God shed upon the person who found them, and it was common as late as early modern Europe to think that fossils had been molded by magic forces within the Earth. Nowadays fossil remains convey lessons for the preservation of our environment for the greater good (Ford, Chapter 28; Rosenberg and Coorough Burke, Chapter 29).

AN EVOLUTION OF PALEONTOLOGICAL ART

Our Memoir 218 samples paleontological art from archaic times through the early emergence of modern paleontological science and on to the present day. Our categories are broad, and many paleontological art applications transcend categorization.

Early Paleontological Art Conceptions

Prehistoric paleoart and zoomorphic representations were rooted in mythology and folklore (Bakker, Chapter 2; Goldstein and Getty, Chapter 16; Rosenberg and Coorough Burke, Chapter 29). But even these fantasies probably had some grounding in observations that were influenced by the culture of the time. The early authors of the Old Testament were constrained by laws against visual imagery, and their written words 'paint an image' without illustrations (Bakker, Chapter 2). Throughout the centuries, multiple interpretations of the Biblical narrative have identified various beasts for Job's monsters, Leviathan and Behemoth. Young Earth Creationists have envisioned these as Mesozoic beasts—a Cretaceous sea reptile and a dinosaur, respectively—to support their young Earth model. Bakker's analysis of Job's anatomical and behavioral interpretations of the monsters led him to identify the Leviathan and Behemoth as modern animals, with a surprising twist. Bakker concluded that Leviathan, with an armor of scales and creator of roiling seas, is the Nile Crocodile, while the Behemoth, with its cedar-like tail, is a young male African Elephant (Bakker, Chapter 2).

The turn of the nineteenth century is identified as the period when modern paleontology emerged, with French anatomist Georges Cuvier (1769–1832) as one of the leading founders. Prior to this, with the late eighteenth-century development of Linnaeus' standardized rules for description and classification, scientists examined fossils, but they nevertheless frequently identified the organism incorrectly (Sendino, Chapter 10; Kryzwiec and Arndt, Chapter 11; Lipps, Chapter 22). The 1800s witnessed an exponential explosion in scientific understanding of fossils, exemplified by publications of James Sowerby (1757–1822) as well as Parkinson. Both Parkinson's three volumes of fossil images (Lewis, Chapter 3) and Sowerby's multi-part *Mineral Conchology* (1812–1829 [1846]) organized fossils in compendia in the early to mid-1800s, with written descriptions accompanied by hand-colored illustrations. The latter are still useful to scientists today.

English surveyor William Smith (1769–1839) is credited with understanding the principle of faunal succession and using it to create the first geological map of an entire country. Smith recognized the *utility* of fossils for correlation and drew detailed and accurate illustrations that can still be carefully matched to their original fossil specimens today (Wigley, Chapter 4); his collaboration with James Sowerby resulted in four parts of *Strata Identified by Organized Fossils,* which formed the foundation of subsequent stratigraphic research. Biostratigraphic correlation using fossils was not the exclusive domain of the English, however. Alexandre Brongniart (1770–1847) and Cuvier used fossils to interpret the Paris Basin's stratigraphy in the early 1800s (Bork, Chapter 5). Their 1811 publication included a geologic map accompanied by fossil illustrations and geologic columns; the paleontological illustrations demonstrated the value of fossils in deciphering ancient environments of alternating freshwater and marine deposits. Brongniart further recognized the similarity of the Paris Basin deposits to those in other regions of France, Poland, and Italy, and included an illustration of common fossils between the Paris Basin and northern Italy in his 1823 *Mémoire*.

Illustrations of fossils became increasingly important as their stratigraphic utility was demonstrated. Roderick Murchison (1792–1871) published illustrations of Paleozoic fossils in his *Geology of Russia* (Murchison, 1845), which effectively documented the Silurian and Devonian Paleozoic systems, as well the Permian whose type section he established (Diemer and Diemer, Chapter 14). The large format of the two-volume book facilitated use of multiple illustrative techniques, including wood engravings with simple graphic patterns, but also higher-resolution lithographs, a zincograph, and copper plate engravings (Diemer and Diemer, Chapter 14). Murchison had fossil images printed with higher-resolution techniques, primarily lithography.

Scientific paleoart prior to 1830 typically illustrated fossils as they were found, e.g., as shells or disarticulated bones. Even in cases where the skeleton of an extinct vertebrate was reconstructed from its bones, those reconstructions did not include soft tissue. Furthermore, the restorations were of individual animals without the context of the environment in which they lived. Around 1830, Henry De la Beche (1796–1855) collaborated with William Buckland (1784–1856) to publish paleoart that was revolutionary in two ways. Drawn as a fundraiser for fossil collector Mary Anning (1799–1847), their lithograph, *Duria antiquior,* was the first paleoecological reconstruction of ancient invertebrates as well as vertebrates with flesh restored, cavorting together within their presumed life habitat (Sharpe and Clary, Chapter 6).

Artworks interpreting the progression of paleoecosystems, documenting different periods in geological history, were to follow. Paleontologist and botanist Franz Unger (1800–1870) and artist Josef Kuwasseg (1802–1877) were the first to portray plants in paleoecological scenes (in 1853) in order to document habitat changes in life history (Collins, Chapter 8). Such paleoecological progressions through time remained popular; in the mid-twentieth century, Erich Thenius (*b.* 1924) collaborated with artist Fritz Zerritsch (1888–1985) to produce scenes from deep time for his book, *The History of Life on Earth* (Thenius, 1955) (Rowland, Chapter 20). The paleoecological scenes were also reproduced as roll-up wall charts for classroom use and display.

Because paleontological illustrations accompany the dissemination of new scientific discoveries, visual accuracy is important. Eduard Suess' (1831–1914) first scientific paper focused upon fossil graptolites, and Suess took great care to illustrate the details that were being *discussed*, with other fossil parts represented in outline form only, in what geologist Hans Cloos termed "the art of leaving out" (Şengör, Chapter 9). Subsequent investigations via electron microscopy corrected errors in Suess' graptolite interpretations. Şengör concluded that Suess' attention to detail, evidenced by carefully constructed illustrations, is nevertheless a defining characteristic of a superior field geologist.

Accurate illustrations of small fossils require magnification, which the expanding technology of microscopy facilitated. Jere Lipps (Chapter 22) demonstrated how multiple perspectives, as well as accuracy of depiction, were critically important when foraminifera became the primary vehicle for petroleum exploration in the mid-1900s; microfossils retained their prominence for correlation until seismic technologies diminished their importance. With more than 50,000 species described and illustrated to date, foraminiferal images likely number in the 200,000–300,000 range (Lipps, Chapter 22). Swiss paleontologist Manfred Reichel's (1896–1984) quest for perfection resulted in exquisite Alveolinid (larger, macroscopic foraminifera) illustrations that are still found in specialized textbooks. Reichel's attention to detail extended to his illustrations of early Jurassic birds and pterosaurs, even though these illustrations were never published (Wannier, Chapter 24).

An Expansion of Paleontological Art

Paleontological art has become an invaluable teaching tool by providing images and models for study. William Buckland wrote to De la Beche that he used the first paleoecological scene, *Duria antiquior*, as a syllabus for his classes—the image presumably encapsulated the content that Buckland covered in his instruction (Sharpe and Clary, Chapter 6). The Thenius/Zerritsch paleontological paintings were reproduced as wall charts for classroom teaching aids to illustrate scenes from Earth history (Rowland, Chapter 20); and Reichel constructed paleoart as visual aids, especially for his students' use (Wannier, Chapter 24). Since students could not have access to all important paleontological specimens, Ward's plaster models offered them an opportunity to investigate outstanding examples of ancient life (Brice, Chapter 15). Therefore, paleoart ensures an optical consistency—or standardized visual representation—among the classrooms that adopt it for instruction.

The experimental socialistic community of New Harmony, Indiana, established in 1826 by Robert Owen (1771–1858) and William Maclure (1763–1840), offers another early example of paleontological art as a teaching tool (Elliott, Chapter 7). New Harmony adopted a pedagogy that was pioneered in Europe and that merged art and science. The Pestalozzian educational method used a "whole child approach" that facilitated all aspects of growth, including mental, emotional, and practical. This embraced nurturing of hands-on artistic skills such as coloring of scientific illustrations. New Harmony's pedagogical approach remains validated by its effectiveness in communicating paleontology in the modern classroom (Elliot, Chapter 7).

Paleontological art has proven to be important well beyond scientific presentations and formal classrooms. The Geological Survey of Ireland began "reaching out" to the public in 1854 with an evening series of "Popular Lectures" that were free and open to the public. Geologist and artist George Victor Du Noyer (1817–1869) produced a series of large watercolors of paleontological illustrations, geological field sections, and alpine scenes that permitted viewing from a distance in the lecture hall. Parkes (Chapter 12) characterized these nineteenth-century paintings as metaphorical PowerPoint presentations. Also, in 1854, Benjamin Waterhouse Hawkins unveiled his dinosaur sculptures at the Crystal Palace, which hundreds of thousands of visitors viewed to satisfy their curiosity about ancient life (Peck and Rowland, Chapter 17). In 1926, Charles Knight started production on a series of panels depicting the progression of life throughout Earth history for Chicago's Field Museum. They enthrall visitors to the museum to the present day, proving that Knight's murals (created between 1926 and 1931) are touchstones in the history of visual outreach in paleontology, despite the fact that many of his interpretations have become archaic. Modern interpretive signage corrects Knight's earlier misconceptions and addresses evolving scientific knowledge for the visitor, demonstrating that historic reconstructions of ancient life have value in revealing that science itself is an evolving enterprise that can engage everyone (Clary, Chapter 18).

Women as notable paleontological artists are finally given their due in this volume. Reitmeyer, Morgan, and Baione (Chapter 19) introduced us to Elisabeth Rungius Fulda (1879–1968), Helen Ziska (1880–1951), Lindsey Morris Sterling (1876–1931), and Margret Joy Flinsch Buba (1904–1998), all of whom made significant paleoart contributions for the American Museum of Natural History at the same time Charles Knight was producing murals there. Ziska's line drawings of *Baluchitherium*, then thought to be the largest terrestrial mammal, accompanied multiple scientific papers, while Fulda reconstructed other specimens from the museum's Central Asiatic Expedition (1921–1930), including adult *Protoceratops* with their young and dinosaurs hatching from eggs. Sterling and Buba drew fossil elephants and mastodonts for Osborn's final book, *Proboscidea*. Knight apparently had a special antipathy toward working with Fulda despite the quality of her work, and he resisted Henry Fairfield Osborn's suggestion that he collaborate with her.

Turner and Berta (Chapter 21) take us beyond the American Museum of Natural History in examining the role of women who drew ancient vertebrates; the recognized early-nineteenth-century women paleoartists, such as Mary Morland Buckland (1797–1857) and Orra White Hitchcock (1796–1863), illustrated for their relatives. Later in the nineteenth century, paleoart began to reflect evolutionary theory. Ann Redfield's (1800–1888) wall chart of the animal kingdom demonstrated this important new trend, with her biodiversity tree of life illustrating relationships among major animal groups. In the twentieth century, more women contributed to evolutionary paleoart's increasing scientific accuracy and accessibility in books and electronic media especially for the public. Despite their evident accomplishments, women paleoartists still constitute fewer than 7% of the winners of the Lanzendorf–National Geographic PaleoArt Prize that recognizes outstanding paleoart and illustration (Turner and Berta, Chapter 21).

New Niches for Paleontological Art

As the public's fascination with fossils grew in the twentieth and twenty-first centuries, paleontological art found expression in new mediums, as well as an expanded presence in public spaces. Examples include the *Jurassic Park* movies, television sitcoms (e.g., the 1991–1994 series, *Dinosaurs*), documentaries (e.g., *Walking with Dinosaurs*), and children's literature (e.g., *Dinotopia*) and programming (e.g., *The Land Before Time* movies, Dinosaur Train television series).

Arguably the most universally accessible venue for paleontological art is postage stamps (Lipps, Vartak, Eijden, Rajshekhar, Vaddadi, and Vartak, Chapter 25). Beginning in 1951, paleontological stamps have constituted portraits of a veritable assemblage of fossils ranging from prokaryotes to dinosaurs and other vertebrates including human ancestors; body fossils and ichnofossils; fossils and their habitats from the Precambrian to Recent; as well as an homage to the paleontologists who discovered and identified them, and the unique field sites where fossils were unearthed. Since 1951, nearly 200 countries have issued ~4000 stamps with paleontological themes. The low cost and small size of stamps facilitate an interest in paleontology around the globe; their value extends beyond philately into classrooms and exhibits. Fossil stamps demonstrate the worldwide curiosity for and love of fossils; diverse multicultural perspectives on ancient life are exhibited *within* the stamps, as well as by the wonderful diversity of nations that issued them. As with the differences in the scientific character of paleontological art evidenced by other works discussed in this volume, the variation in the quality of science exhibited by fossil stamps from across the globe illustrates that science evolves and is an activity in which everyone can participate. It is an implicit and important theme throughout this volume.

Paleoart continues to inspire visitors to explore the planet's geologic history at small regional as well as national museums. Young visitors to the Dunn-Seiler Museum, a small museum at Mississippi State University, point to the brilliant splashes of blue and orange of a mosasaur and *Triceratops* coursing around the room in a mural above the display cabinets—the mural accomplishes visually what the museum guides try to communicate verbally: enthusiasm grows as children and students of all ages gaze at prehistoric animals that actually lived a long time ago in a very different environment in Mississippi from the one in which they now stand (Rowan, Funderburk, and Clary, Chapter 27).

Modern artists use a variety of new mediums to bring ancient creatures to life. Traditional pencil, watercolor, and oil/acrylic paints are now augmented by digital technologies; three-dimensional sculptures are now created with a variety of mediums including metal, polyurethane, and polymer clay, or cast with resin and fiberglass. Artist Tibor Pecsics (Chapter 26) created an artwork of a coelophysoid dinosaur from its only fossil evidence—its tracks in Hungarian deposits. He also reconstructed a pterosaur—the first found in the country—and an unusual freshwater mosasaur. The latter was originally suspected of being a terrestrial lizard, but additional fossil remains helped scientists correctly identify the reptile as a freshwater mosasaur, estimated to grow up to 6 m in length. Pecsics used original fossil specimens and the local zoo's monitor lizards and crocodiles to guide his mosasaur creation. His paintings and models bring ancient creatures from Hungary to life and provide the window through which we can view Hungary's Cretaceous history.

Artists have come to realize, and are increasingly eager to communicate, that paleontological art has an important cultural context. Furthermore, that context has itself evolved. Giles Ford's appropriation of microfossil forms—the repeating images and rhythms that he observed in thin sections which his father had made in the 1960s—led to his exploration of important issues facing society, such as the relationships between industrial production of fossil fuels, plastics, pollutants, and climate change (Chapter 28). Alexis Rockman's dystopian collisions between humans and other extant as well as extinct life forms (Rosenberg and Coorough Burke, Chapter 29) are based on lessons from paleontology. For example, organisms and their environments are interdependent, anthropomorphic damage to one is damage to the other, extinction of either is forever, and consequently the anthropogenic despoiling of our planet does permanent harm to the human condition.

A FUTURE FOR PALEONTOLOGICAL ART

Visual imagery increases the opportunity for successful communication, and, in the absence of the original object, a well-done illustration serves as the concrete reference (Pettersson, 1993, p. 6). Paleontological art has functioned to scientifically communicate extinct life forms; pique public interest; educate about biodiversity, extinction, evolution, and geologic time; and it compels us to explore—and change—our impact on a fragile planet. It encapsulates Earth history—our prehistory—as well as the scientific history of fossil investigation. Paleoart proxies visually summarize and communicate scientific research, serving as standardized visual representatives of the original fossil specimens for future reference (Lewis, Chapter 3; Wigley, Chapter 4; Bork, Chapter 5; Şengör, Chapter 9; Sendino, Chapter 10; Krzyweic and Arndt, Chapter 11; Diemer and Diemer, Chapter 14; Turner and Berta, Chapter 21; Lipps, Chapter 22; Allmon, Chapter 23), in two-dimensional representations and three-dimensional models (Brice, Chapter 15; Peck and Rowland, Chapter 17; Pecsics, Chapter 26). Without accompanying pictures, narratives can be misinterpreted or misappropriated for selective use (Bakker, Chapter 2). Today, paleoart proxy images are gaining increasing importance as records of fossils from outcrops that are disappearing due to the 'progress' of urbanization, human expansion of agriculture, mining, forestry, and other human intrusions into the natural environment. In sum, paleoart may be the *only* way that we can experience many of these fossils in the future.

Beyond the representation of fossil organisms, paleontological art helps us envision ancient ecosystems (Sharpe and Clary, Chapter 6; Collins, Chapter 8). Its impact now radiates far beyond scientific research and classroom instruction (Elliott, Chapter 7; Rowland, Chapter 20; Wannier, Chapter 24). It extends to public outreach in museums and other public spaces as well as to books, stamps, and new media (Parkes, Chapter 12; Lipps et al., Chapter 25; Jovanovic-Kruspel and Harzhauser, Chapter 13; Clary, Chapter 18; Rowan et al., Chapter 27; Reitmeyer et al., Chapter 19). Paleoart has come to challenge our perspectives and cultural values, to prompt us to question what is human progress, and to heighten awareness of human-induced diminishment of the environment and consequent extinction (Ford, Chapter 28; Rosenberg and Coorough Burke, Chapter 29). Above all and in conclusion, it reminds us of our infinitesimally small, but exponentially powerful role as one of the many contributors to Earth and life history. Thus, paleontological art gives "the mind an eye" as it illustrates an argument, enforces visual comparison, and combines the real and the imagined to abolish the separation between art and life—becoming a gift to understanding (Tufte, 1997).

ACKNOWLEDGMENTS

We thank Dr. Robert Bakker, Curator, Paleontology Department, Houston Museum of Natural Science, for suggesting our cover image, Benjamin Waterhouse Hawkins' *Cretaceous Life of New Jersey*, and for discussing its significance within the progression of paleoart. We are also thankful for the tireless efforts of Amy Moe-Hoffman, Collections Manager, Dunn-Seiler Museum, Mississippi State University, in designing multiple variations and iterations of our cover art.

REFERENCES CITED

Brongniart, A., 1823, Mémoire sur les terrains de sédiment supérieurs calcaréo-trappéens du Vicentin, et sur quelques terrains d'Italie, de France, d'Allemagne, etc., qui peuvent se rapporter à la même époque: Paris, F.-G. Levrault, 84 p.

Clary, R.M., and Wandersee, J.H., 2011, DinoViz: The history and nature of science through the progression of dinosaur visualization: Science Scope, v. 34, no. 6, p. 14–21.

Clary, R.M., and Wandersee, J.L., 2015, The evolution of non-quantitative geological graphics in texts during the formative years of geology (1788–1840): Earth Sciences History, v. 34, no. 1, p. 59–91, https://doi.org/10.17704/1944-6187-34.1.59.

Hineline, M.L., 1993, The Visual Culture of the Earth Sciences, 1863–1970 [Doctoral dissertation]: San Diego, University of California, San Diego, Dissertation Abstracts International, v. 55, 713.

Knight, C.R., 1935, Before the Dawn of History: New York, Whittlesey House McGraw Hill, 119 p.

Latour, B., 1990, Drawing things together, *in* Lynch, M., and Woolgar, S., eds., Representation in Scientific Practice: Cambridge, Massachusetts, MIT Press, p. 19–68.

Monaghan, N.T., 2001, Irish palaeontological illustrations of the 19th century, *in* Rushton, B.S., Hackney, R.P., and Tyrie, R.R., eds., Biological Collections and Biodiversity: Otley, UK, Westbury, p. 83–90.

Murchison, R.I., de Verneuil, E., and von Keyserling, A., 1845, The Geology of Russia in Europe and the Ural Mountains, Volume 1, Geology: London, John Murray, 700 p.; Volume 2, Paléontologie: Paris, P. Bertrand, 512 p.

National Research Council (NRC), 2012, A Framework for K–12 Science Education: Practices, Crosscutting Concepts, and Core Ideas: Washington, D.C., National Academies Press, 367 p. + index.

Pettersson, R., 1993, Visual Information (2nd edition): Englewood Cliffs, New Jersey, Educational Technology Publications, 374 p.

Rudwick, M.J.S., 1976, The emergence of a visual language for geological science 1760–1840: History of Science, v. 14, p. 149–195.

Rudwick, M.J.S., 1992, Scenes from Deep Time: Early Pictorial Representations of the Prehistoric World: Chicago, University of Chicago Press, https://doi.org/10.7208/chicago/9780226149035.001.0001.

Thenius, E., 1955, Die Geschichte des Lebens auf der Erde (The History of Life on Earth): Vienna, St. Pölten, and Munich: Hippolyt-Verlag.

Titus, A.L., Knoll, K., Sertich, J.J.W., Yamamura, D., Suarez, C.A., Glasspool, I.J., Ginouves, J.E., Lukacic, A.K., and Roberts, E.M., 2021, Geology and taphonomy of a unique tyrannosaurid bonebed from the upper Campanian Kaiparowits Formation of southern Utah: Implications for tyrannosaurid gregariousness: PeerJ, v. 9, e11013, https://doi.org/10.7717/peerj.11013.

Tufte, E.R., 1997, Envisioning Information: Cheshire, Connecticut, Graphics Press, 156 p.

Vinther, J., Briggs, D.E.G., Prum, R.O., and Saranathan, V., 2008, The colour of fossil feathers, Biolology Letters, v. 4, no. 5, https://doi.org/10.1098/rsbl.2008.0302.

REFERENCED CHAPTERS FROM THIS VOLUME

Allmon, W.D., 2022, "Extreme dinosaurs" and the continuing evolution of dinosaur paleoart, *in* Clary, R.M., Rosenberg, G.D., and Evans, D.C., eds., The Evolution of Paleontological Art: Geological Society of America Memoir 218, Chapter 23, https://doi.org/10.1130/2021.1218(23).

Bakker, R.T., 2022, Imaging dragons in the Old Testament: Were Leviathan and Behemoth Mesozoic monsters?, *in* Clary, R.M., Rosenberg, G.D., and Evans, D.C., eds., The Evolution of Paleontological Art: Geological Society of America Memoir 218, Chapter 2, https://doi.org/10.1130/2021.1218(02).

Bork, K.B., 2022, The illustrations of Brongniart and Cuvier illuminate paleontology in the early nineteenth century, *in* Clary, R.M., Rosenberg, G.D., and Evans, D.C., eds., The Evolution of Paleontological Art: Geological Society of America Memoir 218, Chapter 5, https://doi.org/10.1130/2021.1218(05).

Brice, W.R., 2022, Fossil illustrations in three dimensions: Ward's models at Cornell University, *in* Clary, R.M., Rosenberg, G.D., and Evans, D.C., eds., The Evolution of Paleontological Art: Geological Society of America Memoir 218, Chapter 15, https://doi.org/10.1130/2021.1218(15).

Clary, R.M., 2022, The present is the key to the paleo-past: Charles R. Knight's reconstruction of extinct beasts for the Field Museum, Chicago, *in* Clary, R.M., Rosenberg, G.D., and Evans, D.C., eds., The Evolution of Paleontological Art: Geological Society of America Memoir 218, Chapter 18, https://doi.org/10.1130/2021.1218(18).

Collins, L.B., 2022, Franz Unger and plant evolution: Representations of plants through time, *in* Clary, R.M., Rosenberg, G.D., and Evans, D.C., eds., The Evolution of Paleontological Art: Geological Society of America Memoir 218, Chapter 8, https://doi.org/10.1130/2021.1218(08).

Diemer, J., and Diemer, L., 2022, The use of artwork to document geologic systems in *The Geology of Russia* (1845), *in* Clary, R.M., Rosenberg, G.D., and Evans, D.C., eds., The Evolution of Paleontological Art: Geological Society of America Memoir 218, Chapter 14, https://doi.org/10.1130/2021.1218(14).

Elliott, W.S., Jr., 2022, Significance of New Harmony, Indiana, USA, to nineteenth-century paleontological investigations of North America: Progressive education through arts and sciences, *in* Clary, R.M., Rosenberg, G.D., and Evans, D.C., eds., The Evolution of Paleontological Art: Geological Society of America Memoir 218, Chapter 7, https://doi.org/10.1130/2021.1218(07).

Ford, G., 2022, Fossilarium: Paintings inspired by micropaleontological thin sections, *in* Clary, R.M., Rosenberg, G.D., and Evans, D.C., eds., The Evolution of Paleontological Art: Geological Society of America Memoir 218, Chapter 28, https://doi.org/10.1130/2021.1218(28).

Goldstein, D.H., and Getty, P., 2022, The illustration of dinosaur tracks through time, *in* Clary, R.M., Rosenberg, G.D., and Evans, D.C., eds., The Evolution of Paleontological Art: Geological Society of America Memoir 218, Chapter 16, https://doi.org/10.1130/2021.1218(16).

Jovanovic-Kruspel, S., and Harzhauser, M., 2022, Nineteenth-century paleontological art in the Natural History Museum Vienna, Austria: Between demystification and mythologization, *in* Clary, R.M., Rosenberg, G.D., and Evans, D.C., eds., The Evolution of Paleontological

Art: Geological Society of America Memoir 218, Chapter 13, https://doi.org/10.1130/2021.1218(13).

Krzywiec, P., and Arndt, A., 2022, Development of paleontological art in Poland, *in* Clary, R.M., Rosenberg, G.D., and Evans, D.C., eds., The Evolution of Paleontological Art: Geological Society of America Memoir 218, Chapter 11, https://doi.org/10.1130/2021.1218(11).

Lewis, C., 2022, The fossilist and his engraver: Samuel Springsguth's illustrations of James Parkinson's *Organic Remains*, *in* Clary, R.M., Rosenberg, G.D., and Evans, D.C., eds., The Evolution of Paleontological Art: Geological Society of America Memoir 218, Chapter 3, https://doi.org/10.1130/2021.1218(03).

Lipps, J.H., 2022, Foraminiferal art through the ages, *in* Clary, R.M., Rosenberg, G.D., and Evans, D.C., eds., The Evolution of Paleontological Art: Geological Society of America Memoir 218, Chapter 22, https://doi.org/10.1130/2021.1218(22).

Lipps, J.H., Vartak, A., Van Eijden, T., Rajshekhar, C., Vaddadi, S., and Vartak, R., 2022, Paleontological postage stamps in art and education, *in* Clary, R.M., Rosenberg, G.D., and Evans, D.C., eds., The Evolution of Paleontological Art: Geological Society of America Memoir 218, Chapter 25, https://doi.org/10.1130/2021.1218(25).

Parkes, M.A., 2022, George Victor Du Noyer's large format paintings: Nineteenth-century lecture slides, *in* Clary, R.M., Rosenberg, G.D., and Evans, D.C., eds., The Evolution of Paleontological Art: Geological Society of America Memoir 218, Chapter 12, https://doi.org/10.1130/2021.1218(12).

Peck, R.M., and Rowland, S.M., 2022, Benjamin Waterhouse Hawkins and the early history of three-dimensional paleontological art, *in* Clary, R.M., Rosenberg, G.D., and Evans, D.C., eds., The Evolution of Paleontological Art: Geological Society of America Memoir 218, Chapter 17, https://doi.org/10.1130/2021.1218(17).

Pecsics, T., 2022, Ancient creatures of Hungary: Bringing the animals to life, *in* Clary, R.M., Rosenberg, G.D., and Evans, D.C., eds., The Evolution of Paleontological Art: Geological Society of America Memoir 218, Chapter 26, https://doi.org/10.1130/2021.1218(26).

Reitmeyer, M., Morgan, R., and Baione, T., 2022, Beyond Charles Knight: Women paleoartists at the American Museum of Natural History in the early twentieth century, *in* Clary, R.M., Rosenberg, G.D., and Evans, D.C., eds., The Evolution of Paleontological Art: Geological Society of America Memoir 218, Chapter 19, https://doi.org/10.1130/2021.1218(19).

Rosenberg, G.D., and Burke, P.C., 2022, Art about ancient life as a chronicle for the human condition, *in* Clary, R.M., Rosenberg, G.D., and Evans, D.C., eds., The Evolution of Paleontological Art: Geological Society of America Memoir 218, Chapter 29 https://doi.org/10.1130/2021.1218(29).

Rowan, T.M., Funderburk, T.B., and Clary, R.M., 2022, "But why paint a dinosaur blue?": Envisioning the Cretaceous—A vitalizing, multidisciplinary project in a university museum, *in* Clary, R.M., Rosenberg, G.D., and Evans, D.C., eds., The Evolution of Paleontological Art: Geological Society of America Memoir 218, Chapter 27, https://doi.org/10.1130/2021.1218(27).

Rowland, S.M., 2022, The Fritz Zerritsch/Erich Thenius suite of paleontological wall roll-ups and the pageant-of-life-through-time genre of paleontological art, *in* Clary, R.M., Rosenberg, G.D., and Evans, D.C., eds., The Evolution of Paleontological Art: Geological Society of America Memoir 218, Chapter 20, https://doi.org/10.1130/2021.1218(20).

Sendino, C., 2022, The influence of scientific knowledge on mollusk and arthropod illustration, *in* Clary, R.M., Rosenberg, G.D., and Evans, D.C., eds., The Evolution of Paleontological Art: Geological Society of America Memoir 218, Chapter 10, https://doi.org/10.1130/2021.1218(10).

Şengör, A.M.C., 2022, Eduard Suess on graptolites: His very first scientific paper and illustrations, *in* Clary, R.M., Rosenberg, G.D., and Evans, D.C., eds., The Evolution of Paleontological Art: Geological Society of America Memoir 218, Chapter 9, https://doi.org/10.1130/2021.1218(09).

Sharpe, T., and Clary, R.M., 2022, Henry De la Beche's pioneering paleoecological illustration, *Duria antiquior*, *in* Clary, R.M., Rosenberg, G.D., and Evans, D.C., eds., The Evolution of Paleontological Art: Geological Society of America Memoir 218, Chapter 6, https://doi.org/10.1130/2021.1218(06).

Turner, S., and Berta, A., 2022, Illustrating the unknowable: Women paleoartists who drew ancient vertebrates, *in* Clary, R.M., Rosenberg, G.D., and Evans, D.C., eds., The Evolution of Paleontological Art: Geological Society of America Memoir 218, Chapter 21, https://doi.org/10.1130/2021.1218(21).

Wannier, M.M.A, 2022, A quest for perfection in science and art: The paleontological legacy of Manfred Reichel (1896–1984), *in* Clary, R.M., Rosenberg, G.D., and Evans, D.C., eds., The Evolution of Paleontological Art: Geological Society of America Memoir 218, Chapter 24, https://doi.org/10.1130/2021.1218(24).

Wigley, P., 2022, Fossil illustrations from the work of William Smith, *in* Clary, R.M., Rosenberg, G.D., and Evans, D.C., eds., The Evolution of Paleontological Art: Geological Society of America Memoir 218, Chapter 4, https://doi.org/10.1130/2021.1218(04).

Printed in the USA

The Geological Society of America
Memoir 218

Imaging dragons in the Old Testament: Were Leviathan and Behemoth Mesozoic monsters?

Robert T. Bakker
Department of Paleontology, Houston Museum of Natural Science, Houston, Texas 77030-1799, USA

ABSTRACT

For much of the nineteenth century, the majority of respected stratigraphers were serial creationists who read the rocks as recording successive extinctions followed by new creations, a process that generated progress in vertebrate structure. Beginning after World War I, Leviathan and Behemoth were cited by Young Earth Creationists—a minority among anti-Darwinians—as Mesozoic species observed by humans. This view spread rapidly after World War II. However, the anatomy and behavior of these beings, as portrayed in Ugaritic and Hebrew literature, leads to a firmer identification. The Leviathan of Job has powerful jaws armed with great teeth; skull armor renders hooks impotent; body armor of scales set so close together that they repel spears; water is thrashed into foam by twisting death rolls; this is altogether an accurate rendition of the Nile Crocodile. The Behemoth is a young, adult male African Elephant distinguished by grass-eating habits and an enormous, uncontrolled male organ: "tail like a cedar tree."

INTRODUCTION

Figures 1 and 2 show two methods for imaging famous monsters whether Biblical or fossilized. William Blake (1818) gives us a rotund yet lively Behemoth, his mouth full of hippo-esque tusks, his tail surprisingly long (remember this caudal detail; it will be of use later). Blake follows centuries of Protestant zoo-theology, finding clues in Job of the Old Testament that the Behemoth was a mutant malevolent *Hippopotamus.* In legends of the End Times, the Behemoth stars as one of the two beasts who will be cooked to feed a multitude of saints celebrating the final defeat of Satan (Early Victorian naturalists puzzled about alternative identifications—Cadbury, 2000). The scene of Figure 2 captures the creatures preserved in the Middle Carboniferous lake shales and petrified forests of Nova Scotia.

Drawn in the early 1860s, the scene is still canonical paleontology; few modifications are required to fit the latest analysis. The art comes from the greatest explorer of the Coal Age, Sir William Dawson, founding father of the Redpath Museum at McGill University in Montreal. Dawson applied his own results from analysis of bones and snail shells, pollen, wood thin sections, and leaf macro-fossils. As a kid, he led Sir Charles Lyell to the hollow tree stumps at Joggins (Dawson, 1868). Here they discovered skeletons of the oldest known true reptile: *Hylonomus,* a stout-limbed beastie who stimulates deep thoughts to this day. Many an undergrad in the late twentieth century, drawn to Coal Age research, hoped for a thesis at the Redpath.

One may ask, which picture adheres more closely to what the Bible actually says? Blake? He had an exuberant piety mingled with free-flowing, New Age visions, a theology that makes mainline Protestants nervous then and now. Dawson, on the other hand, was an eloquent advocate for Scottish Presbyterianism who was unashamed of the Gospel. Dawson was most emphatically an anti-transmutationist who argued for multiple, sequential creations. No one species morphed into another. Dawson became an 1870s version of Richard Dawkins, writing erudite critiques of science education and political philosophy and the societal effects of Darwinism (in Dawson's view, mostly bad). A superb

Bakker, R.T., 2022, Imaging dragons in the Old Testament: Were Leviathan and Behemoth Mesozoic monsters?, *in* Clary, R.M., Rosenberg, G.D., and Evans, D.C., eds., The Evolution of Paleontological Art: Geological Society of America Memoir 218, p. 9–18, https://doi.org/10.1130/2021.1218(02).

Figure 1. William Blake's (1818) interpretation of the Behemoth in Job shows a hippo-like head and body terminating in a long, tufted tail. From a loose sheet in the Romer Library, Harvard.

offer came from the Princeton College (Sheets-Pyenson, 1996): a full professorship in geology, plus an endowed lectureship in theology, plus a light teaching load, and funding for fieldwork in the American West, where Princeton undergraduates were excavating Eocene mammals. Dawson agonized and then declined the whole package with regrets.

Dawson was the last of what I label "Punctuated Serial Creationists" (PSCs)—not to be confused with today's "Young Earth Creationists" (YECs), who have a simpler view of geo-history. Between 1820 and 1880, respected PSC stratigraphers mapped out the dramatic changes in life forms through thousands of feet of strata. The final creation, the one we live in, was seen to be the product of many stages where each had just the right menagerie of critters perfectly formed to enjoy their environment. Since Dawson and his co-religionists rejected Lamarck and Darwin, Punctuated Serial Creationists did wonder how one creation stage ended and the next began. Another Presbyterian, Hugh Miller, was the first best-selling author on Scottish fossil fish. His lyrical *Old Red Sandstone* debuted in 1843, was updated by his widow, Lydia, through fourteen more editions (Miller, 1872), and still is in print, arguably the most popular volume on fossil fishes anywhere. A series of energetic volumes showed that the Old Red Period, aka "Devonian," transitioned abruptly into the following Carboniferous period (Miller, 1872). The Old Red ocean swarmed with Panzer Sharks, aggressive predators some ten meters long, clothed in bony armor plate that was cleverly jointed to provide snap-action for the bolt-cutter jaws. When the Old Red time expired, the Panzer Sharks were done. They had fulfilled their purpose. Extinction wiped them out totally. A new wave of creation refilled the seas with new fishes, perfectly outfitted for the next period.

Miller frowned at the "Anti-Geologists" (his label, 1872), uninformed critics who pushed a Young Earth agenda. At the time, Anti-Geologists had little street cred among scholars of either the Bible or paleontology, but they were annoying.

Miller's senior colleague, the magisterial PSC William Buckland of Oxford, had been dealing with the skeptics since the early 1820s, when he was banned from a county science fair because he was "against Moses" (Mortenson, 2004; Buckland, 1837; Rupke, 1983; Rudwick, 2004). Buckland invented the best weapon for defending an Old Earth: vertebrate taphonomy (Rudwick, 2004). An English cave full of hyena bones, according to Buckland, was not a repository of sodden predators washed in from Africa by Noah's Deluge. Bite marks on prey bones and piles of hyena poo proved the cavern served the extinct hyenas as a lair for raising their hyena pups. Buckland's opposite number in the Connecticut Valley in the 1840s and 1850s was Edward Hitchcock, Congregationalist president of Amherst and another foe of "Anti-Geologists." Hitchcock decoded the mysterious fossil tracks of the Jurassic by mapping every toe joint (Hitchcock, 1854). This digital examination revealed the trackmakers to be big ground birds, some as ponderous as elephants. Hitchcock was correct; we now know that his creatures were dinosaurs: feathered members of the avian clan.

These giants of vertebrate paleontology—Buckland, Hitchcock, Miller, Dawson, and co-workers—worried that good Christians were flummoxed by multiple cycles. Hitchcock left us the delightful *Religion of Geology and Its Connected Sciences* (1854), a skein of sermons that tackled theodicy of animal pain and the necessity of death to produce the upward progress seen in the fossil record.

None of the Punctuated Creationists accepted any form of evolution. After the publication of Darwin's *On the Origin of Species by Means of Natural Selection* in 1859, the reputation of Dawson et al. remained high even among the vertebrate paleontologists who accepted some sort of evolution, for example Edward Drinker Cope (1886).

Creationists, punctuated or not, spent little time worrying about the Behemoth and Leviathan (Numbers, 1993). World War I brought horrors of poison gas, bombing of civilians, and abuse of science to justify racism. Vernon Kellogg's (1917) *Headquarters Nights*, written by an American civilian embedded in the German High Command, reported officers justifying invasion. Their reasoning was along these lines: Belgian people are lower evolutionary stages, far inferior to us, and so they deserve to be suppressed, and we deserve their land.

Evolutionism got a black eye from such attitudes. Postwar, German philosophy, including a distorted Darwinism, became unwelcome in American public schools (Numbers, 1993). Higher Criticism, another German export, seemed to attack all the cherished notions of inspiration and inerrancy of Scripture. William Jennings Bryan assumed leadership of the movement to outlaw tadpole-to-monkey-to-man instruction, hence the Scopes Monkey Trial of 1925 (Larson, 1997). Still, the issue wasn't with earth history. Bryan was quite content with the PSC views like those of Dawson, Miller, and Buckland. The Great Depression, another world war, and the advance of Godless Communism began to make a Young Earth position more attractive. Unrestrained emphasis on science in the public schools of the 1950s threatened the place of Christian values. Behemoth and Leviathan now were weaponized, drafted by an invigorated YEC movement to fight Liberalism. If the Jobian monsters were really dinosaurs

Figure 2. Dawson's restoration of Mid-Pennsylvanian coal swamp ecology, from Dawson's (1868) *Acadian Geology*. (Left to right) *Baphetes,* large amphibian. Below, *Anthracopupa,* landsnail. Making tracks, *Dendrerpeton*, strong limbed amphibian. Below land snail. *Hylonomus*, true reptile. *Hylerpeton*, strong limbed amphibian. Below, small millipede.

and Cretaceous sea reptiles seen alive by the Bible writers, then these beasts could indeed erase Deep Time. Plus, once you were alert to the possibilities, you could find clues of other living "prehistoric" beasts in the ancient art of the Assyrians and Sumerians, Egyptians and Persians, peoples contemporary with Old Testament writers (Mortenson, 2004; Numbers, 1993). Here I present a hunt for Job's living monsters and their role in art and culture.

Non-Geological Sources

For a clear explanation of "Higher Criticism," see Friedman's (1987) *Who Wrote the Bible?* The most elegant translation of the Leviathan and Behemoth as written in the Book of Job is found in Alter's (2011) *The Art of Biblical Poetry*. But because the King James Version (KJV) is so easily available, and recommended by Alter, my quotes mostly come from this still excellent translation.[1]

FAMOUS MONSTERS OF THE ANCIENT MIDDLE EAST

Visualizing the Un-Illustratable

When we search for unambiguous images of Biblical beasts, we have a problem: the oldest writers and editors of the Old Testament, with few exceptions, did not work with illustrators. They could not because of proscriptions against imagery in the Law; therefore, they did not include pictures of just what they had in mind for the anatomy and behavior of Leviathan and Behemoth. Ancient Egyptians, on the other hand, delighted in sculpture and color paintings of their semi-divine creatures. Hippos, elephants, crocodiles, and sundry other Mammalia and Reptilia, often accompanied by birds and fish, decorate public buildings and tomb interiors. Sumerians too had zoo-morphic art; Assyrians, Babylonians, and Persians left artistic records of real and imagined creatures (Kee et al., 1999; Black et al., Green, 1992; Day, 1983, 1993; Mackensie and Murphy, 1992).

And so, to understand the jaws and paws in the Psalms and the Book of Job, we must dissect verbal tropes and compare them to pagan animal art made by peoples at the same time and before. Our challenge is a little like that taken up by Mayor, who sought the real fossil skulls and claws that inspired ancient peoples to imagine Rocs and dragons, chimaeras, and cyclopean monsters (Mayor, 2005).

Apocalyptic Bad Dragons: The Hepta-Cephs

St. John's Red Dragon

Evangelicals are most familiar with Leviathan as he is in the final book of the New Testament, the Apocalypse of St. John, also known as Revelation. Leviathan is the Red Dragon. He attempts to swallow the Woman Clothed with the Sun and her newborn. She is Israel or the Christian Church or both. Her son is the new Church or Messiah or both. The Red Dragon is none other than Satan of old. And he has seven heads. All through Old Testament times, and before, hepta-cephalia is a mark of superpowers, usually but not always, evil.

Sumerian 7-Headed? Cheetah

Hepta-Dragons go way back in art. Nearly 3000 years before Revelation was written, the seven-headed dragon was threatening (or listening to) a noble hero in Sumer (Fig. 3). The Sumerian dragon, portrayed in an engraved plate at the Bible Lands Museum in Jerusalem, is puzzling. He/she/it doesn't fit the later standard seven-headed dragon mold. Instead of a massive maw

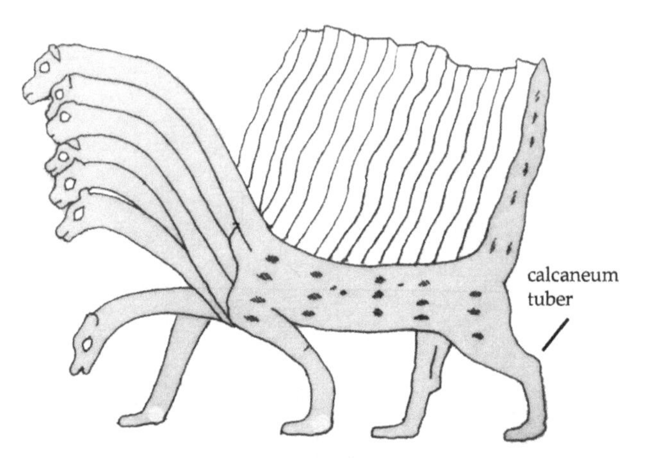

Figure 3. Cheetahs as models for ancient seven-headed dragons. Outline by author from Sumerian engraving, ca. twenty-fifth century B.C.E. Outline extracted from photograph provided by Bible Lands Museum Jerusalem, Israel.

studded with cruel fangs, the seven snouts are dainty, abbreviated, and smallish compared to the bulk of torso. None of the mouths is open in a growl or snarl. Each cranium is diminutive compared with the head of the hero? kneeling in front of the beast. The dragon's forehead is flat on top, not bulging with muscle and mane hair, a sharp distinction from the way lions and lionesses were painted or engraved in Egyptian scenes or later at Nineveh and Babylon. The Sumerian beast has small ears, low and rounded and perky. The tail is quite elongated and held high above the buttocks, as if in greeting. The limb apparatus is striking: most Christian descriptions of Leviathan suggest reptilian arms and legs, conferring a low-slung, flat-footed, malevolent posture. Not so for the Sumerian creature. The animal carries its body mass high on elegantly long legs fore and aft. Carriage is *digitigrade*, ankle and heel (calcaneum tuber) elevated far above the ground surface. Forearm and ankle bones are slender. The Sumerian creature appears to be cat-footed: the paws are compact, rounded, with claws tucked back into the rounded furry mass. Finally, the Sumerian species is adorned with a double row of spots, a feature of most wild felid species of the Ancient Near East.

The Sumerian *incognita* comes very close to the most delicate and swiftest of all the cat family, *Acinonyx jubatus,* the cheetah. Unlike their ponderous cousins, leopards and lions, cheetahs can be trained to hunt, thus filling the role of quadrupedal furry falcon. Trained cheetahs were valued in Egypt and Mesopotamia in the third and second millennium B.C.E.; cheetah hunting was practiced through Pakistan and northern India into the 1800s (Forbes, 1832). Cheetahs were welcomed as tribute when Pharaoh Heptaptshut returned from the land of Punt in the fifteenth century B.C.E., an event recorded in exquisite line art on the temple walls of Deir El-Bahair (Fig. 4).

We must entertain the possibility that the engraving depicts a sometimes benign, perhaps semi-divine cheetah. The lesson for

[1]*Editor's note:* Scripture quotations from The Authorized (King James) Version. Rights in the Authorized Version in the United Kingdom are vested in the Crown. Reproduced by permission of the Crown's patentee, Cambridge University Press.

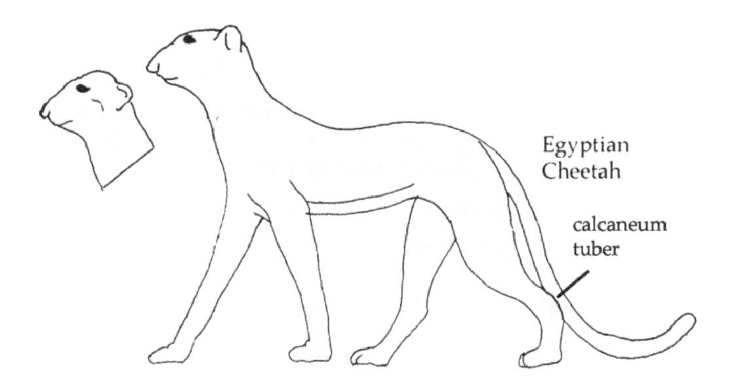

Figure 4. Cheetahs in Ancient Egypt, outlines by author taken from photograph of mural "Parade of Tribute from Expedition by Pharaoh Hatshepsut," Deir El-Bahafi, Egypt. Fifteenth century B.C.E. Taken from photograph in Allsen (2006).

those wishing to decode the Biblical seven-headed beasts is that these mythic "monsters" can fulfill several opposing roles—both dangerous to and helpful to humans.

The hepta-cephalic dragon, in various non-cheetah guises, fought heroes and do-gooders across the Ancient Near East. The hero often had to slay the seven-headed monster who loved darkness, swirling seas, and disorder. Best example: the Ugaritic literature in Shamra, Syria, discovered in the 1920s (Day, 1983, 1993). In Ugaritic legend, the hero Baal had to defeat a hepta-cephalic monster to unlock the dry land.

Old Testament Hepta-Cephs

Hebrew scriptures diverge from the Ugaritic/Mesopotamian in the shortness of the Creation Story; heaven and earth come about with no obvious dragon wrestling. God spoke, and it was done. Post-Creation, the Biblical dragon symbolizes evildoers who attack God's Chosen, often when there's backsliding among the Children of Israel. In Exodus, the dragon embodies Pharaoh and his chariots, who try to intercept the Chosen leaving Egypt. Centuries later, the Dragon personifies the Assyrian invaders. The Babylonians too are servants of Leviathan. In Biblical poetry, human invaders often are vivified as images of untamed seas and disastrous floods: Leviathan's favorite haunts in Ugaritic time.

German Bible scholars, noting the Leviathan's dislike of dry land, tidy gardens, and well-planned cities, came up with an apt sobriquet for the beast: "the Chaos Monster" (Day, 1983, 1993). The battle to free the divine plan became the "Kaos-kampf." Each time, when prophets and Psalmists prayed for deliverance, they pleaded for the dragon's destruction. They reminded God that He had smote the evil Dragon before. They prophesied that God would come with his great sword and slice dragon bodies into Prosciutto. Or crush Leviathan's heads:

Isaiah 27

1 In that day the LORD will punish with his great, cruel, mighty sword Leviathan the Elusive Serpent—Leviathan the Twisting Serpent; He will slay the Dragon of the sea.

Isaiah 51

9 Awake, awake, put on strength, O arm of the LORD; awake, as in the ancient days, in the generations of old. *Art* thou not it that hath cut Rahab, *and* wounded the dragon?

Psalm 74

13 Thou didst divide the sea by thy strength: thou brakest the heads of the dragons in the waters.
14 Thou brakest the heads of leviathan in pieces, *and* gavest him *to be* meat to the people inhabiting the wilderness.

Note the plural here. *Heads* of Leviathan. Seven heads are implied.

SINGLE-HEADED AND FROLICSOME

The Creation Psalm

The psalmist celebrates the *beauty* of creation. The wondrous profusion of birds ... the grace of deer and antelope and wild cattle of the hills. Marvelous too are the young lions, who wait upon the Lord for their daily food. Then there are the even richer life forms in salt water:

Psalm 104

24 O LORD, how manifold are thy works! in wisdom hast thou made them all: the earth is full of thy riches.
25 *So is* this great and wide sea, wherein *are* things creeping innumerable, both small and great beasts.
26 There go the ships: *there is* that leviathan, *whom* thou hast made to play therein.

Atop this food web is the Dragon of Psalm 104. He isn't Satan; he most definitely isn't trying to gobble up Israel or the promised Messiah. He's magnificent and awesome and at times cheerful. The beast needs time off to gambol through the waves. To relax in *playful* behavior. Makes you reconsider his long career encouraging the sacking of cities and squashing hopes. It gets better: For this very same verse, the Jewish Publication Society translation of 1985 confounds us with an even more paradigm-busting descriptor (*TANAKH, JPS Translation of Scripture,* 1985):

26 There go the ships,
and the Leviathan that You formed to play *with.*

Why does the Creator play games with the most evil of monsters? Because God *created* Leviathan. Keep that in mind when we plunge into the Book of Job.

Lair of the Dragon: Job

Job as Natural Historian

We've arrived at the main course of Leviathan-ology and Behemoth lore; the famous, long, beautiful passage in Job Chapters 40 and 41.

Job 40

15 Behold now behemoth, which I made with thee; he eateth grass as an ox.
16 Lo now, his strength is in his loins, and his force is in the navel of his belly.
17 He moveth his tail like a cedar: the sinews of his stones are wrapped together.
18 His bones are as strong pieces of brass; his bones are like bars of iron.
19 He is the chief of the ways of God: he that made him can make his sword to approach unto him.
20 Surely the mountains bring him forth food, where all the beasts of the field play.
21 He lieth under the shady trees, in the covert of the reed, and fens.
22 The shady trees cover him with their shadow; the willows of the brook compass him about.
23 Behold, he drinketh up a river, and hasteth not: he trusteth that he can draw up Jordan into his mouth.

"It's a *Brontosaurus*" is a standard claim from YECs. "The tip-off is the giant, powerful caudal organ (Ham, 2009). Brontosaurs come with Brobdingnagian tails. And they were vegetarian!" True, Jurassic and Cretaceous rocks contain brontosaurs with exceptional caudal organs; plus, bronto dentitions and capacious ribcages demonstrate herbivory. However, Behemoth is a grazer, a consumer of grass.

Grass is an angiosperm, a flowering plant. Undoubted angiosperm fossils—stems, seeds, pollen—are rare or absent in Jurassic rocks where brontosaurians are exceptionally common and diverse. The Behemoth, in fact, exploits two contrasting sectors of angiosperm habitat: feeding on grass in hills among gazelles and deer, then retreating to the river for a cool bath under the lotus leaves. Lotus are another family of plants with flowers. Lotus pollen is unknown in any rocks containing any brontosaur-like bones.

The Behemoth carries its great mass on limbs like iron rods. Such locomotor structures eliminate the *Hippopotamus.* Hippo limbs have sharp flexures at shoulder and elbow, knee and ankle. Such appendicular equipment permit river horses to accelerate into a lively trot, fast enough to catch most unwary humans on land. Behemoth is taller and more erect in carriage than any true hippopotamus. When we search for the tallest, strongest, *straightest* limbs among Ancient Near East animals, we find them among the proboscideans, aka elephants. *Loxodonta africana*, the African elephant and *Elephas maximus,* the Indian species, do appear often in art of the time; in Egyptian paintings, porters are shown hauling elephant ivory (Kee et al., 1999; Moss, 1988; O'Connell, 2008, 2015; Shoshani, 1992).

It must be admitted that YEC critics might have a point about elephant tails versus Behemoth tails: if Job's behemoth has a spectacularly large, impressively mobile tail, then a proboscidean is unlikely to be the natural model. The entire elephantine Order, including mastodonts, mammoths, and deinotheres, carries a tail device of quite modest dimensions, an anatomical fly swatter (as is the rule for the hippo and water buffalo and all bovine species, wild and domestic). Hence, we wonder what does "tail like a Cedar tree" mean in Job's culture?

It means "exceptional tall, erect penis" (Fig. 5). Among placental mammals today, public display of the intromittent organ can be a key part of advertising social position and health. Higher primates offer us spectacular examples: the male Patas Monkey, *Erythrocebus patas,* upon reaching sexual maturity, experiences a color change in the skin of the scrotum—it becomes an almost iridescent blue (Bercovitch, 1996). Thus, the package stands out vividly against the warm russet of the body fur. This is a species of open habitat. Males seek an elevation, a boulder or tall tussock, to sit and observe and be observed, with thighs apart. Even the "highest" primates, our own *Homo sapiens*, show dramatic varieties of penile display. Witness the Koteka, the penis sheaths worn in Papua New Guinea. Renaissance dandies of Europe's mid-1500s, with no knowledge of Papuan practices, dabbled in cod pieces of bright colors. Old Testament culture is curious. It was scandalous to have one's groin exposed (see drunken Noah disgracing himself in Genesis 9, post Flood). And yet the anatomical neighborhood of the male member is a sacred place where solemn oaths are witnessed. Abraham charged his best servant to go choose a bride for his son Isaac (Genesis 24:9). When the patriarch made his faithful servant swear he would never, *ever* select a bride from among the unwashed and uncircumcised nations, the servant slid his hand up Abraham's thigh, at or onto the seat of reproduction. In less somber times of the monarchy, rowdy young men indulged in what can only be called "shlong-shaming." They compared their social status and administrative power by bragging on their member's circumference. Famous case: after King Solomon died, his son Rehoboam gathered advisors to chart out the new kingship. Rehoboam was persuaded to be harder headed with the people; to raise levies and taxes (I Kings 12:10). "My pinkie finger is thicker than my Dad's torso!!" proclaimed Rehoboam. No subtlety here. "I'm better

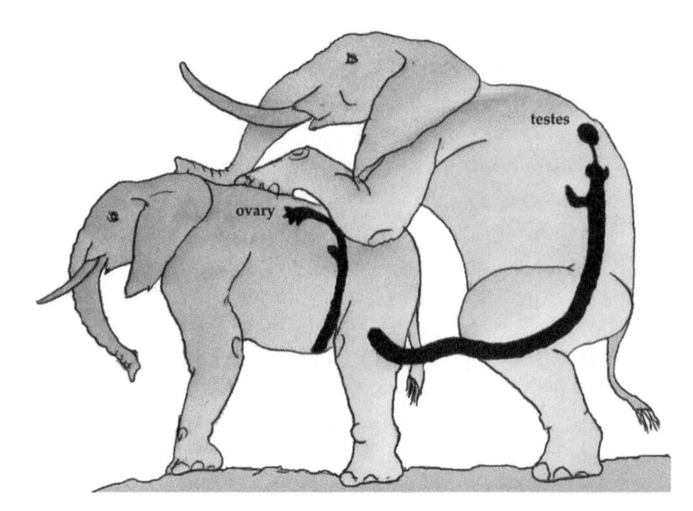

Figure 5. The curious arrangement of testes and ovaries in the African Elephant, *Loxodonta africana*, is shown. Male and female in copulatory posture. Testes do not descend but retain position high within the body cavity. Drawing by author from dissections carried out in 1974 in Zimbabwe.

hung than Dad!!!! And I'll rule that way!" Such bragging always preceded a fall. Rehoboam's rule was a disaster.

Job uses arborescent "like a cedar tree" to convey the male device carried by the Behemoth. A cedar tree has a fabulously straight trunk. It soars skyward. It bends in the high wind but never breaks. The description "swinging like Cedar tree" implies exceptional choreography. Male elephants going through their first musth seem to lose control of the swinging and slapping of their newly enlivened member. Accentuating the motion is the dribbling of aromatic green urine from the tip. Once seen, the demonstration is unforgettable. Males are empowered by hormone drive. A four-ton male will charge a bull two times heavier; the big guy will retreat, knowing that the bantam weight male is a potential berserker (O'Connell, 2015; Poole and Moss, 1981). I am persuaded that someone close to the writer of Job, or the writer him/herself, watched the musth event.

The Jewish Publication Society translation for Job's Behemoth has "sinews of his thighs sewn together." The King James Version has "his stones are knit together." Either way, the reader envisions an impressive scrotal bulge. Job errs here. Go to a zoo; observe the bull proboscidean. He has no package (Shoshani, 1992; Fig. 5). Nothing hangs down, scrotum-wise; in the mating season, the penis does drop impressively but no testicles follow. The two testicular bodies stubbornly cling to their juvenile location: attached high inside the body cavity. (I was taught that undescended testes are primitive for Mammalia; opossums and platypuses are so arranged; DNA evidence is puzzling [Sharma et al., 2018], suggesting that undescended is a secondary condition for elephants.) I imagine that Jobian observers saw big scrota because they expected big scrota.

Job's Armor-Plated Dragon

Job 41

1 Canst thou draw out leviathan with an hook? or his tongue with a cord *which* thou lettest down?
2 Canst thou put an hook into his nose? or bore his jaw through with a thorn?
3 Will he make many supplications unto thee? will he speak soft *words* unto thee?
4 Will he make a covenant with thee? wilt thou take him for a servant for ever?
5 Wilt thou play with him as *with* a bird? or wilt thou bind him for thy maidens?
6 Shall the companions make a banquet of him? shall they part him among the merchants?
7 Canst thou fill his skin with barbed irons? or his head with fish spears?
8 Lay thine hand upon him, remember the battle, do no more.
9 Behold, the hope of him is in vain: shall not *one* be cast down even at the sight of him?
10 None *is so* fierce that dare stir him up: who then is able to stand before me?
11 Who hath prevented me, that I should repay *him? whatsoever is* under the whole heaven is mine.
12 I will not conceal his parts, nor his power, nor his comely proportion.
13 Who can discover the face of his garment? *or* who can come *to him* with his double bridle?
14 Who can open the doors of his face? his teeth *are* terrible round about.
15 *His* scales *are his* pride, shut up together *as with* a close seal.
16 One is so near to another, that no air can come between them.
17 They are joined one to another, they stick together, that they cannot be sundered....
22 In his neck remaineth strength, and sorrow is turned into joy before him.
23 The flakes of his flesh are joined together: they are firm in themselves; they cannot be moved.
24 His heart is as firm as a stone; yea, as hard as a piece of the nether millstone.
25 When he raiseth up himself, the mighty are afraid: by reason of breakings they purify themselves.
26 The sword of him that layeth at him cannot hold: the spear, the dart, nor the habergeon.
27 He esteemeth iron as straw, *and* brass as rotten wood.
28 The arrow cannot make him flee: slingstones are turned with him into stubble.
29 Darts are counted as stubble: he laugheth at the shaking of a spear.
30 Sharp stones *are* under him: he spreadeth sharp pointed things upon the mire....
33 Upon earth there is not his like, who is made without fear.
34 He beholdeth all high *things*: he *is* a king over all the children of pride.

A key clue is here to Leviathan identity: ordinary weapons of war are insufficient to pierce the body. His jaw strength and fangs match those of crocodiles nicely. This monster is outstanding, unforgettable, because of his gnathic prowess: jaws that snap down on prey and cannot be loosened, fangs of frightening aspect. Descriptions that are most appropriate to the muzzle of a crocodile, studded with bone-breaking teeth. Then Job goes on to the coat of armor.

Leviathan's cuirass is distinctively crocodylian (Eudes-Deslongchamps, 1863, and Fig. 6). The individual croc scales are embedded in tough, leathery hide, so there is some mobility. The scales are composite armor plate. The core is dense, hard bone. The outer layer is shiny, but slightly bendable in the manner of a toenail or the outer layer of a bull's horn. In the earliest, simplest crocodyle-oid armor, in Triassic and Jurassic species, there is one double row of scales leaving flanks exposed. In more advanced species, including *Crocodylus niloticus,* the rows increase to four or five on each side so nearly the entire upper surface between shoulder and rump is encased in a suit of armor. Before the introduction of high-powered rifles, killing a big Nile Crocodile was likened to assaulting a fortified position.

Job observes that no one except his Creator can stand up to the monster. The case is closed, almost, in my opinion. The Leviathan is a giant Nile Crocodile, so large, so muscular, so thoroughly armor-plated that no mere mortal can stand to battle him. Just about every detail in Job fits with precision. Except there are a couple of verses that go beyond a crocodilian nature, comments that elevate the Leviathan to semi-divine status.

Job 41

18 By his neesings a light doth shine, and his eyes *are* like the eyelids of the morning.

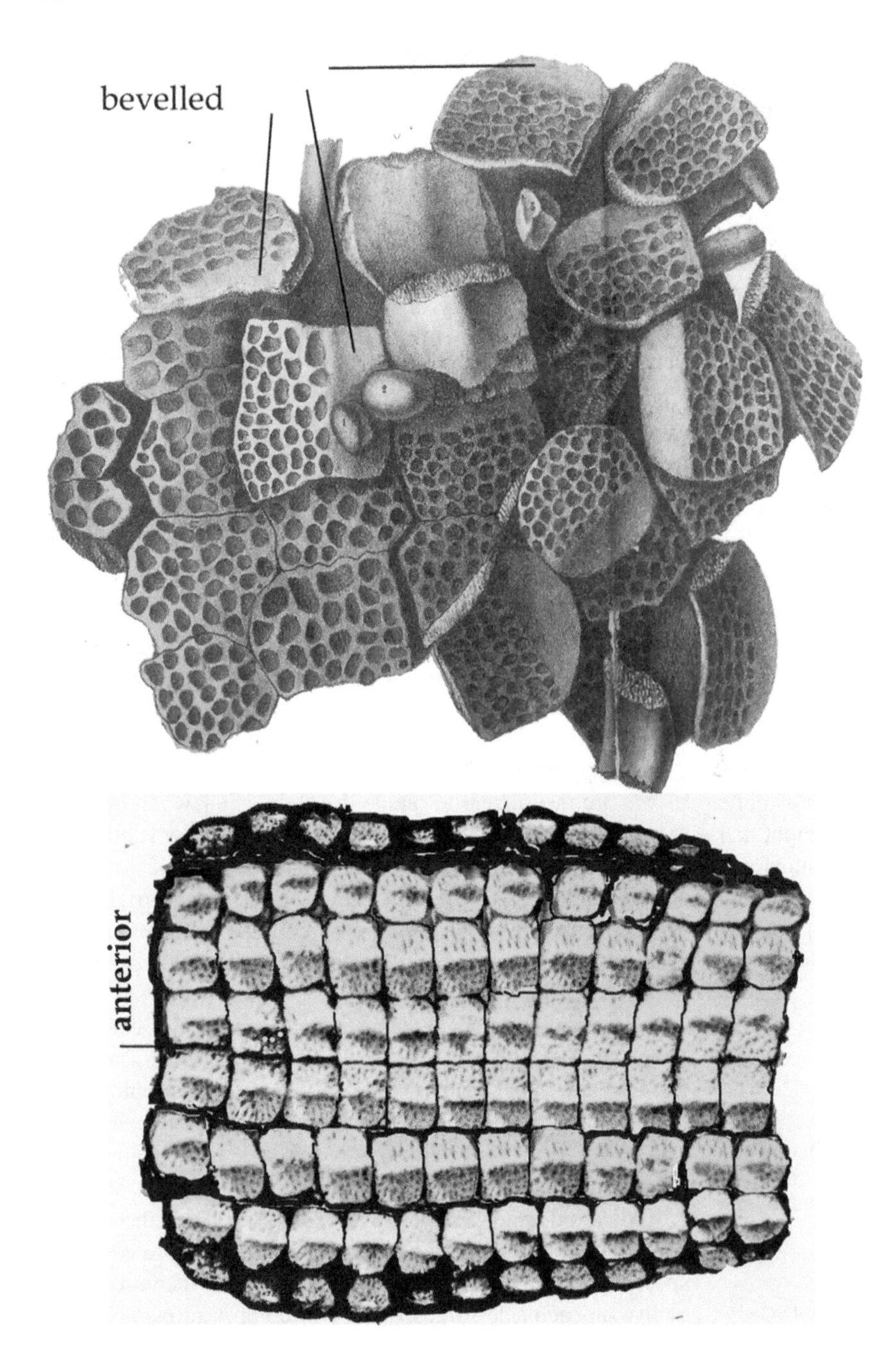

Figure 6. (Top) Jurassic crocodile dorsal armor from Eudes-Deslongchamps (1863). Lithograph shows how the beveled anterior edge of the bone plate makes a hinge for overlap by the next plate anteriorly. (Below) Torso bone armor in a *Crocodylus niloticus*, drawn by author from specimen Field Number 6-3JVII and others collected by B. Patterson from Lake Turkana, in the osteology collections, Museum of Comparative Zoology, Harvard University.

19 Out of his mouth go burning lamps, *and* sparks of fire leap out.
20 Out of his nostrils goeth smoke, as *out* of a seething pot or caldron.
21 His breath kindleth coals, and a flame goeth out of his mouth.

Here is a biomechanical/theological conundrum: Could a real dragon have flame-thrower breath? Young Earth Creationists dabble in igniferous models for the Trombone Duckbill Dinosaur, *Parasaurolophus*, whose skull famously carries long tubular crests with double chambers (Ham, 2009). The tubes might house two separate chemicals for a binary explosive à la Bombardier Beetle. The insect releases streams of two compounds; mixed in air, they produce a hot "bang." But binary inflammable agents are unknown among vertebrates; I am forced to conclude that the flames in Job are zoo-allegory, expressing the frightening visage of the Leviathan.

We return to the nonflammable, less mythological Leviathan:

Crocodylians—all species, living and extinct—differ from most other reptiles in having unusually long and well-muscled necks. During courtship display and threats, bull gators may be seen arching their heads and necks upwards as they swim slowly forward in a dance called "the Ghostly Sea-serpent" (Dinets, 2013). The description of Leviathan's neck fits.

The most intriguing, and perhaps the most tantalizing aspect listed in Job is the *behavior* of the beast, how he moves in water, the manner of his attack:

32 He maketh the deep to boil like a pot: he maketh the sea like a pot of ointment. He maketh a path to shine after him; *one* would think the deep *to be* hoary.

Leviathan churns the water into a whitened froth. The sea is whipped into a bubbling mass. Curious—efficient swimming does not cause mountains of bubbles. Turbulence like that might come from inefficient swimming, a thrashing about. Is there some other activity, perhaps exercised by a crocodile, that might result in such whirling white water:

Of course—The Death Roll (Dinets, 2013). The Death Roll recruits the entire body musculature for pulling pieces off the carcass. The croc predator seizes a limb or a head of the carcass and then performs axial rotations of extraordinary power. Pieces come loose and are swallowed. Any human witnessing the roll for the first time will remember the spectacle. The water is thrashed into sheets of foam. Humans have watched and been watched by person-eating *Crocodylus* for several million years as attested by croc bites on fossil *Homo* and *Australopithecus* bones from Olduvai (Bochu et al., 2010). Crocodyle-phobia had been fixed in our species long before the composition of Job.

CONCLUSIONS

Old Testament authors did not see live Mesozoic giants. With a few exceptions, Jobian critters conform nicely with two of the largest and most formidable animals of the rivers and deltas of the Old Testament world. The Leviathan is the adult male Nile Crocodile, the largest predator of the ancient Near East ecosystem. The Behemoth is the largest herbivore, the male African Elephant. Observers in the Late Bronze Age could not help but be impressed and intimidated by these natural monsters. Jobian monsters did not excite the *scientific* imagination of "Punctuated Serial Creationists," the nineteenth-century PSC stratigraphers who mapped key events of our modern "geological history" (Rudwick, 2004). These rock sleuths accepted the overwhelming evidence for a complex Earth history; they saw multiple, successive creations with each one converting the biota into something closer to that of the modern world. Only the most recent faunas supported people who pondered extinct species and drew their pictures and wrote stories.

ACKNOWLEDGMENTS

First, I'm indebted to Renee Clary for the invitation to this marvelous gathering of artists and paleontologists. Her editorial sense was thoroughly awesome. I thank the College of St. Benedict and St. John for two visits where we had lively exchanges about Richard Dawkins, Church Father Origen, Job, and the myth of conflict between science and Scripture. Thanks to the Bible Lands Museum Jerusalem for an image of the Sumerian seven-headed cheetah, allowing me to trace the body outline. Ron Numbers sent a key critique that reformed my story of young earthers; Martin Rudwick was the first to identify me as a follower of Euhemerus. My mother, Mrs. Nellie VanYperen Bakker, repeatedly schlepped me, as a grade-schooler, to the American Museum at Central Park West. She also urged Scripture study every day. When, as a young Prof, I said I was doing an article on the Bible and evolution, she replied "I'll just have to pray harder…"

REFERENCES CITED

Allsen, T.T., 2006, The Royal Hunt in Eurasian History: Philadelphia, University of Pennsylvania Press, 416 p.

Alter, R., 2011, The Art of Biblical Poetry: New York, Basic Books, 296 p.

Bercovitch, F., 1996, Testicular function and scrotal coloration in patas monkeys: Journal of Zoology, v. 239, p. 93–100, https://doi.org/10.1111/j.1469-7998.1996.tb05439.x.

Black, J.A.A., and Green, A., 1992, Gods, Demons and Symbols of Ancient Mesopotamia (with Illustrations by T. Richards): Austin, University of Texas Press, 165 p.

Blake, W., 1818, Illustrations of the Book of Job, Invented and Engraved by William Blake: London, Methuen.

Bochu, C., Nijau, J., Blumenchine, R.J., and Densmore, L.D., 2010, A new horned crocodile from the Plio-Peistocene hominid sites at Olduvai George, Tanzania: Plos One, 24 February 2010, https://doi.org/10.1371/journal.pone.0009333.

Buckland, W., 1837, The Bridgewater Treatise VI: Geology and Mineralogy: London, William Pickering, 313 p.

Cadbury, D., 2000, The Dinosaur Hunters: London, Fourth Estate, 375 p.

Cope, E.D., 1886, Theology of Evolution: Philadelphia, Arnold, 37 p.

Darwin, C., 1859, On the Origin of Species by Means of Natural Selection, or, the Preservation of Favoured Races in the Struggle for Life: London, John Murray, 502 p.

Dawson, J.W., 1868, Acadian Geology: Edinburgh, MacMillan and Company, 694 p.

Day, J., 1983, God's Conflict with the Dragon: Echoes of a Canaanite Myth in the Old Testament: Cambridge, UK, Cambridge University Press, 411 p.

Day, J., 1993, Leviathan, *in* Freedman, D.N., ed., Anchor Bible Dictionary: New York, Doubleday, v. 4, K–N, p 295–296.

Dinets, V., 2013, Dragon Songs: New York, Arcade Publishing, 318 p.

Eudes-Deslongchamps, J.A., 1863, Mémoires sur les Téléosauriens de l'Époque Jurassique du Département de Calvados: Normandy, Société Linnénne de Normandie 13, 292 p.

Forbes, J., 1832, Oriental Memoirs, a Narrative of Seventeen Years Residence in India: London, Richard Bentley, 579 p.

Friedman, R.E., 1987, Who Wrote the Bible?: New York, Simon & Schuster, 444 p.

Ham, K., 2009, Dinosaurs for Kids: Green Forest, Arkansas, Master Books, 55 p.

Hitchcock, E., 1854, The Religion of Geology and Its Connected Sciences: Boston, Phillips, Sampson and Company, 511 p.

Kee, H.C., Rogerson, J., Meyers, E.M., and Saldariui, A.J., 1999, Cambridge Companion to the Bible: Cambridge, Cambridge University Press, 616 p.

Kellogg, V., 1917, Headquarters Nights, a Record of Conversations and Experiences at the Headquarters of the German Army in France and Belgium: Boston, The Atlantic Monthly Press, 117 p.

Larson, E.J., 1997, Summer for the Gods: New York, Basic Books, 336 p.

Mackensie, R.A.F., and Murphy, R.E., 1992, Job, *in* Suggs, M.J., Sakenfeld, K.D., and Mueller, J.R., eds., The Oxford Study Bible with the Apocrypha, p. 510–550.

Mayor, A., 2005, The First Fossil Hunters: Princeton, New Jersey, Princeton University Press, 400 p.

Miller, H., 1843, The Old Red Sandstone, First Edition: Edinburgh, UK, William P. Nimmo., 315p.

Miller, H., 1872, The Old Red Sandstone, Fifteenth Edition: Edinburgh, UK, William P. Nimmo, 385 p.

Mortenson, T., 2004, The Great Turning Point: New Leaf Publishing, Green Forest, Arkansas, 271 p.

Moss, C., 1988, Elephant Memories: New York, William Morrow, 398 p.

Numbers, R.L., 1993, The Creationists: Berkeley, University of California Press, 457 p., https://doi.org/10.1515/9783110974362.248.

O'Connell, C., 2008, The Elephant's Secret Sense: Chicago, University of Chicago Press, 264 p.

O'Connell, C., 2015, Elephant Don: Chicago, University of Chicago Press, 261 p.

Poole, J.H., and Moss, C.J., 1981, Musth in the African Elephant (*Loxodonta africana*): Nature, v. 292, no. 5826, p. 830–831, https://doi.org/10.1038/292830a0.

Rudwick, M.J.S., 2004, Bursting the Limits of Time: The Reconstruction of Geohistory in the Age of Revolution: Chicago, University of Chicago Press, 732 p.

Rupke, N., 1983. The Great Chain of History: William Buckland and the English School of Geology: Oxford, UK, Clarendon Press 322 p.

Sheets-Pyenson, S., 1996, John William Dawson: Faith, Hope and Science: Montreal, Queen's University Press, 274 p.

Shoshani, J., ed., 1992, Elephants: Majestic Creatures of the Wild: Emmaus, Pennsylvania, Rodale Press, 240 p.

Sharma, V., Lehmann, T., Stuckas, H., Funke, L., and Hiller, M., 2018, Loss of *RXFP2* and *INSL3* in Afrotheria shows that testicular descent is the ancestral condition in placental mammals: PLoS Biology 16, no. e2005293, 22 p.

TANAKH, 1985, JPS Translation of Scripture: Philadelphia, Jewish Publication Society, 1622 p.

Manuscript Accepted by the Society 15 January 2021
Manuscript Published Online 5 November 2021

Printed in the USA

The Geological Society of America
Memoir 218

The fossilist and his engraver: Samuel Springsguth's illustrations of James Parkinson's Organic Remains

Cherry Lewis*
Honorary Research Fellow, School of Earth Sciences, University of Bristol, Queens Road Bristol, BS8 1QU, UK

ABSTRACT

James Parkinson was an apothecary surgeon, political activist, and paleontologist during the latter part of the long eighteenth century. He is most famous for his 1817 work, *An Essay on the Shaking Palsy*, in which he was the first to describe and define the symptoms of *paralysis agitans*, a condition now known as Parkinson's disease. During his lifetime, however, he was internationally renowned for his three-volume study of fossils, *Organic Remains of a Former World*. Sales of this work continued for 25 years after Parkinson's death, even though much of its scientific content had become redundant. This was due to the beauty and fidelity of its illustrations, although Samuel Springsguth, the illustrator and engraver, is never explicitly acknowledged in the work. By examining several extant fossils known to have been in Parkinson's collection and illustrated in his works, it has been possible to gain some insight into the way that Parkinson and Springsguth worked together when illustrating these volumes.

JAMES PARKINSON

James Parkinson (1755–1824) lived and worked all his life in Hoxton in the Borough of Shoreditch, a small village on the northern outskirts of London. His father, John Parkinson (1725–1784), was an apothecary surgeon and at the age of 16 James was apprenticed to him for seven years to learn the "art and mystery" of the trade. At the end of this period Parkinson spent six months as an assistant surgeon at the London Hospital before joining his father in the Hoxton practice. When his father died, Parkinson felt the need to improve his medical education, which he considered had been "misdirected" since he had left the London Hospital still feeling "miserably ignorant" (Parkinson, 1800a, p. 36–37). Thus, in the autumn of 1785 he enrolled in a course of evening lectures given by the famous surgeon John Hunter (1728–1793).

At some point during this period Parkinson visited Hunter's spectacular museum of natural history, which was located on the two floors above the lecture theater that, among many other items, contained over three-thousand fossils. Parkinson later recalled that:

> From the earliest Moment of viewing the splendid and beautifully illustrative Collection of our revered and celebrated Countryman, John Hunter, Remains of Animals ... became the Subject of my anxious Investigations.[1]

**Mailing address:* 6 Monkswell Close, Monmouth, NP25 3PH, UK; *email:* cherrylewis5@gmail.com.

[1]Royal College of Surgeons: GOV-1-1-3, Minutes of the Council of the Royal College of Surgeons, Friday, 11 April 1823, Court of Assistants and Council Minute Book.

Lewis, C., 2022, The fossilist and his engraver: Samuel Springsguth's illustrations of James Parkinson's *Organic Remains*, *in* Clary, R.M., Rosenberg, G.D., and Evans, D.C., eds., The Evolution of Paleontological Art: Geological Society of America Memoir 218, p. 19–27, https://doi.org/10.1130/2021.1218(03).

From that time on, Parkinson began collecting fossils, a passion that was to dominate the rest of his life. Initially he started looking for specimens himself, but when his work commitments made this increasingly difficult he purchased or swapped them. But as his collection grew, he found it progressively difficult to identify and classify many of its rare and beautiful specimens because, as he explains, little had been published in English on fossils at that time.

Geology was still a young science, and enormous questions lay unanswered, such as how fossils could be found on the tops of mountains when they had evidently been deposited at the bottom of an ocean. Parkinson decided to take on the task of addressing such questions and between 1804 and 1811 published his seminal three-volume work on fossils, *Organic Remains of a Former World*. They were written in an epistolary style that was popular at the time, with each letter effectively representing a separate chapter. His acute observational powers, coupled with exquisite drawings, enabled Parkinson to present the first attempt in English to classify fossils scientifically but in a format that would appeal to an audience who had never before seen such exotic and beautiful creatures. Managing to integrate the geological evidence with prevailing religious values—at least to his own satisfaction—he revealed frightening images of "mutilated wrecks of former ages" (1804, p. 10) within a religious context with which the general public was familiar and felt comfortable. As a consequence, his books on *Organic Remains* became extraordinarily popular. Even the Romantic poets such as Byron and Shelley incorporated images conjured up by his works into their poetry (Lewis, 2017). It was partly due to Parkinson's works that fossil collecting became the nation's favorite pastime during the 1820s and 1830s, but he was also responsible for moving it on from a collectors' hobby into the dawn of a real science.

THE COLLECTION

When Parkinson sat down to write the first volume of *Organic Remains*, published in 1804, he had been collecting fossils for almost 20 years and had amassed what he described as a "tolerably large and systematic cabinet" (1804, p. vi). He continued to acquire fossils throughout his life, but after he died in 1824 his magnificent collection was sold at George Brettingham Sowerby's (1788–1854) auction rooms in April 1827. Initially Parkinson's wife, Mary Parkinson (1757–1838), who had been left the collection in Parkinson's will, did not want to split it up, but when she was unable to find an individual or museum willing to pay the £1500 she was asking for the whole collection (Lewis, 2017), she was forced to sell it at auction. That the collection was sold over four days is an indication of its considerable size, and Samuel Parkes's (1761–1825) comments imply it was of international significance (Parkes, 1815, p. 125):

> … there are several collections in England which I suspect far surpass those at Vienna. In confirmation I need only refer to Mr. Parkinson's superb collection in Hoxton Square, London. The polished specimens in his cabinet, of the various kinds of wood in a petrified state, are beautiful beyond comparison.

Parkinson's achievements were also recognized internationally when fossils were named in his honor by fossilists from many countries (Lewis, 2017), including the Jurassic ammonite *Parkinsonia parkinsoni*, dedicated to him by the renowned naturalist James Sowerby (1757–1822).

Parkinson's young friend Gideon Mantell (1790–1852) attended the auction and remembered the sad occasion well (Mantell, 1850, p. 126):

> The matchless collection of Mr. Parkinson (the author of the "Organic Remains of a former World"), which contained most of the specimens figured in his beautiful work, was disposed of by auction, and realized a very inadequate sum.

Prices had dropped considerably since Parkinson had purchased his fossils, largely due to the fact that he had been collecting during England's long wars with France when obtaining specimens, particularly from abroad, was difficult and consequently expensive. Once the wars were over, the number of dealers greatly increased; fossils became easier to obtain and so prices fell. In 1806, for example, Parkinson had dropped out of bidding for a fossil echinoderm when the price reached 15 guineas (£15 15s); it eventually sold for £15 17s 6d. When sold again in 1828, it fetched only £3 15s (Allingham, 1924, p. 45).

No catalogue of the auction has yet been found, though it seems likely that one exists, so we do not know exactly what the collection contained. And even though we do know some of the individuals who were present at the auction and bought specimens, such as Gideon Mantell, Adam Sedgwick (1785–1873), George Featherstonhaugh (1780–1866), and James de Carle Sowerby (1787–1871), identifying where those specimens are now is an almost impossible task since they have been amalgamated into later collections. But thanks to the diligence of Ron Cleevely (1934–2017), former senior scientific officer in the Department of Paleontology at the Natural History Museum, London, who identified some of Parkinson's specimens in their collections several decades ago, I have again managed to locate about a dozen individual fossils that once belonged to Parkinson, although only a few of these are of any significance.

THE ILLUSTRATIONS

Fortunately, we do have the beautiful illustrations that accompanied *Organic Remains*, most of which were drawn from specimens in Parkinson's collection. He tells us that only those plates not colored had been taken from other works (1808, p. xiv), and there are very few of these. Today, it is the illustrations that we particularly cherish, and individual plates (torn from the volumes) cost many hundreds of pounds, but they were also highly regarded at the time. Arthur Aiken (1783–1854), editor of the *Annual Review* and one of the founders, with Parkinson, of the Geological Society of London in 1807, was particularly complimentary about the illustrations when reviewing volume 2 (Aiken, 1809, p. 709):

> The descriptions ... are accompanied by figures from original drawings so admirably executed as to leave all former graphical representations of the subject far behind.

And in a review of volume 3, the *Monthly Magazine* also enthused about the illustrations (Anonymous, 1811, p. 694):

> Mr Parkinson has enriched his work with the most beautiful collection of engravings, colored after nature, that we remember to have seen in any book on these subjects.

But there is no mention in these reviews of the individual who drew and engraved the illustrations, and it is Parkinson on whom the accolades were showered, giving readers the impression that it was Parkinson himself who had created them. However, although Parkinson advocates the importance of taking drawing lessons to enable students to copy anatomical plates while studying surgery (1800a, p. 44) and Mantell says that Parkinson "revised my drawings" (Mantell, 1850, p. 14), Parkinson's own drawing skills were probably inadequate for the task of illustrating his volumes. This is demonstrated by a rather amateurish sketch drawn by Parkinson on the front of *The Villager's Friend and Physician* (Parkinson, 1800b; Lewis, 2017, p. 188). Furthermore, illustrating the fossils himself would have taken Parkinson a lot of additional time—something he was always short of.

Parkinson's daughter Emma Rook Parkinson (1788–1867) is believed to have hand colored the plates, certainly for the first edition and possibly for later editions (Thackray, 1976). Five hundred copies of the first volume were printed and, it is assumed, similar numbers were printed of the subsequent volumes; each plate in all these copies had to be individually hand colored. There are nine plates in the first volume, all of which are colored; only the frontispiece is not colored. The colored diagram on page 127 showing a "Section of Part of the Strata of Coal etc at Bovey" and giving the thickness of each coal seam was probably drawn by Parkinson himself as it has no inscription or imprint. The 19 plates and frontispiece in volume 2 are all colored, except for plate XIII, which is printed in bistre, and plate XIX, which was taken from someone else's work (discussed below), plus a few individual fossils on some of the plates. In volume 3 there are 22 plates and a frontispiece, all of which are colored except for a few individual fossils. This makes a total of at least 25,500 plates (51 plates × 500 copies) that had to be hand colored over the seven years during which the first editions of all three volumes were produced. Nowhere does Parkinson acknowledge this gargantuan task, although he does say that Emma accompanied him on some of his fossil-hunting sojourns (Parkinson, 1804). It is difficult to imagine that Emma colored all the plates on her own, even for just the first edition, and it seems more likely that there was a team of colorists of which she was a part. She would only have been 16 when the first volume was published in 1804.

In common with most authors of the time, Parkinson also does not acknowledge the person who drew almost all the illustrations and engraved all the copper plates, but on close inspection of the illustrations, it can be seen that the inscription that appears on each plate is "S. Springsguth. Del et sculp," where Springsguth both drew and engraved the plate, or "S. Springsguth. Sculp" on the few he only engraved. However, the term "engraver" can be misleading since artists such as Springsguth would be proficient in both etching and engraving. The term engraver generally covered both techniques, as it does in this chapter, unless otherwise stated.

The frontispiece to volume 1 depicts a dramatic landscape of jagged rocks that form the post-diluvian world left behind as the waters of Noah's Flood recede. In the background the Ark sits stranded on Mount Ararat, while in the foreground a few shells lie on the sand waiting to become fossilized. In this first volume Parkinson clearly adheres to the belief that fossils were found in their present locations because their original remains had been washed there during Noah's Flood, which this image illustrates. A full discussion of the evolution of Parkinson's religious beliefs can be found in Lewis (2013, 2017); it is therefore sufficient to say here that by the end of volume 1, he had started to question such views, and by the end of volume 3, due to his improved understanding of geology, he considered Moses's account of the deluge as written in the Bible to be a myth. This frontispiece is annotated: "Designed by R. Corbould, Esqr. Engraved by S. Springsguth." Richard Corbould (1757–1831) was an artist who specialized in landscapes. Like all of the plates, this frontispiece has the imprint "Publish'd as the Act directs, by J. Parkinson, Hoxton, June 1, 1804," although the date changes with the volumes. This printing patent or printing privilege was a precursor of modern copyright and gave Parkinson the exclusive right to have the work printed.

In volume 2 the frontispiece of a large, fossilized sponge and plate XIV of a beautiful "Stone Lily" or "Lily Encrinite" (crinoid) were both drawn by a Mrs. Sheffield, and she is the only person acknowledged in the text as having contributed to the illustrations. When describing the crinoid, Parkinson says (1808, p. 188):

> I am indebted to the correct pencil of Mrs. Sheffield, of the Polygon, Somers' Town, for the exact delineation of this specimen, as well as for the elegant drawing of the fossil which appears in the frontispiece.

Mrs. Sheffield's illustrations were engraved by Springsguth, as was plate IX, the drawings for which were taken from a paper in the *Philosophical Transactions* (see below). In volume 3 all plates, including the striking frontispiece that depicts "The back grinding tooth of the MAMMOTH or MASTODON of Ohio – weight 4 lbs. 7 oz." (Fig. 1), were drawn and engraved by Springsguth, although there are a few individual fossils that are not colored and which Springsguth, therefore, only

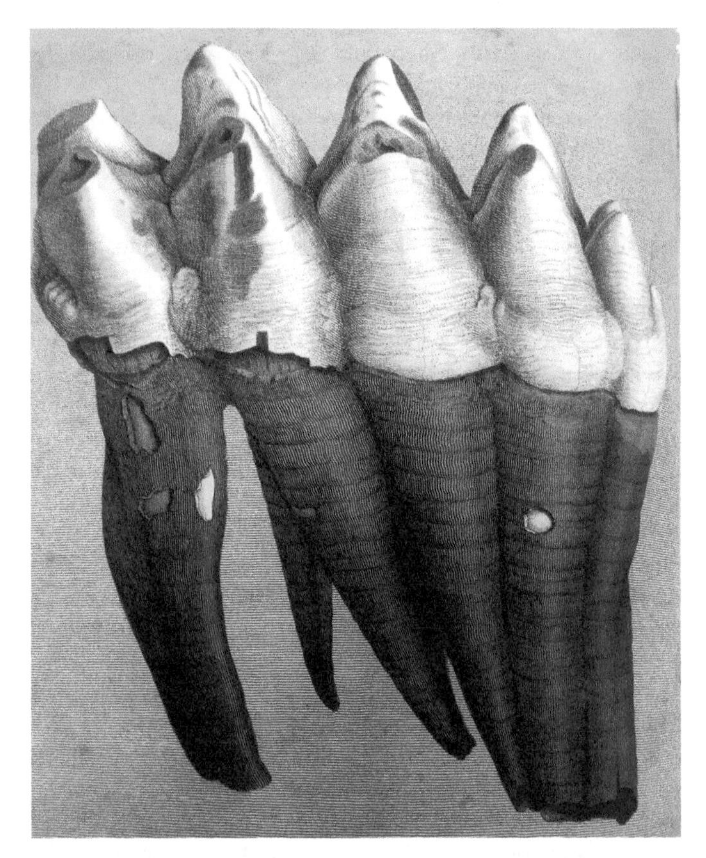

Figure 1. Frontispiece to volume 3 of *Organic Remains of a Former World* (1811) shows the back grinding tooth of the mammoth or mastodon of Ohio weighing 4 lbs. 7 oz.

engraved. It is worth noting that below the frontispiece, in very small print, it says: "Drawn and Engraved by S. Springsguth from the original." This formal credit placed neatly below the illustration, rather than Springsguth's usual abbreviated inscription scrawled on the illustration itself, suggests it may be the only occasion where Parkinson has explicitly acknowledged Springsguth's work.

SAMUEL SPRINGSGUTH

Samuel Springsguth (1769–184?) was born in Covent Garden, London (Parent, 2018), the eldest surviving but third child born to Joachim Samuel Springsguth (1742–1795) and his wife Anne Norwood (1738–1863). Joachim was a habit-maker (tailor) and also known as Samuel. The son Samuel was probably one of twins as another child, Joachim, who died in 1871 aged two, must also have been born in 1769.[2] The exact date of Springsguth's death is unknown. His four-line will was written in 1832 and left everything to his wife Maria (née Jane Maria Hadwen [1764–1863]), but it was not proved until June 1844 wherein it states that Springsguth had been "deceased for several years before." He was recorded as living in Hoxton in the 1841 census so he must have died sometime between June 1841 and June 1844.

In 1783, at the age of 14, Springsguth was apprenticed to the engraver Thomas Cook (1745–1818). Cook worked as a printmaker in a number of contexts, producing portraits for the *Gentleman's Magazine* and frontispieces for book publishers. He was most famous for his reproductions of the works of Hogarth, which were published as *Hogarth Restored* in 1806 (Myrone, 2004). Springsguth's career followed a path similar to that of his master, engraving landscapes, portraits, and illustrations in books, including one by Isaac Weld (1774–1856) that described Weld's travels through the United States and Canada in 1795–1797 (Weld, 1799). In particular Springsguth illustrated books for children such as *Robinson Crusoe* and the *Cabinet of Lilliput*, a series of "instructive stories" in 12 miniature books just 5 cm high. It seems his eldest son, also Samuel Springsguth (1794–1861), followed his father into the engraving trade, producing portraits such as that of George Parker Bidder (1806–1878), "The Extraordinary Mental Calculator Aged 12 Years," which is signed Samuel Springsguth Jr.

Parkinson first seems to have become involved with Springsguth around 1800 when Parkinson published his *Chemical Pocket Book* (1800c) and Springsguth engraved the frontispiece for the 1801 and later editions. As Springsguth lived in and around Shoreditch for much of his life, it would have been convenient for him to visit Parkinson's house where he could draw most of the specimens for *Organic Remains* from Parkinson's own collection. Parkinson probably arranged the fossils for Springsguth beforehand as he wanted them to appear in the volumes. Over the years, Springsguth created over 1000 individual drawings and engravings of fossils for Parkinson, including those on the 10 plates from *Outlines of Oryctology*, the student textbook on fossils that Parkinson published in 1822.

As most engraving apprenticeships were seven years, Springsguth would have had more than 10 years of practice as a journeyman engraver before starting work with Parkinson on *Organic Remains,* so he would have been considerably experienced. But to illustrate the patience, dexterity, and attention to detail required for this work, as well as the extraordinary length of time each plate must have taken, it is worth summarizing the techniques required to produce these plates.

Having first drawn the images on paper, Springsguth would then transfer them onto the copper plates to create printable images using either or both engraving and etching intaglio methods, which required great skill. In etching, the process would start with the highly polished surface of a copper plate, 1–3 mm thick, being coated with a thin layer of a mixture of resins, asphaltum, and wax (the ground or resist). The drawing would be transferred onto this layer by scribing with an etching needle, thereby exposing the copper for etching (biting) the lines with acid. In engraving the lines were incised directly into the bare metal plate using a tool called a burin that was pushed across the highly polished copper surface. Examination of the illustrations suggests that

[2]A family tree and various dates in Springsguth's life can be found at https://caliendi.com/Springsguth/indil18.html (accessed February 2021).

both methods were used; this was common at the time to obtain a wider range of effects, but engraving appears to have been used more frequently.[3]

Before printing took place, the plate was heated and covered with ink, the warm ink seeping into the finest of depressions and filling the lines and textures of the drawing. Surplus ink was then wiped off the surface before dampened imprint paper was placed against the plate, covered by a blanket, and fed through a high-pressure printing press. The paper picked up the ink from the incised lines to make the print, and the process was repeated for each copy required. A copper plate could be used several hundred times to produce a print, by which time the image quality would have deteriorated due to wear of the soft metal. Wear on the copperplate may well have been a factor in Parkinson's decision to print 500 copies of the first edition, as reworking of the plate would have been necessary to improve the print quality after that many copies had been made.

One of the most difficult aspects of Springsguth's work was that he had to reverse the image he was engraving so that it would appear the right way round when printed. To achieve this most engravers would have a mirror on the table which reflected, and thus reversed, the image being copied. Knowing this, and by examining one or two of the specimens known to have been both in Parkinson's collection and illustrated in *Organic Remains*, it is possible to gain some insight into how Springsguth and Parkinson worked together when making the engravings.

Figure 2A shows photographs of both valves of a fossilized oyster that was purchased by the British Museum in 1860 from James de Carle Sowerby, who had presumably purchased it at the auction of Parkinson's fossils in 1827. It is now in the Natural History Museum, London. This specimen is illustrated in figure 1 of plate XV, volume 3 of *Organic Remains*, and on page 217 Parkinson describes it as a

> … shell as large, and even larger, than the common oyster, being plicated, and having the margin formed by acute-angled teeth, like those of the saw, and placed at right angles with the surface of the shell: the margin being finely striated by the apposition of the different lamellae.

Comparison of the photos with the illustration drawn and engraved by Springsguth (Fig. 2B) makes it evident that they are one and the same specimen, and yet careful examination shows one of two possibilities: either the illustration was not reversed when it was engraved, or it was reversed and then "embellished" to look like the less damaged valve. Either way, the illustration looks more complete than the specimen really was and suggests that other specimens may have been "tidied up" in this way to present a more pleasing image.

Similarly, the stem and holdfast of the crinoid photographed in Figure 3A can confidently be identified as figure 5 on plate XV in volume 2 (Fig. 3B). Parkinson named this the Turban encrinite (Parkinson, 1808, p. 196) from the shape of the calyx. The original specimen is now in the Natural History Museum, but it has had a convoluted history. It was identified as having belonged to Parkinson when Benjamin Bright (1823–1900) gave the family collection to the British Museum in 1873 (Kark and Moore, 1981). It had been purchased in 1827 by Benjamin's uncle, Richard Bright (1759–1858) of Bright's disease, from George Sowerby who, in turn, acquired it at Parkinson's auction. Parkinson says the specimen was originally in the collection of John Strange (1732–1799), so he probably bought it at the auction of Strange's

[3]For those wishing to know more about these techniques, see Stijnman (2012).

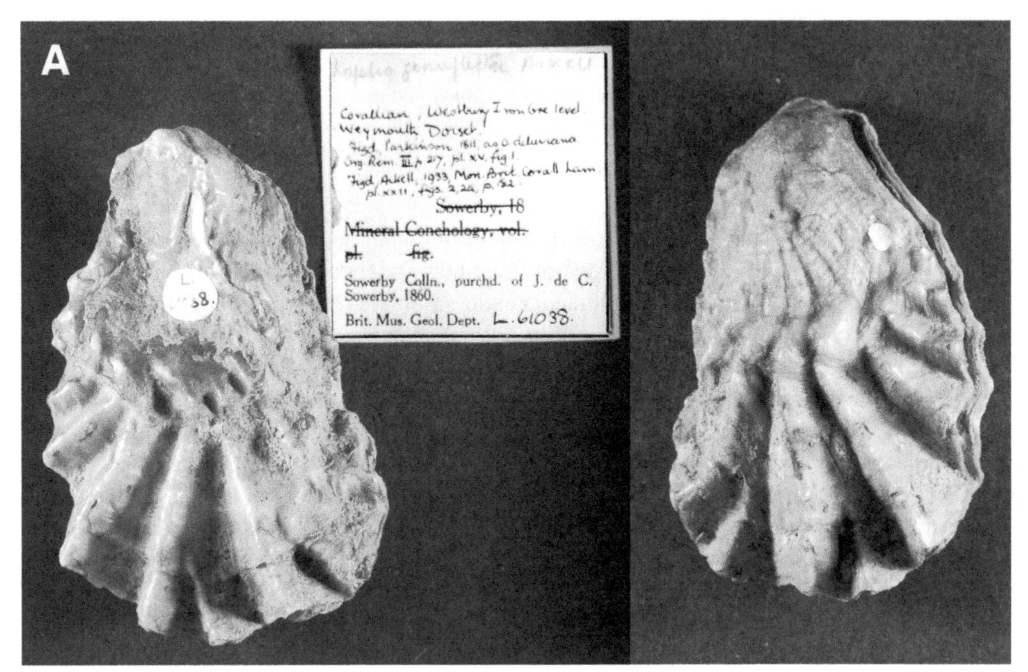

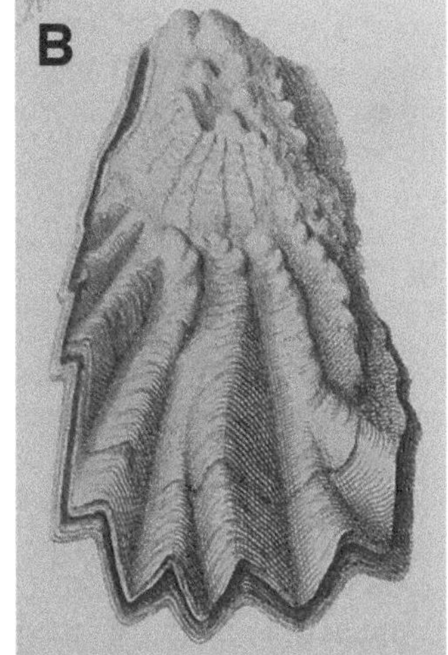

Figure 2. (A) Photographs of both valves of (B) the fossilized oyster illustrated on plate XV, figure 1, in volume 3 of *Organic Remains* (1811).

Figure 3. (A) Photograph of the stem and holdfast of (B) the "Turban encrinite" illustrated on plate XV, figure 5, in volume 2 of *Organic Remains* (1808).

collection in 1801, which Parkinson is known to have attended, "but where it was obtained from [before that] I have had no opportunity of knowing" (Parkinson, 1808, p. 195). Such complex ownership histories illustrate why it is so difficult to locate Parkinson's specimens today.

Examination of the original specimen (Fig. 3A), which is ~13 cm long, shows that the illustration has been drawn the correct way round, but that it is a "compilation" of features that are highlighted in the text (Parkinson, 1808, p. 203) and which Parkinson wanted to demonstrate in the illustration (Fig. 3B):

> The nature and uses of the parts just described are clearly ascertained by the extraordinary and unique specimen, plate XV. Fig. 5 … The extreme thinness of the vertebrae [ossicles], it has been already observed, appears to be one of the characteristics of this species of endocrinite; and, in this specimen, this character is very observable; since although the trunk, from which the roots proceed, is only about an inch in length, upwards of 30 vertebrae enter into its formation.

The pile of five ossicles seen on the left-hand side of the illustration, for example, is not evident anywhere on the original specimen but has been added to the illustration to demonstrate the "extreme thinness of the vertebrae." Likewise, the roots protruding from the base of the stem have been made to look much more like roots than they actually do in the hand specimen. Parkinson was the first to recognize which way up crinoids grew. With a long stalk and cuplike body bearing five feather-like fronds that are usually branched, it was not clear at the time if crinoids were animals or plants, nor which way up they grew. It was Parkinson who first understood that the fronds were actually tentacles and not roots, as had previously been supposed, and it may well have been this specimen, with its rarely preserved roots, that made him realize this. A fellow fossilist enthused about this revelation (Miller, 1821, p. 94):

> It is this ingenious discovery and exposure of an error of former writers on these animals, which has greatly contributed to the better understanding of their economy and anatomical details. Mr. PARKINSON's able work on the Organic Remains of a Former World must indeed be considered as the publication of the greatest importance in the study of these remains….

It was therefore important to Parkinson that the illustration should demonstrate how the roots grew out of the stem, which is not immediately evident from the hand specimen. So it seems he advised Springsguth to enhance the roots in the illustration to make his point absolutely clear to readers.

The only other fossil of any significance that we can now identify as having been owned by Parkinson is the silicified sponge, *Chenendopora michelinii* Hinde, photographed in Figure 4A, which illustrates the frontispiece to the second (1808) volume of *Organic Remains*. It was noted previously that this fossil sponge was drawn by Mrs. Sheffield and engraved by Springsguth, and as the illustration in Figure 4B demonstrates, it is a faithful replica of the original specimen, which is now in the Natural History Museum, London.

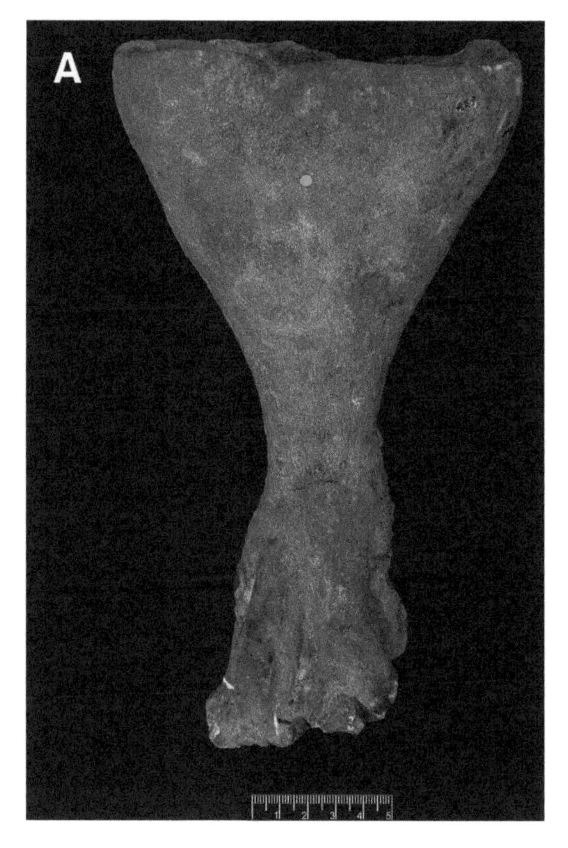

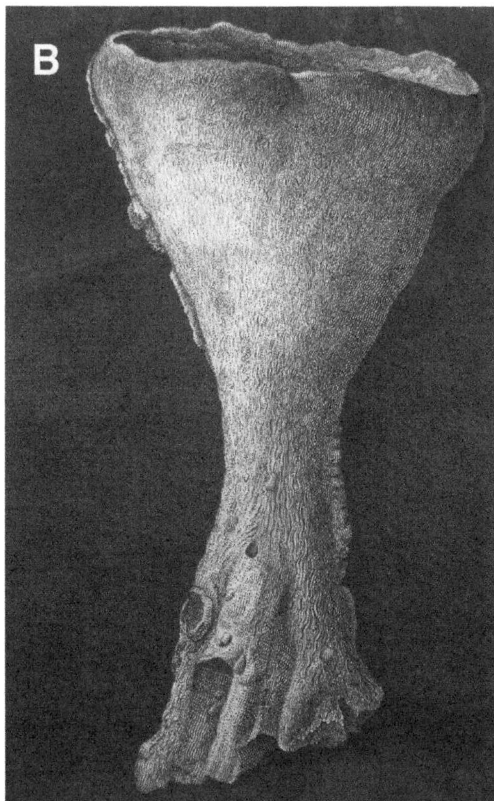

Figure 4. (A) Photograph of the silicified sponge, *Chenendopora michelinii* Hinde. (B) The illustration of this sponge, drawn by Mrs. Sheffield and engraved by Springsguth, adorned the frontispiece to volume 2 of *Organic Remains* (1808).

It is also interesting to note how Springsguth approached engraving images from other people's works. In volume 2, Parkinson quotes extensively from *The Natural History of Many Curious and Uncommon Zoophytes: Collected from Various Parts of the Globe* (Ellis and Solander, 1786), as well as from several of Ellis's (1710?–1776) papers published in the *Philosophical Transactions*. Parkinson's figures 1 and 2 of Plate XIX in volume 2 (Fig. 5A), for example, have been copied from Ellis (1761), plate XIV, figure M, and plate XIII, figure B, respectively (Figs. 5B and 5C). It is worth noting that in the copy of *Organic Remains* held by the University of Bristol from which Figure 5A is taken, figures 2 and 3 are correctly labeled but awkwardly laid out on the page. Although this is a "first edition" as identified by the publishers and booksellers listed (Thackray, 1976), earlier printings have these two figures labeled the other (wrong) way round, which Parkinson must have subsequently corrected.[4] From such details a picture of the volume's printing history can be established. Springsguth, probably using the pin-prick method, has reproduced Ellis's illustrations with great accuracy, except that they are mirror images of how they appeared in Ellis's works. Presumably Springsguth found it easier to do this since he did not have to reverse the image, and Parkinson found it acceptable because in this instance it did not matter which way round they were reproduced.

[4]Karen Cook (2019, personal commun.).

THE VOLUMES

In 1834, James Laird (1779–1841), the Geological Society's first secretary, wrote to George Bellas Greenough (1778–1855), the Geological Society's first president, to reminisce about those heady days when the Society had been inaugurated back in 1807. Laird had been responsible for overseeing the Society's first volume of *Transactions* (to which Parkinson was a contributor) through what seems to have been its rather tortuous publication process in 1811 (Lewis, 2009). Looking back to this time, Laird says:

> Our first volume is interesting as shewing the very imperfect state of Geological Science at the commencement of our Society's proceedings.[5]

Indeed, geology had greatly advanced in the 27 years since the Society had been founded and by the 1830s was entering its "golden age." At no other time in the history of geology did an understanding of the subject increase at such a pace; undoubtedly Parkinson contributed to this progress with *Organic Remains*, which remained in print for over 30 years. A strong advocate for the work of William Smith (1769–1839), at a time when many in the Geological Society dismissed Smith's ideas, Parkinson often insisted at Society meetings that fossils could tell us about the formation of the Earth in a way that nothing else could (Lewis, 2017).

[5]UCL: AD7981 1099, Laird to Greenough, 18 March 1834.

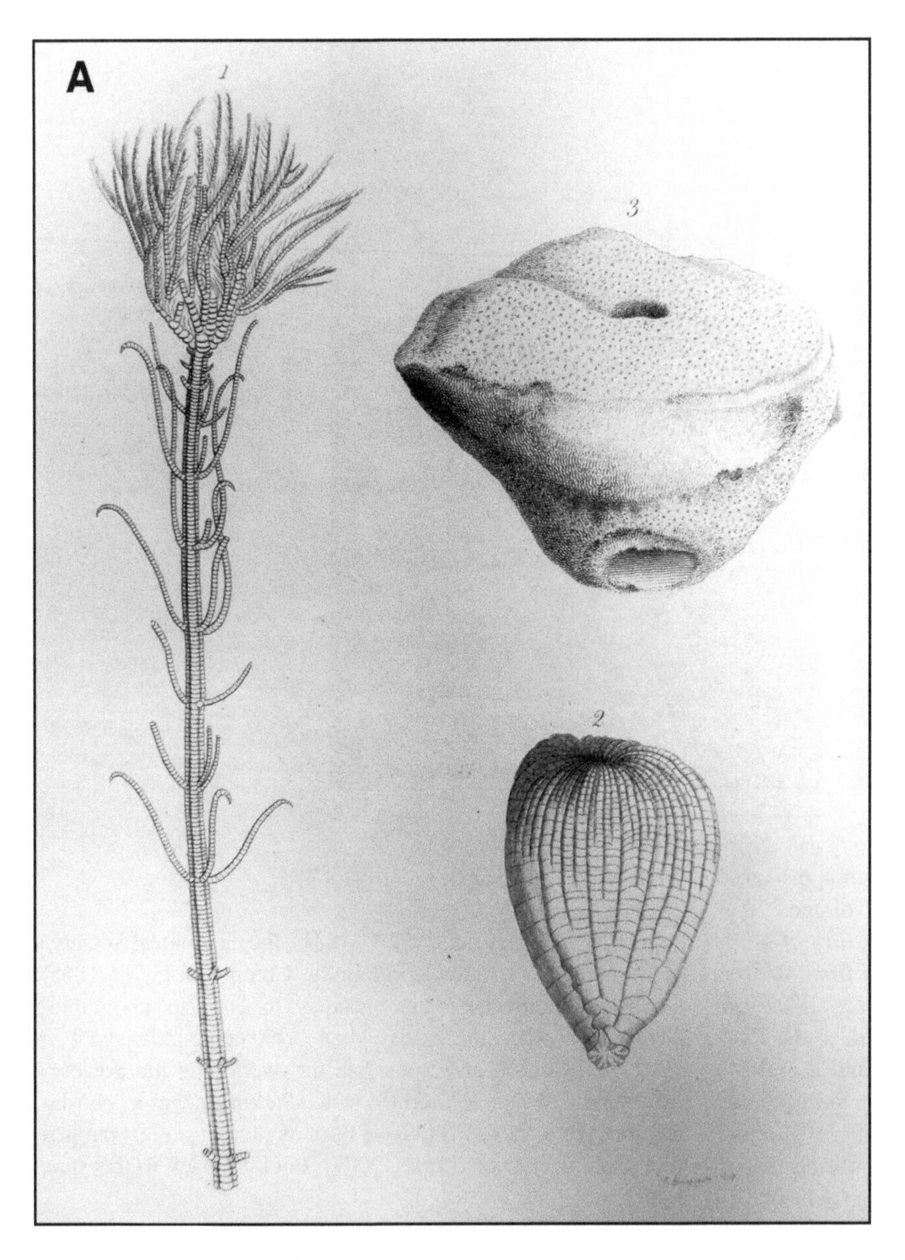

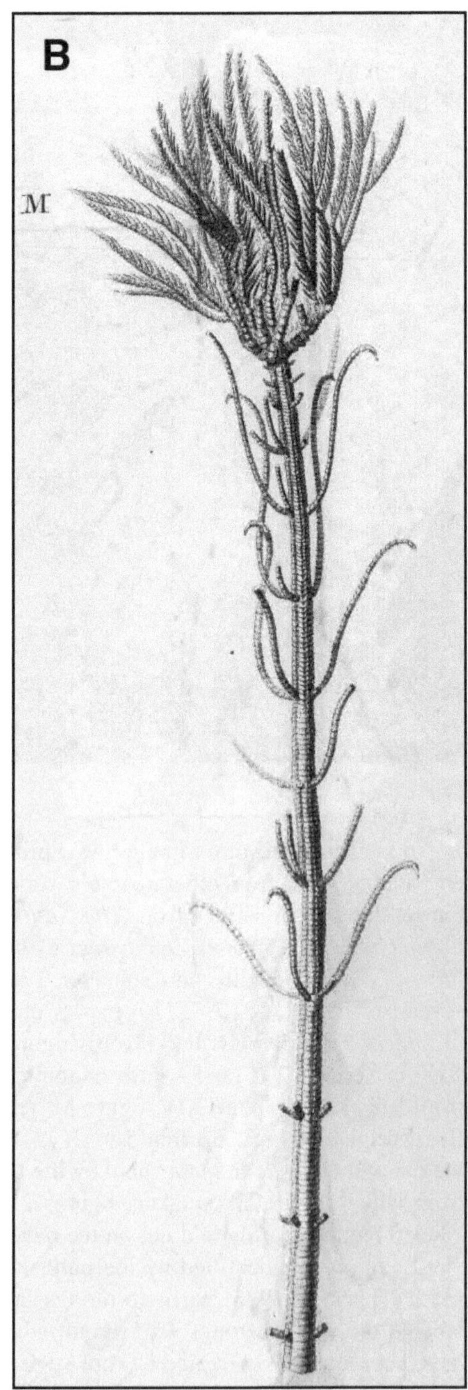

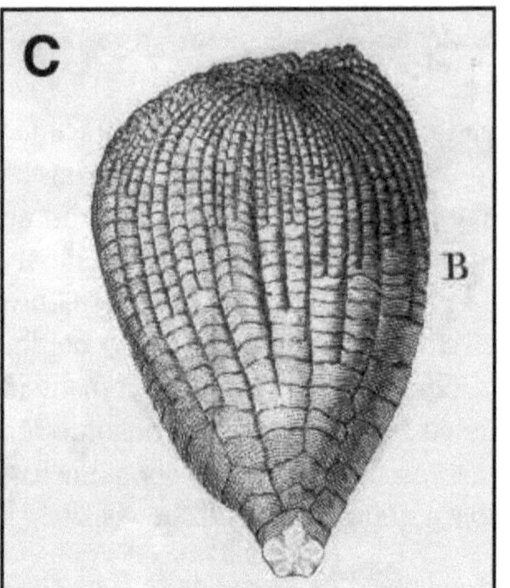

Figure 5. (A) Plate XIX from volume 2 of *Organic Remains* (1808). Figures 1 and 2 on this plate have been copied from Ellis (1761). (B) and (C) show those figures as drawn by Ellis.

The first volume of *Organic Remains* initially sold for £2 2s 6d, rising to £2 12s 6d in 1808, when the second volume was published, which also sold for £2 12s 6d. The third volume, published in 1811, was more expensive at £3 13s 6d but has a larger number of plates. A second edition of volume 1 also appeared in 1811, which enabled the three volumes to be sold together for £8 8s 6d, since the first volume went out of print in 1810. Parkinson did make minor changes to the text for this second edition (and the numbering of the letters was corrected; in the first edition of the first volume, letter XXX was numbered XXI), but these changes were largely grammatical rather than scientific (Thackray, 1976). After Parkinson's death in December 1824, the stock of unbound sheets of the three volumes passed from his current publisher—Sherwood, Neely, and Jones of Paternoster Row—to Michael Angelo Nattali (ca. 1810–1850) of Covent Garden, who had the plates printed on paper watermarked 1825 and sold the three volumes for 10 guineas. Around 1844, the stock passed to another publisher, Henry George Bohn (1796–1884), also of Covent Garden, who printed a "second edition" with plates hand colored by the Sowerbys; this also sold for 10 guineas. Presumably Bohn anticipated making a profit on this venture, but it is interesting to ask why people kept buying the volumes since Parkinson's epistolary style and the volumes' scientific content must have seemed very out of date by the 1840s. It is Gideon Mantell who provides an answer to this conundrum.

In the late 1840s, the stock of Parkinson's volumes finally ran out, but Bohn still had the copper plates that had been engraved by Springsguth, who had also died by this time. In 1850, Mantell arranged with Bohn to reprint all the plates from *Organic Remains* (except the frontispiece to volume 1 of Noah's Ark on Mount Ararat), in his *Pictorial Atlas of Fossil Remains*. Mantell explains why in his introduction (Mantell, 1850, p. 13):

> The publication of Mr Parkinson's "*Organic Remains of a Former World*," at the commencement of the present century, must be regarded as a memorable event in the history of British Palaeontology: it was the first attempt to give a familiar and scientific account of the fossil relics of animals and plants, accompanied by figures of the specimens described.... Although nearly forty years have since elapsed, and hundreds of geological works, of all kinds and degrees of merit, have subsequently been issued, Mr. Parkinson's Plates, owing to their fidelity and beauty, are still in such request, as to induce the proprietor, Mr. Bohn, now that the work is out of print, to publish them, with the descriptions and modern names of the fossils represented.

In reality it was Springsguth's, not Parkinson's, beautiful plates that were still in such demand. Even today, people buying what they think are Parkinson's prints still do not appreciate this.

ACKNOWLEDGMENTS

I am indebted to Special Collections Librarian Michael Richardson, University of Bristol, for access to first editions of Parkinson's three volumes of *Organic Remains* and for being allowed to photograph the plates. I am also grateful to Consuelo Sendino, Collection Manager, Earth Sciences Natural History Museum, London, and others at the Natural History Museum, for helping me to locate specimens from Parkinson's collection and allowing me to photograph them. I had very helpful discussions with Special Collections Librarian Karen Cook, Kenneth Spencer Research Library, University of Kansas, who enlightened me with regard to nineteenth-century engraving techniques.

REFERENCES CITED

Aiken, A., 1809, The Annual Review, and History of Literature for 1809, v. VII, p. 709.

Allingham, E.G., 1924, A Romance of the Rostrum: Being the Business Life of Henry Stevens, and the History of Thirty-eight King Street: London, H.F. & G. Witherby, London, 333 p.

Anonymous, 1811, Review of Organic Remains of a Former World, Volume III: Monthly Magazine, v. XXXII, no. II, p. 694.

Ellis, J., 1761, An account of an Encrinus or Starfish with a jointed stem, taken on the coast of Barbados...: Philosophical Transactions, v. 52, p. 357–365.

Ellis, J., and Solander, D., 1786, The Natural History of Many Curious and Uncommon Zoophytes: Collected from Various Parts of the Globe: London, Benjamin White and Son, and Peter Elmsly, 208 p.

Kark, R.M., and Moore, D.T., 1981, The life, work, and geological collections of Richard Bright, M.D. (1789–1858): Archives of Natural History, v. 10, no. 1, p. 119–151, https://doi.org/10.3366/anh.1981.10.1.119.

Lewis, C.L.E., 2009, Doctoring geology: The medical origins of the Geological Society, in Lewis, C.L.E., and Knell, S., eds., The Making of the Geological Society of London: Geological Society, London, Special Publication 317, p. 49–92, https://doi.org/10.1144/SP317.2.

Lewis, C.L.E., 2013, James Parkinson's 'system of successive creations', in Duffin, C.J., Moody, R.T.J., and Gardner-Thorpe, C., eds., A History of Geology and Medicine: Geological Society, London, Special Publication 375, p. 339–348.

Lewis, C.L.E., 2017, The Enlightened Mr Parkinson: London, Icon Books, Ltd.

Mantell, G., 1850, A Pictorial Atlas of Fossil Remains: London, H.G. Bohn, 207 p.

Miller, J.S., 1821, A Natural History of the Crinoidea or Lily-shaped Animals: Bristol, C. Frost, 150 p.

Myrone, M., 2004, Boydell, John, engravers, in Oxford Dictionary of National Biography: Oxford, UK, Oxford University Press (accessed online December 2019).

Parent, A., 2018, A tribute to James Parkinson: The Canadian Journal of Neurological Sciences, v. 45, p. 83–89, https://doi.org/10.1017/cjn.2017.270.

Parkes, S., 1815, Chemical Essays, Volume V: London, Baldwin, Cradock, and Joy.

Parkinson, J., 1800a, The Hospital Pupil; or, an Essay Intended to Facilitate the Study of Medicine and Surgery: London, H.D. Symonds.

Parkinson, J., 1800b, The Villager's Friend and Physician: London, H.D. Symonds.

Parkinson, J., 1800c, The Chemical Pocket-book: London, Symonds, Murray, and Highley.

Parkinson, J., 1804, Organic Remains of a Former World (Vol. 1): London, J. Robson (and others).

Parkinson, J., 1808, Organic Remains of a Former World (Vol. 2): London, Nornaville and Fell (and others).

Parkinson, J., 1811, Organic Remains of a Former World (Vol. 3): London, Sherwood, Neely, and Jones (and others).

Parkinson, J., 1822, Outlines of Oryctology: London, Sherwood, Neely, and Jones, 346 p.

Stijnman, A., 2012, Engraving and Etching 1400–2000: A History of the Development of Manual Intaglio Printmaking Processes: London, Archetype Publications, 240 p.

Thackray, J., 1976, James Parkinson's "Organic Remains": Journal of the Society for the Bibliography of Natural History, v. 7, no. 4, p. 451–466, https://doi.org/10.3366/jsbnh.1976.7.4.451.

Weld, I., 1799, Travels through the States of North America, and the Provinces of Upper and Lower Canada during the Years 1795, 1796, and 1797: London, John Stockdale, 552 p.

Manuscript Accepted by the Society 15 January 2021
Manuscript Published Online 2 August 2021

Printed in the USA

The Geological Society of America
Memoir 218

Fossil illustrations from the work of William Smith

Peter Wigley
Wells Park, Cullompton, Devon EX15 1LR, UK

Abstract

William Smith's *Strata Identified by Organized Fossils*, published between 1816 and 1819, was one of the most important books in the development of stratigraphy; it was also significant in the evolution of paleontological art and illustration. For the first time, Smith organized fossil illustrations in plates according to the order of the strata. Each stratigraphic plate showed characteristic assemblages of fossils. The publication was a joint venture between Smith and James Sowerby and it was Sowerby who elevated the work into the realm of art. Smith had been influenced by the work of previous authors, in particular Robert Plot and John Morton, who, some 150 years earlier, had published texts illustrated by fossil engravings. The difference between these engravings and those of Sowerby shows the extent to which fossil illustration had evolved. Unlike previous work where the engravings were very mechanical, Sowerby's were extraordinarily naturalistic. By means of subtle lines, stipple, and water coloring, Sowerby was able to achieve extremely realistic and aesthetically pleasing artwork. Unusually, many of Smith's originals fossils are still intact and when photographs of these specimens are compared to the illustrations, the quality of Sowerby's work is striking. Smith also selected earth-colors for the paper on which the illustrations were produced, with colors reflecting the strata in which the fossils were embedded. Although this technique had some disadvantages, it aimed to bridge the gap between science and art.

INTRODUCTION

William Smith (1769–1839) is remembered by many for his famous 1815 map: *A Delineation of the Strata of England and Wales, with Part of Scotland*. However, he also had a profound influence on the science of stratigraphy, particularly in his use of fossils to characterize strata. To Smith, fossils were an important tool, and he was very particular to describe them and to record their locations and the strata in which they occurred. Like many naturalists and geologists of his day, Smith could draw, which in an age before photography was a distinct advantage. In the Smith Collection at the Oxford University Museum of Natural History, there are numerous examples of well-executed sketches of fossils, maps, and sections by Smith.[1] He also had a talent for portraiture and made numerous sketches of friends and acquaintances. Between 1816 and 1819, Smith, in collaboration with James Sowerby (1757–1822), published four parts of *Strata Identified by Organized Fossils* (Smith, 1816–1819). The publication laid the foundation for future stratigraphic studies and remains a pioneering publication. Aside from their scientific importance, the illustrations by Sowerby are exquisite works of art.

[1]Oxford University Museum of Natural History, William Smith Collection Online: http://www.oum.ox.ac.uk/collections/archives.php (accessed March 2021).

Wigley, P., 2022, Fossil illustrations from the work of William Smith, *in* Clary, R.M., Rosenberg, G.D., and Evans, D.C., eds., The Evolution of Paleontological Art: Geological Society of America Memoir 218, p. 29–36, https://doi.org/10.1130/2021.1218(04).

INFLUENCES

William Smith's nephew John Phillips (1800–1874) wrote in his *Memoirs of William Smith* (Phillips, 1844, p. 24) that early in his career, Smith drew inspiration from the work of previous authors. These included Robert Plot, John Morton, and John Woodward. Robert Plot (1640–1696) had written *Natural History of Oxfordshire* (Plot, 1677), which contained descriptions and illustrations of numerous fossils, rocks, and minerals engraved by Michael Burghers (1647/8–1727). John Morton's (?1671–1726) *The Natural History of Northamptonshire* (Morton, 1712) included 10 complete plates of fossils drawn by P. La Vergne (1684–1756) and engraved by M. Vandergucht (1660–1725). Two examples of these engravers' work are shown in Figures 1A–1B. Both Burghers and Vandergucht were traditional engravers, and although their work is extremely competent it appears somewhat mechanistic. For example, Vandergucht's line-work on the echinoid (Fig. 1B) was created using either a French curve or possibly a mechanical device, and the rendering of the radial plates seems to be an afterthought. Vandergucht also used hatched shading around the objects, a traditional engraver's device to give depth. Similarly, Burghers' spiral drawn on the ammonite (Fig. 1A) looks geometric, and the overall effect is more like metalwork than a fossil, especially when compared to Sowerby's naturalistic style (Fig. 1C). The plates are mostly signed by the artist and the engraver, and on early plates dedications to various dignitaries often include their armorial emblems. While these extravagant embellishments were, no doubt, well-intentioned, they tend to overpower the illustrated fossils.

Robert Plot had some strange ideas concerning the origin of his fossils; he did not believe they were organic remains but rather chemically derived from crystallization of various compounds including urine. His classification system of fossils and minerals was equally eccentric. He conceived their origin as either from heavenly bodies—belemnites resulting from thunderbolts—air, or the watery kingdom and also figured specimens that resembled human and animal body parts—heart, kidneys, and even feet. By modern standards, these ideas may seem ridiculous, but nevertheless these early published plates represent the beginning of scientific illustration of fossil material. It is unlikely that Smith would have had much time for Plot's fanciful theories, but he was influenced by the descriptions and illustrations of the fossils in both Plot's and Morton's books, and in time he would incorporate some of them into his own work.

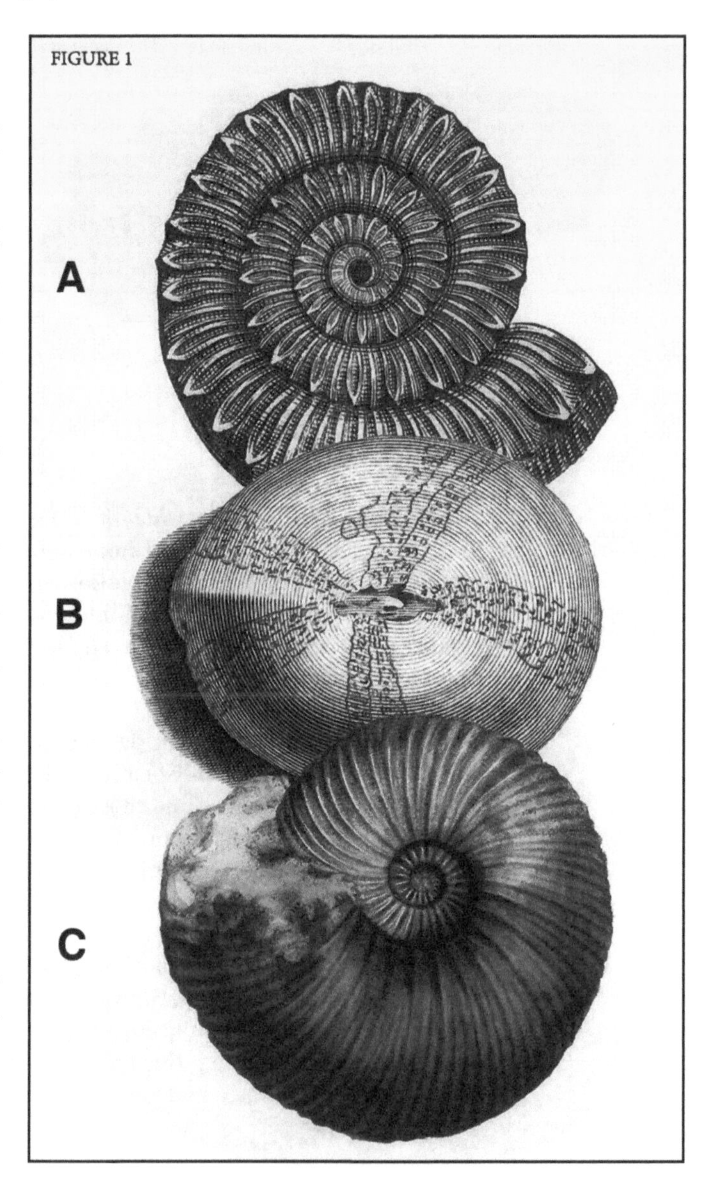

Figure 1. Illustrative styles of fossil engravings from the seventeenth, eighteenth, and early nineteenth centuries are shown. (A) Illustration of an ammonite from Plot's (1677) *Natural History of Oxfordshire*, table 5, no. 13, p. 112, engraved by Michael Burghers. Plot used the term "Ophiomorpit" to describe this ammonite, which is probably a *Stephanoceras*. (B) Illustration of an echinoid from John Morton's *Natural History of Northamptonshire* (Morton, 1712, table 10, no. 11, p. 246). Morton named it "Galeatus" because of its helmet shape. Engraved by Michael Vandergucht. Courtesy Dave Williams. (C) Illustration of an ammonite from Sowerby's (1812–1818) *The Mineral Conchology of Great Britain*; table CVIII is described by Sowerby as *Ammonites Nutfieldiensis*. Courtesy of Dave Williams.

STRATA IDENTIFIED BY ORGANIZED FOSSILS

In the first decade of the nineteenth century, Smith—while busy with his great map of the strata of England and Wales, land draining, and other schemes—also found time to prepare his groundbreaking publication *Strata Identified by Organized Fossils* (Smith, 1816–1819). In this endeavor he was ably assisted by James Sowerby, an eminent natural historian, artist, and engraver. In 1808 Smith contacted Sowerby by letter (Cox, 1942). The purpose of this letter, apart from introducing himself, was to reassure Sowerby that his planned publication would in no way conflict with Sowerby's (1812–1818) *The Mineral Conchology of Great Britain*. Later that year (Cox, 1942) Smith met Sowerby, and from the letter he wrote after the meeting, it is clear that the pair had much in common. Smith went on to propose a joint venture to publish his work. This publication was planned by Smith to be issued to subscribers on a monthly basis in seven parts. Only four parts were ever published between 1816 and 1819, but despite this, Smith and Sowerby have left a legacy of 18 wonderful colored plates that show fossil assemblages stratigraphically arranged from the Craig (Crag, Plio-Pleistocene) down to the Fuller's Earth Rock (Middle Jurassic).

SMITH'S FOSSIL COLLECTION

William Smith had avidly collected fossils throughout his life. His fossils were the tools of his trade, and they were essential to his "Science of the Strata." In 1815, when his financial circumstances were at an all-time low, he started negotiations to sell this valuable resource to the British Museum. The story of the sale has been well documented by Joan Eyles (Eyles, 1967) and Hugh Torrens (Torrens, 2016), and it is not a happy one. Principal librarian Joseph Planta of the British Museum and his under librarian Charles Konig were indifferent to Smith and the proposed sale of his fossils. In particular, Konig was extremely opposed to Smith's stratigraphic system of classification. Nevertheless, the sale was finally agreed upon, and Smith eventually received £700, spread over a two-year period, for a total of 2657 specimens (Phillips, 1844). For many years, the specimens remained in their boxes, and it was not until after the Natural History Museum was opened in 1881 that the specimens were transferred to the building in South Kensington. When the new paleontological galleries were opened in 1885–1886, Smith's fossils were at last put on display (Eyles, 1967), and they remain in the Natural History Museum to the present day.

COMPARISONS WITH ACTUAL FOSSILS

Smith collected many of his fossils in the late seventeenth and early eighteenth centuries, and by good fortune much of his collection still survives in the twenty-first century. Smith selected individual specimens from this collection that were illustrated by Sowerby in *Strata Identified by Organized Fossils* (Smith, 1816–1819) and described in detail in *Stratigraphical System of Organized Fossils with Reference to the Specimens of the Original Geological Collection in the British Museum* (Smith, 1817). Both publications were unfinished, and copies of the books are extremely rare and often in poor condition. To mark the bicentennial of these publications, the author and his colleagues Jill Darrell, Diana Clements, and Hugh Torrens have republished Smith's original works with previously unpublished manuscript material that includes his sketches for additional plates and new photographs of his fossils from the Natural History Museum (Wigley et al., 2019). This was no small undertaking and took over two years to complete, but it did provide the opportunity to make detailed comparisons of Sowerby's original engravings with modern fossil photographs. Initially, high-resolution color scans were made of all four parts of Smith's publication including the plates and the letter press. Scanned text was recognized using optical character recognition (OCR) and manually edited and formatted to match the original letter press. After scanning, the plates were digitally processed in an attempt to restore their original color. As part of the processing, the engraved fossils were extracted from the textured paper background and the background was then replaced by an averaged solid color into which the images were re-inserted. The engraved plates were then each presented with a matching facing page containing the fossil photographs at the same size and orientation as the originals. Figures 2A–2D show four examples of engraved fossils extracted from their original plates and juxtaposed with corresponding fossil photographs. All of these examples demonstrate Sowerby's extraordinary ability to graphically represent the essence of the fossils with deceptively simple lines, stipple, and color. In some ways, the engravings are even more instructive than the photographs since he was able to emphasize important parts of the fossils while subduing less important aspects. His eye for detail was remarkable, with individual cracks and blemishes often being replicated. Many of the engravings are in their correct orientations but, as in the case of Figure 2C, some are mirror images. This is due to the image being drawn directly on the plate rather than transferred through reversed tracing or use of a mirror. Interestingly, a century before, we know that John Morton experienced similar problems, for in the preface to *Natural History of Northamptonshire* he writes of the engraver Vandergucht, "[he] has done his Part with due Care. Only there is an Error, that was committed unawares, as to the turbinated shells; which is that the Convolutions of all of them… are from Right hand to the Left; whereas they should have the contrary turn" (Morton, 1712, p. iii).

ILLUSTRATION TECHNIQUES

Printed images of fossils produced in the eighteenth and early nineteenth centuries were almost always obtained using the intaglio technique, in which the image is incised into a metal plate, often copper, which when inked and wiped allows ink to remain in the incisions. Paper is then pressed onto the inked plate, and the image is transferred to the paper. Two important members of the intaglio family of techniques are engraving and etching. In engraving, the image is incised directly into the plate using a sharpened tool called a burin or graver, which creates a distinctive line with clean edges. By contrast, in etching, the plate is first coated with a layer of acid-resistant wax or resin (ground). The image is then incised through the ground with an etching needle, which tends to give free-flowing lines albeit often blunt-ended. To produce sharp-ended lines and lines of variable thickness, an échoppe tool with a slanted oval section can be used, either through the ground or to directly enhance the etched plate. When immersed in acid (mordant), the acid "bites" into the exposed metal and creates the image. After the ground is removed, the plate is used to make the paper print.

The exact technique used by Sowerby is uncertain (J. Wilson, 2019, personal commun.), but it is probably a combination of engraving, etching, and enhancing of a copper plate followed

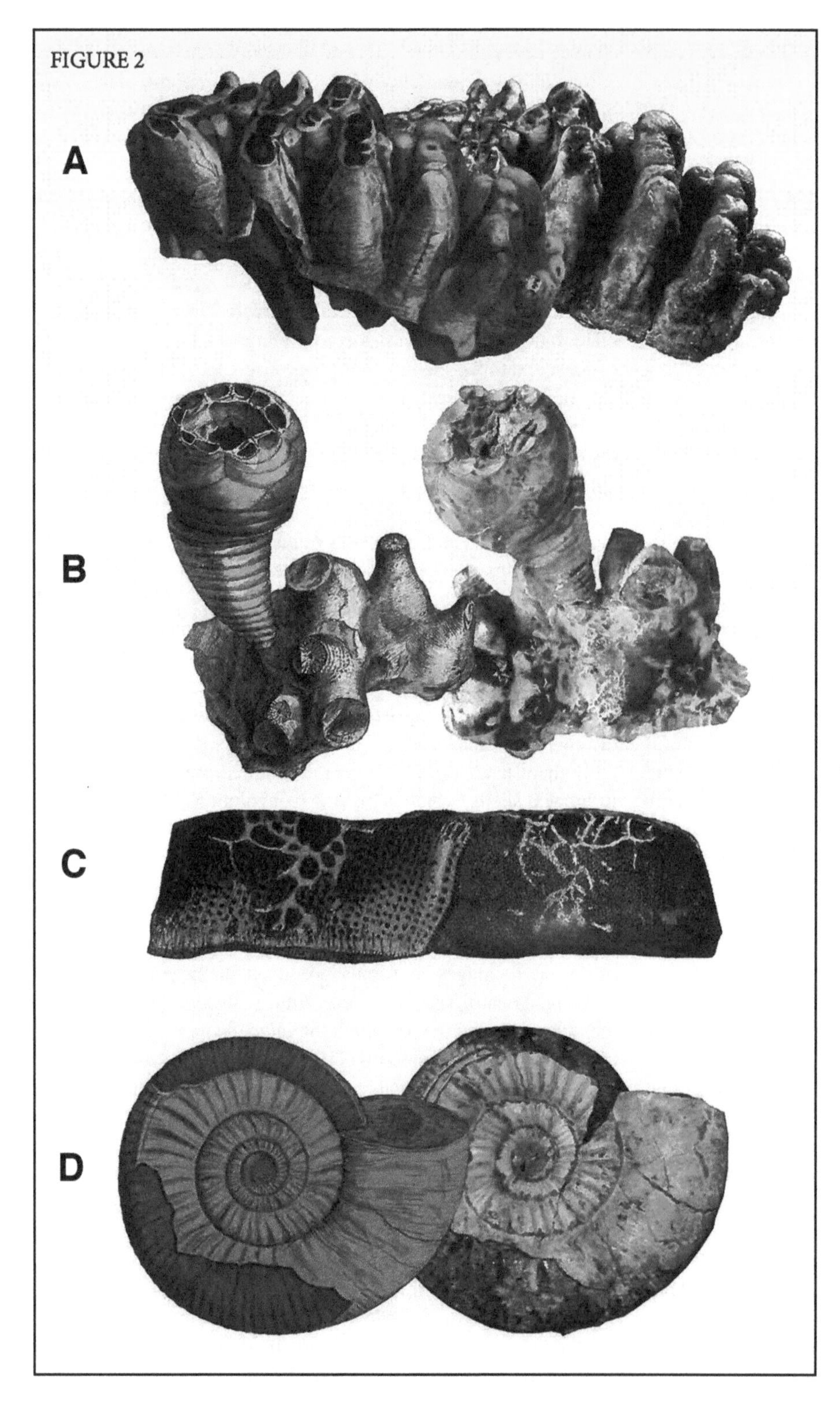

Figure 2. (Left) Engravings from *Strata Identified by Organized Fossils* are compared with (right) corresponding fossils from the Smith Collection at the Natural History Museum. Photographs were provided courtesy of the Natural History Museum. Photographs licensed under the terms of a Creative Commons Attribution License (CC-BY) © The Trustees of the Natural History Museum, London. Some Rights Reserved. https://creativecommons.org/licenses/by/4.0/legalcode. (A) Frontispiece plate of a mastodon tooth (*Anancus arvernensis*), which Smith referred to as "a singular Fossil Tooth, of some extinct monstrous unknown animal." Approximate width of fossil is 17 cm. (B) Pear encrinus [now identified as *Apiocrinites elegans*] from the Clay over the Upper Oolite plate [16] no. 1. The specimen was found in a field at Berfield, near Bradford, which belonged to Smith's friend, the Rev. Benjamin Richardson. Approximate width of fossil is 7 cm. (C) Fish palate [?*Asteracanthus magus*] figured in the Forest Marble plate [15] no. 9, which was found in a quarry at Pickwick in Wiltshire. Approximate width of fossil is 4 cm. (D) Ammonites [*Pictonia balyei*] no. 7 from the Oak-Tree Clay [Kimmeridge Clay] plate [9]. Approximate width of fossil is 10 cm.

by hand coloring of the paper prints. Examples of Sowerby's illustrations for *Strata Identified by Organized Fossils* (Smith, 1816–1819) are shown in Figures 3A–3C. The detail shows fairly simple lines, cross hatching, and stippling all used to great effect and enhanced with subtle water coloring. Sowerby (1812–1818) seems to have used the same techniques for many illustrations in *The Mineral Conchology of Great Britain*. However, in other cases (see Figs. 1C and 3D) there is strong evidence that other tools were used to create a textured background. These include a grooved wheel tool (roulette wheel) and a dry-point rocker,

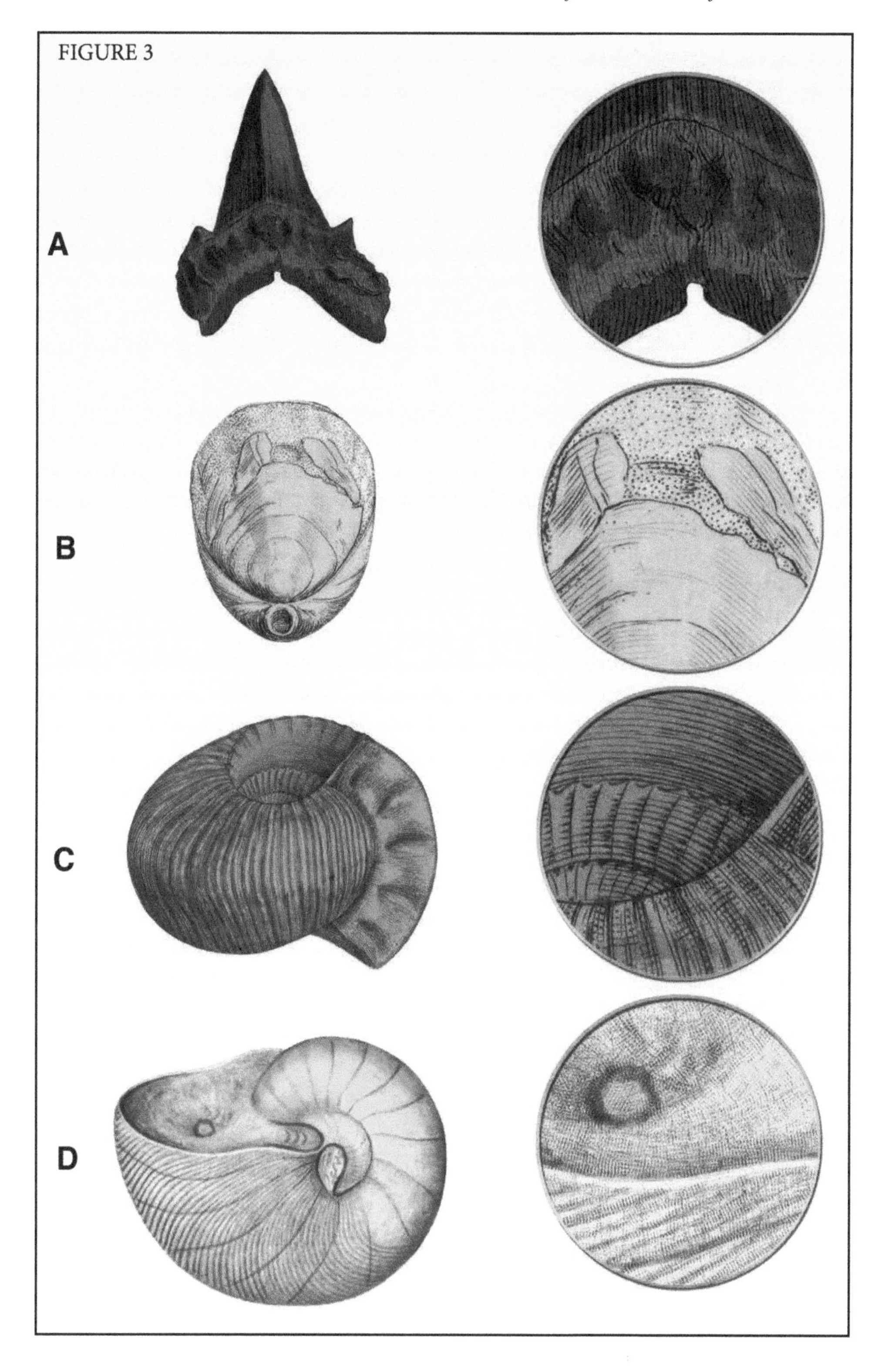

Figure 3. Illustrations show various engraving techniques used by James Sowerby in *Strata Identified by Organized Fossils* (Smith, 1816–1817) and *The Mineral Conchology of Great Britain* (Sowerby, 1812–1818). (Left) The engraving extracted from the plate is shown; (right) circles show magnified detail. (A) Shark's tooth from the London Clay plate, no. 9, table 2. (B) *Terebratula subundata* [*Concinnithyris subundata*] no. 9 from the Upper Chalk plate [3]. (C) *Ammonites sublaevis* [*Cadocera sublaevis*] no. 2 from the Kelloways Stone plate [13]. (D) Illustration from Sowerby's *The Mineral Conchology of Great Britain* table CXVI described as *Nautilus elegans*. Specimen from the chalk at Ringmer in Sussex and courtesy of Gideon Mantell.

which would have been used directly on the copper plate and scratched back where necessary with a scraper tool. In dry-point, the tool used leaves a rough burr of metal in the grooves that holds the ink prior to printing. Some of Sowerby's fossil engraving also shows a rather irregular, blotchy tonal texture; this may be the result of the aquatint process, in which the acid is allowed to partially penetrate the resin ground, creating a pattern of small pits in the plate.

Whatever the technique, Sowerby used it to stunning effect particularly in *The Mineral Conchology of Great Britain*

(1812–1818). His illustrations for *Strata Identified by Organized Fossils,* though perhaps not quite at the same peak of perfection as seen in *The Mineral Conchology of Great Britain*, are nonetheless extremely precise and aesthetically pleasing. Probably due to cost, engravings with textured backgrounds are not seen in *Strata Identified by Organized Fossils*. Creation of these textures, particularly when using a rocker and a scraper, is very time consuming. While Sowerby may have been prepared to spend time and energy on his magnum opus, he was, perhaps, less enthusiastic about other ventures.

The achievements of Sowerby are all the more remarkable considering that he also did most of the original fossil drawings from which the prints were made. In addition to being a gifted naturalist and engraver he was also a true artist. For his part, Sowerby also acknowledged the talent of William Smith, for when naming an ammonite (*Asteroceras smithi*) after him he says, "This is named in honor of Mr. W. Smith, the Author of a Geological map of England, etc. whose discoveries of the regular succession of the strata, and the means of distinguishing them by their organised contents, has laid the foundation of all our Geological knowledge of England" (Sowerby, 1812–1818, vol. 4, p. 148, plate 406).

PLATE EDITING

A copy of *Strata Identified by Organized Fossils* in the Smithsonian Libraries provides rare insight into the editing process the plates underwent.[2] Attached to the Smithsonian's copy are a number of proof or pattern plates including an uncolored and unlettered version of the Fuller's Earth Rock plate. Also, a proof Clunch [Oxford Clay] plate that Sowerby sent to Smith at his 15 Buckingham Street address requested, "Will Mr. Smith please to find, if he can one or two small subjects to fill this vacancy." Smith responded with two rather small serpulids! These proof plates also show that they were lettered and numbered after the line-work was produced, and in some cases small changes to the line-work were also made. The lettering was engraved, not impressed, and one example shows proofreader's marks and subsequent corrections (see Fig. 4A). It is evident that Sowerby used similar editing processes for *The Mineral Conchology of Great Britain.* The Sheridan Library (OCLC: 53927833) holds nearly 650 so-called pattern plates, many of which have been annotated with editing comments often relating to color and shading.[3] It would seem that these pattern plates were intended as a guide for those coloring the engraved plates.

[2]See William Smith, 1769–1839, Washington, Smithsonian Library, DSI, Collections: Biodiversity Smithsonian. Burndy Library, donor; https://library.si.edu/digital-library/book/strataidentifie00smit (accessed March 2021).

[3]See James Sowerby, pattern plates for *The Mineral Conchology of Great Britain*: Johns Hopkins University Sheridan Libraries, produced between 1810–1845?, 643 plates, hand-colored copper engravings, 29 cm, https://www.library.jhu.edu (accessed March 2021).

USE OF COLORED PAPER

A montage of the types of paper used in *Strata Identified by Organized Fossils* is shown in Figure 4B. In parts 1 and 2, the paper itself is colored (or plain); in parts 3 and 4, the paper has been color-washed and the reverse side left uncolored. Smith noted in his Introduction to *Strata Identified by Organized Fossils* that "figures of organized Fossils in each Stratum are printed on coloured paper, to correspond with the most general colour of the matter in which they are imbedded" (Smith, 1816–1819, on wrappers for Nos. 1, 2, and 3). In general, except for the chalk, the colors have also been chosen to match the colors used for strata on his geological maps; the concept is interesting and innovative but has some drawbacks. Paper color varies considerably between different copies of *Strata Identified by Organized Fossils.* Some of this variation may be due to age and discoloration and some due to changes in tint of the color wash. Both Smith and Sowerby were interested in the systematic use of color. Sowerby invented a chromatic scale of 63 colors (Henderson, 2015), and Smith used this scale to define the soil color in his description of the London Clay (Orange brown, Y.R.B.2). However, the main disadvantage of the colored papers is that on the darker papers, the illustrations tend to be dull and rather flat. This is particularly evident when they are compared to Sowerby's illustrations from *The Mineral Conchology of Great Britain*, which were printed on plain paper.

PAPER MAKERS

From watermarks in the paper used in *Strata Identified by Organized Fossils*, it has been possible to identify some of the manufacturers. Perhaps the most famous maker was J. Whatman, who originally made the paper at Turkey Mill and later at Springfield Mill, both of which are in Maidstone, Kent. This high-quality paper was favored by Thomas Gainsborough, J.M.W. Turner, and William Blake. Other makers were Ruse and Turner (1816), Rye Mill (1813), and Cobb's (1812). Watermarks from Rye Mill (1813, High Wycombe, Buckinghamshire) and Cobb's Patent are shown in Figure 4C. The latter watermark is interesting since it appears on very early machine-produced paper made using a patented invention by Thomas Cobb Junior of Banbury, Oxfordshire.

CONCLUDING REMARKS

The fossil illustrations published by Smith in *Strata Identified by Organized Fossils* between 1816 and 1819 are historically important both scientifically and artistically. In his publication, Smith arranged the fossil plates in stratigraphical order, grouping key assemblages for each stratum on a single plate. Smith's choice of Sowerby as the engraver was inspired. Not only was he one of the most talented engravers of his generation, but he was also an extremely competent naturalist. Sowerby, the artist, created fossil illustrations that were accurate and realistic. With his

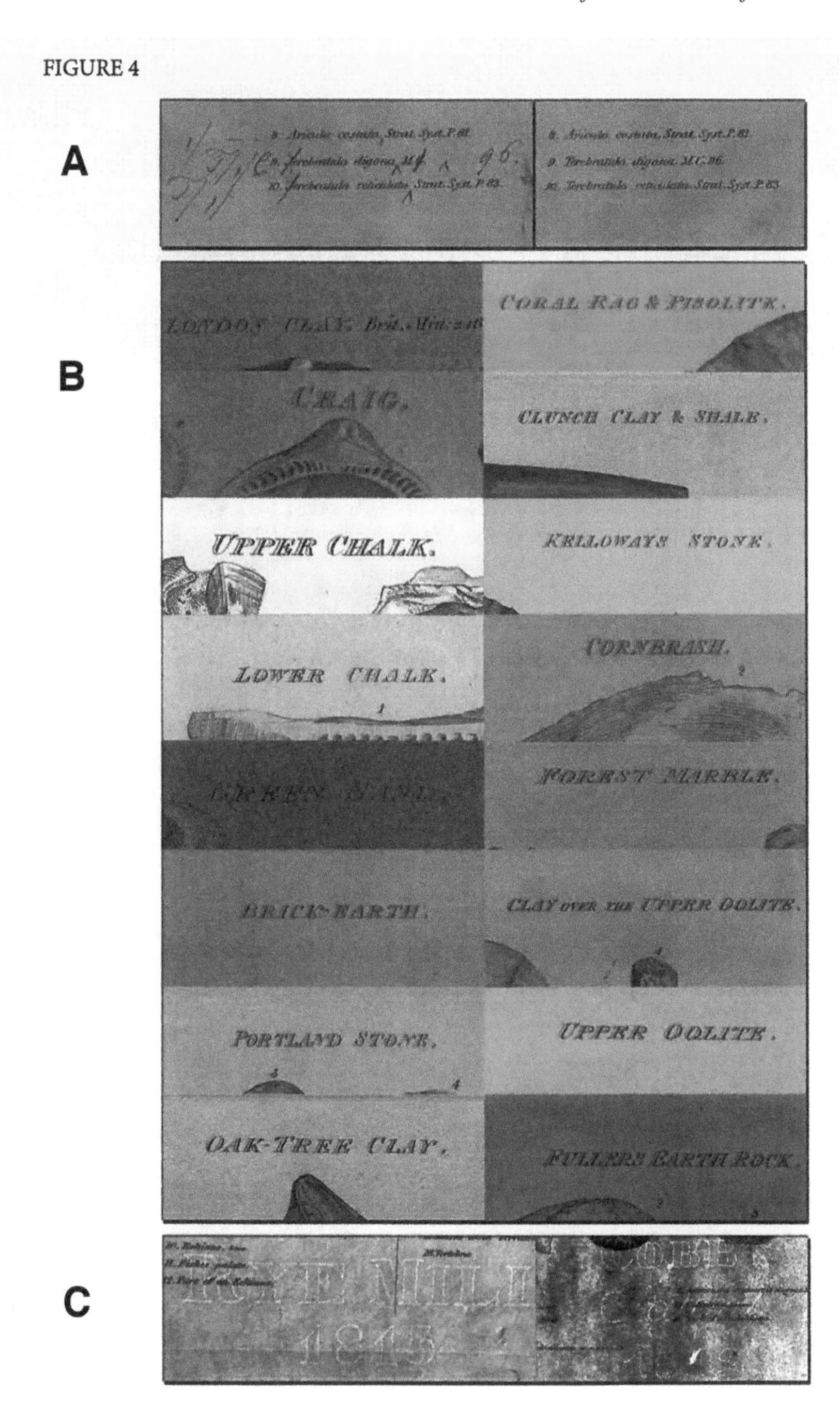

Figure 4. Colored papers, engraved lettering, and watermarks from *Strata Identified by Organized Fossils.* (A) Engraved lettering from a proof plate of the Clay over the Upper Oolite plate [16] showing proofreader's marks to the left and the corrections to the right. Courtesy of the Smithsonian Libraries. (B) Montage of colored papers used in *Strata Identified by Organized Fossils*. Most of the papers were color washed prior to illustration; others, like the London Clay, Craig [Crag], and Greensand plates, are actually on colored paper. (C) Two examples of watermarked paper used in *Strata Identified by Organized Fossils*: Rye Mills 1813 and Cobb's Patent 1812, both of which were photographed in transmitted light.

naturalist's eye, Sowerby could also bring into focus significant paleontological features while subduing those of less importance. Unlike earlier fossil engravings, Sowerby's illustrations were individually hand-colored using subtle tints to further enhance the final effect. Under Smith's instruction, the illustrations were reproduced on a variety of colored and color-washed papers with each paper color mimicking the color of the strata in which the fossils were embedded. Also, these colors mostly match those that Smith used for his geological maps and sections.

Smith's publications were intended to communicate to both men of science and the wider public his concept of "the Science of the Strata." The graphical representations of the fossils were part of that concept, but such is the quality of Sowerby's illustrations that they are indeed elevated to works of paleontological art.

REFERENCES CITED

Cox, L.R., 1942, New light on William Smith and his work: Proceedings of the Yorkshire Geological Society, v. 25, p. 1–99, https://doi.org/10.1144/pygs.25.1.1.

Eyles, J.M., 1967, William Smith: The sale of his geological collection to the British Museum: Annals of Science, v. 23, p. 177–212, https://doi.org/10.1080/00033796700203276.

Henderson, P., 2015, James Sowerby: The Enlightenment's Natural Historian: London, Kew, Royal Botanic Gardens, 336 p.

Morton, J., 1712, The Natural History of Northamptonshire: With Some Account of the Antiquities. To Which Is Annex'd a Transcript of Doomsday-book So Far as It Relates to That County: London, R. Knaplock and R. Wilkin, 597 p.

Phillips, J., 1844., Memoirs of William Smith LLD: London, John Murray, 150 p.

Plot, R., 1677, A Natural History of Oxfordshire Being an Essay Toward the Natural History of England: London, Leon Lichfield, 366 p.

Smith, W., 1816–1819, Strata Identified by Organized Fossils Containing Prints on Colored Paper of the Most Characteristic Specimens in Each Stratum: London, W. Arding, 32 p., 18 plates + frontispiece.

Smith, W., 1817, A Stratigraphical System of Organized Fossils with Reference to the Specimens of the Original Geological Collection in the British Museum Explaining Their State of Preservation and Their Use in Identifying the British Strata: London, E. Williams, 118 p.

Sowerby, J., 1812–1818, The Mineral Conchology of Great Britain; or, Coloured Figures and Descriptions of Those Remains of Testaceous Animals or Shells, Which Have Been Preserved at Various Times and Depths in the Earth: London, 4 vols. cited herein: v. 1, B. Meredith, 234 p.; v. 2, W. Arding and Merrett, 251 p., v. 3, W. Arding, 194 p.; v. 4, W. Arding, 160 p.

Torrens, H.S., 2016, William Smith (1769–1839): His struggles as a consultant, in both geology and engineering, to simultaneously earn a living and finance his scientific projects, to 1820: Earth Sciences History, v. 35, no. 1, p. 1–46, https://doi.org/10.17704/1944-6187-35.1.1.

Wigley, P., Darrell, J., Clements, D., and Torrens, H., eds., 2019, William Smith's Fossils Reunited: Wellington, UK, Halsgrove, 160 p.

Manuscript Accepted by the Society 13 January 2021
Manuscript Published Online 30 June 2021

The Geological Society of America
Memoir 218

The illustrations of Brongniart and Cuvier illuminate paleontology in the early nineteenth century

Kennard B. Bork
Emeritus, Department of Geosciences, Denison University, Granville, Ohio 43023, USA

ABSTRACT

The concept of biostratigraphy was a significant step in the evolution of geoscience. Alexandre Brongniart (1770–1847) and Georges Cuvier (1769–1832) were key contributors to developing the subdiscipline as they worked to decode the stratigraphy of the Paris Basin in the first decades of the nineteenth century. Their illustrations of fossils, local geologic columns, and a regional geologic map played a decisive role in furthering an understanding of the value of paleontology in the service of illuminating Earth history.

ILLUSTRATIONS IN PALEONTOLOGY: THE CASE OF BRONGNIART AND CUVIER

Early in the nineteenth century, Alexandre Brongniart (1770–1847) and Georges Cuvier (1769–1832) worked together to decode the stratigraphy of the Paris Basin. Their *Essai sur la géographie minéralogique des environs de Paris* (read before the Institut Impérial on 11 April 1808) documented, in epic scope, novelty, and clarity their field-based observations and interpretations (Cuvier and Brongniart, 1808). Their brief essay listed fossil species, put them in stratigraphic order, associated them with named geologic formations, and placed them in a map of geographic settings around Paris. One of their powerful insights was that fossils could serve as valuable aids in determining ages and sequences of strata. Rather than relying on lithology or elevation, which were then widely used, they concluded that fossils are key indices of age. Fossils became "a sign" that never deceived them as to age and position within a geologic column.

Cuvier and Brongniart's (1808) statement of 33 pages underwent a mega-revision to 278 pages in 1810 (with a publication date of 1811, it was revised again in 1822). Using the term "mineral geography" indicated a focus on field-based fact and not mere "theory." Along with voluminous added details about lithologies and fossils, the revision (1822) incorporated illustrations of fossils, sketches of geologic columns from the Paris region, and a colored geological map (at 1:200,000) (Fig. 1). As Taylor (2008) noted, maps illustrating geological elements pre-dated 1800, but Brongniart and Cuvier's (1810) map introduced key aspects of modern geologic maps five years before William Smith's classic map of 1815. Distribution of formations was shown using coded colors, age sequence of beds was established, strata could be tied to topography, and one could infer Earth history from the graphically illustrated strata.

The significance of the team's work was widely recognized and applauded (Webster, 1814; d'Archiac, 1862; Rudwick, 1972; etc.). Gohau (1990) concluded that Brongniart was a key founder of biostratigraphy, partly because of his work on the Tertiary sequence in the Paris Basin, but also because he used fossils as correlation keys well beyond Paris. Brongniart called attention (Brongniart, 1821) to similar relations of chalk in France and Poland, and he generated a beautifully illustrated *Mémoire* (Brongniart, 1823) relating Paris Basin fossils to those in Northern Italy. When considering the relative reliability of petrographic versus paleontological criteria for time recognition, Brongniart voted strongly for fossils. He firmly stated that age associations of similar fossils could be made over huge horizontal distances despite the fact that fossil species changed dramatically in the vertical sense. Brongniart and Cuvier were certainly not claiming that "transformation of species" (evolution) was the driving mechanism of the observed changes, but their hard evidence of

Bork, K.B., 2022, The illustrations of Brongniart and Cuvier illuminate paleontology in the early nineteenth century, *in* Clary, R.M., Rosenberg, G.D., and Evans, D.C., eds., The Evolution of Paleontological Art: Geological Society of America Memoir 218, p. 37–45, https://doi.org/10.1130/2021.1218(05).

Figure 1. The hand-colored geologic map from Cuvier and Brongniart's *Carte Géognostique des environs de Paris* (original date of 1810), which appears at the end of their *Essai sur la géographie minéralogique des environs de Paris* (Cuvier and Brongniart, 1811). (Light green = sandstone, millstone; light blue = siliceous limestone; deep blue = gypsum; very light tan = coarse limestone; mid-tan along the Seine = detrital silt.) Courtesy of Linda Hall Library.

change in organic morphology through time was not lost on Lamarck, Darwin, and others.

During the first decades of the nineteenth century both men were extremely busy with professional obligations that made time-consuming fieldwork difficult. In 1800, Napoleon's brother Lucien Bonaparte, minister of the interior during the Consulate (1799–1804), appointed Brongniart to the directorship of the Sèvres Porcelain Manufactory, and he held this position until his death in 1847 (Préaud, 1997). That was not as random as it may seem. Brongniart had training in chemistry and mineralogy, was the son of celebrated architect Alexandre-Théodore Brongniart (1739–1813), and was recognized for his abilities in science, art, and administration. As director he employed and befriended such artists as Jacques-Louis David (1748–1825) and J.A.D. Ingres (1780–1867). Brongniart and his wife entertained artists Eugène Delacroix (1798–1863) and Ingres, along with celebrated scientists such as Ampère, Faraday, Humboldt, Lamarck, and Oersted (de Launay, 1940). While not himself a gifted painter, Brongniart integrated ceramic chemistry, visual art, and fine porcelain. His life bridged the gap between the Enlightenment and the Industrial Revolution. He commissioned a Sèvres series of plates on "Service des Arts Industriels," echoing Diderot's attempts in *L'Encyclopédie* to illustrate the work of industrial workers in society. Early in his time as director at Sèvres, a plate (Fig. 2) was made that, while not strictly paleontological, shows Brongniart's interest in having Sèvres products convey noteworthy messages through the medium of ceramic art. In this case, it portrays the ravages of time as the landscape and human artifacts erode, and a woodcutter is pursued by Death.

Travel played a role in Brongniart's real-world education. Time in London, in 1790, introduced him to first-tier British scientists, ceramicists, and then-current ideas about how to conduct natural history. The possibility exists that contact with William Smith's ideas planted productive seeds in Brongniart's mind (d'Archiac, 1862; Hancock, 1977; Rudwick, 1972). A 1795 trip into the Alps, accompanied by Déodat Dolomieu (1750–1801), impressed him with the beauty and majesty of mountains and triggered his interest in tectonics (de Launay, 1940). But that impact did not deter him from an appreciation of Earth's scale, as he commented that mountains were but "wrinkles" on the Earth's surface. Fieldwork in Normandy, in 1811, demonstrated his fealty to the "facts first" vision shared with Cuvier but also allowed him to reach major "theoretical" conclusions (Bork, 2013). For example, he negated Werner's widely held views that igneous rocks had to be Primary in age and that deposition from the waters of a diminishing universal sea created the world's strata. But for us, in considering the power of art in the service of paleontology, of primary significance was the 1820 geologic excursion into Northern Italy with his son Adolphe (soon to be a force in paleobotany). Brongniart père was struck by the similarity of fossil forms he observed in the Vicentin Alps with what he had seen in the Paris Basin.

Thus, the outstanding examples of Brongniart's use of art as related to paleontology are the six plates of his 1823 *Mémoire sur les terrains de sédiment supérieurs calcaréo-trappéens du Vicentin, et sur quelques terrains d'Italie, de France, d'Allemagne, etc., qui peuvent se rapporter à la même époque* (henceforth, simply *Mémoire*).[1] Those plates (Fig. 3) portray beautifully engraved fossils that directly correlated genera found in the environs of Paris with fossils in Northern Italy. And, in topographic contrast to their siblings in the low-lying Paris Basin, the Italian fossils were situated high in impressive mountains. They are graphic evidence of his recognition of the power of fossils to tell time and to aid in correlation over large distances. They also reflect a great amount of fieldwork, classification ability, and desire to share the important potential of fossils. The engraver of the plates was C. Constans, and the sketch artist was N. Boullemier, both of whom were employed at the Sèvres Porcelain Manufactury.

Figure 2. Sèvres hard-paste porcelain plate, 1806, is shown; *Restes de quelques Tombeaux antiques*; a gift from Napoleon to J. J. R. de Cambacérès, a Consul member and author of the Napoleonic Code. Note the ruins and death skeleton; these are comments on the passage of time. Produced in Brongniart's sixth year as director of Sèvres. Préaud (1997), with permission from the Bard Graduate Center.

As noted above, Brongniart's ability to reach large-scale conclusions, while pursuing facts-first methodologies, allowed him to visualize correlation potential over great distances. He could see geology from the point of view of a naturalist whose knowledge went beyond mere description and classification. Cautious but confident, he asserted (1823, p. 33; my translation), "Such is the confidence that one can now have in the rules of geology deduced from the nature of fossils that specimens suffice to enable one to recognize formations with great probability." Along with Cuvier, he was calling attention to Earth history and providing visual images that could be used by other naturalists to recognize fossils of a given age in their own areas. Thus, the attentive viewer could reach important conclusions about correlation of strata.

Brongniart and Cuvier also saw fossils as not only indicators of geologic age, but as clues to ancient environments of deposition. A specific case is their recognition of freshwater deposition alternating with marine deposits (Brongniart, 1810). Thomas Webster, in his discussion of freshwater formations on the Isle of Wight, commented (1814, p. 161):

> Among the geological researches which have lately been made in various parts of the globe, none have been more interesting than those of MM Cuvier and Brongniart in the environs of Paris... These naturalists have described a series of mineral strata distinguished by their numerous and singular organic remains. The animals whose exuviae had hitherto been more commonly noticed in regularly stratified rocks were the inhabitants of oceans: but many of the Parisian fossils belonged to freshwater lakes and marshes, thus developing new and unsuspected agents in the forming of mineral beds.

[1]My copy of Brongniart's *Mémoire* (1823) was gifted to the Library of Bowdoin College, Brunswick, Maine, in 2019. The inside cover included Brongniart's handwritten note to Professor Parker Cleaveland, of the Bowdoin faculty, as well as Cleaveland's nameplate. The two men had exchanged correspondence concerning their early texts on mineralogy (Bork, 1999).

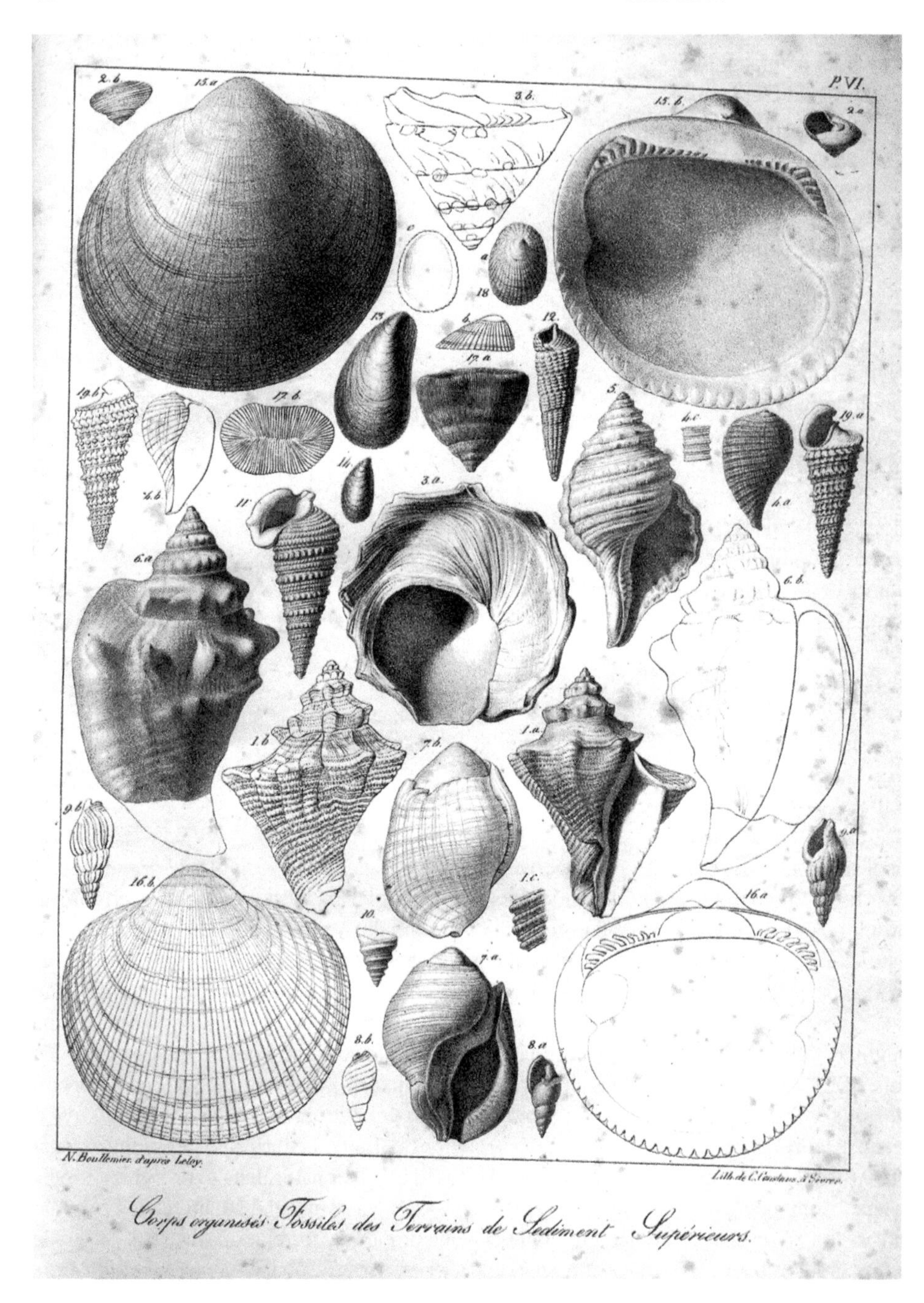

Figure 3. Plate VI of Brongniart's 1823 *Mémoire*, which illustrates fossils found at both the Paris Basin and the Vicentin region of Northern Italy. The superb work was done by C. Constans and N. Boullemier, both of whom worked at Sèvres under Brongniart's directorship. Personal copy.

Thus, well before Amanz Gressly's (1838) definition of "facies," Brongniart and Cuvier were describing interfingering of marine and freshwater strata. They perceived the field evidence as proving past shifts in the relation of land and sea and as an argument against Werner's concept of a universal marine sea gradually diminishing in size. Their classic figure of the column of Parisian strata did not provide a modern vision of interfingered units, but their text spoke directly to the dynamics of the stratigraphic relationships between marine and freshwater deposits and between rock types of different chemical and physical natures. Thus, the stratigraphic record revealed a dynamic past world.

If Brongniart was busy, Cuvier was involved with a whirlwind of activities. His seminal contributions to vertebrate paleontology, comparative anatomy, and the concept of organic extinction are well known to geologists. His overall impact on French science, education, and culture during his Paris years of 1795–1832 may be less familiar. A potent index of Cuvier's reception in France is the fact that his name is one of 72 inscribed on the Eiffel Tower. Philippe Taquet, a former director of the Muséum d'histoire naturelle (Paris) and a past president of the French Académie des sciences, both home bases for Cuvier, has been in a unique position to discuss Cuvier's life and work. His detailed book-length biographies (Taquet, 2006, 2019) greatly enrich our understanding of a complex man treating complex issues in a complex time.

While Cuvier had a well-developed ego, and his name appeared first on joint publications, he was candid in admitting that Brongniart had done most of the fieldwork, detailed invertebrate paleontology, and recognition of freshwater and marine lithologies (Schneer, 1969; Rudwick, 2005). Anglophones can profit from Rudwick's 1997 book, *Georges Cuvier, Fossil Bones, and Geological Catastrophes*, which contains (p. 183–252) a valuable translation of Cuvier's *Discours préliminaire* to his extraordinary *Recherches sur les ossemens fossiles.* Cuvier stated (*in* Rudwick, 1997, p. 205), "Why has not anyone seen that fossils alone gave birth to a theory about the formation of the earth, that without them, no one would have ever dreamed that there were successive epochs in the formation of the globe?" That potent question was likely a function of his shared work with Brongniart. Taquet (2009) provided valuable insights into the shared and individual contributions of Brongniart and Cuvier while also discussing recently found private diaries of Brongniart and his wife Cécile Coquebert de Montbret (P. Taquet, 2012, personal commun.).

In the context of art in the service of zoology and paleontology, Cuvier is a striking case. He was himself a gifted artist (Taquet, 2006), and his sketches of organisms are not only impressively rendered, they also carry deep messages informed by his encyclopedic knowledge of comparative anatomy. On the zoological front, he wrote scientific notices for Nicolas Maréchal's (1753–1803) beautiful paintings of living animals in the Ménagerie of the Muséum d'histoire naturelle in Paris. His hand-drawn sketches of teeth of proboscideans showed that Asian and African elephants differed from each other. But Cuvier went further, claiming that illustrations of jaws and teeth proved that mammoths and mastodons are no longer with us. Thus, informed art became powerful evidence for extinction. As Rudwick noted (1992, p. 219), artistic renditions of ancient animals and their places in Earth history go back to Cuvier.

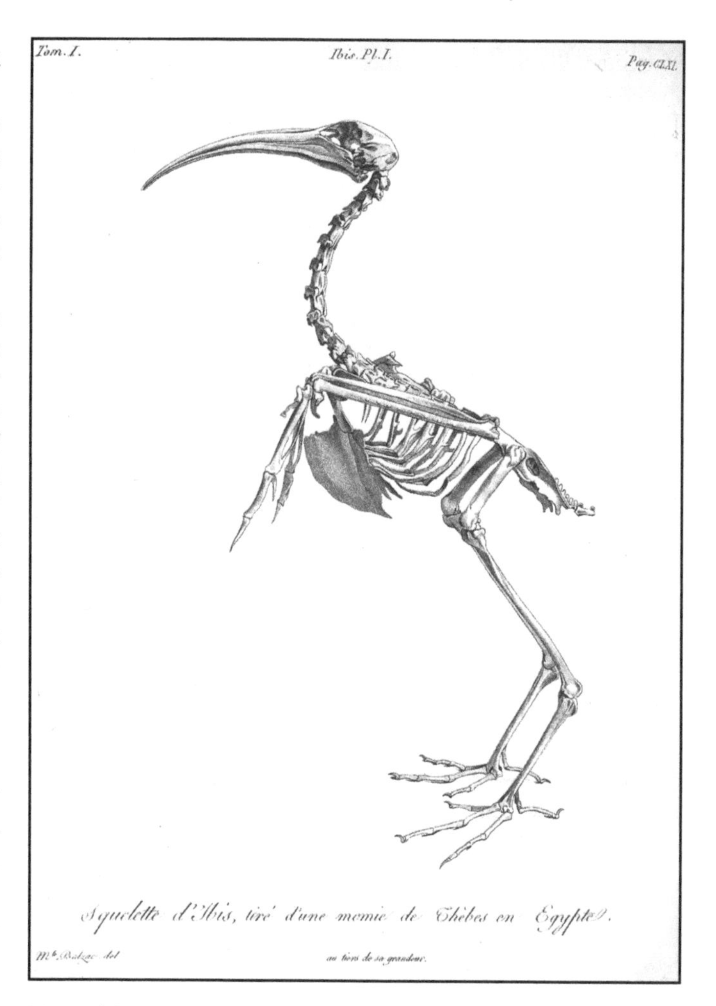

Figure 4. The rendering (Cuvier, 1821, *Recherches*, Vol. 1, Plate 1, foll. p. CLX) of a modern *Ibis* makes the point that it had not changed at all as determined from skeletons found in tombs of ancient Egypt and thus argues against "transformation" (evolution). Courtesy of Linda Hall Library.

While serving as a key catalyst for recognizing the reality and importance of extinction, Cuvier argued forcefully against organic evolution. His beautiful sketch of the skeleton of a living *Ibis* (Fig. 4) made the case that "transformation" of species did not take place, because modern forms of the genus were identical to the structure of the mummified *Ibis* from an ancient Egyptian tomb that was brought to Paris by French naturalists. (For Egyptians, *Ibis* represented Thoth, the deity of writing, math, and magic.) Although Cuvier saw Earth history as extensive, he did not have a deep understanding of the tiny percentage of Earth time represented by the few millennia between Old Kingdom Egypt (ca. 2500 B.C.E.) and the early-nineteenth century.

The line drawings in *Ossemens fossiles*, sketched by or commissioned by Cuvier, have a clarity and information potential that will be familiar to paleontologists who work with ostracods and forams. But his prime subjects were large vertebrates. The interaction of art and paleontology is powerfully evident as his illustrations of bones evoke structures and functions in mammoths, sloths, ruminants, plesiosaurs, pterodactyls, and other fossil vertebrates. By scanning evocative illustrations, readers could visualize functional anatomy operating in ancient organisms. And they could understand Cuvier's claim that a few well-preserved bones, interpreted through the power of comparative anatomy, and his principle of correlation of parts had the power to lead to identification of fossil vertebrates. They might even realize why Cuvier was so insistent on not allowing anatomical "transformations" through time; because to do so could undermine the phenomenally interdependent engineering of skeletal structures and inferred complex functions.

Just a few examples will have to suffice to document the relevance of artistic images to Cuvier's key arguments about fossils as windows on understanding the past. Fossil vertebrates from the New World included *Megatherium* from Paraguay and the "Ohio Animal" from the young United States. A year after settling in Paris, Cuvier (1796) compared *Megatherium* to sloths, suggested that the huge animal had to be related to modern sloths, and stated that the fossil was sufficiently different from living forms that it had to be extinct. Turning to the imposing fossil skeleton from Ohio, he again used art to formulate exciting conclusions. Having authored *Mémoires sur les espèces d'éléphants vivants et fossiles* (1799), Cuvier did detailed work on jaws, tooth structure, and bones of elephants and their predecessors (Fig. 5). The resultant pictures really were worth thousands of words. His verdict was that the "Ohio Animal" was related to, but not identical to, large proboscideans of Africa and Asia. He also argued that it was extinct. Because individual mammary-form teeth differed from the flat, grinding teeth of mammoths, Cuvier named the impressive beast *Mastodon*.

Fossil finds in the era of 1800–1832 were revealing noteworthy ancient animals from the land, sea, and air. It was a golden age for a vertebrate paleontologist well versed in comparative anatomy. Cuvier took advantage of several amazing finds, and his renderings of their skeletal structures became iconic. The famous Solnhofen Limestone beds of Bavaria had not yet yielded *Archaeopteryx* (1859), but an unusual set of bones had come to light. (We should also acknowledge the amazing skills of preparators.) Working from sketches, Cuvier correctly envisioned a flying reptile (Fig. 6), a conclusion informed by his encyclopedic knowledge of comparative anatomy. Interpreting the detailed structures of wing and finger, he supplied the classic name *Ptero-*

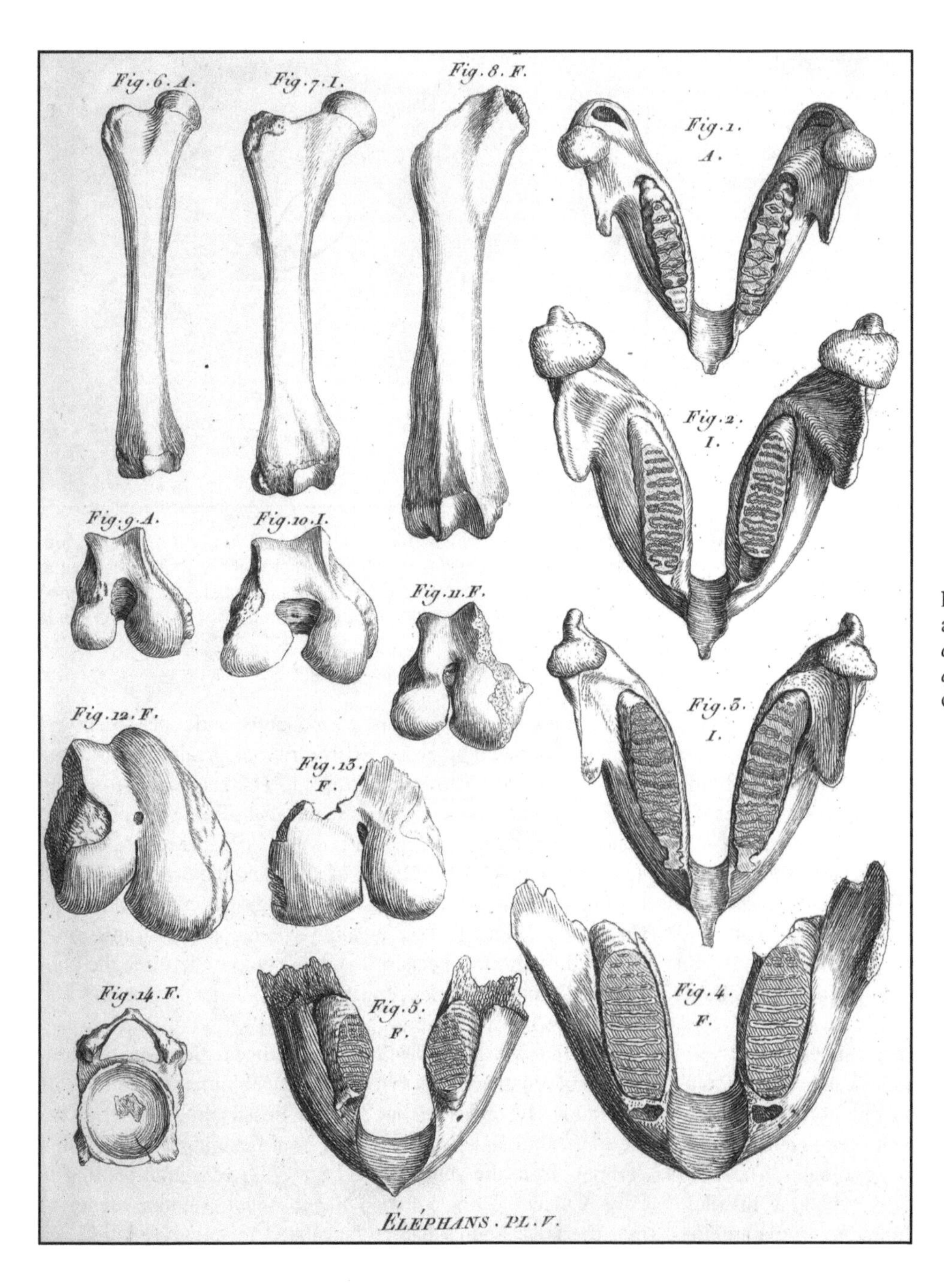

Figure 5. Jaws and bones of elephants are shown from Cuvier's (1812) *Recherches sur les ossemens fossiles de quadrupèdes*, Vol. 2, Plate V. Courtesy of Linda Hall Library.

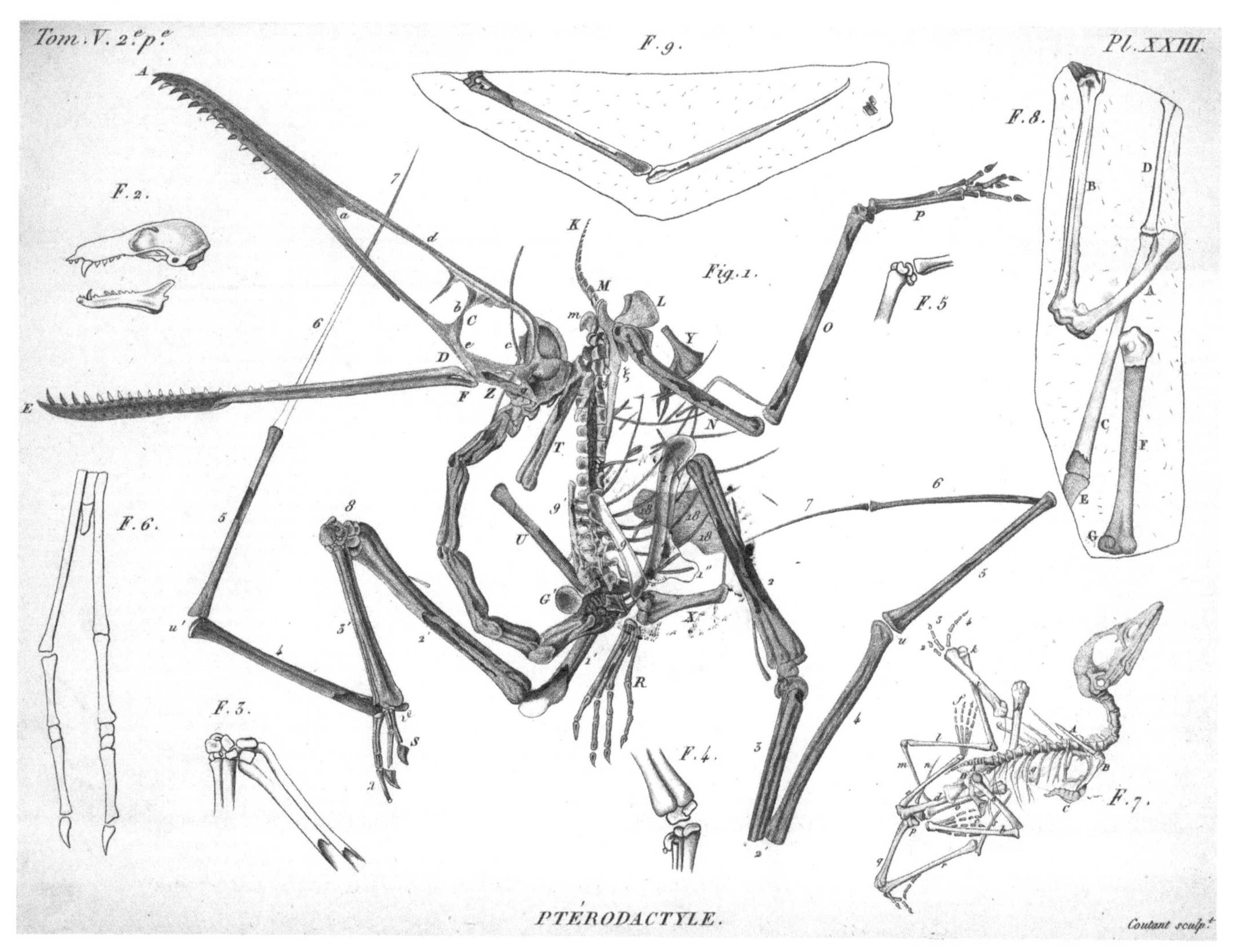

Figure 6. Rendering of a *Pterodactyle* from Cuvier (1824, Vol. 5, Part 2, Plate 23) is shown. The exquisite detail is characteristic of illustrations in Cuvier's work and provided viewers with valuable clues as to anatomy, structure, and function. Courtesy of Linda Hall Library.

dactyle (Cuvier, 1809). Meanwhile, evidence of large vertebrates (including "Sea dragons") inhabiting ancient seas was attracting attention (Howe et al., 1981). Cuvier (1824), deeply interested in form and function, presented viewers with paired illustrations (Fig. 7) of streamlined skeletons of an ichthyosaur and a plesiosaur. The drawings show the power illustration has to lead to significant conclusions about life of the distant past.

CONCLUSION

Illustrative art has, indeed, informed paleontology. Its visual power has greatly aided our understanding and interpretation of nature. Classic examples of that synergism are provided by the seminal work done by Brongniart and Cuvier in the first decades of the nineteenth century. Their excellent visuals allowed identification of fossils, correlation of strata, building of a geologic column, and an early appreciation of Earth history.

ACKNOWLEDGMENTS

Staff members of the Linda Hall Library of Science, Engineering, and Technology, in Kansas City, Missouri, were exemplary in their courtesy and productivity. Vice president for research and scholarship Benjamin Gross, digital initiatives manager Benjamin Gibson, and digital initiatives technician Jon Rollins consistently provided prompt and valuable responses. Information from the Manufacture Nationale de Sèvres (Porcelain) is appreciated. Philippe Taquet, in Paris, and Kenneth Taylor, in Norman, Oklahoma, USA, provided generous and constructive advice concerning the text and figures. Also appreciated is input from Renee Clary, Gary Rosenberg, and Dallas Evans, volume editors and session conveners with the History and Philosophy of Geology Division of the Geological Society of America (GSA), and two anonymous reviewers.

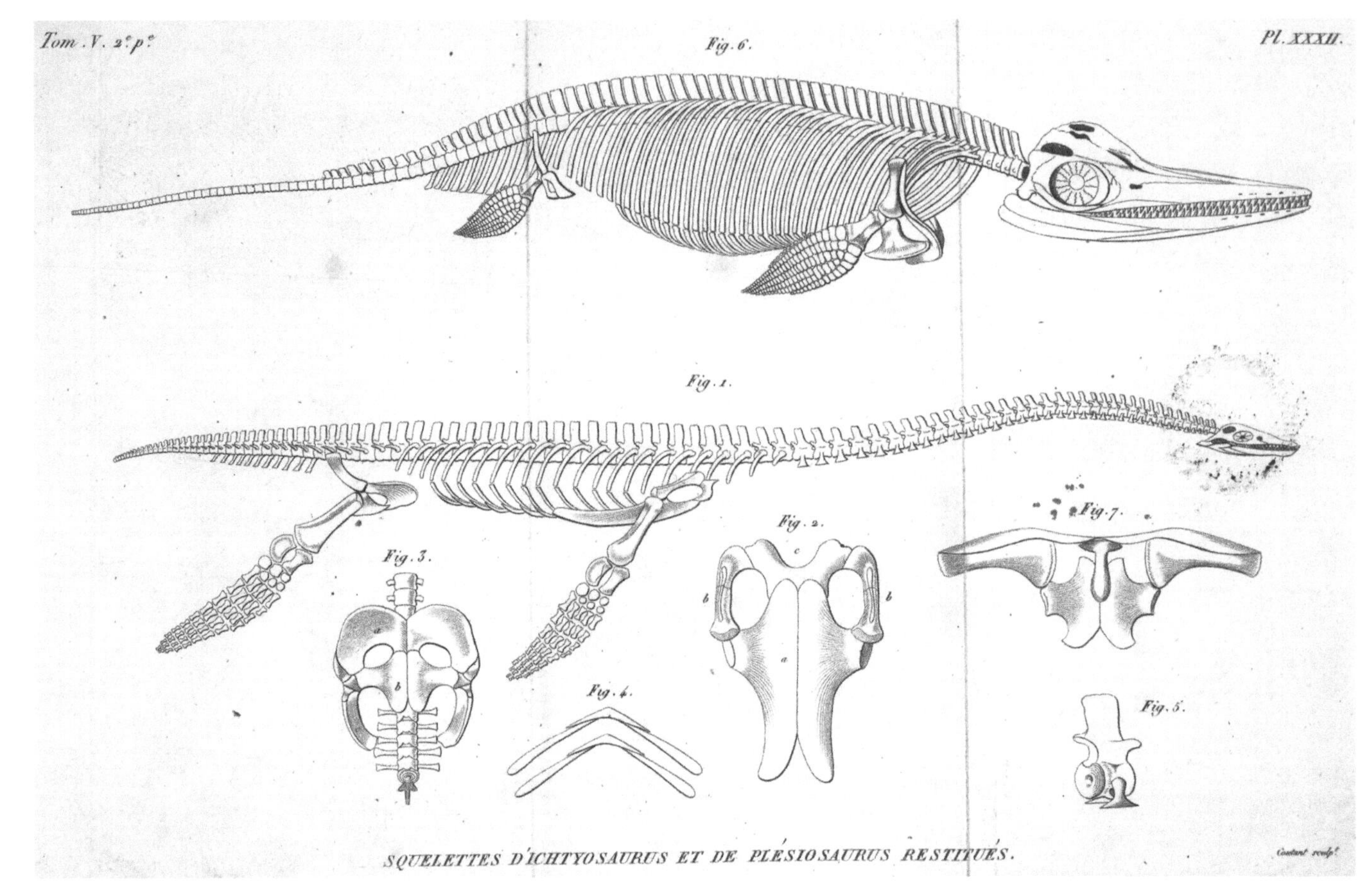

Figure 7. A lesson in form and function: Cuvier (1824, Vol. 5, Part 2, Plate 32) presented readers with striking views of ichthyosaur and plesiosaur skeletons. Courtesy of Linda Hall Library.

REFERENCES CITED

d'Archiac, E.-J.-A., 1862, Cours de paléontologie stratigraphique: Professé au Muséum d'histoire naturelle (Paris): Paris, Librairie de la Société Géologique de France, 491 p.

Bork, K.B., 1999, Correspondence as a window on the development of a discipline: Brongniart, Cleaveland, Silliman and the maturation of mineralogy in the first decades of the nineteenth century: Earth Sciences History, v. 18, no. 2, p. 198–245, https://doi.org/10.17704/eshi.18.2.e250tuw214t1l808.

Bork, K.B., 2013, Alexandre Brongniart (1770–1847) shows that a 'Facts First' scientific approach can lead to large-scale conclusions: Earth Sciences History, v. 32, no. 1, p. 9–22, https://doi.org/10.17704/eshi.32.1.x8757468r35215h1.

Brongniart, A., 1810, Sur les terrains qui paraissent avoir été formés sous l'eau douce: Annales du Muséum d'histoire naturelle, v. 15, p. 357–405.

Brongniart, A., 1821, Sur les caractères zoologiques des formations: Avec application de ces caractères à la détermination de quelques terrains de craie: Annales des Mines, v. 6, p. 541–552.

Brongniart, A., 1823, Mémoire sur les terrains de sédiment supérieurs calcaréo-trappéens du Vicentin, et sur quelques terrains d'Italie, de France, d'Allemagne, etc., qui peuvent se rapporter à la même époque: Paris, F.-G. Levrault, 84 p.

Cuvier, G., 1799, Mémoire sur les espèces d'éléphans vivantes et fossiles, lu le premier pluvose an 4 (21 January 1796): Mémoires de l'Institut National des Sciences et des Arts, sciences mathématiques et physiques, v. 2, p. 1–22, plates 2–6.

Cuvier, G., 1809, Mémoire sur le squelette fossile d'un reptile volant des environs d'Aichstedt, que quelques naturalistes ont pris pour un oiseau, et dont nous formons un genre de Sauriens, sous le nom de Petro-Dactyle (Ptéro-Dactyle): Annales du Muséum d'histoire naturelle, Paris, v. 13, p. 424–437.

Cuvier, G., 1812, Recherches sur les ossemens fossiles de quadrupèdes: Où l'on rétablit les caractères de plusieurs espèces d'animaux que les révolutions du globe paroissent avoir détruites. Tome troisième. Les os fossiles des environs de Paris: Paris, Chez Déterville, 4 vols.

Cuvier, G., 1821–1824, Recherches sur les ossemens fossiles: Où l'on rétablit les caractères de plusieurs animaux dont les révolutions du globe ont détruit les espèces. Nouvelle édition, entièrement refondue, et considérablement augmentée, 5 vols. in 7: Paris, chez G. Dufour et E. d'Ocagne.

Cuvier, G., 1824, Recherches sur les ossemens fossiles de quadrupèdes, où l'on rétablit les caractères de plusieurs espèces d'animaux dont les révolutions du globe ont détruites les espèces: Paris, G. Dufour et E. Ocagne, 23 p.

Cuvier, G., and Brongniart, A., 1808, Essai sur la géographie minéralogique des environs de Paris: Journal des mines, v. 23, p. 421–458. (Also: Annales du Muséum d'histoire naturelle, v. 11, p. 299–328.)

Cuvier, G., and Brongniart, A., 1811, Essai sur la géographie minéralogique des environs de Paris, avec une carte géognostique, et des coupes de terrain (lu le 11 avril 1808), *in* Mémoires de la Classe des Sciences mathématiques et physiques de l'Institut Impérial de France 1810: Paris, Baudouin, p. 1–278.

Cuvier, G., and Brongniart, A., 1822, Description géologique des environs de Paris. Nouvelle édition, dans laquelle on a inséré la description d'un grand nombre de lieux de l'Allemagne, de la Suisse, de l'Italie, etc., qui présentent des terrains analogues à ceux du bassin de Paris, par M. Alex. Brongniart: Paris and Amsterdam, G. Dufour et E. d'Ocagne, 428 p.

Gohau, G., 1990, A History of Geology, revised and translated by A. V. Carozzi: New Brunswick, New Jersey, Rutgers University Press, 259 p.

Hancock, J.M., 1977, The historic development of concepts of biostratigraphic correlation, *in* Kauffman, E.G., and Hazel, J.E., eds., Concepts and Methods of Biostratigraphy: Stroudsburg, Pennsylvania, Dowden, Hutchinson, and Ross, p. 3–22.

Howe, S.R., Sharpe, T., and Torrens, H.S., 1981, Ichthyosaurs: A History of Fossil "Sea Dragons": Cardiff, National Museum of Wales, UK, 31 p.

de Launay, L., 1940, Les Brongniart: Une grande famille de savants: Paris, G. Rapilly et fils, 208 p.

Préaud, T., 1997, The Sèvres Porcelain Manufactory: Alexandre Brongniart and the Triumph of Art and Industry, 1800–1847: New Haven, Connecticut, Yale University Press, 416 p.

Rudwick, M.J.S., 1972, The Meaning of Fossils: Episodes in the History of Palaeontology: London and New York, Macdonald, 287 p.

Rudwick, M.J.S., 1992, Scenes from Deep Time: Early Pictorial Representations of the Prehistoric World: Chicago, University of Chicago Press, 280 p., https://doi.org/10.7208/chicago/9780226149035.001.0001.

Rudwick, M.J.S., 1997, Georges Cuvier, Fossil Bones, and Geological Catastrophes: Chicago, University of Chicago Press, 301 p., https://doi.org/10.7208/chicago/9780226731087.001.0001.

Rudwick, M.J.S., 2005, Bursting the Limits of Time: The Reconstruction of Geohistory in the Age of Revolution: Chicago, University of Chicago Press, 708 p., https://doi.org/10.7208/chicago/9780226731148.001.0001.

Schneer, C.J., ed., 1969, Toward a History of Geology: Cambridge, Massachusetts, The M.I.T. Press, 469 p.

Taquet, P., 2006, Georges Cuvier: Naissance d'un Génie: Paris, Odile Jacob, 539 p.

Taquet, P., 2009, Les contributions respectives de Georges Cuvier et d'Alexandre Brongniart à l'élaboration de l'Essai sur la géographie minéralogique des environs de Paris, d'après les manuscrits retrouvés d'Alexandre Brongniart: Travaux du Comité français d'histoire de la géologie (COFRHIGEO): Troisième série 23, no. 1, p. 1–16.

Taquet, P., 2019, Georges Cuvier: Anatomie d'un naturaliste (1795–1803): Paris, Odile Jacob, 779 p.

Taylor, K.L., 2008, Early geoscience mapping, 1700–1830, *in* The Earth Sciences in the Enlightenment: Studies on the Early Development of Geology: Aldershot, Hampshire, UK, & Burlington, Vermont, USA, Ashgate Publishing. Republished from Proceedings of the Geoscience Information Society, 1985, v. 15, p. 15–49.

Webster, T., 1814, On freshwater formations in the Isle of Wight, with some observations over the Chalk in the south-east part of England: Transactions of the Geological Society of London, v. 2, p. 161–254, https://doi.org/10.1144/transgsla.2.161.

Manuscript Accepted by the Society 14 January 2021
Manuscript Published Online 11 May 2021

The Geological Society of America
Memoir 218

Henry De la Beche's pioneering paleoecological illustration, Duria antiquior

Tom Sharpe*
4 Abbey Mains Cottages, Haddington, East Lothian EH41 3SB, Scotland

Renee M. Clary*
Department of Geosciences, Mississippi State University, Box 5448, Mississippi State, Mississippi 39762, USA

ABSTRACT

In late 1829 or early 1830, Henry Thomas De la Beche (1796–1855), in collaboration with William Buckland (1784–1856), published *Duria antiquior* [*A more ancient Dorsetshire*], the earliest known paleoecological illustration of ancient life. De la Beche's interpretation was based largely on fossils then recently uncovered from Lower Jurassic (Lias) rocks near Lyme Regis on the south coast of England. Many of these were brought to scientific attention by local fossil collector and dealer Mary Anning (1799–1847). De la Beche published *Duria antiquior* as a lithograph, copies of which were sold as a fundraiser for Anning, who was then in straitened circumstances. *Duria antiquior* represented a new style of paleontological illustration that pioneered a new scientific genre addressing the history of nature and an innovative viewpoint where the observer glimpses lifeforms *through* the water. Other authors modified and adopted De la Beche's visionary illustration, and the style became commonplace in popular geological publications in the later nineteenth century. *Duria antiquior* can be acknowledged as the pioneering graphic from which fossil organisms' reconstructions and modern computer-generated paleoecosystem animations trace their origins.

INTRODUCTION

Prior to the mid-nineteenth century, fossils were illustrated just as they had been collected. A sketch of invertebrate fossils, such as brachiopods, mollusks, and corals, closely resembled the organisms as they appeared in life. However, this was not the case with vertebrates. Paleontologists might assemble the individual bones into a correct (or incorrect) sequence, but soft tissue anatomy was rarely preserved and therefore not included in the illustration. This changed in late 1829 or early 1830 with *Duria antiquior* [*A more ancient Dorsetshire*] (Fig. 1), a ground-breaking illustration by Henry Thomas De la Beche (1796–1855), who imagined the fossil ecosystem of the Early Jurassic (Lias) rocks exposed in coastal cliffs and foreshore around the small Dorset town of Lyme Regis on England's southern coast. De la Beche's lithograph, its variants, and derivatives have appeared in numerous paleontology and history of science publications for almost two centuries (Rudwick, 1992; Clary and Wandersee, 2009).

*Emails: tom@tomsharpe.co.uk; RClary@geosci.msstate.edu

Sharpe, T., and Clary, R.M., 2022, Henry De la Beche's pioneering paleoecological illustration, *Duria antiquior*, *in* Clary, R.M., Rosenberg, G.D., and Evans, D.C., eds., The Evolution of Paleontological Art: Geological Society of America Memoir 218, p. 47–54, https://doi.org/10.1130/2021.1218(06).

Figure 1. In late 1829 or early 1830, De la Beche sketched and painted *Duria antiquior* [*A more ancient Dorsetshire*], a watercolor image of extinct Jurassic life based upon the fossils gathered from the Lias by Mary Anning and other collectors. From this watercolor, *Duria* was turned into a lithograph, and copies were sold as a fundraiser for Mary Anning, who faced financial hardships. *Duria* is the first published scene from Deep Time and the first published illustration with an aquarium viewpoint. Reproduced with permission of the National Museum of Wales.

THE ARTIST: HENRY DE LA BECHE

Henry De la Beche was born in London in 1796 but spent much of his childhood in the West Country of England with his mother (McCartney, 1977; Sharpe, 2008, 2013). His father died in 1801 during a visit to the family's Jamaican sugar plantation from which their wealth derived (Sharpe, 2013). While at school at Keynsham in Somerset (ca. 1805–1808), Henry developed an interest in the local Lias fossils and collected ammonites and belemnites (Sharpe, 2013). In 1812, Henry and his mother, now with her third husband, settled in Lyme Regis, where Henry's interest in fossils was encouraged both by his stepfather and the local physician, Dr. Thomas Coulson Carpenter (ca. 1778–1833). Like Carpenter, Henry De la Beche assembled a collection of local specimens, including ichthyosaurs, and made the acquaintance of other Lyme collectors including the fossilist Mary Anning (1799–1847) who, with her mother and brother, was bringing to light a previously unknown fossil vertebrate fauna from the coastal strata (Howe et al., 1981; Torrens, 1995). These, and the geology of the Dorset coast, were studied by De la Beche, at times in collaboration with William Buckland (1784–1856) and William Daniel Conybeare (1787–1857), both of whom also had Dorset connections.

As an adult, De la Beche emerged as a noted and respected geologist—a Fellow of the Royal Society and Fellow and later President of the Geological Society of London. Upon the loss of his family income in the 1830s, he successfully transitioned from gentleman geologist to paid professional, becoming the first Director of what is now the British Geological Survey (McCartney, 1977; Secord, 2004; Sharpe, 2008; Clary and Wandersee, 2009, 2014). De la Beche was knighted for his service in 1842.

In addition to being an accomplished geologist, De la Beche was also a skilled draftsman and artist. He wrote that he taught himself to draw while living at Sidmouth with his mother (ca. 1807–1810) at a time when drawing manuals were popular, but undoubtedly his drawing skills were honed at Military College at Marlow in Buckinghamshire, where the drawing master was the landscape artist William Delamotte (1775–1863) (Sharpe, 2013; Clary and Wandersee, 2014). De la Beche used his artistic skills throughout his geological career both formally in the preparation of his plates and diagrams and informally through sketches and cartoons critically commenting on scientific developments or poking fun at friends and colleagues (McCartney, 1977; Clary and Wandersee, 2010, 2011). His earliest surviving sketches (1815) are of foreign visitors to Lyme Regis, but his first landscapes and geological scenes are preserved in his 1816 diary of a tour of northern England and Scotland. Diaries of his later tours in England, Wales, and on the continent through the 1820s are often beautifully illustrated (McCartney, 1977; Sharpe and McCartney, 1998; Antognini and Sharpe, 2002; Clary, 2003; Clary and Wandersee, 2014).

A PIONEERING ILLUSTATION: *DURIA ANTIQUIOR*

In 1820, Lieutenant-Colonel Thomas James Birch (ca. 1768–1829) was motivated to sell his fossil collection to aid the Annings, who were in desperate financial need (Torrens, 1979, 1995; Sharpe, 2020). By the end of that decade, Mary and her mother were again on the brink of poverty. Fossil sales were an unreliable and irregular income source. In 1826, unable to sell some of her better specimens, Anning had expressed thoughts of giving up fossil dealing altogether (Taylor and Torrens, 1986). To assist them financially, De la Beche constructed and published a lithograph illustrating the Lias ecosystem, with proceeds from sales of the print going to the Annings (Clary, 2019). In a letter dated 13 May 1830 to Gideon Mantell (1790–1852), Charles Lyell (1797–1875) tells him that "The Plate [*Duria*] was done for Mary Anning and will put much money in her pocket"[1] (Torrens, 1995; Sharpe, 2008).

De la Beche's *Duria antiquior* is the first reconstruction to show extinct fossil organisms as living animals within an ecosystem, and as such, pioneered a new scientific genre depicting the history of nature (Rudwick, 2014) (Fig. 2). Another remarkable feature of *Duria* is the innovative "aquarium" viewpoint, which reveals activity below the surface of the sea, on its surface, and on a hilly and island landscape beyond. This novel viewpoint may have arisen from De la Beche's enthusiasm for boating and swimming in the waters of Lyme Bay or from new marine salvage devices such as the diving helmets developed in the 1820s by the diving engineer brothers Charles (1796–1848) and John Deane (1800–1884) (Rudwick, 1992). The aquarium view was not readily adopted in other illustrations until after the Victorian parlor aquarium craze (Clary and Wandersee, 2005).

Duria summarizes the remarkable vertebrate fossils discovered, mainly by the Anning family, in the Lias strata of Lyme Regis between 1811 and 1829 (Howe et al., 1981; Torrens, 1995). While ichthyosaurs, plesiosaurs, and pterosaurs are the dominant elements of the illustrated fauna, other vertebrates include several different species of bony fish and sharks. Ward and Bizley (2007) suggested that the fish represented are *Dapedium politum* (Leach 1822), a pycnodont similar to the modern Atlantic wolffish; *Caturus heterurus* (Agassiz 1844); *Pholidophorus bechei* Agassiz 1844; *Acrodus anningae* Agassiz 1839; and an unidentifiable three-spined fish.

On land, the vegetation includes palm trees and other plants that may reflect the vegetation seen by De la Beche on his visit to Jamaica about six years earlier (Sharpe, 2008). Cycads were known to De la Beche from later Jurassic rocks to the east of Lyme at Portland in Dorset, and these Late Jurassic strata may be the source of the crocodile and turtles that De la Beche includes in *Duria*.

Several of the animals are depicted in the act of producing proto-coprolites, either voluntarily or through an involuntary evacuation brought on by stress in the case of the plesiosaur whose neck is being bitten by a large ichthyosaur. Although first described by Buckland (1829, 1835b), who introduced the term, coprolites were likely first recognized as fossil feces by Mary Anning, who had noted their frequent occurrence in the abdominal areas of ichthyosaur skeletons (Duffin, 2012). Buckland realized that coprolites provided evidence of the eater and the eaten in the Lias food chain, and this is illustrated by De la Beche in *Duria* as different animals consume one another. Here the illustration is of serious intent, unlike De la Beche's humorous *A Coprolitic Vision*, which shows Buckland amongst defecating pterosaurs, as well as Pleistocene hyaenas and deer, a reference to Buckland's earlier excavation at Kirkdale Cavern in Yorkshire (McCartney, 1977; Clary and Wandersee, 2011).

Duria antiquior's Inspiration

On 6 February 1829, in his paper at the Geological Society on Anning's 1828 pterosaur discovery, Buckland's description brought the Lias vertebrates to life: "With flocks of such-like creatures flying in the air, and shoals of no less monstrous Ichthyosauri and Plesiosauri swarming in the ocean, and gigantic crocodiles and tortoises crawling on the shores of the primæval lakes and rivers, air, sea, and land must have been strangely tenanted in these early periods of our infant world" (Buckland, 1835a, 1836). In *Duria*, De la Beche realized not only Buckland's vivid vision (McCartney, 1977; O'Connor, 2007; Rudwick, 2014) but also incorporated William Daniel Conybeare's 1824 description of the plesiosaur's mode of life: "I suppose he swam on the surface and fished with his long neck, or lurked in Shoal water … catching all the small fry that came within reach of his long sweep, but he must have kept as much as possible out of reach of Ichthyosauri, a very junior member of whom with his powerful jaws would have bit his neck in two without ceremony,"[2] a thought perhaps reinforced by the 1823 specimen's displaced cervical vertebrae implying ichthyosaur predation (Norman, 2000).

[1]Charles Lyell to Gideon Mantell, 13 May 1830, Mantell MSS, Alexander Turnbull Library, Wellington, New Zealand.

[2]Conybeare to De la Beche, 4 March 1824, NMW84.20G.D302 (Sharpe and McCartney, 1998).

Figure 2. Proceeds from the sale of lithographic copies of *Duria antiquior* helped provide much needed funding for the Anning family. The lithograph is the first published paleoecological scene and illustrates Jurassic organisms interacting within terrestrial and marine ecosystems; even future coprolites are drawn. Private collection, used with permission.

Buckland's (1835a) description of *Pterodactylus macronyx* as "resembling … the dragons of romance and heraldry" inspired George Ernest Howman (ca. 1797–1879) to reconstruct a scene of the animal (Torrens, 1995; O'Connor, 2007). Although Martill (2014) described the illustration as the earliest of a pterosaur in its life environment (predating *Duria* by a year), Howman's depiction illustrates a winged dragon flying over a stormy sea in which a sailing ship lists heavily offshore of a ruined castle on a rocky headland; unlike De la Beche's Jurassic scene, the illustration places the pterosaur in more recent historical time.

DURIA DISTRIBUTION AND DISSEMINATION

William Buckland adopted *Duria* immediately in his teaching at Oxford. He wrote to De la Beche on Tuesday 25 May [1830],[3] telling him how useful *Duria* had been: "I have a capital class and your Duria has contributed to its numbers and my entertainment of them." He mentions *Duria* again almost a year later,[4] "I have a capital Class which I am sure is 30 per cent better for your Duria Antiquior by way of a Syllabus." At the end of his lectures at Oxford, Buckland distributed copies of *Duria* "in order to bring to the minds of his audience the reality of the subjects on which he had been conversing," according to his son Frank (Buckland, 1886, p. xi). He also had an enlarged version made as a teaching aid (Boylan, 1984).

Buckland was also selling copies of *Duria* and forwarding the money to Mary Anning. In his letter of 25 May [1830], he

[3]NMW84.20G.D182 (Sharpe and McCartney, 1998).

[4]Buckland to De la Beche, 1 May 1831, NMW84.20G.D180 (Sharpe and McCartney, 1998).

wrote, "I have sent M. Anning £5 for copies sold to Stokes, Lonsdale and Broderip." These were Charles Stokes (1783–1853), William Lonsdale (1794–1871), and William Broderip (1789–1859). *Duria* prints sold for £2 10s each (Rudwick, 1992), so for Anning to receive £5 from the sale of three, the proceeds per copy sold were likely £1 13s 4d and production or other costs 16s 8d per copy.

Buckland may have held a significant stock of *Duria* (Gordon, 1894). According to Boylan (1984), Buckland paid for additional prints to be made at his own expense. In a draft of his letter of 14 October 1831,[5] but not included in the final letter sent to De la Beche,[6] Buckland mentioned that he "sent M. Anning 100 copies" of *Duria*. From this we may surmise that Anning, too, was distributing or, more likely, selling copies from her shop in Broad Street in Lyme Regis. If she sold all 100 copies at £2 10s each, her income would have been £250. A print of *Duria* was an expensive purchase; the same amount would have purchased Thomas Hawkins' (1834) Imperial folio volume *Memoirs of Ichthyosauri and Plesiosauri*, and it was only 13 shillings less than the cost of an annual subscription to the Geological Society (which today is about £200).

Buckland also distributed *Duria* to his European contacts, sending a copy to Georges Cuvier (1769–1832) in Paris (Brignon, 2016)[7] and in 1837–1838 presenting a copy to the Geological Society of France.[8] Buckland may also have sent a copy to Georg August Goldfuss (1782–1848), professor of zoology and mineralogy at Bonn, to whom he had already sent a copy of his pterosaur paper (Rudwick, 1992).

A copy had reached Berlin by early 1831. On 5 February of that year, Prussian geologist Leopold von Buch (1774–1853), who had visited Buckland in Oxford in 1816 and was known to De la Beche by 1829, discussed *Duria* at a meeting of the Berliner Gesellschaft der Freude der Humanität, a Berlin intellectual society (Kröger, 2013). This was the first public presentation in what is now Germany of the work of Buckland and De la Beche on the English Lias fossils and of *Duria* (Kröger, 2013). In the notes of his talk, "Bemerkungen Über ein Bild, Welches die Urwelt Vorstellt" ["Remarks on a Lithographic Print, Depicting the Primeval World"], which survive in the Museum für Naturkunde Berlin, von Buch described *Duria*'s contents in detail and how "… Mr Buckland and Mr De la Beche have brought all this information into one drawing in which most of the recently discovered creatures are represented in a charming hustle and bustle; all following their destiny, that is devouring each other" (quoted in Kröger, 2013, p. 26).

That Buckland was closely involved with the production of *Duria* is suggested not only by von Buch's statement that Buckland and De la Beche "have brought all this information into one drawing" but also by a mention in the 13 May 1830 letter from Charles Lyell to Gideon Mantell:[9] "Have you seen the admirable plate of Buckland and Delabeche's … of Duria antiquior or Dorsetshire as it existed at the era of the lias?" So *Duria* was regarded, at least by some contemporaries, as a joint production of De la Beche and Buckland, both of whom were close friends of Mary Anning and were no doubt keen to help ease her financial difficulties through the sale of lithographs.

DURIA'S ADOPTION AND REPRODUCTIONS

A German "Parody"

On 14 October 1831, William Buckland wrote to De la Beche that he had just received a "German Parody" of *Duria antiquior* from William Lonsdale (1794–1871) at the Geological Society, who had, in turn, received it from the German fossil collector Friedrich Wilhelm Hoeninghaus (1770–1854).[10] Although it was not truly a parody, *Jura Formation* was a plagiarized elaboration of *Duria antiquior* that was probably drawn by the University of Bonn lithographer and scientific draftsman (and professor of art) Nicolaus Christian Hohe (1798–1868) to promote the publication of the third part of *Petrefacta Germaniae* by Goldfuss despite its irrelevance to the contents of that volume (Rudwick, 1992, 2008).

Buckland encouraged De la Beche to forestall further plagiarism by drawing more such scenes and suggested a series of geological time periods for De la Beche's consideration. None, at least not on the scale of *Duria*, appear to have been done by De la Beche. By this time, De la Beche was more deeply involved in his geological mapping of Devon and in his writing. In 1830, De la Beche published two volumes, *Geological Notes* and *Sections and Views Illustrative of Geological Phaenomena*, and 1831 saw publication of the first edition of *A Geological Manual*. De la Beche also held a position as Secretary to the Geological Society from 1831 to 1832. Buckland, however, does appear to have had several new scenes drawn; one depicted a late Carboniferous coal forest and the other another Jurassic scene (O'Connor, 2007). These, like his enlargement of *Duria* and De la Beche's 1830 lithograph *Awful Changes,* were prepared as visual aids, perhaps by Buckland's wife, Mary Morland (1797–1857), who was an accomplished illustrator.

Like *Duria*, *Jura Formation* (the phonetic similarity between *Jura* and *Duria* is coincidental) features a large ichthyosaur at its center (though swimming to the right rather than to the left), ammonites swimming on the surface with "sails," crocodiles and turtles on land among various terrestrial plants, and pterosaurs in the air (Fig. 3). Ammonite shells litter the lower right corner of the view and crinoids grow in the lower left, positions which,

[5]Buckland Archive, Oxford University Museum of Natural History.

[6]Buckland to De la Beche, 14 October 1831, NMW84.20G.D183 (Sharpe and McCartney, 1998).

[7]BCM Ms627/103 Bibliothèque central du Muséum national d'Histoire naturelle, Paris.

[8]*Bulletin de la Société Géologique de France*, v. 9, p. 452.

[9]Lyell to Mantell, 13 May 1830, Mantell MSS, Alexander Turnbull Library, Wellington, New Zealand.

[10]Buckland to De la Beche, 14 October 1831, NMW84.20G.D183 (Sharpe and McCartney, 1998).

Figure 3. In 1831, a plagiarized version of *Duria* surfaced to promote Goldfuss' third part of *Petrefacta Germaniae*. Based on the *Jura Formation*, the lithograph lacks the paleoecological interactions of De la Beche's *Duria*, although it features finer details of the invertebrate marine organisms included. The aquarium viewpoint is also partly masked by the surface ripples. Reproduced with permission of the Geological Society of London.

when combined with the reversed facing direction of the central ichthyosaur, suggest that *Duria* was at least the starting template for the engraving of the stone for *Jura Formation*. The *Jura Formation* lithograph measures 397 mm × 261 mm and is significantly larger than *Duria* (321 mm × 228 mm).

However, it is a more static view, lacking many of the faunal interactions shown by De la Beche, although some animals are feeding. It offers the same aquarium view as *Duria*, but shading representing water ripples renders the underwater section much less clear. However, on close inspection, it is evident that *Jura Formation* contains much more detail than *Duria*, not just in the density of the benthic fauna but also in the finer details of the individual organisms, such as ammonite ornamentation, echinoid spines, and detailed crinoid calyxes. In fact, with the exception of the large, central ichthyosaur and the crocodile on shore behind it, *Jura Formation* is much more finely drawn than *Duria*. Hohe seemed to have been more comfortable drawing the invertebrates. The densely packed benthic fauna includes limulids, lobsters, shrimp, starfish, and the distinctive stemless crinoid *Saccocoma*, which, along with the dragonflies sharing the air with pterosaurs and other faunal elements, suggest that *Jura Formation* is based largely on fossils from the Tithonian Solnhofen Plattenkalk lagerstätte of southern Germany (the source of the stone on which both *Jura Formation* and *Duria antiquior* were most likely drawn). So, while *Duria* primarily illustrates the English Lower Jurassic, *Jura Formation* seems more representative of the Bavarian Upper Jurassic.

Jura Formation was the first of many versions, adaptations, and derivatives of *Duria* to appear, initially, in more peripheral publications aimed at general readers rather than in the specialized geological literature (Rudwick, 2008). The images helped a general readership visualize ancient ecosystems, however, and their importance was eventually recognized. Rudwick (1992) and other authors (O'Connor, 2007; Clary and Wandersee, 2009; Glendening, 2009) considered the importance and significance of *Duria antiquior* and discussed its legacy in detail.

While De la Beche's *Duria antiquior* has a cheerful, almost comic aspect to it that probably contributed to its enduring appeal

(Rudwick, 1992), the paleoecological interactions of animals eating or being eaten led to the adoption of a visualization of viciousness in a much darker style by later saurian artists such as John Martin (1789–1854) (see Mantell, 1838; Hawkins, 1840; Rudwick, 2008). These images may have anticipated or inspired the vision of "Nature, red in tooth and claw" of Alfred, Lord Tennyson (1809–1892) (Canto 56, *In Memoriam A.H.H.*, 1849) (Rupke, 1983).

DURIA'S LASTING INFLUENCE

Duria antiquior is one of at least six illustrations that De la Beche produced and had printed between 1829 and 1841: *A Coprolitic Vision* (ca. 1829), *Awful Changes* (1830), *The Light of Science* (1832), *A Scientific Annual* (1837), and *The Irregularities of Sol Visited upon His System* (1841) (see McCartney, 1977; Rudwick, 1992). *Duria antiquior* is by far the best known and had significant influence on subsequent geological authors and illustrators. Lyell described it as "a glorious restoration and has done much to popularize the subject."[11] In this single image, De la Beche encapsulated nearly two decades of research that he, Conybeare, Buckland, and others had conducted on the Lias fossils of Dorset. It is a concise summary of a remarkable period of paleontological discovery.

However, *Duria antiquior* is important for several other reasons. It was the first reconstructed paleoecological scene published and quickly influenced subsequent geological illustration. Other authors attempted to depict extinct organisms as they once lived, whether by close adoption of De la Beche's version (e.g., Richardson, 1842; see Rudwick, 1992, for other examples) or a progression of illustrations that resulted from *Duria*'s pioneering image (see, for example, Allmon, 2017, for evolution of ammonite illustrations). Within a decade, other artists applied the paleoecological reconstruction technique to illustrations of other organisms (e.g., Mantell, 1838).

De la Beche's aquarium viewpoint was not as readily adopted. Even within paleoecological reconstructions in his own texts, De la Beche reverted to the overhead view of a plesiosaur in a vignette scene of deep time (De la Beche, 1832). Two decades after *Duria antiquior*, parlor aquaria became popular in Victorian society, offering a direct view of aquatic life through glass. However, period illustrations did not immediately incorporate a dual phase view of water and air (Clary and Wandersee, 2005). Today, multiple phase scenes are the default view in geological textbooks.

De la Beche's *Duria antiquior* was a visionary illustration that ushered in a new genre of imagery. The subsequent influences of this graphic cannot be underestimated, especially when we consider that geological murals, dioramas, and modern movie animations (e.g., *Jurassic Park*) can trace their heritage to De la Beche's first paleoecological reconstruction.

[11]Lyell to Mantell, 13 May 1830, Mantell MSS, Alexander Turnbull Library, Wellington, New Zealand.

ACKNOWLEDGMENTS

For assistance with the preparation of this paper, sourcing references, permission to reproduce images, and providing access to material in their care, we thank Emily Chen (Oxford University Museum of Natural History); Cindy Howells and Kay Kays (National Museum of Wales); Caroline Lam, Wendy Cawthorne, and Fabienne Michaud (Geological Society Library, London); Hellen Pethers (Natural History Museum, London); Charlotte Topsfield (National Galleries of Scotland); David Tucker and Richard Bull (Lyme Regis Museum); Alastair Macrae; and the library staff at both the Wellcome Collection, London, and the Alexander Turnbull Library, Wellington, New Zealand. We thank Chris Duffin (Natural History Museum, London) for his assistance with Lias fish identifications; reviewers Paul Brinkman (North Carolina Museum of Natural Sciences) and David Martill (University of Portsmouth), and Volume Editor Gary Rosenberg for comments and suggestions that improved the presentation of this research.

REFERENCES CITED

Allmon, W.D., 2017, Life-restorations of ammonites and the challenges of taxonomic uniformitarianism: Earth Sciences History, v. 36, no. 1, p. 1–29, https://doi.org/10.17704/1944-6178-36.1.1.

Antognini, M., and Sharpe, T., 2002, Le osservazioni sulla geologia del luganese di H.T. De la Beche (1796–1855): Dal diario di viaggio alla pubblicazione: Bollettino della Società ticinese di Scienze naturali, v. 90, p. 17–28.

Boylan, P.J., 1984, William Buckland, 1784–1856: Scientific institutions, vertebrate palaeontology, and Quaternary geology [Ph.D. thesis]: Leicester, UK, University of Leicester, 443 p.

Brignon, A., 2016, Revue historique des premières études sur les poissons fossiles (Teleostei) des ardoises d'Engi (Oligocène inférieur, canton de Glaris, Suisse): Revue de Paléobiologie, Genève, v. 35, no. 2, p. 459–490.

Buckland, F.T., 1886, Curiosities of Natural History, 2nd Ser., Popular edition: London, Richard Bentley and Son, 360 p.

Buckland, W., 1829, On the discovery of a new species of Pterodactyle; also of the faeces of the Ichthyosaurus; and of a black substance resembling sepia, or Indian ink, in the Lias at Lyme Regis: Proceedings of the Geological Society of London, v. 1, p. 96–98.

Buckland, W., 1835a, On the discovery of a new species of Pterodactyle in the Lias at Lyme Regis, and in other formations. Read 6th February 1829: Transactions of the Geological Society of London, 2nd Ser., v. 3, p. 217–222.

Buckland, W., 1835b, On the discovery of coprolites, or fossil faeces, in the Lias at Lyme Regis, and in other formations. Read 6th February 1829: Transactions of the Geological Society of London, 2nd Ser., v. 3, p. 223–236.

Buckland, W., 1836, Geology and Mineralogy Considered with Reference to Natural Theology, Volume 1: London, William Pickering, xvi + 596 p.

Clary, R.M., 2003, Uncovering strata: An investigation into the graphic innovations of geologist Henry T. De la Beche [Ph.D. thesis]: Baton Rouge, Louisiana, Louisiana State University, x + 470 p.

Clary, R.M., 2019, Mary Anning: She sold (fossil) sea shells by the seashore: GSA Today, v. 29, no. 5, p. 62–63, https://www.geosociety.org/gsatoday/archive/29/5/pdf/i1052-5173-29-5-62.pdf.

Clary, R.M., and Wandersee, J.H., 2005, Through the looking glass: The history of aquarium views and their potential to improve learning in science classrooms: Science & Education, v. 14, p. 579–596, https://doi.org/10.1007/s11191-004-7691-1.

Clary, R.M., and Wandersee, J.H., 2009, All are worthy to know the Earth: Henry De la Beche and the origins of geological literacy: Science & Education, v. 18, p. 1359–1375, https://doi.org/10.1007/s11191-008-9177-z.

Clary, R.M., and Wandersee, J.H., 2010, Scientific caricatures in the earth science classroom: An alternative assessment for meaningful science learning:

Science & Education, v. 19, no. 1, p. 21–37, https://doi.org/10.1007/s11191-008-9178-y.

Clary, R.M., and Wandersee, J.H., 2011, A "Coprolitic Vision" for earth science education: School Science and Mathematics, v. 111, no. 6, p. 262–273, https://doi.org/10.1111/j.1949-8594.2011.00087.x.

Clary, R.M., and Wandersee, J.H., 2014, The journey from elite society to government geologist: Henry De la Beche's (1796–1855) powerful impact on the importance of observation within an emerging professional science: Earth Sciences History, v. 33, no. 2, p. 259–278, https://doi.org/10.17704/eshi.33.2.b0764512965g836u.

De la Beche, H.T., 1832, A Geological Manual. 2nd edition: London, Treuttel & Würtz, Treuttel Jun. and Richter, 564 p.

Duffin, C.J., 2012, Coprolites and characters in Victorian Britain, *in* Hunt, A.P., Milàn, J., Lucas, S.G., and Spielmann, J.A., eds., Vertebrate Coprolites: New Mexico Museum of Natural History and Science Bulletin 57, p. 45–60.

Glendening, J., 2009, 'The World-Renowned Ichthyosaurus': A nineteenth century problematic and its representations: Journal of Literature and Science, v. 2, no. 1, p. 23–47, https://doi.org/10.12929/jls.02.1.02.

Gordon, Mrs. [E.O.], 1894, The Life and Correspondence of William Buckland, D.D., F.R.S.: London, John Murray, xvi + 288 p.

Hawkins, T., 1840, The Book of the Great Sea-dragons, Ichthyosauri and Plesiosauri Gedolim Taninim, of Moses Extinct Monsters of the Ancient Earth: London, William Pickering, 27 p.

Howe, S.R., Sharpe, T., and Torrens, H.S., 1981, Ichthyosaurs: A History of Fossil 'Sea-dragons': Cardiff, National Museum of Wales, 32 p.

Kröger, B., 2013, Remarks on a scene, depicting the primeval world: A talk given by Leopold von Buch in 1831, popularizing the *Duria antiquior*: HiN—Humboldt Im Netz: Internationale Zeitschrift für Humboldt-Studien, XIV, v. 27, p. 7–35.

Mantell, G.A., 1838, The wonders of geology; or, a familiar exposition of geological phenomena: London, Relfe and Fletcher, 373 p., https://doi.org/10.5962/bhl.title.153153.

Martill, D.M., 2014, *Dimorphodon* and the Reverend George Howman's noctivagous flying dragon: The earliest restoration of a pterosaur in its natural habitat: Proceedings of the Geologists' Association, v. 125, no. 1, p. 120–130.

McCartney, P.J., 1977, Henry De la Beche: Observations on an Observer: Cardiff, Friends of the National Museum of Wales, xii + 77 p.

Norman, D., 2000, Henry De la Beche and the plesiosaur's neck: Archives of Natural History, v. 27, no. 1, p. 137–148, https://doi.org/10.3366/anh.2000.27.1.137.

O'Connor, R., 2007, The Earth on Show: Fossils and the Poetics of Popular Science, 1802–1856: Chicago, University of Chicago Press, xiii + 541 p.

Richardson, G.F., 1842, Geology for Beginners: London, Baillière, 530 p.

Rudwick, M.J.S., 1992, Scenes from Deep Time: Early Pictorial Representations of the Prehistoric World: Chicago, University of Chicago Press, xiii + 280 p.

Rudwick, M.J.S., 2008, Worlds Before Adam. The Reconstruction of Geohistory in the Age of Reform: Chicago, University of Chicago Press, xxii + 614 p.

Rudwick, M.J.S., 2014, Earth's Deep History. How It Was Discovered and Why It Matters: Chicago, University of Chicago Press, ix + 360 p.

Rupke, N., 1983, The Great Chain of History, William Buckland and the English School of Geology (1814–1849): Oxford, UK, Clarendon Press, 332 p.

Secord, J.A., 2004, Beche, Sir Henry Thomas De la (1796–1855), *in* Oxford Dictionary of National Biography. From the Earliest Times to the Year 2000, v. 4: Oxford, UK, Oxford University Press, p. 686–688.

Sharpe, T., 2008, Slavery, sugar and the Survey: Open University Geological Society Journal, v. 29, no. 2, p. 88–94.

Sharpe, T., 2013, New insights into the early life of Henry Thomas De la Beche (1796–1855), *in* Morris, R., ed., A Journal of Sir Henry De la Beche Pioneer Geologist (1796–1855) Written in His Own Hand: Swansea, Royal Institution of South Wales, p. 5–21.

Sharpe, T., 2020, The Fossil Woman: A Life of Mary Anning: Wimborne Minster, UK, Dovecote Press, 240 p.

Sharpe, T., and McCartney, P.J., 1998, The Papers of H.T. De la Beche (1796–1855) in the National Museum of Wales: Cardiff, National Museum of Wales, 257 p.

Taylor, M.A., and Torrens, H.S., 1986, Saleswoman to a new science: Mary Anning and the fossil fish *Squaloraja* from the Lias of Lyme Regis: Proceedings of the Dorset Natural History and Archaeological Society, v. 108, p. 135–148.

Torrens, H.S., 1979, Collections and collectors of note 28. Colonel Birch (c. 1768–1829): Newsletter of the Geological Curators' Group, v. 2, no. 7, p. 405–412.

Torrens, H.S., 1995, Mary Anning (1799–1847) of Lyme; 'the greatest fossilist the world ever knew': British Journal for the History of Science, v. 28, p. 257–284, https://doi.org/10.1017/S0007087400033161.

Ward, D., and Bizley, R., 2007, *Duria antiquior*, A More Ancient Dorset. A 21st century interpretation of a famous painting: privately printed pamphlet.

Manuscript Accepted by the Society 13 January 2021
Manuscript Published Online 30 June 2021

The Geological Society of America
Memoir 218

Significance of New Harmony, Indiana, USA, to nineteenth-century paleontological investigations of North America: Progressive education through arts and sciences

William S. Elliott Jr.
Department of Geology and Physics, University of Southern Indiana, 8600 University Boulevard, Evansville, Indiana 47712, USA

ABSTRACT

William Maclure, Father of North American Geology, partnered with Robert Owen in 1825 to establish an experimental socialistic community focusing on equitable reform in New Harmony, Indiana, USA. Artists, educators, and natural scientists recruited from Philadelphia arrived on a keel boat named *Philanthropist* in January 1826. Upon their arrival, Maclure established the New Harmony schools using a modified Pestalozzian educational approach under the guidance of Madame Fretageot. The New Harmony schools focused on practical education through direct observation of nature as well as a curriculum involving drawing, music, science, writing, and trade skills such as carpentry, engraving, and printing. Furthermore, the integration of arts and sciences with hands-on experiences led to a productive community of natural scientists who published significant works on the conchology, geology, ichthyology, and paleontology of North America.

In the mid-nineteenth century, hand-drawn illustrations were reproduced through engravings, etchings, or lithography prior to the invention of the daguerreotype process in 1839, collodion wet plate process in 1851, and flexible celluloid film in 1888. In particular, the published works of David Dale Owen demonstrate the increasing importance of evolving reproduction techniques to paleontological illustration as well as the significance of hand-drawn artistic renderings. Interestingly, the modified Pestalozzian educational approach introduced by Maclure in New Harmony has several implications for the modern classroom. For instance, recent studies suggest that drawing improves spatial reasoning skills and increases comprehension of complex scientific principles. Likewise, engaging students in the drawing of fossils delivers a meaningful learning experience in the paleontology classroom.

INTRODUCTION

The Harmonists, led by Father Johann Georg Rapp (1757–1847), established the town of New Harmony in 1814 in southwestern Indiana, USA (Fig. 1). The settlers of this self-sustaining pioneer town on the American frontier used natural resources such as local stone for building, clay for brick, and water for milling (Pitzer and Elliott, 1979; Johansen, 1997). The Harmonists grew citrus trees using seasonal greenhouses, established a viniculture, and produced market goods such as rope and textiles

*wselliott@usi.edu

Elliott, W.S., Jr., 2022, Significance of New Harmony, Indiana, USA, to nineteenth-century paleontological investigations of North America: Progressive education through arts and sciences, *in* Clary, R.M., Rosenberg, G.D., and Evans, D.C., eds., The Evolution of Paleontological Art: Geological Society of America Memoir 218, p. 55–65, https://doi.org/10.1130/2021.1218(07).

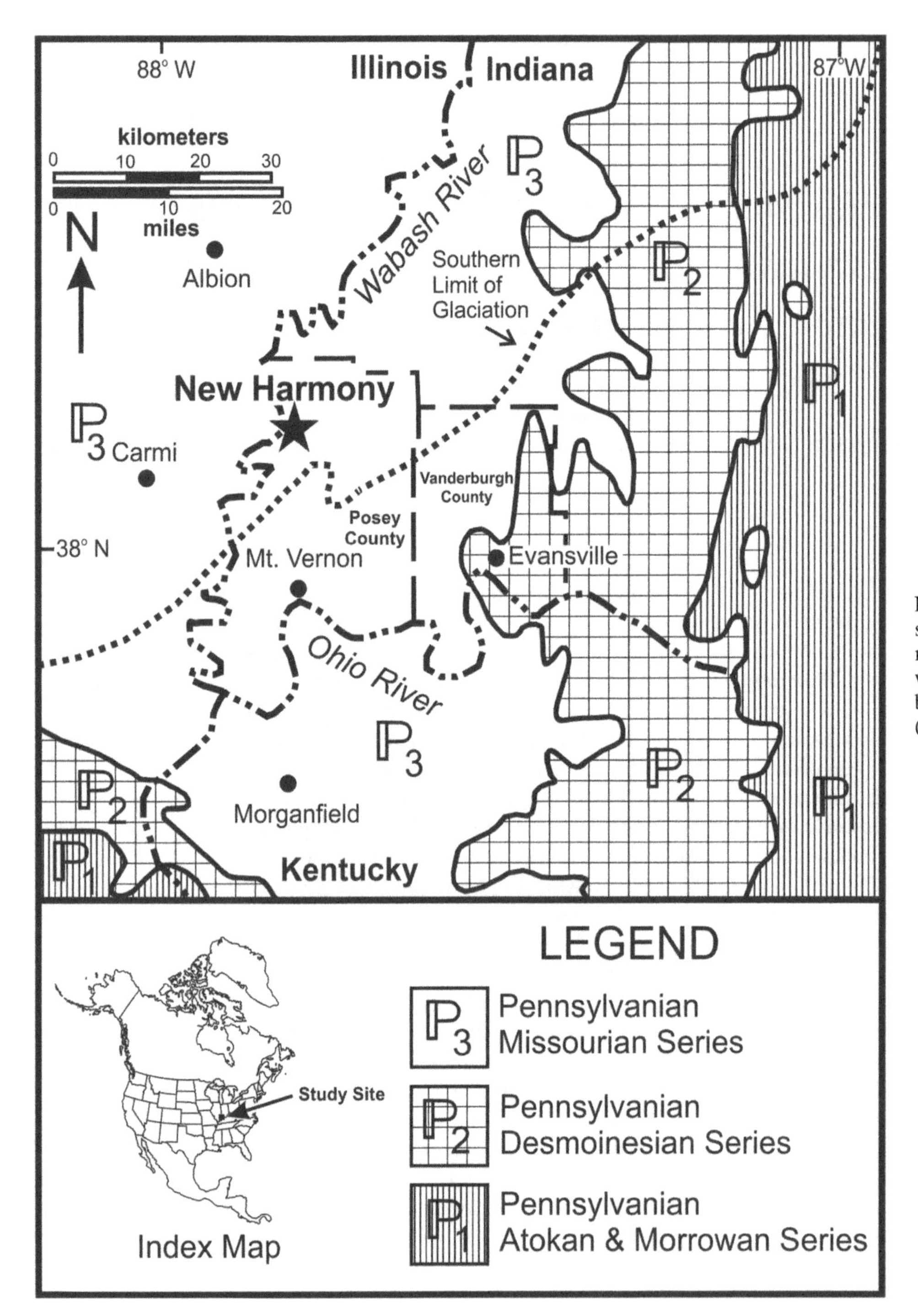

Figure 1. Generalized geologic map shows the area surrounding New Harmony along the Wabash River in southwestern Indiana. Geological units and boundaries are from King and Beikman (1974).

from hemp and wool (Arndt, 1997). Because of difficulties in transport to eastern markets, the Harmonists moved their community to western Pennsylvania, USA, and founded the town of Economy in 1824 (Wilson, 1964; Pitzer and Elliott, 1979).

To expand his ideas on social reform to America, Robert Owen (1771–1858) purchased the town of New Harmony, Indiana, from the Harmonists in January 1825 and established a socialistic community of artists, educators, scientists, and social reformers (Browne, 1936; Wilson, 1964; Carmony and Elliott, 1980; McLaren, 1996). Robert Owen collaborated with William Maclure (1763–1840), who recruited educators and natural scientists to join the community in New Harmony (Burgess, 1998; Pitzer, 1998; Warren, 2009).

On 8 December 1825, the first group of intellectuals embarked on their journey from Pittsburgh, Pennsylvania, to New Harmony, Indiana, on a boat named *Philanthropist*, which was also referred to as the "Boatload of Knowledge" (McLaren, 1996; Burgess, 1998; Pitzer, 1998; Straw and Doss, 2008). The passengers on the *Philanthropist* included notable natural scientists such as Thomas Say (1787–1834), an American entomologist and conchologist, and Charles Alexandre Lesueur (1778–1846), a French artist, ichthyologist, and zoologist (Pitzer, 1998). Additionally, many prominent educators of the time made the journey on the *Philanthropist*, including Marie Duclos Fretageot (1783–1833) and William S. Phiquepal (1779–1855), who were French educators, along with Lucy Sistare Say (1801–1886), a student of Fretageot, and Virginia Poullard DuPalais (1804–1864), a student of Lesueur (Pitzer, 1998). Others joining the experimental community included social reformer Francis Wright (1795–1852), skilled Pestalozzian teacher Joseph Neef (1770–1854), and geologist Gerard Troost (1776–1850). Upon their arrival, Maclure was put in charge of organizing the New Harmony schools; he implemented his modified Pestalozzian educational approach under the guidance of Madame Fretageot (Pitzer, 1998).

The early to mid-nineteenth century was also an important time for the development of the geological sciences, and in particular, the use of illustrations in geologic and paleontologic reports (Rudwick, 1976; Clary and Wandersee, 2015; Davidson, 2017). The evolution of reproduction techniques of artistic renderings in paleontology is documented by the works of David Dale Owen, who headquartered his geological surveys from 1837 to 1860 in New Harmony. The purpose of this paper is to (1) explore the impact of the modified Pestalozzian educational method established by William Maclure on scientific and paleontological investigations of North America; (2) summarize the work of David Dale Owen, including his artistic ability, use of experimental printing techniques, and his training of geologists and paleontologists; and (3) discuss the implications of the educational approach used by Maclure in the New Harmony schools for the modern science classroom.

PESTALOZZIAN EDUCATION IN AMERICA

The Pestalozzian method of education originated from the work of Johann Heinrich Pestalozzi (1746–1827), a Swiss social reformer known as the "Father of Modern Education" (Pitzer, 1998). Pestalozzi believed in a tailored educational experience based upon the maturity of individual students through a curriculum involving direct observation of nature and physical activity (Chernin, 1986; Pitzer, 1998). In other words, the Pestalozzian method is predicated on the balance of hands, heart, and head, with an instructional approach encouraging intellectual, moral, and physical development, empirical sensory learning, and a focus on nature (Chernin, 1986; Gutek, 1999).

During Maclure's European travels, he visited Pestalozzi's school in Yverdon, Switzerland, at least six times beginning in 1805 and introduced the Pestalozzian method to the United States by commissioning Joseph Neef to establish a school in Philadelphia, which opened in 1809 (Burgess, 1963; Donnachie, 2000). In 1819, Maclure also established a Pestalozzian school in his Paris home under the direction of William S. Phiquepal, and shortly thereafter was introduced to Marie Duclos Fretageot (Donnachie, 2000).

Coincidently, Maclure also played an important role in expanding the use of lithography in North America; he viewed the technique as an inexpensive way to print scientific illustrations and supply educational materials. Accordingly, Maclure made a request of Fretageot in Paris to purchase materials necessary for lithographic printing, and in September 1821, Fretageot arrived in Philadelphia with lithographic limestone, specialized ink, and a papirographic press (Weimerskirch, 1989).

In 1825, Robert Owen partnered with William Maclure to establish a community of artists, educators, and scientists to conduct a socialistic experiment in America. After acquiring the town of New Harmony, Maclure recruited artists, educators, and natural scientists to join the new community (Burgess, 1998; Pitzer, 1998; Warren, 2009).

PROGRESSIVE EDUCATION IN NEW HARMONY

In 1826, Maclure was placed in charge of the New Harmony schools by Owen and instituted his educational approach, which incorporated trade skills such as carpentry, engraving, and printing (Burgess, 1963; Warren, 2009). Maclure also recognized the importance of drawing to the educational process: "The art of drawing or delineation … must be ranked amongst those which are useful, as it is probably the most expeditious, correct, easy and pleasant mode, of giving ideas both to children and adults" (Maclure, 1831, p. 48). In recognizing the importance of art to education, Maclure ensured that drawing and painting were taught in the New Harmony schools by a diverse group of talented artists that included Martha Chase (?–1834), Charles Alexandre Lesueur, Balthazar Obernesser, Virginia Poullard DuPalais, and Lucy Sistare Say (Carmony and Elliott, 1980; Pitzer, 1998). In addition, science was taught in the New Harmony schools by Lesueur, Maclure, Say, and Troost.

New Harmony also attracted Cornelius Tiebout (1777–1832), an accomplished artist, engraver, and printer who arrived in September 1826. Tiebout immediately became engaged with teaching engraving in the New Harmony schools, supplementing the instruction of Phiquepal and Lesueur. In 1827, Maclure purchased an additional printing press in New Orleans for New Harmony to aid in the production of educational and scientific materials (MacPhail and Sutton, 1998). The new printing press was used to publish scientific monographs, including *American Ichthyology* (1827) by Lesueur and *American Conchology* (1830–1834) by Thomas Say. Incidentally, almost all of the scientific illustrations for *American Conchology* (58 of the 60 plates) were drawn by Lucy Sistare Say, with the prints from copper plates being hand-colored by the children in the New Harmony schools (Pitzer, 1998; Thomas and Hannibal, 2008). The hand-coloring of the printed plates was part of the children's educational experience as they learned about conchology and the application of artistic techniques for the purpose of scientific illustration.

The integration of arts and sciences with practical skills in engraving and printing led to a unique educational institution in New Harmony (Patton et al., 1983; Spencer, 1986; Pitzer, 1998). This educational and scientific enterprise continued through the nineteenth century, primarily through the efforts of David Dale Owen, the fourth son of Robert Owen (Patton et al., 1983; Johnson, 1977a).

DAVID DALE OWEN: FRONTIER GEOLOGIST

David Dale Owen (1807–1860) was born in Lanarkshire, Scotland, on 24 June 1807, privately tutored at home until the age of 17, and then attended the Philipp Emanuel von Fellenberg's School in Hofwyl, Switzerland (Straw and Doss, 2008). Von Fellenberg's School followed an immersive Pestalozzian approach with instruction in chemistry, geography, mathematics, mineralogy, natural history, and zoology that involved hands-on activities and field trips (Hendrickson, 1943, p. 7–8). David Dale and his brother, Richard Dale Owen (1810–1890), returned to Scotland in 1826 and continued their studies under Andrew Ure (1778–1857) at the Andersonian Institute at Glasgow. In 1827, David Dale Owen traveled to America with his father and two of his brothers: Robert Dale Owen (1801–1877) and Richard. In January 1828, he traveled to New Harmony, Indiana, to live in the community established by his father and Maclure. In 1830, David Dale Owen spent a year learning to draw and paint in New York City while living with his brother Robert Dale and working in the printing office of *The Free Enquirer* (Hendrickson, 1943, p. 15). From 1831 to 1833, he studied chemistry under the instruction of Edward Turner (1796–1837) at London University and most likely attended lectures on geology given by Charles Lyell (1797–1875) and Roderick Murchison (1792–1871), both of whom were members of the Geological Society of London (Hendrickson, 1943, p. 16; Lane, 1966).

David Dale Owen returned to New Harmony in 1833 ready to pursue a career in geology and remodeled the Harmonist Shoemaker's Shop into a geological laboratory from 1834 to 1835 (Lane, 1966). In 1835, Owen pursued a degree from the Ohio Medical College in Cincinnati, and in 1836 served as an assistant to Gerard Troost in conducting a geological survey of Tennessee (Hendrickson, 1943). After returning to New Harmony in March 1837, Owen accepted an appointment to conduct a geological reconnaissance of Indiana.

In 1839, Owen was appointed to conduct a survey of the Mineral Lands district including parts of Illinois, Iowa, and Wisconsin (Hendrickson, 1943; Johnson, 1977b). Although Owen published the preliminary results of this work in 1840, a more complete monograph including geologic maps with plates of picturesque landscapes, correlated stratigraphic sections, and fossil illustrations was published in 1844 (Figs. 2 and 3). The plates were reproduced primarily by lithography after hand-drawn renderings by Owen, who emphasized the realistic illustration of fossils that included weathered surfaces, irregularities in morphology and form, and taphonomic features such as fractures.

Figure 2. Plate XI of Owen (1844) illustrates two fossiliferous slabs from the Devonian Cedar Valley Group of Iowa (referred to as Carboniferous Limestone by Owen) that contain crinoid columnals, fenestrate bryozoans, and the tabulate coral *Thamnopora magniventra* Stumm, 1961 [*Striatopora (Cyanthopora) iowensis* (Owen, 1844)]. Sketches were drawn by David Dale Owen with lithography by E. Weber and Co. of Baltimore, Maryland.

The geologic map, several of the stratigraphic sections, and one of the fossil plates (Fig. 2) included with Owen's report were hand-colored after lithographic reproduction. Color was selectively used in geologic publications of the early-nineteenth century, especially prior to the invention of direct color printing techniques such as chromolithography, which became widely available by the late nineteenth century (Cook, 1995).

The invertebrate fossil illustrations in Owen (1844) included bivalves, brachiopods, bryozoans, crinoids, gastropods, nautiloids, receptaculitids, rugose and tabulate corals, sponges, and

Figure 3. Plate XIII of Owen (1844) illustrates fossils collected from the coralline beds of the Silurian Hopkinton and Scotch Grove Formations (referred to as Upper Magnesian Cliff Limestone by Owen) of Iowa: (1) *Ptychophyllum stokesi* Milne-Edwards and Haime, 1850; (2) *Syringopora tenella* Rominger, 1876; (3) *Ptychophyllum expansum* (Owen, 1844); (4) *Cyclocrinites dactioloides* (Owen, 1844); (5) *Ptychophyllum stokesi* Milne-Edwards and Haime, 1850; (6) *P. expansum*; (7) *Favosites favosus* Goldfuss, 1826; (7a, 7b) details of individual corallites of *F. favosus*; (8) *Plasmopora follis* Milne-Edwards and Haime, 1849; (9) *Hexameroceras* Hyatt, 1884; (10) *P. expansum*; and (11) *Lyellia americana* Milne-Edwards and Haime, 1851. Sketches were drawn by David Dale Owen and lithography is by E. Weber and Co. of Baltimore, Maryland.

trilobites. The plates in the report were organized by stratigraphic unit with 10–12 detailed sketches of invertebrate fossils diagnostic to each interval. Several individual sketches depict symbiotic and/or epibiont relationships. The fossil illustrations are not embellished, but are drawn realistically with weathered surfaces, natural irregularities, and morphological variation, which in some cases are highlighted in magnified, detailed sketches focusing on diagnostic features of the genus and/or species (Fig. 3).

Owen (1844) focused on the realistic portrayal of fossils and their practical application to stratigraphy, in line with David Dale Owen's conviction that "the Science of Geology, of comparatively modern date, is now universally conceded to be one, not of mere curious inquiry, but of vast practical utility" (Owen, 1839, p. 5). Coincidently, the paleontological research conducted by Owen (1844) was one of the first works in North America funded by the U.S. government. Likewise, David Dale Owen viewed illustration as a practical utility to "enable the student of American geology to draw comparisons for the identification and parallelism of strata" (Owen, 1852, p. 91). Thus, it is not surprising that David Dale Owen's fossil illustrations are drawn realistically with irregularities and weathered forms that would likely be collected by a geologist in the field. It is this realistic approach that makes the fossil illustrations produced by David Dale Owen unique and artistic.

The detailed observations of Owen, along with his artistic and field abilities, gained him almost immediate recognition as one of the most capable field geologists of North America (Hendrickson, 1943, p. 70).

Owen firmly believed in teaching through hands-on experiences, direct observations, and the use of numerous maps, stratigraphic sections, and illustrations (Straw and Doss, 2008). Accordingly, New Harmony became an important institution for the training of geologists and paleontologists in the mid-nineteenth century of North America (Johnson, 1977a; Kimberling, 1996; Straw and Doss, 2008).

PALEONTOLOGICAL LEGACY OF NEW HARMONY

In 1846, Charles and Mary Lyell were guests at Owen's home in New Harmony for several days (Browne, 1936; Hendrickson, 1943). While visiting, Charles Lyell spent time inspecting fossil and mineral specimens in Owen's cabinets. The visit of Lyell in 1846 attests to Owen's reputation and the significance of New Harmony to the science of geology in North America.

In 1847, David Dale Owen was appointed by the U.S. Congress to conduct a geological survey of the Chippewa Land District of Wisconsin and northern Iowa (Merrill, 1924, p. 271; Hendrickson, 1943, p. 88). In preparation for this work, Owen began recruiting and training a team of geologists to work under his supervision, including John Evans (1812–1861), Fielding Bradford Meek (1817–1876), Joseph Granville Norwood (1807–1895), his younger brother Richard Dale Owen (1810–1890), Henry Pratten (?–1857), and Benjamin Franklin Shumard (1820–1869) (Johnson, 1977a). These geologists were trained by Owen in his laboratory at New Harmony through hands-on instruction using fossils, minerals, and rocks; applied chemical analyses of rocks; and lectures using maps, charts, and sections (Hendrickson, 1943). Owen emphasized realistic sketching of specimens through direct observation of fossils from his cabinet. With the established printing operations in New Harmony, Owen was also able to train geologists on the use of various reproduction techniques for illustrating fossils, such as wood cuts, wood and metal engraving, and lithography. Owen also valued the practical application of paleontology in identifying natural resources and recognizing age relationships among sedimentary rocks of North America and Europe (Johnson, 1977b; Straw and Doss, 2008). Owen also championed "on the job training" that involved many of the geologists learning while conducting work on the geological survey and making direct observations and sketches from nature (Hendrickson, 1943; Straw and Doss, 2008). David Dale Owen's integration of the arts and sciences in New Harmony provided a unique learning environment that educated some of the most notable paleontologists of North America in the mid- to late nineteenth century (Table 1).

To best highlight his maps and illustrations, Owen requested that his 1852 report be printed using quarto-size rather than the standard octavo-size (Hendrickson, 1943, p. 94). After some hesitation, the U.S. Congress appropriated funding to print Owen's report in quarto-size in two volumes, one of which was dedicated to illustrations (Owen, 1852). The larger page size permitted Owen to reproduce many of his fossil illustrations at the same scale as the specimens. Furthermore, this report standardized the method of geological surveys and the format of federal reports, including narratives, maps, and illustrations (Hendrickson, 1943; Kimberling, 1996; Johnson, 2008).

Owen (1852) included 15 plates of invertebrate fossils, three plates of plant fossils, and nine plates of vertebrate fossils using a variety of reproduction techniques, including wood and metal engraving, lithography, and the experimental techniques of medal ruling and photoengraving. Medal ruling machines are a type of mechanized device that permits a probe to transverse back and forth over a three-dimensional object resulting in a simultaneous engraving of the specimen on a steel plate (Frazier, 1975). Owen (1852) used this technique for 10 plates of fossils included in his geologic report, including one dedicated to trilobites (Fig. 4). The illustrations produced by medal ruling accurately capture the detailed morphology of the fossils but lacked textural details because the image is created primarily by engraved lines, which produces an Op Art appearance. Ultimately, the goal of Owen in using the experimental technique of medal ruling was probably to reproduce the most accurate illustrations possible of the trilobite fossils.

Likewise, Owen (1852) used daguerreotypes to produce five engraved plates of vertebrate fossils included in his geologic report, highlighting remains recovered from Cenozoic deposits of Nebraska (Fig. 5). This represents one of the earliest examples of a photographic technique being used to illustrate fossils in North America and attests to David Dale Owen's desire to include realistic renderings of fossils within his geologic reports.

In 1854, Owen was appointed state geologist of Kentucky and once again trained several geologists in his New Harmony laboratory to assist with this work. Most noteworthy are Edward Travers Cox (1821–1907) and Sidney Lyon (1808–1872), who executed detailed paleontological investigations of Paleozoic invertebrate fossils of Kentucky. In particular, Edward Travers Cox was educated in the New Harmony Schools and was probably one of the children who had hand-colored the illustrations for Say's *American Conchology*. After being trained by Owen, both Edward Travers Cox and Sidney Lyon pursued paleontological research, with Sidney Lyon becoming an expert on Paleozoic crinoids and Edward Travers Cox being appointed state geologist of Indiana from 1869 to 1880 (Table 1).

TABLE 1. PALEONTOLOGISTS TRAINED BY DAVID DALE OWEN IN NEW HARMONY, INDIANA

Paleontologist	New Harmony	New Harmony association and relevant accomplishments
Edward Travers Cox (1821–1907)	1825–1869	Educated in New Harmony Schools; assisted David Dale Owen on geological surveys of Kentucky from 1854 to 1859 and Arkansas from 1857 to 1860; published reports on molluscan and plant fossils of Pennsylvanian strata of Indiana, Illinois, and Kentucky; state geologist of Indiana from 1869 to 1880.
John Evans (1812–1861)	1847–1850	Assistant to David Dale Owen during the geological surveys of Iowa, Minnesota, and Wisconsin from 1847 to 1850; explored western Nebraska with Shumard in 1849; appointed as U.S. geologist to Oregon and Washington Territories from 1850 to 1861; published three papers with Shumard on Cretaceous and Tertiary fossils of Nebraska.
Sidney S. Lyon (1808–1872)	1856, 1857	Assistant to David Dale Owen during geological surveys of Kentucky from 1854 to 1859; thereafter published paleontological research on blastoids and crinoids collected from Paleozoic rocks of Indiana, Kentucky, and Ohio.
Fielding Bradford Meek (1817–1876)	1848–1850	Assistant to David Dale Owen during geological survey of Iowa, Minnesota, and Wisconsin from 1848 to 1850; assistant to James Hall from 1852 to 1858; exploration of western Nebraska with Ferdinand V. Hayden in 1853 and assistant to the geological of survey of Missouri in 1854 and 1855; extensive paleontological research; chief paleontologist at Smithsonian Institution from 1858 to 1876.
Joseph Granville Norwood (1807–1895)	1847–1853	Conducted investigation of Paleozoic invertebrate fossils of Kentucky with David Dale Owen in 1846; assistant to David Dale Owen during geological surveys of Iowa, Minnesota, and Wisconsin from 1848 to 1851; state geologist of Illinois from 1851 to 1858 headquartered in New Harmony until 1853; co-authored three papers with Pratten describing Paleozoic brachiopods of Illinois.
Henry Pratten (?–1857)	1848–1850; 1852–1853	Assistant to David Dale Owen during geological surveys of Iowa, Minnesota, and Wisconsin from 1848 to 1849; trip to California from 1850 to 1852; joined Illinois Geological Survey as assistant to Norwood in 1852, headquartered in New Harmony until 1853, then moved to Springfield, Illinois; co-authored three papers with Norwood describing Paleozoic brachiopods of Illinois.
Benjamin Franklin Shumard (1820–1869)	1846–1850	Assistant to David Dale Owen during geological surveys of Iowa, Minnesota, and Wisconsin from 1847 to 1849; assistant to Evan's survey of Oregon and Washington Territories from 1850 to 1852; appointed paleontologist and assistant geologist of Missouri from 1853 to 1858; state geologist of Texas from 1858 to 1860; published research on Pennsylvanian and Permian fossils of Texas and New Mexico, Cretaceous fossils of Texas, and Cretaceous and Tertiary fossils of Nebraska, Oregon, and Washington.

Note: Compiled from Merrill (1924), Hendrickson (1943), and Johnson (1977a).

IMPLICATIONS FOR THE MODERN SCIENCE CLASSROOM

Following the modified Pestalozzian method introduced in New Harmony by Maclure, recent studies also indicate that sketching and the direct observation of nature improve student retention of scientific knowledge. For instance, many studies indicate that students who are encouraged to explore, document, and justify their understanding through drawing are more motivated to learn and retain scientific knowledge (Ainsworth et al., 2011; Henderson et al., 2011; Forbus and Ainsworth, 2017). Furthermore, research from cognitive science suggests that drawing improves spatial reasoning skills and assists with retention of complex scientific principles (Lane et al., 2009; Ainsworth et al., 2011; Quillin and Thomas, 2015; Clary et al., 2015; Garnier et al., 2017). Additionally, the use of concept sketching—annotated drawings that illustrate the complex natural processes and components of a system—improves student retention of information presented in the Earth science classroom (Johnson and Reynolds, 2005).

In the New Harmony Schools, arts and sciences were integrated to provide students with a holistic educational experience. This was accomplished by children directly observing nature, learning artistic techniques to document first-hand observations, and gaining hands-on experiences with printing techniques. The children in the New Harmony Schools were also taught by the natural scientists in the community, which provided unique educational experiences such as the children hand-coloring the printed plates for Thomas Say's *American Conchology*. Likewise, many recent studies indicate that integrating art across

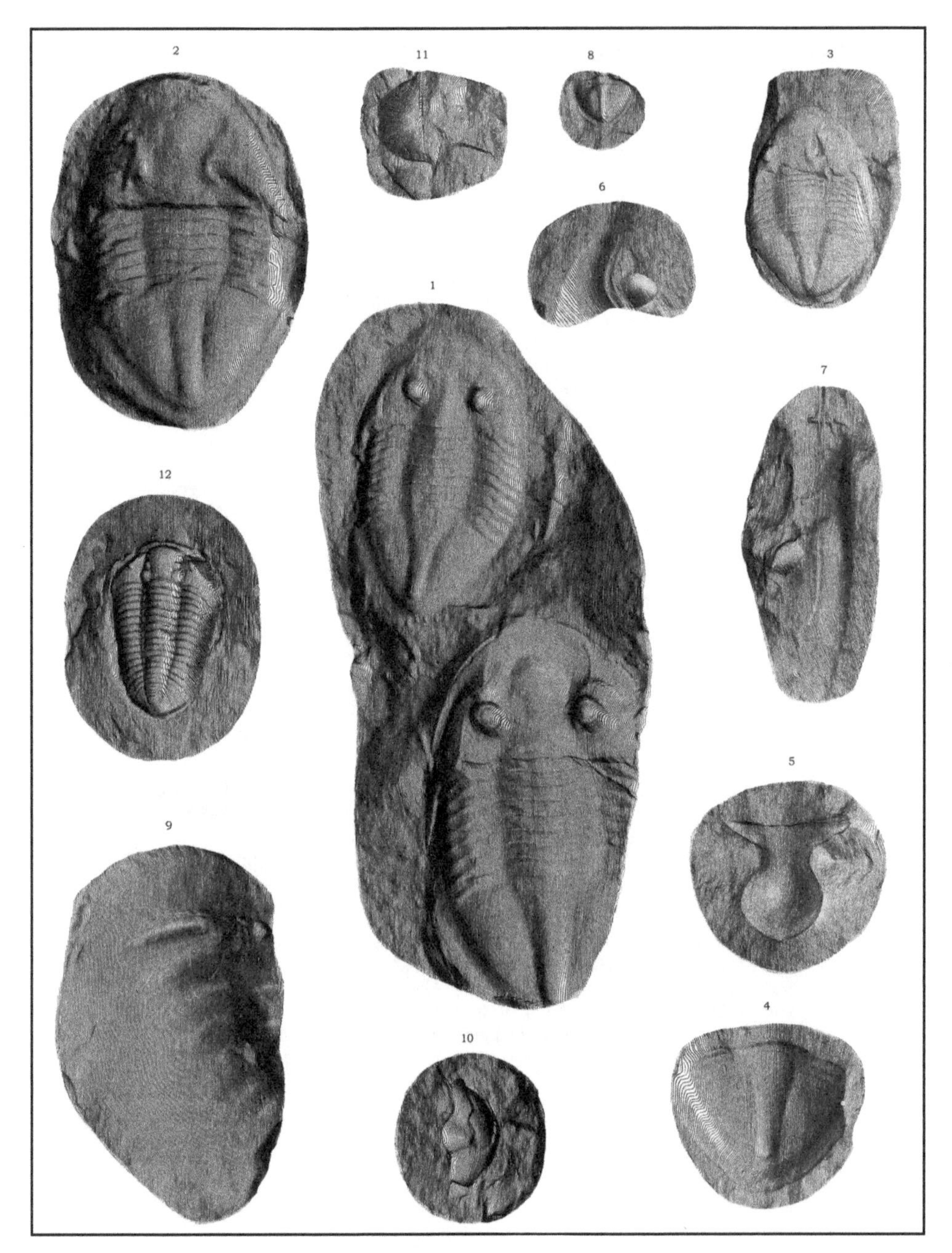

Figure 4. Table II from Owen (1852) was originally printed from an engraved steel plate scribed by the process of medal-ruling of the fossil specimens by J.M. Butler in Philadelphia, Pennsylvania. This was probably the earliest use of medal-ruling on steel to illustrate fossils in America (Merrill, 1924, p. 273). The fossils include: (1, 2, 3) *Isotelus iowensis* (Owen, 1852); (4) pygidium of *I. iowensis*; (5) glabela of *I. iowensis*; (6, 7) compound eye with cephalic shield of *I. iowensis*; (8) pygidium of *Phacops* Emmrich, 1839; (9) thoracic segments of *Dikelocephalus minnesotensis* Owen, 1852; (10) cephalic shield of an *Illaenus* Dalman, 1827; (11) *Sowerbyella sericea* (Sowerby, 1839); (12) *Flexicalymene senaria* (Conrad, 1841).

the curriculum, as was done at the integrative schools of New Harmony, contributes to increased problem-solving skills and improved observational competency (Ainsworth et al., 2011; Root-Bernstein and Root-Bernstein, 2013; Clary et al., 2015; Garnier et al., 2017). Moreover, providing instruction to students on sketching techniques may decrease anxiety and build self-confidence in their abilities to document their observations through illustration (Ainsworth et al., 2011).

Finally, the modern study of paleontology continues to require the inclusion of high-quality, hand-drawn illustrations that are realistic representations of fossils (Budd, 2000; Foote and Miller, 2007; Hoad, 2013). Although David Dale Owen did not produce line drawings for interpretive purposes in his geological reports, his fossil illustrations focused on realistic renderings of features observed in specimens. In some instances, a line drawing may be more helpful in illustrating a fossil than a photograph, especially when there are significant taphonomic variations in fossil preservation, the color of the fossil is similar to the sediment, or details of the fossil are obscured by matrix (Budd, 2000; Foote and Miller, 2007). In these cases, it is important that the artist only draw anatomical features that are evident in the original specimen (Foote and Miller, 2007). Thus, it is vital to have the expertise of a paleontologist involved in the rendering of artistic and/or hand-drawn illustrations of fossils.

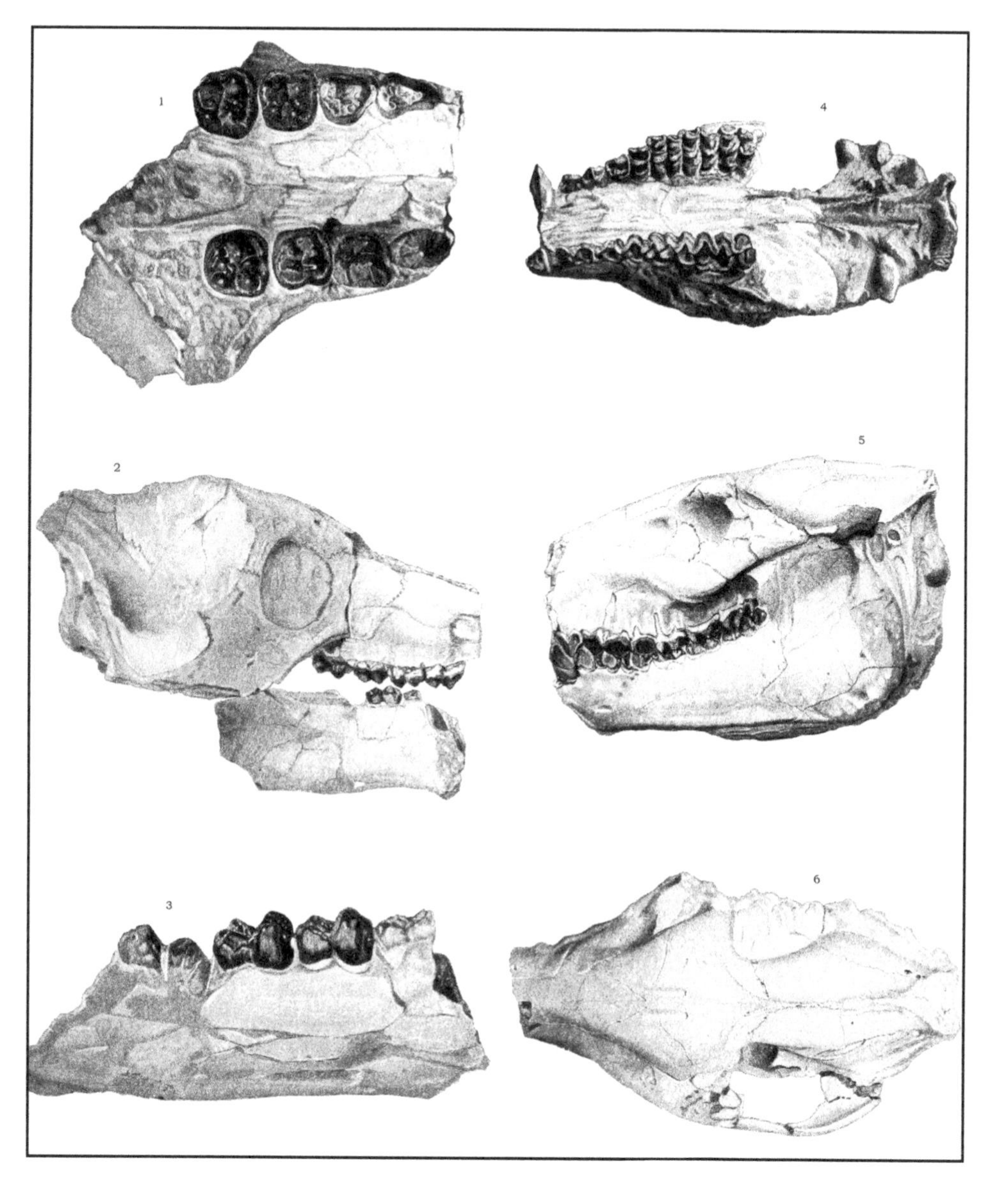

Figure 5. Table X of Owen (1852) represents one of the earliest examples of the use of a photographic technique to illustrate fossils in America. Original plates were printed from photoengraved copper plate from a daguerreotype of the fossil specimens engraved by A.B. Walter (Davidson, 2008). Fossils include: (1) inferior view of the upper jaw of *Archaeotherium mortoni* Leidy, 1850; (2) side view of the head of *A. mortoni*; (3) portion of the left side of the lower jaw of *A. mortoni*; (4) inferior view of a male skull of *Merycoidodon culbertsonii* Leidy, 1848; (5) side view of a female skull of *M. culbertsonii* with the lower jaw; (6) upper view of the female skull of *M. culbertsonii*.

CONCLUSIONS

The use of artistic hand-drawn illustrations in paleontology has an interesting history that progressed through the application of evolving reproduction techniques prior to the invention of photography. Paleontological studies in the early-nineteenth century of North America benefited from the integration of arts and sciences with hands-on and field experiences introduced as an educational approach by William Maclure in New Harmony in 1826 and exemplified by the extensive work of David Dale Owen from 1837 to 1860. In particular, the educational efforts of Owen had a lasting impact on the study of paleontology through the many works of his students.

Hand-drawn illustrations continue to be vital in paleontological research and significant to the teaching of paleontology in the modern classroom. The use of drawing exercises in the paleontology classroom is shown to have a meaningful impact on student learning. Finally, reflections on the history of education, artistic renderings of fossils, and progression of reproduction techniques contribute to the continued evolution of paleontological art.

ACKNOWLEDGMENTS

This paper benefited from critical reviews conducted by Renee Clary, Joe Hannibal, Gary Rosenberg, and an anonymous reviewer. The author is also grateful to Leslie Townsend, director of Historic New Harmony, and Connie Weinzapfel, the former director, for their support. This work also profited from discussions about New Harmony with Amanda Bryden, Paul Doss, Lois Gray, Nils Johansen, Anton Maria, Ryan Rokicki, and Thomas Straw.

REFERENCES CITED

Ainsworth, S., Prain, V., and Tytler, R., 2011, Drawing to learn in science: Science, v. 333, p. 1096–1097, https://doi.org/10.1126/science.1204153.

Arndt, K.J.R., 1997, George Rapp's Harmony Society, *in* Pitzer, D.E., ed., America's Communal Utopias: Chapel Hill, North Carolina, University of North Carolina Press, p. 57–87.

Browne, C.A., 1936, Some relations of the New Harmony movement to the history of science in America: The Scientific Monthly, v. 42, no. 6, p. 483–497.

Budd, J., 2000, Them and us: Why biologists don't care about palaeontology: The Palaeontology Newsletter, v. 45, p. 12–15.

Burgess, C., 1963, William Maclure and education for a good society: History of Education Quarterly, v. 3, no. 2, p. 58–76, https://doi.org/10.2307/367241.

Burgess, C., 1998, The boatload of trouble: William Maclure and Robert Owen revisited: Indiana Magazine of History, v. 94, p. 138–150.

Carmony, D.F., and Elliott, J.M., 1980, New Harmony, Indiana: Robert Owen's seedbed for Utopia: Indiana Magazine of History, v. 76, no. 3, p. 161–261.

Chernin, M., 1986, A practical application of an eighteenth-century aesthetic: The development of Pestalozzian Education: College Music Symposium, v. 26, p. 53–65.

Clary, R.A., and Wandersee, J.H., 2015, The evolution of non-quantitative geological graphics in texts during the formative years of geology (1788–1840): Earth Sciences History, v. 34, no. 1, p. 59–91, https://doi.org/10.17704/1944-6187-34.1.59.

Clary, R.A., Remo, J.P., Walker, R., and Wandersee, J.H., 2015, Chapter 15: Drawing scientists together, University faculty's perceptions of art and perceived barriers to constructing and implementing visual data in science classrooms, *in* Finson, K.D., and Pedersen, J., eds., Application of Visual Data in K16 Science Classrooms: Charlotte, North Carolina, Information Age Publishing, p. 357–376.

Conrad, T.A., 1841, Fifth annual report on the paleontology of the state of New York: New York State Geological Survey Annual Report 5, p. 25–57.

Cook, K.S., 1995, False starts to firm beginnings: Early colour printing of geological maps: Imago Mundi, v. 47, p. 155–172, https://doi.org/10.1080/03085699508592818.

Dalman, J.W., 1827, Om palaeaderna eller sa kallade Trilobiterna: Stockholm, Kungliga Svenska Vetenskapsakademiens Handlingar, p. 113–152.

Davidson, J.P., 2008, A History of Paleontological Illustration: Bloomington, Indiana, Indiana University Press, 217 p.

Davidson, J.P., 2017, Patrons of Paleontology, How Government Support Shaped a Science: Bloomington, Indiana, Indiana University Press, 232 p., https://doi.org/10.2307/j.ctt1zxxzp1.

Donnachie, I., 2000, Robert Owen: Owen of New Lanark and New Harmony: Glasgow, United Kingdom, Tuckwell Press, 290 p.

Emmrich, H.F., 1839, De Trilobitis: Dissertatio petrefactologica quam consensu et auctoritate amplissimi philosophorum ordinis in alma litterarum universitate Friderica Guilelma pro summis in philisophia honoribus: Berlin, Friderica Guilelma, 60 p.

Foote, M., and Miller, A.I., 2007, Principles of Paleontology (3rd edition): New York, W.H. Freeman, 480 p.

Forbus, K.D., and Ainsworth, S., 2017, Editors' introduction: Sketching and cognition: Topics in Cognitive Science, v. 9, p. 864–865, https://doi.org/10.1111/tops.12299.

Frazier, A.H., 1975, Joseph Saxton and His Contributions to the Medal Ruling and Photographic Arts: Washington, D.C., Smithsonian Institution Press, Smithsonian Studies in History and Technology 32, 17 p.

Garnier, B., Chang, M., Ormand, C., Matlen, B., Tikoff, B., and Shipleye, T.F., 2017, Promoting sketching in introductory geoscience courses: CogSketch Geoscience Worksheets: Topics in Cognitive Science, v. 9, p. 943–969, https://doi.org/10.1111/tops.12291.

Goldfuss, G.A., 1826, Petrefacta Germaniae, I: Düsseldorf, Germany, Anstalt, Arnz, and Company, 76 p.

Gutek, G.L., 1999, Pestalozzi and Education: Prospect Heights, Illinois, Waveland Press, 178 p.

Henderson, C., Beach, A., and Finkelstein, N., 2011, Facilitating change in undergraduate STEM instructional practices: An analytic review of the literature: Journal of Research in Science Teaching, v. 48, no. 8, p. 952–984, https://doi.org/10.1002/tea.20439.

Hendrickson, W.B., 1943, David Dale Owen, Pioneer Geologist of the Middle West: Indianapolis, Indiana, Indiana Historical Bureau, 180 p.

Hoad, J., 2013, Art of ancient life: The value of artistic interpretation and the role of art in reconstructive palaeontology: The Palaeontology Newsletter, v. 84, p. 35–37.

Hyatt, A., 1884, Genera of fossil cephalapods: Proceedings of the Boston Society of Natural History, v. 22, p. 253–338.

Johansen, N.I., 1997, New Harmony, Indiana, a century and a half of science and engineering: Proceedings of the Indiana Academy of Sciences, v. 106, p. 257–266.

Johnson, C.S., 2008, The evolution of illustrated texts and their effect on science: Examples from early American State Geological Reports: Leonardo, v. 41, no. 2, p. 120–127, https://doi.org/10.1162/leon.2008.41.2.120.

Johnson, J., and Reynolds, S.J., 2005, Concept sketches using student- and instructor-generated, annotated sketches for learning, teaching, and assessment in geology courses: Journal of Geoscience Education, v. 53, no. 1, p. 85–95, https://doi.org/10.5408/1089-9995-53.1.85.

Johnson, M.E., 1977a, Geology in American education: 1825–1860: Geological Society of America Bulletin, v. 88, p. 1192–1198, https://doi.org/10.1130/0016-7606(1977)88<1192:GIAE>2.0.CO;2.

Johnson, M.E., 1977b, Early geological explorations of the Silurian System in Iowa: Proceedings of the Iowa Academy of Science, v. 84, no. 4, p. 150–156.

Kimberling, C., 1996, David Dale Owen and Joseph Granville Norwood: Pioneer geologists in Indiana and Illinois: Indiana Magazine of History, v. 92, no. 1, p. 2–25.

King, P.B., and Beikman, H.M., 1974, Geologic Map of the United States (Exclusive of Alaska and Hawaii): U.S. Geological Survey, scale 1:2,500,000, 3 sheets.

Lane, D., Seery, N., and Gordon, S., 2009, The understated value of freehand sketching in technology education: Engineering Design Graphics Journal, v. 73, no. 3, p. 13–22.

Lane, N.G., 1966, New Harmony and pioneer geology: Geotimes, v. 11, no. 2, p. 18–22.

Leidy, J., 1848, On a new fossil genus and species of ruminantoid Pachydermata: *Merycoidodon culbertsonii*: Proceedings of the Academy of Natural Sciences of Philadelphia, v. 4, p. 47–50.

Leidy, J., 1850, Observations on two new genera of mammalian fossils: *Eucrotaphus jacksoni* and *Archaeotherium mortoni*: Proceedings of the Academy of Natural Sciences of Philadelphia, v. 5, p. 90–93.

Lesueur, C.A., 1827, American Ichthyology, or Natural History of the Fishes of North America with Coloured Figures from Drawings Executed from Nature: New Harmony, Indiana, School Press, 5 plates, 15 p.

Maclure, W., 1831, Opinions on Various Subjects, Dedicated to the Industrious Producers: New Harmony, Indiana, School Press, 483 p.

MacPhail, I., and Sutton, M., 1998, William Maclure as publisher in the New Harmony Reform Tradition: Indiana Magazine of History, v. 94, p. 167–177.

McLaren, D.J., 1996, Robert Owen, William Maclure and New Harmony: History of Education, v. 25, no. 3, p. 223–233, https://doi.org/10.1080/0046760960250302.

Merrill, G.P., 1924, The First One Hundred Years of American Geology: New Haven, Connecticut, Yale University Press, 773 p.

Milne-Edwards, H., and Haime, J., 1849, Recherches sur les polypiers, Mémoire 4, Monographie des Astréides: Annales des Sciences Naturelles, Zoologie, serial 3, no. 12, p. 95–197.

Milne-Edwards, H., and Haime, J., 1850, A Monograph of the British Fossil Corals; Part 1, Introduction: Paleontological Society of London Monograph, v. 3, 71 p.

Milne-Edwards, H., and Haime, J., 1851, Monographic des polypiers fossiles des terrains palaeozoïques: Paris, Archives du Muséum d'Histoire Naturelle, v. 5, 502 p.

Owen, D.D., 1839, A geological reconnaissance and survey of the State of Indiana, made in the years 1837 and 1838: Indiana Geological Survey Bulletin B61, 121 p.

Owen, D.D., 1840, Report of a Geological Exploration of a Part of Iowa, Wisconsin and Illinois, Made in Year 1839 in the Mineral Lands of the United States: First Session of the Twenty-Sixth U.S. Congress, House Executive Document 239, 161 p.

Owen, D.D., 1844, Report of a Geological Exploration of a Part of Iowa, Wisconsin and Illinois, Made in Year 1839 with Charts and Illustrations: First Session of the Twenty-Eighth U.S. Congress, Senate Executive Document 407, 191 p.

Owen, D.D., 1852, Report of a Geological Survey of Wisconsin, Iowa, and Minnesota, and Incidentally of a Portion of Nebraska Territory: Philadelphia, Pennsylvania, Lippincott, Grambo, and Company, 638 p.

Patton, J.B., Millbrooke, A., and Nelson, C.M., 1983, The New Harmony geologic legacy (Field Trip 11), *in* Shaver, R.H., and Sunderman, J.A., eds., Field Trips in Midwestern Geology: Bloomington, Indiana, Annual Meeting of the Geological Society of America with the Indiana Geological Survey and the Department of Geology, Indiana University, v. 1, p. 225–243

Pitzer, D.E., 1998, William Maclure's boatload of knowledge: Science and education into the Midwest: Indiana Magazine of History, v. 94, p. 110–137.

Pitzer, D.E., and Elliott, J.M., 1979, New Harmony's first Utopians, 1814–1824: Indiana Magazine of History, v. 75, no. 3, p. 225–300.

Quillin, K., and Thomas, S., 2015, Drawing-to-learn: A framework for using drawings to promote model-based reasoning in biology: CBE Life Sciences Education, v. 14, p. 1–16, https://doi.org/10.1187/cbe.14-08-0128.

Rominger, C., 1876, Part II: Paleontology—Fossil Corals: Geological Survey of Michigan, Lower Peninsula 1873–1876 Accompanied by a Geological Map: New York, Julius Bein, 55 plates, 161 p.

Root-Bernstein, R., and Root-Bernstein, M., 2013, The art and craft of science: Educational Leadership, v. 70, no. 5, p. 16–21.

Rudwick, M.J.S., 1976, The emergence of a visual language for geological science 1760–1840: History of Science, v. 14, p. 149–195, https://doi.org/10.1177/007327537601400301.

Say, T., 1830–1834, American Conchology; or Descriptions of the Shells of North America, with Coloured Figures from Drawings Executed from Nature, Parts 1–6: New Harmony, Indiana, School Press, 60 plates, 390 p.

Sowerby, G.B., 1839, A Conchological Manual: London, England, Bloomsbury, 130 p.

Spencer, L.T., 1986, Filling in the gaps: A survey of nineteenth century institutions associated with the exploration and natural history of the American west: American Zoologist, v. 26, p. 371–380, https://doi.org/10.1093/icb/26.2.371.

Straw, W.T., and Doss, P.K., 2008, David Dale Owen and the geological enterprise of New Harmony, Indiana, with a companion roadside geology of Vanderburgh and Posey Counties, *in* Maria, A.H., and Counts, R.C., eds., From the Cincinnati Arch to the Illinois Basin: Geological Field Excursions along the Ohio River Valley: Geological Society of America Field Guide 12, p. 105–117, https://doi.org/10.1130/2008.fld012(07).

Stumm, E.C., 1961, Corals of the Transverse Group of Michigan, Part VI, *Cladopora, Striatopora*, and *Thamnopora*: Contributions from the Museum of Paleontology: University of Michigan, v. XVI, no. 4, p. 275–285.

Thomas, S.F., and Hannibal, J.T., 2008, Revisiting New Harmony in the footsteps of Maximilian, the Prince of Wied; David Dale Owen; Charles Lesueur; and other early naturalists, *in* Maria, A.H., and Counts, R.C., eds., From the Cincinnati Arch to the Illinois Basin: Geological Field Excursions along the Ohio River Valley: Geological Society of America Field Guide 12, p. 25–45, https://doi.org/10.1130/2008.fld012(03).

Warren, L., 2009, Maclure of New Harmony, Scientist, Progressive Educator, Radical Philanthropist: Bloomington, Indiana, Indiana University Press, 343 p.

Weimerskirch, P.J., 1989, Lithographic stone in America: Printing: Historical Journal, v. 11, p. 2–14.

Wilson, W.E., 1964, The Angel and the Serpent: The Story of New Harmony (2nd edition): Bloomington, Indiana, Indiana University Press, 242 p.

Manuscript Accepted by the Society 20 January 2021
Manuscript Published Online 21 Septmber 2021

The Geological Society of America
Memoir 218

Franz Unger and plant evolution: Representations of plants through time

Larry B. Collins
Delta State University, Division of Mathematics and Sciences, 111A Walters Hall, Cleveland, Mississippi 38733, USA

ABSTRACT

This chapter will highlight a series of lithographs produced by Franz Unger and Josef Kuwasseg that emphasize how Unger used plants to represent different periods of earth history. While Henry De la Beche is credited with the first depiction of ancient life through art (*Duria antiquior*), Unger's work was the first to illustrate how plants could be used as indicators of changes in life history. In collaboration with artist Josef Kuwasseg, he embarked on a project entitled *The Primitive World in Its Different Periods of Formation* that consisted of 14 lithographs that were published in 1851. The title was unique in that it combined the concepts of a "primitive world," or the widely accepted contemporary idea of undifferentiated deep time, with our modern concept of different periods of earth history. Unger selected periods for this project based upon major strata, but his botanical roots led him to emphasize the importance of plants in each lithograph. The series begins with the "Transition Period," or the strata that contain the most fossil evidence to develop a reconstruction, and ends with a depiction of the arrival of man in a plant-filled world. This series of lithographs offers a unique contribution to the history and philosophy of geology as Unger recognized the importance of plants to our understanding of geology and deep time in the nineteenth century.

INTRODUCTION

Franz Xaver Unger (1800–1870), director of the Botanical Garden at the University of Graz, is arguably a revolutionary figure in the discipline of paleobotany given his combined expertise in paleontology and biogeography (Fig. 1). While most of his formal training was in law, medicine, and natural history, Unger was recruited to the University of Vienna because of his significant contributions to several fields such as paleobotany, plant physiology, and cell biology, which included the proposal of a theory of evolution prior to Charles Darwin. A condition of his new appointment was that he had to play an important role in making the University of Vienna a leader in scientific research. After the death of his sister in 1835, he sought to leave Vienna and moved on to a new position at the University of Graz. As a custodian at the Landesmuseum Joanneum and director of the botanical garden at the University of Graz, he conducted research in botany (e.g., research on plant habitats and plant geography) and geology, which strengthened his reputation (particularly in paleobotany) within the nineteenth-century scientific community.

He strengthened his reputation by publishing his views on evolution and by using these views to shape the paleontological art that his colleague and fellow artist, Josef Kuwasseg, painted. Unger theorized that cells come from pre-existing cells and did not believe in spontaneous generation. Thus, his conceptions of evolution aligned with common descent. In addition to his

Collins, L.B., 2022, Franz Unger and plant evolution: Representations of plants through time, *in* Clary, R.M., Rosenberg, G.D., and Evans, D.C., eds., The Evolution of Paleontological Art: Geological Society of America Memoir 218, p. 67–72, https://doi.org/10.1130/2021.1218(08).

Figure 1. Lithograph of Franz Unger (1876) by Josef Kriehuber (public domain, Wikimedia Commons).

conceptions of evolution, Unger also had a strong religious background from being raised in the Catholic community (Dröscher, 2015). When he was born, he was named after a Jesuit, Francis Xavier. These religious beliefs are displayed within this series of lithographs since they culminate in a depiction of the present world where humans arrive with Adam and Eve in the Garden of Eden (Unger, 1851). Unger intended this series to be synonymous with the seven days of creation that are described in the book of Genesis. The last lithograph describes the sixth day of creation, when Adam and Eve arrived before God rested on the seventh day (Gliboff, 1998).

Unger's views on evolution were matched with controversy in the Catholic community. He pioneered a disputative argument surrounding pre-Darwinian conceptions of evolution. The newspapers in 1851 began stirring up this debate when Unger argued that all plants were descended from a common ancestor, and he implied that the same was true for animals and humans (Unger, 1851). A Catholic priest, Sebastian Brunner, was one of Unger's rivals who made his disapproval of Unger's ideas about evolution known. The views of evolution challenged the contemporary Catholic views, and Brunner believed that these were ideas that a scholar from the University of Vienna (a Catholic University) should not be publishing. He depicted Unger and his ideas as "the worst kinds of products" of the Revolutions of 1848 that resulted in educational reform (Gliboff, 1998).

Unger argued that plants were made up of cells, and life continued to evolve. Unger documented the evolution of life within the sequence of lithographs (Unger, 1853). In contrast to Lamarckian views of evolution, Unger supported the proposal that all living things were descended from earlier life. He stated this position when he wrote that the first known plants likely contained the "germs of all later developments" (Gliboff, 1998). As Unger declared, "the plant world is not based on a linear pattern of development, but an expansion that radiates" (Unger, 1851, p. 144). He was not a geologist by training, and Unger illustrated his conceptions of evolution through art when he began with the Transition Period, which he described as the time in which the first evidence of plants could be found within the strata, so that a scene could be reconstructed (Unger, 1853). It is not clear whether Unger believed these were the first "official" plants on the scene in Earth's history or if they were simply the ones that he and his colleagues could find sufficient evidence of within the fossil record.

The Primitive World in Its Different Periods of Formation

The inspiration behind this series of lithographs emerged from one of Unger's students whose name was not revealed in Unger's works. As Unger was one of the only known scholars to focus on plants rather than animal life, his student suggested that he publish an entire series of scenes focused on plant life. However, Unger was hesitant to do this because he was not an artist himself and because he anticipated criticism from his peers in the scientific community. Consequently, Unger collaborated with a popular artist, Josef Kuwasseg, whose work impressed him and who he thought could help him visualize something with which he was unfamiliar. He completed the introduction to the series in a defensive tone. He stated:

> I felt, however, that difficulties almost insurmountable obstructed the execution of this project; the attempt was consequently delayed, until the inspection of some experimental drawings, submitted to me by the talented artist Josef Kuwasseg, not only convinced me of the possibility of levelling gradually all obstacles to the success of the undertaking, but induced a hope that these representations of the primitive world might be found not wholly to lack that mysterious charm which belongs to the contemplation of the distant past, and to the memory of our dreams. (Unger, 1851, p. ii)

Given Unger's botanical roots, it is no surprise that he emphasized the importance of plants in this series of lithographs, but he also struggled with titling the series of lithographs. During this time, non-scientists thought of deep time as undifferentiated (Rudwick, 1992), meaning continuous and not divided into different periods. In contrast, scientists (especially geologists) then thought of time as differentiated into periods identified by changes in life forms. Unger and Kuwasseg sought to disrupt everyone's conceptions of deep time by combining both the scientific concept of differentiated deep time with the non-scientists' concept of undifferentiated deep time within the title. Unger intended "primitive" in the title to indicate pre-human, and no concept of different geologic periods giving rise to the scientific view of "different periods of formation" referenced the current scientific consensus on deep time. It is important to recognize that Unger did not use "primitive" to refer to the earliest stratigraphic period, but to reference the previous context of undifferentiated geologic time. He further emphasized that "primitive" referred to pre-human times.

Origins of Fossils

Unger was not a geologist by training and had a limited understanding of the physical Earth. To him, the ideal world was one that was filled with plants. The fossils that appear within the lithographs described below are primarily from central Europe (Unger, 1855b). Reconstruction was difficult for Unger as most of the rocks that he described rarely contained fossils. However, Unger later described a major sandstone formation that is after "The Coal Period" that also contains volcanic rocks known as the Totliegende. These rocks were later correlated with those from the Permian Period that directly followed the Carboniferous (Rudwick, 1992). The abundance of conifers that appear in later scenes can be attributed to the Bunter Sandstone of central Europe, which is the oldest of three formations within central Europe. Unger also displays fossils from the "Period of the Chalk," which emerge from a limestone formation that is prominent in Europe.

Transition Period

Henry T. De la Beche is credited with the first visualization depicting an assemblage of animals and plants in deep time in his *Duria antiquior*, which was published around 1830 (Clary, 2003). He was a pioneer in educating all social classes (Clary and Wandersee, 2009), as was Franz Unger. Unger sought to make the lithographs accessible to the general public, as well as to those within higher social classes as he sought to have a uniform understanding of deep time among all classes (Unger, 1855a). Unger and Kuwasseg designed the first scene of the series around the first time period in which there was sufficient fossil evidence to justify a reconstruction. Unger termed this "The Transition Period," and it is likely identifiable today as components of the Carboniferous Period. In this scene, he shows a coal forest on a few islands within an ancient ocean. Numerous tree-sized cryptograms are depicted throughout the scene instead of modern palm trees. It is also worth noting that plant fossils are rarely whole when found but need to be reconstructed from tiny fragments. This presented challenges to Unger.

The presence of *Stigmaria* corroborates the claim that this scene best represents the modern Carboniferous Period. *Stigmaria* are thought to represent the root structures of lycopsid trees within coal forests. They are also associated with *Sigillaria* and *Lepidodendron* (Unger, 1855b). *Stigmaria* do not often appear attached to other plant structures within the fossil record; hence, they are depicted independently in this scene. Unger, at the time, did not fully understand this aspect of preservation of *Stigmaria*, which explains why it is depicted as a dwarf plant in this and other past scenes.

Diversity of Plants

In an effort to document the progression of plant evolution throughout deep time, Unger shows different plants throughout the series (Unger, 1855a). They depict several paleoenvironments. For example, another representation of *The Coal Period* (see Fig. 2) indicates a swamp environment consisting of trees (Lepidodendrons) in the foreground, several ferns, plants clinging to the ferns which are likely parasitic plants, and the background contains tall *Calamites.* In another example known as *The Keuper Sandstone*, a marsh is illustrated with the outskirts of a forest (Unger, 1855a). The scene includes horsetails (*Equisetum sylvaticum*), *Preisleria antiqua* climbing up the trunks of the trees in the picture, and *Calamites arenaceus* with branches hanging freely comprise a portion of a forest with numerous ferns such as *Anomopteris mougeotii* with *Equisetites columnaris* towering over them (Unger, 1855a). Cycadae are also present (see Fig. 3).

Throughout Earth's history, there were five mass extinction events. Unger was not aware of the concept of extinction, and he makes no mention of organisms that went extinct. The Muschelkalk illustrates what Unger conceptualized as a disruption to plant life when the sea advanced. Most of the plants are portrayed as disheveled, and coral reefs and crinoids are exposed. It is a time in which there were no plants in this area, and Unger viewed it as a very dark time (Unger, 1851). It is hypothesized that the moonlight in this scene represents Unger's disappointment in a world that is not full of plants (Rudwick, 1992). In another example, he displays the *Period of the Chalk* as emerging (Fig. 4) from a large limestone formation in Europe. While Unger recognized that there are numerous types of organisms that would have contributed to the marine origin of this chalk, he instructed Kuwasseg to only portray a few mollusks along the shoreline (Unger, 1851). He further demonstrated his lack of interest in marine fossils by having Kuwasseg display this marine scene being pummeled by a storm (Unger, 1851). In this *Period of the Chalk*, he still demonstrates his love for plants with palm trees and conifers that are along the coastal rocks.

The Present World

In the final scene of the 14 lithographs, we see Unger's vision of an ideal world that is truly dominated by plants. While Unger does not explicitly describe every plant displayed in the lithograph, it is clear that he sought to emphasize the "modern world" dominated by plants titled *The Present World* as indicating the arrival of humans into the history of life. Adam and Eve are shown, and the tree dominating the center takes on biblical meaning, namely as the tree that figured in the sixth day of creation when God created Adam and Eve as described in the Book of Genesis.

Figure 2. *The Coal Period*, photographic print from the *Primitive World in Its Different Periods of Formation, 1851,* by Josef Kuwasseg; from the U.S. Geological Survey (public domain).

Figure 3. *The Keuper Sandstone*, photographic print from the *Primitive World in Its Different Periods of Formation, 1851,* by Josef Kuwasseg; from the U.S. Geological Survey (public domain).

Figure 4. *Period of the Chalk*, photographic print from the *Primitive World in Its Different Periods of Formation, 1851,* by Josef Kuwasseg; from the U.S. Geological Survey (public domain)

The dominance of plant life within each of the lithographs in this series and the lack of animal life clearly demonstrate Unger's desire to draw attention to the significance of plants to the history of life. The plants that Unger depicted in these lithographs clearly do not represent all that were found in the fossil record; Unger simply wanted to demonstrate his desire for a plant-dominated world (Unger, 1851, 1852).

CONCLUSIONS

Unger leveraged the expertise of Kuwasseg to shape the audience's views of deep time. *The Primitive World in Its Different Periods of Formation* is a pioneering sequence of lithographs in which the artist (Kuwasseg) is given the majority of the prestige and credit for its success. As Unger himself stated:

> But it is due to the Artist himself that my gratitude is chiefly due. Unwearied by frequent trials, he finally attained such a perfect comprehension of the conceptions I had formed of these remote periods, that the undefined visions of my fancy were, by his genius, developed into clear and vigorous images. I can claim, then, as my part in the performance of this undertaking, only the communication of my thoughts and conjectures: if these have given inspiration to the Artist, if to these is attributable the existence of his productions, not to me, but to him with whom the scheme originated, belong alike the merit and the praise. (Unger, 1851, p. ii)

Unger was one of the first scientists to introduce plants as a way of characterizing the different periods of life history. The significance of plants is not often at the forefront of attention of geologists and other scholars; 15° Laboratory researchers Wandersee and Schussler (1998) defined it as the inability to see or notice plants in one's own environment. They further noted that this could lead to: (1) the inability to recognize the importance of plants in the biosphere and in human affairs; (2) the inability to appreciate the aesthetic and unique biological features of the life forms belonging to the Plant Kingdom; and (3) the misguided, anthropocentric ranking of plants as inferior to animals, leading to the conclusion that plants are not worthy of human consideration (Wandersee, and Schussler, 1998).

Several "symptoms" of plant blindness have been described in the literature. One symptom that can be addressed here is an individual's failure to distinguish between the differing time scales of plant and animal activity (Attenborough, 1995). Illustrating the evolution of plant life through time provides a pictorial history. Unger and Kuwasseg's lithographs were a first step toward showing the diversity of plants through time and how those plants evolved. Unger and Kuwasseg's visualizations provide an important avenue for illustrating the importance of plants in the history and philosophy of geology, and they also offer a unique opportunity for educators to highlight in their classrooms the significance of plants in the history of life.

ACKNOWLEDGMENTS

The author thanks Renee Clary for her invitation to contribute to this volume and her thoughtful comments and feedback on the ideas that shaped this manuscript as part of the T91: "Evolution of Paleontological Art" technical session at the 2018 Geological Society of America Annual Meeting in Indianapolis, Indiana. Thoughtful comments from Gary Rosenberg, Dallas Evans, and two anonymous reviewers helped to improve this manuscript.

REFERENCES CITED

Attenborough, D., 1995, The Private Lives of Plants: A Natural History of Plant Behavior: Princeton, New Jersey, Princeton University Press, 230 p.

Clary, R.M., 2003, Uncovering strata: The graphic contributions of geologist Henry T. De la Beche [Ph.D. diss.]: Baton Rouge, Louisiana State University, 481 p.

Clary, R.M., and Wandersee, J.H., 2009, All are worthy to know the Earth: Henry De la Beche and the origin of geological literacy: Science & Education, v. 18, p. 1359–1375, https://doi.org/10.1007/s11191-008-9177-z.

Dröscher, A., 2015, Gregor Mendel, Franz Unger, Carl Nägeli and the magic of numbers: History of Science, v. 53, no. 4, p. 492–508, https://doi.org/10.1177/0073275315594972.

Gliboff, S., 1998, Evolution, revolution, and reform in Vienna: Franz Unger's ideas on descent and their post-1848 reception: Journal of the History of Biology, v. 31, p. 179–209, https://doi.org/10.1023/A:1004379402154.

Rudwick, M.J., 1992, Scenes from Deep Time: Early Pictorial Representations of the Prehistoric World: Chicago, University of Chicago Press, 280 p., https://doi.org/10.7208/chicago/9780226149035.001.0001.

Unger, F., 1851, Die Urwelt in ihren verschiedenen Bildungsperioden: Wien, Fr. Beck.

Unger, F., 1852, Iconographia plantarum fossilium: Abbildungen und Beschreibungen Fossiler Pflanzen: Vienna, Imperial Royal Court and State Printing Office, 40 p.

Unger, F., 1853, Botanical Letters to a Friend: London, Samuel Highley, 116 p.

Unger, F., 1855a, Anatomie und Physiologie der Pflanzen: Pest, Wien, und Leipzig, Verlag von C. A. Hartleben, 461 p.

Unger, F., 1855b, Ideal Views of the Primitive World, in Its Geological and Palaeontological Phases, Illustrated by Fourteen Photographic Plates, Being an Introduction to the Series: London, Samuel Highley, 8 p.

Wandersee, J.H., and Schussler, E.E., 1998 (13 April), A model of plant blindness, presented at 3rd Annual Associates Meeting of the 15° Laboratory: Baton Rouge, Louisiana, Louisiana State University.

Manuscript Accepted by the Society 20 January 2021
Manuscript Published Online 6 December 2021

Printed in the USA

The Geological Society of America
Memoir 218

Eduard Suess on graptolites: His very first scientific paper and illustrations

A.M.C. Şengör*
ITU Maden Fakültesi, Jeoloji Bölümü and Avrasya Yerbilimleri Enstitüsü, Ayazağa 34469 Istanbul, Turkey

To the memory of my first and greatest teacher in paleontology, Walter Georg Kühne (1911–1991), "the legendary explorer of Mesozoic mammals" and a graptolite worker in his spare time.

ABSTRACT

The very first scientific paper by Eduard Suess (1831–1914) treats the graptolites of Bohemia in the present-day Czech Republic (in the Upper Proterozoic to Middle Devonian "Barrandian" extending between Prague and Plzeň). This paper is accompanied by superb drawings of his observations in which Suess took great care not to insert himself between Nature as he perceived it in the framework of the knowledge of his day and his readers. His only limitation was the one imposed by the size of his study objects. His technological means did not allow him to see what we today consider the "right" picture. Nevertheless, we can see what he saw and interpret it through a modern lens of understanding. In his drawings, Suess exercised what the great German geologist Hans Cloos later called "the art of leaving out." This meant that in the drawings, the parts not relevant to the discussion are left only in outline, whereas parts he wished to highlight are brought to the fore by careful shading. Even the parts left only in outline are not schematic, however; instead they are careful reconstructions true to Nature as much as the material and his technological aids allowed. This characteristic of Suess' illustrations is seen also in his later field sketches concerning stratigraphy and structural geology and in his depiction of the large tectonic features of our globe representing a window into his manner of thinking.

INTRODUCTION

Eduard Suess (1831–1914; Fig. 1) is one of the greatest geologists who ever lived, if not the greatest. His entry into geology took place via paleontology (see especially his memoirs: Suess, 1916; also see Şengör, 2014, 2015). As a student in the Polytechnical School in Vienna (the present-day Technical University of Vienna), he was entangled in the 1848 March revolution as a member of the "Academic Legion." After the failure of the revolution, his father sent him to Prague to his grandparents' house, fearing that he might be arrested. It was in Prague that Suess' great love for geology was awakened. During a visit to the "Fatherland Museum" in Prague, he saw the early Paleozoic fossils collected from the classical Barrandian (from its Silurian parts) around Prague and fell in love with them. In his memoirs he reminisced:

*sengor@itu.edu.tr

Şengör, A.M.C., 2022, Eduard Suess on graptolites: His very first scientific paper and illustrations, *in* Clary, R.M., Rosenberg, G.D., and Evans, D.C., eds., The Evolution of Paleontological Art: Geological Society of America Memoir 218, p. 73–80, https://doi.org/10.1130/2021.1218(09).

> The sight of a long extinct marine population, the thought of the immense changes that the country had experienced and the realisation that a strike of my hammer might expose an image that nobody before me had seen gripped my fantasy to such an extent that it was impossible to keep my attention on any other study. As soon as my foot recovered, I spent every free day at some rich fossil locality near Prague…. (Suess, 1916, p. 71–72)

Figure 1. Eduard Suess during the years when he wrote his graptolite paper (courtesy of Stephen Suess).

SUESS AND THE BARRANDIAN GRAPTOLITES

In Prague, Suess began undertaking his own excursions to the surroundings of the city during which he developed an interest in and some original ideas on graptolites. Apart from a few pages he had contributed to a tourist guide about the spa town of Karlsbad (now Karlovy Vary in the Czech Republic) (Anonymous, 1851), the paper here discussed is the first geological publication by Suess (Suess, 1851a). It appeared in a journal published by the most eminent earth scientist of Austria in those days, namely the great mineralogist Wilhelm Ritter von Haidinger (1795–1871), after Suess made a presentation of its contents to the third meeting of the "Friends of the Natural Sciences in Vienna" on 19 April 1850 (Suess, 1851b). Suess' broad knowledge of paleozoology and its methods as displayed in this paper, written when its author was not yet 20 years of age, awakens one's admiration. He minutely studied his graptolites using a microscope and discovered many new aspects of these tiny creatures.

Suess' paper is illustrated with four plates (his plates VII–X; of these I reproduce here in my Figure 2 only his plate VII) drawn most likely by himself, not only because they show his characteristic "light touch" and style of drawing, but also because in those days he had no institutional support. He was simply a young, private individual of 19 years of age. Suess' paper was reviewed in the "History of Research" section of the famous Monograph by Elles and Wood (1902, p. xxii–xxv). They consider Suess' paper not to have improved on that of Barrande (1850) and his illustrations "indifferent" (their p. xxii), yet they then proceed to describe in detail how and where Suess differed from Barrande and what improvements he made.

Suess' plate VII illustrates a still-valid species, namely *Retiolites geinitzianus* BARRANDE (1850)[1] and belongs to a group of graptoloids, which was studied most intensively by scanning electron microscope by later graptolite paleontologists and zoologists. In fact, Maletz (2008, p. 286) said that the retiolitid graptolites are the "most complex biological structures known from the fossil record," but often their preservation is poor, owing to the delicate meshwork of lists forming their only preservable parts. When Suess wrote his paper, our knowledge of graptolites was very rudimentary and that has since progressed so much in its fundamental aspects (see Bulman, 1970; Maletz, 2017; and Lenz et al., 2018, for convenient guides to recent developments) that although the species studied by Suess remains valid, the scientific value of his observations has long been very greatly reduced. This makes his drawings even more interesting from the viewpoint of the development of paleontological illustration.

First, however, presentation of some very simplified terminology of the graptolite biology is in order to be able to describe Suess' drawings (see Figs. 2 and 3): Graptolites belong to the phylum Hemichordata and the class Graptolithina, thus being close relatives of the vertebrates. They are colonial invertebrate marine animals. Their rhabdosomes, (from the Ancient Greek ῥάβδος meaning a rod or a wand and σῶμα meaning body), are a colony around a stem, which may appear straight or curved, or even with a spiral form; they may be single- or double-branched ("bifid"), or even multi-branched. This great diversity makes them excellent index fossils. They existed between the medial Cambrian and the late Carboniferous (Bulman, 1970; Maletz, 2015, 2017; Lenz et al., 2018) or perhaps even into the Recent (Dilly, 1993; Mitchell et al., 2012). The prominent "stem" seen in a graptolite rhabdosome, the sicula (from the Latin meaning a small dagger), has a spike-like conical nema (from the Ancient Greek νῆμα, via Latin *nema*, thread, yarn, anything with a filiform appearance) at its apex. After the free-floating graptoloid larvae find themselves an appropriate substratum to attach to, this

[1]Suess used capital G in the species name, which reflects the custom of the day in capitalizing species names if taken from a proper name as opposed to a descriptive name. In a footnote on his p. 68, Barrande (1850) wrote that "if, because the generic name *Gladiolites* has an affinity to *Gladiolus* designating a plant, an objection is raised against the former, we propose substituting it with *Retiolites*." To my knowledge, Suess (1851a) was the first to use Barrande's suggested alternative, because Barrande himself continued using *Gladiolites* in his 1850 book. Modern authors credit Barrande with the introduction of the name *Retiolites*, but this is inappropriate, because although Barrande suggested it, he did not follow his own suggestion in his book of 1850. *The Treatise on Invertebrate Paleontology*, part V, second edition (Bulman, 1970), retains *Retiolites* as a synonym in *R. geinitzianus*, but gives no reference to Suess' paper because of the problem just mentioned. Holm (1890) returned to Suess' designation in 1890 and today, *Retiolites geinitzianus* (BARRANDE, 1850) is the accepted form although Suess is usually not credited with the first usage of the full name. I believe this ought to change.

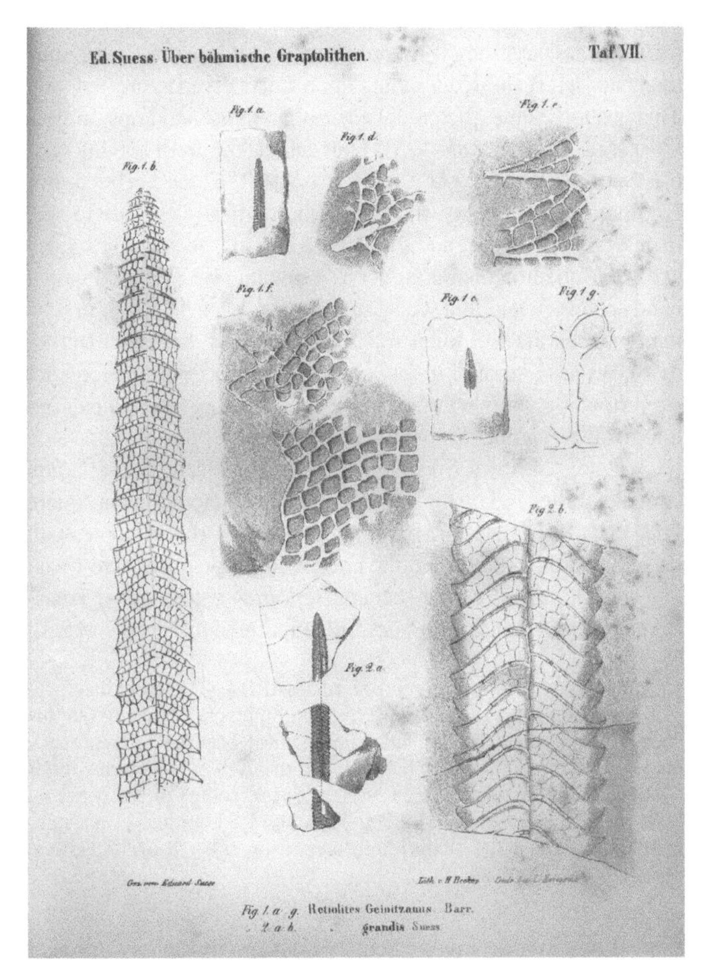

Figure 2. Plate VII from Suess (1851a) showing the appearance and details of the structure of *Retiolites geinitzianus* BARRANDE. See text for further explanation.

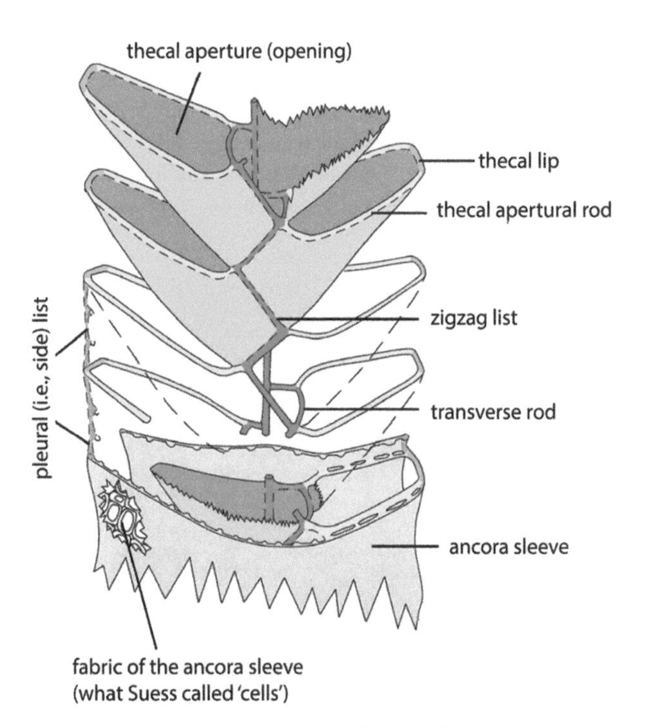

Figure 3. Basic structure of *Retiolites* BARRANDE (slightly modified from Lenz et al., 2018, fig. 9).

is the first part that grows. From this sicula stipes (from the Latin *stipes*, branch of a tree, main branch of a candlestick) branch away, on which grow numerous theca (cup-like buds; plural *thecae*; from the Ancient Greek θήκη meaning a box or any receptacle, via Latin *theca* meaning a sheath or a case). The graptolite animal (the zooid, which is never preserved as a fossil) lived in these miniscule thecae.

In retiolite graptoloids, a secretion from the tip of the sicular aperture forms a fusselar growth called the ancora (from the Ancient Greek ἄγκυρα, anchor) enveloping or joining the thecae at their bottom (first defined by Eisenack, 1951, p. 134; see also Bates, 1990; Bates et al., 2005; Lenz et al., 2018, their fig. 9; herein Fig. 2). The ancora looks like a fishing net woven with threads or bands called lists (from Middle English *list*: band, strip, barrier, enclosing an area for jousting; in German it is called *Strebe*, i.e., rod, stiffener, brace, which is more apposite). Suess could see the rhabdosome, the sicula, and the stipes with a naked eye and the ancora sleeve (his "cells") under 8× magnification. The magnification available to him and the preservation of his fossils in squashed form in slates did not allow distinguishing the thecae and the detailed structure of the thecal walls. Our knowledge of them became possible mainly after the development of scanning electron microscopy and the study of fossils preserved in three-dimensional form in limestones (first separated by Wilhelm Gümbel in 1878 and then by G. Holm in 1890), although already in 1850 Barrande did distinguish some thecae (see, for example, his plate 1).

Below I describe Suess' plate VII (Fig. 2 herein) reflecting what he thought he was seeing. He misidentified a number of things ("cells") and did not at all recognize others (e.g., the ancora, although he did see it and drew it!). This description illustrates the importance of what Goethe once wrote to his friend Friedrich von Müller, the able Chancellor of the Duchy of Saxe-Weimar-Eisenach, on 24 April 1819, "Man erblickt nur, was man schon weiß und versteht" (one sees only what one already knows and understands) (von Goethe, 1948). The graptolite research was in its very infancy when Suess got into it, and the technical means, especially microscopic magnification, were not nearly sufficient to get into the details of the graptolite anatomy. This is one very important aspect that one needs to bear in mind when studying old paleontological illustrations depicting complex organisms, parts of which cannot be seen without powerful magnification.

Before we get into the anatomical details illustrated, let me emphasize a technique Suess used in his sketches, which might help in appreciating the style of his illustrations: Suess chose, in some cases, to illustrate an entire hand specimen (in Fig. 2 herein, his figs. 1a, 1c, 2a). In these, both the fossil and the entombing rock are drawn, and in one case (his fig. 2a), even the missing pieces from the original outcrop are indicated. Yet in others, only the organ to be illustrated is sketched with no other detail (e.g., his fig. 1g) or some shading of the background (his figs 1d, 1e, 1f). In yet others, an intermediate degree of detail is shown where the reader sees the fossil, but not the surrounding rock. This is deliberate: Suess shows in each drawing the detail he wants his reader to see. All detail he considers "overcrowding" and thus likely to divert the reader's attention unnecessarily are left out. This is a technique, the great German geologist and consummate artist Hans Cloos (1885–1951) later called "the art of leaving out" ("*Kunst des Weglassens*": see Carlé, 1988, p. 268). The author "illuminates," so to say, those parts he wishes his reader to see. In Suess' figs. 1a, 1c, and 2a, (Fig. 2 herein) we see a few lines and some shading enough to let us know that we are looking at a hand specimen and that we learn about its shape and even in how many pieces the specimen was recovered from the rock. But no more, because "more" in this context is considered unnecessary overcrowding. Now we can examine his drawings from a paleontological viewpoint.

Figure 4. A rhabdosome, with its sicula and its stipes and the ancora enveloping the invisible thecal "cups," of the species *Retiolites geinitzianus* BARRANDE. (Estonian geocollections database; image 84066, taken by I. Paalitis, TÜ LM geoloogilised kogud, 25 January 2014; http://geocollections.info/specimen/246925; accessed January 2021).

Figure 2 shows Suess' plate VII. I translate Suess' long, explanatory legend on his p. 98–99 with my annotations in square brackets: [Figure 4 shows a photograph of a rhabdosome with its sicula and its stipes and the ancora enveloping the here invisible thecal "cups," of the species *Retiolites geinitzianus* BARRANDE, to compare with Suess' illustration of the same species.]

1a. Upper end of *Retiolites geinitzianus* BARRANDE, from the slates of Kuchelbad near Prague. Left 29, right 28 branches [stipes]. On this specimen one sees that the branches [stipes] become fully present, namely (counted in the left) the 10th and the 29th, which corresponds to the 28th on the other side [These are Suess' counts of the stipes on both sides of the sicula]. The entire length of an anomaly [i.e., nonmatching sides of the sicula] here comprises only 18 or 17 vertical distances of a branch.

Although the stipes seem prominent in Suess' drawing (Fig. 2, i.e., his plate VII, fig. 1b), they are not everywhere accurate because of the insufficient magnification and his (and, of course, everybody else's in those days) insufficient knowledge of the graptolite anatomy that prohibited him from recognizing the ancora (although he drew what is actually the ancora!).

1b. (Fig. 2 herein) The same specimen, magnified 8 times [compare with Fig. 5 showing a transmitted light photo of *Retiolites geinitzianus* BARRANDE specimen displaying the net-like ancora sleeve and the well preserved thecal walls inside it (from Maletz, 2008, fig. 1A).]. One sees that it was in the third phase of its development; the uppermost branches form only the second row of cells [in reality ancora openings; every time Suess writes cell, read ancora opening]. On the right edge one can see the irregularities peculiar to this species, which on the left side are less conspicuous because of the deviation towards the interior of the peripheral walls and the strong forward pressing of the youngest cells. The four last branches on the right show clearly the strengthened horizontal part as the strengthened cell in its inner end.

1c. (Fig. 2 herein) A torn specimen of Retiolites geinitzianus BARRANDE with the free, downward-hanging axis [i.e., sicula]; 18 branches on both sides. From the slates of Hodkowiček.

1d. (Fig. 2 herein) The same specimen, the left side magnified many times. This short specimen has almost completed the fourth phase of the separation in its 15th–18th branches and displays in all its parts a luxuriant distribution of mass. The axis [here the stipes] is strong, the walls separating the cells and the rows are very strong, the latter are completely distorted by the rapid growth. At the tips of the of the side

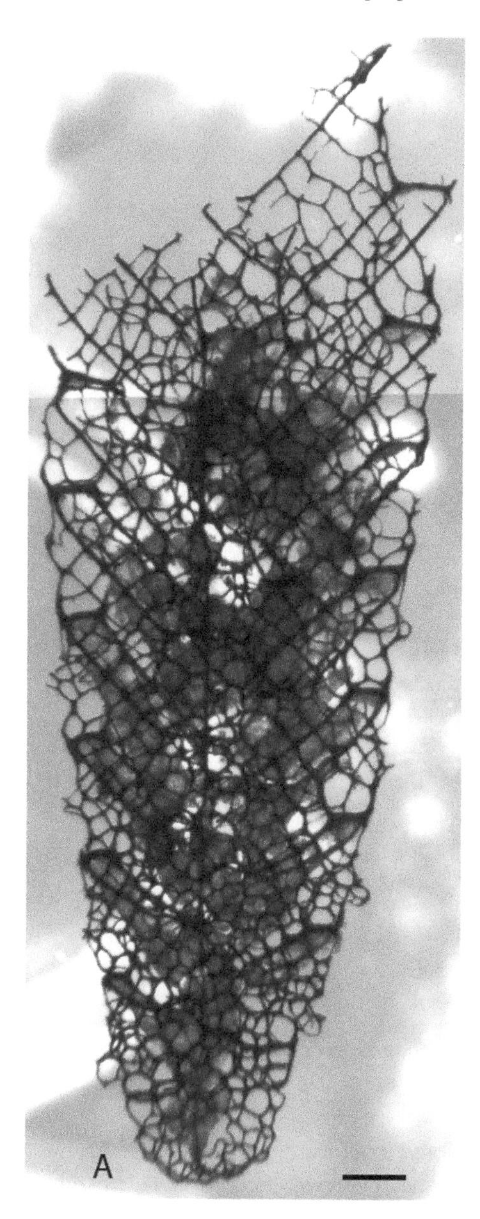

Figure 5. Transmitted light photos of retiolitid species *Retiolites geinitzianus* BARRANDE (from Maletz, 2008, fig. 1A; courtesy of Dr. Jörg Maletz). The length of the black bar is 1 mm.

branches are still significant accumulations of irregular boundaries of the ancoral lists [Here the magnification that was available to Suess could not identify separately the thecae walls and the ancora sleeve (compare Figs. 2 and 3)].

1e. (Fig. 2 herein) The left side of a specimen in the fourth phase of development, magnified many times. Here two rows of cells remained behind in their development, that is why the horizontal part is very conspicuous. The wall of the contour is torn, but one still sees the same delimiting indentations at the ends of the side branches, which begins in the fifth separation. This specimen represents an example of the opposite extreme with respect to the previous one, not only through the lagging behind of so many cell rows, but also through the spare distribution of the mass. Characteristic is the circumstance, however, that the cell walls are concave towards the interior. From the yellow (Graptolite) slates of Hodkowiček.

1f. (Fig. 2 herein) The lowermost known end of Ret. Geinitzianus BARRANDE Left half, magnified many times. From the thin limestones going through the Graptolite-slates of Wisločilka near Prague.

1g. (Fig. 2 herein) The horizontal part that forms through the irregular formation of this species with the strengthened cell and the indentation of the contours at the junction of the side branch, many times magnified.

2b. (Fig. 2 herein) Detail showing the sicula, the stipes and the ancora of the Retiolites genitzianus BARRANDE.

The descriptions above were taken verbatim from Suess' paper (in my translation from the German) and the figures show how carefully Suess studied his material within the limits of what was then known of graptolites and the limits of the available technology. That we can today identify in terms of our present knowledge what he drew and described is a tribute to his skill not only as a geologist, but also as a draftsman.

I have chosen only this plate from Suess' paper, because it illustrates his view of a still-valid species that happens to be one of the best-known and most intensively studied graptoloid species, the internal structure of which has been laid bare mainly by electron microscopy (Bates and Kirk, 1987, 1992, 1997). Herein lies the lesson of the aid technology has given to paleontological observations and illustrations. Suess' drawings of the *Retiolites geinitzianus* BARRANDE is extremely realistic as a comparison of Figures 2, 4, and 5 shows. However, when we compare the thecae and the ancora sleeve in Figure 5 with his most detailed drawings (his figs. 1b and 2b; herein Fig. 3) we can see that he was able to see only the ancora lists and even those not in any detail. He thought them to be cell walls, which is incorrect. His sketches illustrate a mixture of what he really saw and what he thought he was seeing. Yet any comparison with a modern drawing, depending on the magnification, will show significant differences (see Figs. 2 and 5).

But, let us look at his technique of drafting again, the *Kunst des Weglassens*: This is a technique that characterized all of Suess' drawings throughout his professional life; drawings of fossils, outcrops, and panoramas, as well as fossils other than graptolites. I here reproduce two examples: one from his paper on the *Terebratula*-bearing rocks in Austro-Hungary (Fig. 6) and the other only a small cutout from a long, unpublished cross section, drawn for student excursions in the early 1860s, showing the geology in the surroundings of Eggenburg in Lower Austria (Fig. 7). In Figure 6, one sees the scenery around the Czorsztyn (formerly Scharfstein) area in the Western Carpathians illustrating the geometry of the Carpathian Klippen in all their splendor, because Suess wanted to emphasize the appearance of the then-enigmatic limestone blocks cropping out amidst the surrounding *Scaglia Rossa*–type marly limestones and flysch. By contrast, in Figure 7, notice how the "incidental" house is shown only

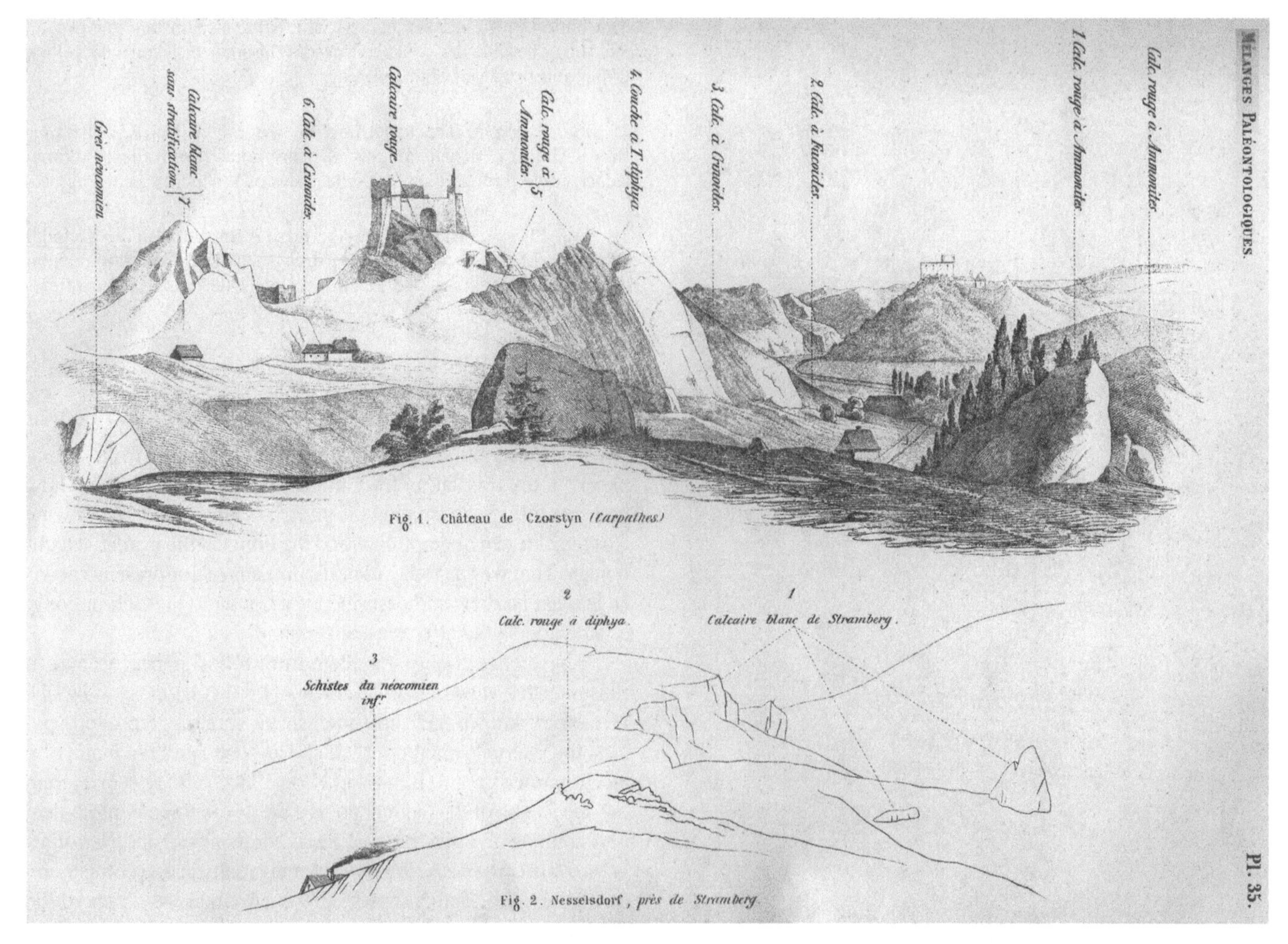

Figure 6. Eduard Suess' field sketch showing the Panorama of the Czorsztyn area illustrating the geometry of the Carpathian klippen. View to the north showing the Czorsztyn castle and the River Dunazec (from Suess, 1867).

in outline, its basement with slight indication of three window frames. Here Suess wanted to show that the outcrop was under the house into which the basement had been dug, the further details of the house itself being irrelevant. No illustration of detail of the kind we see in Fig. 6 is here attempted, because there was no need for it.

"The art of leaving out" ("*Kunst des Weglassens*") should not be confused with schematization. Schematization is made to give a rough idea of what something is with a few lines not necessarily true to scale or even to the shape (Fig. 8). "The art of leaving out" preserves both the scale and the shape, yet leaves out overcrowding details. Schematization may completely mislead the beholder; the art of leaving out does not. In most cases of paleontological illustration, the latter aids the beholder, the former, by contrast, may confuse and misinform her or him.

CONCLUSIONS

This attention to detail in drawing natural objects characterized Suess' illustrations all his life, in all branches of geology. He endeavored to let Nature speak through his publications. His explanations, hypotheses, were formulated only after he presented the relevant data in the greatest possible precision. In our age of cameras and computers, the field geologist has much to learn from Suess. No photograph can possibly convey the perception of the geologist reporting on his study objects. The ideal in informing the reader is to present a detailed drawing, made at outcrop of the rocks and fossils in addition to their photographs, *not* a hasty sketch, or a schema. I think Eduard Suess remains, in this regard, the unsurpassed master of the field geologist.

We also realize here the immense contribution that the development of advanced microscopy made to our knowledge of graptolites and our ability to depict them in drawings and photography. Technology has had similar influence in all branches of geology, especially in the latter half of the twentieth century. Without the submarine mapping devices and the sensitive seismographs and magnetometers there could have been no plate tectonics. In his time, Suess had done the best that could be done also in tectonics by considering the continents only, because he had no means of observing the seafloor and knowing the precise

Figure 7. Cutout from an unpublished cross section near Eggenburg in Lower Austria by Suess (drawn in the early 1860s). The original is in the Institut für Geologie der Universität Wien.

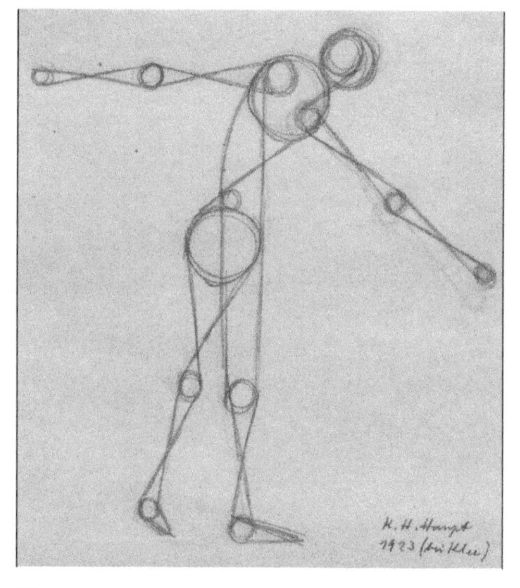

Figure 8. Schematic drawing of a human figure. (Anatomical and geometrical study for Paul Klee's course, 1923. Creator: Karl Hermann Haupt [German, 1904–1983]. Graphite on paper. 27.5 × 22.1 cm. Bauhaus Student Work, 1919–1933. The Getty Research Institute, Los Angeles, 850514.)

location of and sense of slip in earthquakes (except in rare cases where a fault offset observed in the field could be associated with an earthquake). That knowledge and the magnetic anomalies made plate tectonics possible. Thus, the good field geologist is not only the one who looks at and records the rocks in detail in the field and laboratory, but also one who keeps close tabs on the developing technology that has the potential of vastly improving the quality of his or her observations—and the illustrations recording them.

ACKNOWLEDGMENTS

I thank Renee Clary, Gary Rosenberg, and Dallas Evans for inviting this paper for their volume, and Clary and Rosenberg plus two other reviewers for providing detailed reviews. Jörg Maletz is thanked for his truly immense help in guiding me through the graptolite biology and the associated literature. However, I wish to absolve him of any errors that might have remained herein. Christian Koeberl, Suess' compatriot and the scholarly editor of the GSA books, handled this paper with great competence and finesse.

REFERENCES CITED

Anonymous, 1851, *Carlsbad und Seine Umgebungen—Kürzester und Zuverlässigster Wegweiser für Curgäste und Reisende beim Besuche dieses Curortes*: Carlsbad und Prag, A.C. Kronberg'sche Buchhandlung, VIII + 161 p.

Barrande, J., 1850, *Graptolites de Bohême—extrait du Systême Silurien de la Bohême*: Privately printed, Prague, VI + [I] + 74 p. + 4 plates and captions.

Bates, D.E.B., 1990, Retiolite nomenclature and relationships: Journal of the Geological Society, v. 147, p. 717–723, https://doi.org/10.1144/gsjgs.147.4.0717.

Bates, D.E.B., and Kirk, N.H., 1987, The role of extrathecal tissue in the construction and functioning of some Ordovician and Silurian retiolitid graptolites: Bulletin of the Geological Society of Denmark, v. 35, p. 85–102.

Bates, D.E.B., and Kirk, N.H., 1992, The ultrastructure, mode of construction and functioning of a number of Llandovery ancorate and retiolitid graptolites: Modern Geology, v. 17, p. 1–270.

Bates, D.E.B., and Kirk, N.H., 1997, The ultrastructure, construction and functioning of the genera *Stomatograptus* and *Retiolites*, with an appendix on the incremental construction of the rhabdosome in *Petalolithus*, and its comparison with that of the thecal framework in *Retiolites* and in

Stomatograptus: Institute of Geography and Earth Sciences, University of Wales, Aberystwyth, Publication no. 10, p. 1–168.

Bates, D.E.B., Kozłowska, A., and Lenz, A.C., 2005, Silurian retiolitid graptolites: Morphology and evolution: Acta Palaeontologica Polonica, v. 50, p. 705–720.

Bulman, O.M.B., 1970, *Graptolithina, in* Teichert, C., ed., Treatise on Invertebrate Paleontology, Part V, second edition: Lawrence, Kansas, USA, Geological Society of America and University of Kansas Press, xxxii + 163 p.

Carlé, W., 1988, Werner-Beyrich-von Koenen-Stille ein Geistiger Stammbaum Wegweisender Geologen: Geologisches Jahrbuch (A), no. 108, 499 p.

Dilly, P.N., 1993, *Cephalodiscus graptolitoides* sp. nov. a probable extant graptolite: Journal of Zoology, v. 229, p. 69–78, https://doi.org/10.1111/j.1469-7998.1993.tb02621.x.

Eisenack, A., 1951, Retioliten aus dem Graptolithengestein: Palaeontographica, v. 100, p. 129–163.

Elles, G.L., and Wood, E.M.R., 1902, *A Monograph of British Graptolites*, edited by Charles Lapwort. *Introduction and Part I*: Palaeontographical Society, London, xxviii p. + p. 55–102 + plates V–XIII.

von Goethe, J.W., 1948, Schriften zur Kunst, Propyläen, Einleitung, zitiert nach: *Gedenkausgabe der Werke, Briefe und Gespräche*: Zürich und Stuttgart, v. 13, p. 142, https://gutezitate.com/zitat/183167.

Holm, G., 1890, Gotlands graptoliter: *Svenska Vetenskap-Akademiens Handlingar*: Bihang, v. 16, p. 1–34.

Lenz, A.C., Bates, D.E.B., Kozłowska, A., and Maletz, J., 2018, *Treatise Online Number 114, Part V, Second Revision, Chapter 26: Family Retiolitidae: Introduction, Morphology, and Systematic Descriptions*: Lawrence, Kansas, USA, Paleontological Institute, The University of Kansas, 37 p.

Maletz, J., 2008, Retiolitid graptolites from the collection of Hermann JAEGER in the Museum für Naturkunde, Berlin (Germany). I. *Neogothograptus* and *Holoretiolites*: Paläontologische Zeitschrift, v. 82, no. 3, p. 285–307, https://doi.org/10.1007/BF02988896.

Maletz, J., 2015, Graptolite reconstructions and interpretations: Paläontologische Zeitschrift, v. 89, p. 271–286, https://doi.org/10.1007/s12542-014-0234-4.

Maletz, J., 2017, *Graptolite Paleobiology*: Chichester, Wiley Blackwell, viii + 336 p.

Mitchell, C.E., Melchin, M.J., Cameron, C.B., and Maletz, J., 2012, Phylogenetic analysis reveals that Rhabdopleura is an extant graptolite: Lethaia, v. 46, p. 34–56, https://doi.org/10.1111/j.1502-3931.2012.00319.x.

Şengör, A.M.C., 2014, Die Korrespondez zwischen Albert Oppel und Friedrich Rolle als Schlüssel zu Eduard Sueß' Bedeutung bei der Korrelation der Kössener Schichten: Wien, Jahrbuch der Geologischen Bundesanstalt, v. 154, p. 213–246.

Şengör, A.M.C., 2015, The founder of modern geology died 100 years ago: The scientific work and legacy of Eduard Suess: Geoscience Canada, v. 42, p. 181–246, https://doi.org/10.12789/geocanj.2015.42.070.

Suess, E., 1851a, Ueber böhmische Graptolithen: *Naturwissenschaftliche Abhandlungen* gesammelt durch Subskription herausgegeben von Wilhelm Haidinger, v. 4, p. 87–134 + plates 7–9.

Suess, E., 1851b, Graptolithen- oder Utica-Schiefer: *Berichte über die Mittheilungen von Freunden der Naturwissenschaften in Wien*, v. 7: Wilhelm Braumüller, Wien, p. 124–125.

Suess, E., 1867, Note sur le Gisement des Térébratules du groupe de Diphya dans l'Empire d'Autriche, *in* Pictet, F.-J., ed., *Mélanges Paléontologiques*, troisième livraison: Genève, Ramboz et Schuchardt, p. 185–201 + Plate 35.

Suess, E., 1916, *Erinnerungen*: Leipzig, S. Hirzel, IX + 451 p.

Manuscript Accepted by the Society 13 January 2021
Manuscript Published Online 14 April 2021

The Geological Society of America
Memoir 218

The influence of scientific knowledge on mollusk and arthropod illustration

Consuelo Sendino*
Natural History Museum, London, SW7 5BD, London, UK

ABSTRACT

Our attraction to fossils is almost as old as humans themselves, and the way fossils are represented has changed and evolved with technology and with our knowledge of these organisms. Invertebrates were the first fossils to be represented in books and illustrated according to their original form. The first worldwide illustrations of paleoinvertebrates by recognized authors, such as Christophorus Encelius and Conrad Gessner, considered only their general shape. Over time, paleoillustrations became more accurate and showed the position of organisms when they were alive and as they had appeared when found. Encyclopedic works such as those of the Sowerbys or Joachim Barrande have left an important legacy on fossil invertebrates, summarizing the knowledge of their time. Currently, new discoveries, techniques, and comparison with extant specimens are changing the way in which the same organisms are shown in life position, with previously overlooked taxonomically important elements being displayed using modern techniques. This chapter will cover the history of illustrations, unpublished nineteenth-century author illustrations, examples showing fossil reconstructions, new techniques and their influence on taxonomical work with regard to illustration, and the evolution of paleoinvertebrate illustration.

INTRODUCTION

Fossil illustration is still the main resource available to us for displaying detailed representations of specimens and demonstrating how these fascinating forms of early life appeared when alive. Paleoinvertebrate illustration is an extensive subject due to its history, the sheer number of fossils illustrated (also being the first fossil group illustrated), and the variety of organisms that are included. Therefore, this chapter will deal with two of the most historically important fossil invertebrate groups studied: the mollusks and the arthropods. The evolution of the study of these groups is reflected in their illustration. Artistic representations of fossil invertebrates appeared earlier in the record than their written descriptions. The first representations are reported during Egyptian times (Lehmann, 1981). But it is not until the Renaissance that we see the first ever published work with illustrations of fossil invertebrates. Since then, fossils have been increasingly studied under microscopes and have been compared to recent specimens for a better understanding of their anatomy. Attempts have also been made to reconstruct the appearance of those organisms when they were alive and even their movements. This is reflected in the figures that accompany fossil descriptions, with the quality of the figures increasing with new techniques and tools.

The early study of fossils during the Renaissance had been undertaken using a magnifying glass, the only tool available at the time, but this was soon followed by rudimentary microscopes

*c.sendino-lara@nhm.ac.uk

Sendino, C., 2022, The influence of scientific knowledge on mollusk and arthropod illustration, *in* Clary, R.M., Rosenberg, G.D., and Evans, D.C., eds., The Evolution of Paleontological Art: Geological Society of America Memoir 218, p. 81–89, https://doi.org/10.1130/2021.1218(10).

at the end of the sixteenth century. From then on, precision of microscopes improved exponentially. Illustrations evolved until the twentieth century from woodcuts to copper plate engravings and etchings. Large expeditions in the late nineteenth and early twentieth centuries provided discoveries of new taxa to be described, and this crucial time also saw the expansion of universities and scientific knowledge. Textbooks and catalogues written on paleontology at the beginning of the twentieth century used mainly drawings, and this gave way to conventional photographs in the second part of the century. The use of photographs during the era of mass media with offset printing made the publications affordable, and it was at this time that textbooks dealing with all fossil groups became popular. Paleontological monographs and encyclopedic works gave way to articles that increased rapidly in number. From the 1970s, fossils were studied under X-ray, and their photographs helped to identify morphological elements that were not seen earlier. The necessity to illustrate the microscopic world led to scanning electron microscopy (SEM) which, along with the development of digital photography at the end of the twentieth century to the beginning of the twenty-first century, helped popularize the fossil world. SEM images are produced by a high-energy beam of electrons giving high resolution images of the specimen; viewing fossils using high magnification allows the opportunity to see morphological elements that otherwise are missed. SEM is also useful for obtaining the chemical composition of a specific area of the specimen. Parallel to the use of SEM, a new digital photographic technique was born in the digital revolution: focus stacking. This technique allows the combination of multiple photographs of a 3-D specimen, with photographs taken at different focal lengths, and then combined to produce a unique image.

Finally, in the twenty-first century, a new X-ray technology combined with computing is revolutionizing paleontology: computerized tomography (CT) scanning. It allows the study of fossils in 3-D and is the beginning of virtual paleontology, providing accurate visual illustrations of formerly unseen morphological elements. It is also a non-destructive technique. The use of CT, which combines a series of X-ray images, is being popularized, and most of the fossil groups are now benefiting. Images of the internal parts are processed digitally and show new structures and elements never seen before. It is, without doubt, a further advancement in paleontology.

MOLLUSKS

This taxonomic group, the first to be illustrated and also one of the most abundant, is therefore very suitable for studying the evolution of invertebrate paleoillustration. The first widely accepted illustrations of this phylum in the western world were published by Encelius (1551). He showed woodcuts of a gastropod and a pectinid bivalve in the same work. Both figures are schematic and have enough information to identify the groups to which they belong. At that time, knowledge on fossils was included in the Oryctologia (the study of specimens that come from the earth), which did not differentiate between minerals and fossils. Fossils were not considered remains of living organisms but simply objects. Some years after Encelius' work (1565), the first printed paleontological work with fossil illustrations was written by the Swiss naturalist Gessner, who is generally considered to be the first true paleontologist. This was the first attempt to illustrate fossils systematically. Although during the Renaissance fossils were believed to be stones formed in the earth and not organic remains, Gessner was one of the first naturalists who acknowledged the resemblance between some fossils and extant organisms.

In the following century (seventeenth), Aldrovandi was one of the first leading figures in Oryctologia. He built one of the most important collections on natural history of his time and compiled an encyclopedic work on his collection that was not completely published during his lifetime. *Musaeum Metallicum,* his masterpiece with fossil illustrations, was not published until 1648. This work was a landmark in paleontology and contains numerous illustrations of fossil invertebrates. A further advance is made by Colonna who, although a diluvialist being a man of his time, recognized the organic origin of fossils. In his work of 1616, he displayed fossil and extant specimens on the same plate, considering their resemblance and allowing comparative study (Colonna, 1616, plate liii).

In the eighteenth century, the posthumous work of the mathematician Hooke (1705) was another step forward in paleontology; it showed detailed figures of ammonite sutures. Hooke realized the similarities and differences that ammonoids and nautiloids share, and he displayed them on the same plate. A few years later, Lang (1708) published a monograph on fossils from the Alps, collected by him or his friends, where he showed a partial ammonite section revealing the internal chambers and septa, clear frontal views additional to the lateral ammonite view and an image of a nautiloid with a view of the siphuncle internal position. In the second part of the eighteenth century, Brander (1766) published a monograph on a collection from Hordwell Cliff (Hampshire, England) with a systematic arrangement of mollusks described in the text. This is a balanced combination of descriptions and figures to identify specimens and represented a milestone in the paleontological world, as it is also the first publication to describe a collection of fossils using the Linnaean system. With the use of microscopes, the interest in small organisms and fossil microstructure began. We owe to Soldani (1780) one of the first figures of a cross section of a bivalve shell. This is described as laminate, fibrosus, and opaque.

At the turn of the eighteenth to nineteenth century, the railway and mining industries started in earnest, and it is during this Industrial Revolution when multiple engineering projects took place that new fossil discoveries were revealed. They were published in works that were the basis of paleontology as we know it today. The necessity to describe the specimens and show them in illustrations became established. Illustrations are the main protagonists of these systematic works, which researchers used to identify their specimens. A better knowledge of the morphology of organisms developed thanks to comparison with extant specimens. At this time, paleontological works increased exponentially, not only in monographs but also in papers, with the establishment of scientific societies and their publications. Monographs were published on fossil groups or fossils from specific stratigraphic layers. Cuvier and Brongniart (1822) published a monograph on the French Chalk, with accurate descriptions accompanied by specimen illustrations, and they figured ammonites with different views and clear drawings of their suture lines. The Sowerbys, James and James De Carle, published one of the largest encyclopedic works on mollusks, *The Mineral Conchology of Great Britain* (1812–1846), which set a precedent regarding comprehensive works on shells. The specimen descriptions are complemented with illustrations, site locations, and stratigraphy of the fossils. The Sowerbys described and illustrated for the first time many British fossil invertebrates and making them types. Most of these are kept at the Natural History Museum (NHM), London. James Sowerby was one of the first to illustrate some nautiloid species from the Eocene London Clay Formation. After Montfort (1799) and Parkinson (1811), he was the third person to illustrate *Turrilites*, and his figure was one of the most complete specimens figured in hand-color (Sowerby, 1815) at a time when color printing was not available. He was probably also the first in Britain to illustrate *Pinna* in color, by hand. His son, James De Carle Sowerby, was the first person in Britain to illustrate what he believed to be '*Crioceratites emerici*,' but this was never published (Fig. 1A) (Sowerby, 1837). The NHM keeps this illustration with Sowerby's handwritten notes about other species that have been compared to '*C. emerici*' in the literature. We can also see, on the same illustration, a drawing of another species, *Hamites beanii*, that he compared to '*C. emerici*' (Fig. 1A, upper-left corner) and considered (Sowerby, 1840) to be synonymous with *C. emerici* (see Figs. 1B–1C). His illustration resembles that of *Crioceratites honoratii,* also pubished by Levéillé (1837), except in the cross-section outline. The work of the Sowerbys was a milestone in the study of shells (including mollusks and brachiopods). The seven volumes include 648 etched copper plates that are works of art. Some of the drawings notably enhance the identification of the specimens; for example, some show morphological elements such as umbo, hinge teeth and muscle scars in bivalves or lips, siphonal canal, umbiculus, columella, and sutures in gastropods. These drawings show an understanding of perspective with specimens mostly displayed in the same standardized position we know today.

Greater scientific specialization within paleontology took place during the latter half of the nineteenth century. Alberti (1864) wrote on the Triassic of Germany, recording species and stratigraphic layer. The specimen descriptions are complemented with numerous drawings of mollusks with different specimen views on lithographic plates at the end of the monograph. The bivalves are drawn showing the internal morphology of the shells, and most of the gastropods show the aperture as a morphological element for identification, apart from the final plate. One year later, Austin (1865) made reconstructions of some shells (Fig. 2). Comparison to other complete fossils and extant specimens allowed Austin to reconstruct how the bivalve had appeared. Another work at the end of the nineteenth century to highlight is that of Geyer (1893) on cephalopods from the Jurassic of Austria, which includes plates showing numerous cephalopod forms with detail of specimen profile, transverse sections, and sutures.

At the beginning of the twentieth century, many publications combined drawings with photographs so that both techniques complemented each other. The drawings, mainly made with pen-and-ink and pencil, were used for detailed morphological elements. Some of the publications that used both techniques for illustrations are *Palaeontographica Americana*, *Proceedings of*

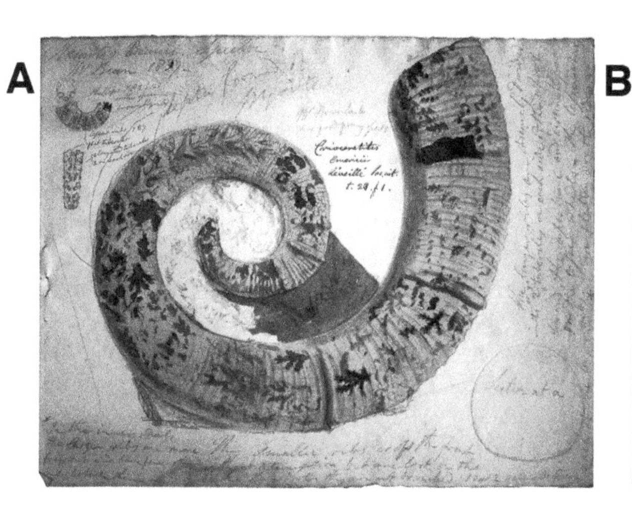

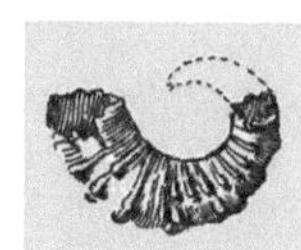

Figure 1. (A) Original colored drawing of '*Crioceratites emerici*' from Cretaceous of Speeton, England, never published (Sowerby, 1837). This has Sowerby's handwriting with notes and comparison to '*Hamites beanii*' in the upper-left corner. Source: Library and Archives, Natural History Museum, London. (B) *Crioceratites emerici* from Cretaceous of France published by Levéillé (1837). The image is rotated and flipped with isolated cross section to compare to A. (C) *Hamites beanii* published by Phillips (1829) (same site location as A). Image is rotated to compare to A (upper-left corner). B–C are images from the Biodiversity Heritage Library.

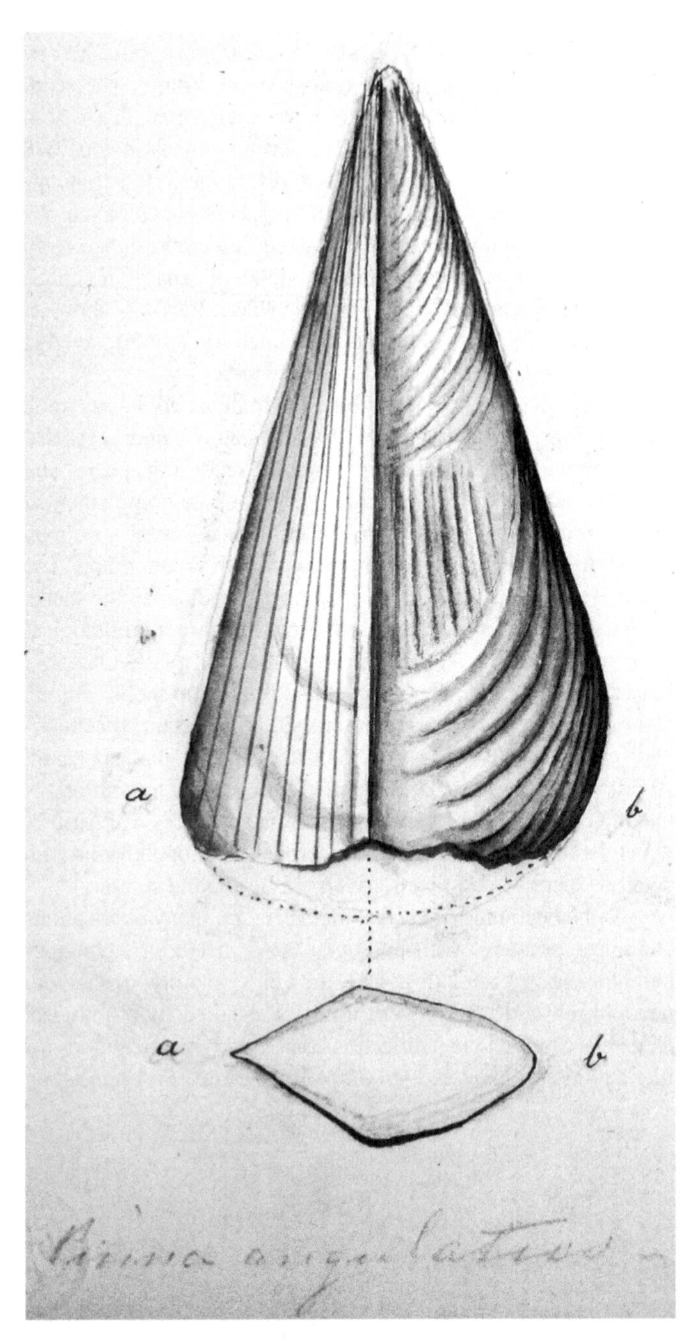

Figure 2. Original plate proof of *Pinna angulatus* from Carboniferous of Bristol, England, described and figured by Austin (1865, plate 1). Source: Library and Archives, Natural History Museum, London.

the Academy of Natural Sciences of Philadelphia, and *The Quarterly Journal of the Geological Society of London*. They published glossy black-and-white photographs. Probably some of the earliest photographs of fossil mollusks are those from 1913, with Brown (1913) showing mollusks from the Island of Antigua. It was also at the beginning of this century when reconstructions of fossils as living organisms were widely extended, while schematic figures with morphological elements were identified. Grabau (1922) published a reconstruction of a nautiloid orthocone and defined the morphological elements in a figure. However, he criticized his own illustration, being aware of the limitations of knowledge at the time.

The second half of the twentieth century produced comprehensive works on fossil revisions and multiple articles in specialized journals. Conventional photographs introduced a scale into the image. More recently, new discoveries and new technologies have allowed the opportunity to study very small specimens, such as ammonite plates that were used to close their aperture and which have been the focus of much controversy. SEM photographs of aptychi showing different layers and compared to modern nautilid jaws have recently been published (Kruta et al., 2014). This is an example of comparative anatomy with the use of twenty-first-century resources.

Recent papers on cephalopods studied under CT scan give clear images of the septa. The use of this resource allows us to see these and other internal morphological elements that were previously not seen and helps to improve our taxonomic knowledge. This opens a door to new research fields in addition to the taxonomy, evolution, and paleoecology of the organism. This technique could also be used in pyritized specimens for better identification and assessment of condition (Fig. 3).

ARTHROPODS

Fossil arthropods are probably the group that has suffered most in terms of "transformation" in paleoillustration. This can be seen, for instance, from the small size depicted of some insects or through the lack of awareness of some extinct fossil forms. This group is also the most abundant, which is one reason why it has been chosen, along with mollusks, to explain the evolution of paleoillustration. The first illustration of this group in the western world may be that of an almost complete fossil crab shown in a woodcut and named *Pagurus lapideus* by Gessner (1565). We have to wait until the seventeenth century to see more figures. Some of the examples came with Scilla (1670), who displayed a fossil chela from the Strait of Messina embedded in matrix, and Lhwyd (1699), who illustrated not only crustaceans but also some insects and an arachnid, possibly also cirripeds, and trilobites. By the eighteenth century, Bonanni (Buonanni) (1709) figured a decapod belonging to the *Musaeum Kicherianum* catalogue and Lang (1708), in his monograph on fossils, showed another almost complete decapod and also a cirriped, and a complete insect, which was probably a fly. Later, Mercati (1717) illustrated and described different species of decapods. It was during the eighteenth century when numerous specialized publications in Europe showed different kinds of arthropods, such as insects, arachnids, and crustaceans in copal or amber displayed on plates (e.g., Bloch, 1776). Walch (1768, 1769, 1771) illustrated different trilobites and cirripeds. A trilobite pygidium, illustrated with Knorr (1755) copper engravings, was believed to be a "bivalve pectuculum," and Walch (1769) called it "conchae trilobae." However, in 1771, Walch established that these organ-

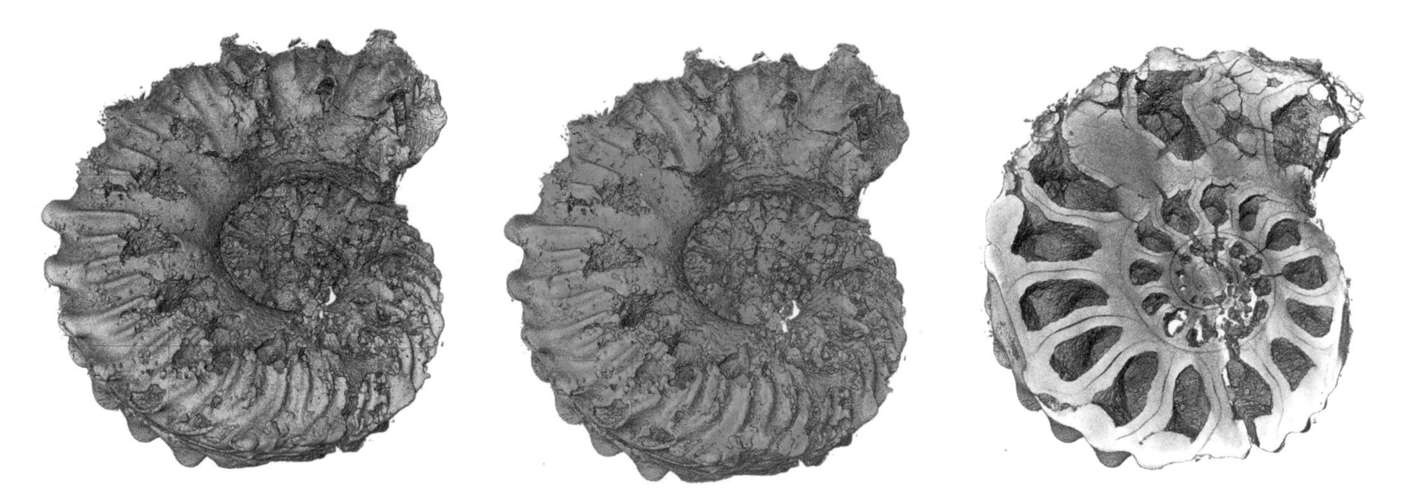

Figure 3. *Euhoplites bucklandi* Spath, 1925 from the Albian Gault at Folkestone in Kent. Digital manipulation of the 3-D data gives clear images of the internal structure of a pyritized specimen.

isms were most likely arthropods. In 1769, Walch also displayed numerous barnacles, some of which were attached to pectinids.

In the last quarter of the eighteenth century, one of the first engravings in color appeared. Burtin (1784) figured decapods and cirripeds with a varied paleofauna from near Brussels with fine brown and colored figures, which signified a landmark in paleoillustration. Faujas de Saint-Fond (1798–1799) recognized that crustacean claws are very common in the Cretaceous of Mount Saint Peter (Maastricht in the Netherlands) and illustrated various shapes of decapod chelipeds based on feeding requirements of the organism, for example a "bivalve eater" and a "plant- and meat-eater."

By the nineteenth century, Brocchi (1814) presented a clear figure, in an engraving plate, of a barnacle from the Tertiary of the Italian Subapennines. This is the beginning of taxonomic studies using illustrations to accompany descriptions. As they were considered mollusks (Cuvier, 1817), there are numerous figures of cirripeds in works on mollusks from the eighteenth and nineteenth centuries. Sowerby (1815) and Sowerby and Sowerby (1829) published some species of cirripeds in their *Mineral Conchology of Great Britain.* Other works on arthropods from the nineteenth century include those of Brongniart and Desmarest (1822), who published *Histoire Naturelle des Crustacés Fossiles*, which included trilobites. These accurate plates displayed ventral and dorsal positions and schematic drawings of the crustaceans with diagnostic characteristics. Mantell (1822, 1850) illustrated different species of crabs, shrimps, insects, and trilobites on engraving plates with high quality. With the nineteenth-century advances in the new discipline of "paleontology," there were more works on fossil groups. It was also the time when paleontologists began to compare fossils with recent specimens and to see morphological elements of the extant invertebrates in the extinct ones. DeKay (1825) presented a eurypterid for the first time; the illustration was enough to identify the taxonomic group, but it lacked detailed morphology. Unfortunately, DeKay identified the eurypterid as a crustacean. Later, Buckland (1837) displayed what could be a possible intestinal canal of a scorpion. The paleontologist Samuel Peckworth Woodward, a specialist in mollusks, figured detailed crustacean morphology with watercolor drawings that he never published (Smith, 1845) (Fig. 4).

A nineteenth-century paleontologist whose excellence should be highlighted is Joachim Barrande (1799–1883), who published what has been considered the largest encyclopedic work written by one person. It was written over more than 30 years (starting in 1846) and had more than 1000 lithographic plates. In it he devoted some volumes to trilobites and also crustaceans from the Lower Paleozoic of the Prague Basin. He described and designed the illustrations of numerous new arthropod species. His work on trilobites is a respected reference, and his name has been used for the Barrandian area and to differentiate three of the four periods to divide trilobite research within it. His illustrations range from trilobite ontogeny to detailed exoskeleton morphology and show different trilobite enrollment with longitudinal and transverse sections, and reconstructions of incomplete morphological elements. Although Barrande may not be an innovator in trilobite illustration, he was one the most prolific, and his illustrations are essential for identification of many species and marked a great advance in trilobite knowledge.

In the second half of the nineteenth century, Alberti (1864) was one of the first paleontologists to show detailed morphological illustrations of decapods. He illustrated three different species from the Triassic of the Alps. Heer (1865) studied and showed the paleoflora and paleofauna of Switzerland, including detailed plates of entomological specimens from the Jurassic Schambelen Member. Roemer (1876) published *Lethaea Geognostica* with numerous plates that included different crustaceans (malacostracans, branchiopods, maxilopods), eurypterids, phyllocarids, trilobites, myriapods, arachnids, and insects from the Paleozoic that were mainly from Europe. Scudder (Goldsborough, 1919, and references therein) was a prolific researcher of fossil arthropods,

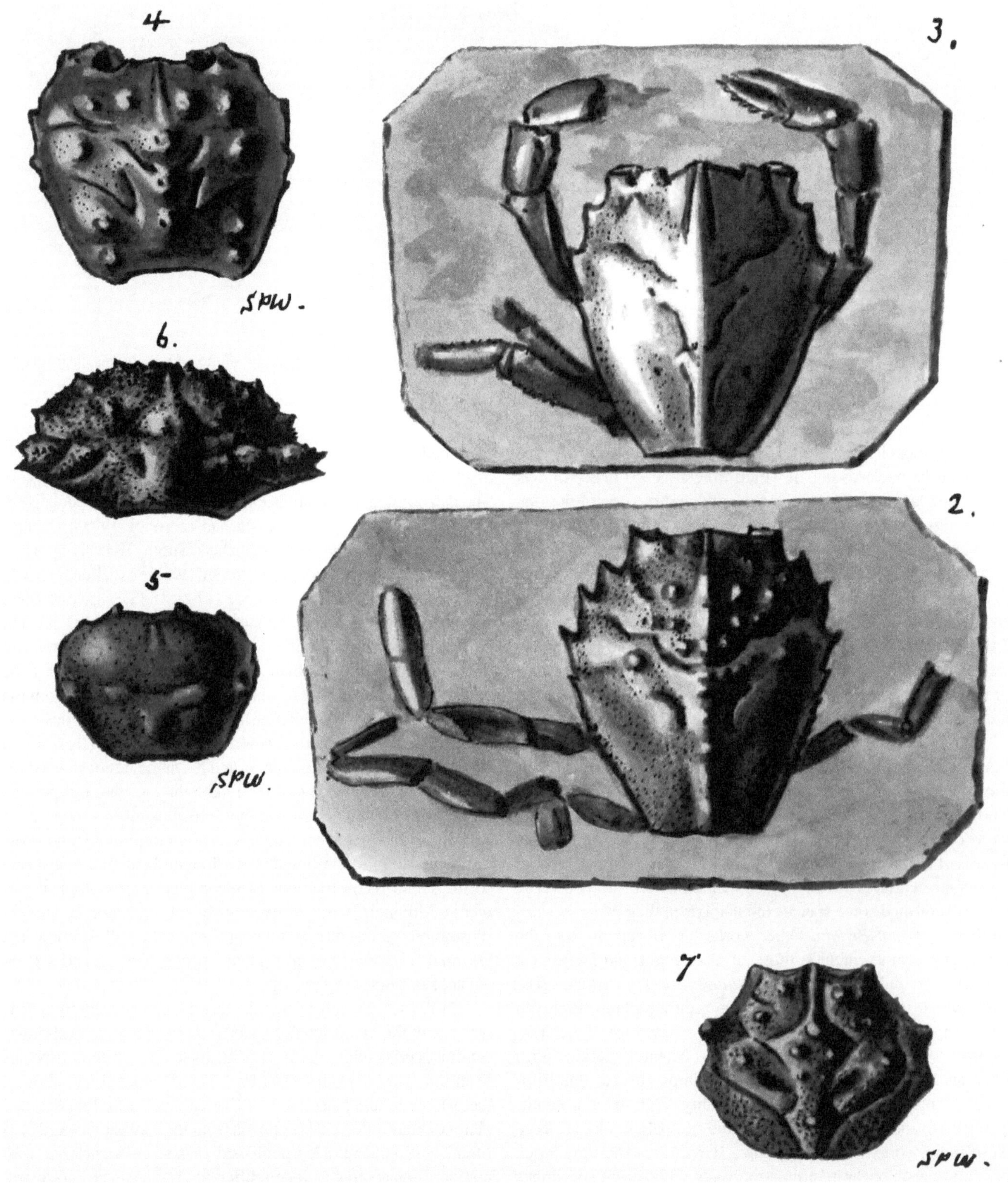

Figure 4. Decapods of different species: (2) *Corystes stokesii*, (3) *C. broderipii*, (4–5 and 7) *C.* sp., and (6) *Etyus martini* from the Gault Formation of Maidstone in Kent, England, drawn by S.P. Woodward in Mary Hone Smith's unpublished manuscript (1845). Source: Library and Archives, Natural History Museum, London.

mainly insects, that accompanied his fossil descriptions with accurate and schematic engraving plates. Reconstructions of fossil arthropods preserved in amber were published by Koch and Berendt (1854), but unfortunately these drawings did not show enough diagnostic detail (Selden and Penney, 2017). Taxonomic studies by stratigraphic unit continued into the twentieth century. Grabau and Shimer (1909–1910) published a two-volume monograph with numerous North American fossil drawings of specimens, with mollusks and arthropods including insects, for stratigraphic correlations.

It is with new discoveries in the twentieth century that paleontology advanced with the increased understanding of evolution. In 1909, the Burgess Shale was discovered, and with this Lagerstätte, new arthropod species appeared that have been published in numerous papers, starting with Walcott (1912), who produced some of the first photographs in paleontology of different arthropod taxa. More publications on new discoveries of Lagerstätten with arthropods have continued to the present day. Microscope technology using photography helped to depict diagnostic details, and a new complementary process became available for enhancing photographs in case contrast was needed: smoking with ammonium chloride. This involved the application of a thin, white coating that was widely used when the material studied occurred in a dark matrix. Publications with photographs of fossils used this method to present specimens, though with decreasing use over time due to museum policies for specimen safety. Some of the first photographs of fossil insects were also widely published at the beginning of the 1910s. Calvert (1913) displayed drawings made with camera lucida next to photographs of odonates on the same plate to complement them. At the end of the twentieth century, paleontologists re-examined the Burgess Shale fossils to reach new interpretations and noticed what were believed to be remains of different specimens belonging to different groups (scyphozoans in the case of the anomalocaridid mouth and decapod remains in the case of anomalocaridid appendages; see Collins, 1996). The conclusion was reached that they belonged to the same group, anomalocaridids, which was widely accepted as closely related to the ancestral or stem group arthropods. Accurate reconstructions of the anomalocaridids were published in the last decade of the twentieth century. It is also at the end of the twentieth century when the conventional photograph, with enhanced contrast and images in color, displayed morphological elements more clearly than the previous black-and-white photographs from the beginning of the century.

At the end of the twentieth century, the study of past forms of life is brought into closer relation with biological research, and this is reflected in illustrations that make comparisons among extinct and extant organisms. Shu et al. (1999) compared the bradoriid *Kunmingella* from the Chengjiang fossil Lagerstätte with extant phyllocarid crustaceans for a better reconstruction of the anatomy and to infer the "life attitude" that was illustrated. Recently, new techniques such as CT scanning and computational analysis have helped with specimen reconstruction as has been done with arthropods and arthropod-like taxa (Lamsdell et al., 2015). These new reconstructions differ from their predecessors in displaying detailed morphological elements. New findings with new technologies have improved the way fossil organisms are represented.

CONCLUSION

The history of paleoillustration, in this case shown through invertebrates, is intertwined with the state of knowledge and the available resources of the time. The first illustrations only tried to show shapes found in the earth that, with time, were later understood to be organic remains. Artistic depictions began with woodcuts that later were replaced by engravings. With advancing knowledge came more accurate illustrations with detailed morphology to complement specimen descriptions and standardization of the fossil representation. These milestones facilitated the exchange of knowledge among researchers. It is in the nineteenth century, with the birth of the science of paleontology, that fossil reconstructions begin, and these were common by the end of the century. It became essential to find out how a specimen had appeared in life and to compare it to extant taxa. Monographs were mainly replaced by journals with varied articles in the twentieth century. In these, drawings of morphological elements were the normal form of illustration with general view photographs of the specimen for taxonomic studies. The further development of microscopy and digital photography showed more detail of morphological elements. This proved very useful for showing the anatomy of insects and other small arthropods. At the end of the twentieth century, SEM photographs provided more detail on shell microstructure and specimen anatomy, and now in the twenty-first century, the treatment of the digital photographs and CT scans opens a door to new research methods and more accurate reconstructions. This is a new era for paleontology and its illustration.

ACKNOWLEDGMENTS

I thank my colleagues at the Natural History Museum, London: Lu Allington-Jones, Andrea Hart, Hellen Pethers, Laura Brown, Paul Martyn Cooper, Brett Clark, David Notton, Brian Rosen, and Svetalana Nikolaeva; also, Mikel A. López Horgue (Universidad del País Vasco, Spain) and Kevin Page (University of Plymouth, UK) as experts on ammonites and the reviewers who have improved this text.

REFERENCES CITED

Alberti, F., 1864, Ueberblick über die Trias, mit Berücksichtigung ihres Yorkommeiis in den Alpen: Stuttgart, Buchhandlung, 353 p., 7 plates.

Austin, T., 1865, The Millstone Grit, Its Fossils and the Relation It Bears to Other Groups of Rocks, More Particularly as It Occurs in the Bristol District, and South-West of England Generally: London, H. Baillière, 58 p., 5 plates.

Bloch, M.E., 1776, Beytrag zur Naturgeschichte des Kopals. Beschäftigungen der Berlinischen Gesellschaft Naturforschender Freunde: Berlin, Bey Joachim Pauli, v. 2, p. 91–196, plates 3–5.

Bonanni, P., 1709, Musaeum kircherianum, sive Musaeum a P. Athanasio Kirchero in collegio romano Societatis Jesu jampridem incoeptum, nuper restitutum, auctum, descriptum et iconibus illustratum: Roma, Plachi Caelaturam Profitentis, 522 p., https://doi.org/10.5962/bhl.title.120244.

Brander, G., 1766, Fossilia Hantoniensia Collecta, et in Musaeo Britannico Deposita: London, 43 p., 9 plates.

Brocchi, G., 1814, Conchiologia fossile subappennina: Con osservazioni geologiche sugli Appennini e sul suolo adiacente: Milan, v. 1 (240 p.), v. 2 (241–712 p., plates 1–16).

Brongniart, A., and Desmarest, A.G., 1822, Histoire naturelle des crustacés fossiles, sous les rapports zoologiques et géologiques. Savoir: Les Trilobites: Paris, F.G. Levrault, 154 p., 11 plates.

Brown, A.P., 1913, Notes on the geology of the Island of Antigua: Proceedings of the Academy of Natural Sciences of Philadelphia, v. 65, p. 584–616, plates 18–20.

Buckland, W., 1837, The Bridgewater Treatises on the Power, Wisdom and Goodness of God as Manifested in the Creation. Treatise VI. Geology and Mineralogy Considered with Reference to Natural Theology, Volume 2: Philadelphia, Carey, Lea and Blanchard, 131 p.

Burtin, F.X., 1784, Oryctographie de Bruxelles ou description des fossiles tant naturels qu'accidentels découverts jusqu'à ce jour dans les environs de cette ville: Le Maire, Brussels, 152 p., 32 plates.

Calvert, P.P., 1913, The fossil odonate Phenacolestes, with a discussion on the venation of the legion Podagrion Selys: Proceedings of the Academy of Natural Sciences of Philadelphia, v. 65, p. 225–272, plate 14.

Collins, D., 1996, The "evolution" of *Anomalocaris* and its classification in the arthropod class Dinocarida (nov.) and order Radiodonta (nov.): Journal of Paleontology, v. 70, p. 280–293, https://doi.org/10.1017/S0022336000023362.

Colonna, F., 1616, Fabii Columnae Lyncei Pvrpura. Hoc est de Purpura ab Animali testaceo fusa, de hoc ipso Animali, alijsq[ue] rarioribus testaceis quibusdam. Ad Ill.mum et Reuer.mum Principem ac Dominum Iacobvm Sannesivm S.R.E. Cardinalem amplissimvm Cum Iconibus ex aere ad viuum representantis, Elencho rerum et Indice: Rome, Apud Jacobum Mascardum, xlii + 73 p.

Cuvier, G., 1817, Le règne animal distribué d'après son organisation: Pour servir de lase a l'histoire naturelle des animaux et d'introduction a l'anatomie comparée, Volume 2. Content: Les reptiles, les poisons, les mollusques et les annelids: Paris, Déterville, 532 p.

Cuvier, G., and Brongniart, A., 1822, Description géologique des environs de Paris: Amsterdam, G. Dufour et E. d'Ocagne, 428 p., 11 plates.

DeKay, J. E., 1825, Observations on a fossil Crustaceous animal of the order Branchiopoda: Annals of the Lyceum of Natural History, v. 1, p. 375–383, plate 29.

Encelius, C., 1551, De Re Metallica, hoc est, de origene, varietate, et natura Corporum Metallicorum, Lapidum, Gemmarum, atq. aliarum, quae ex fodinis eruuntur, rerum, ad Medicinae usam deseruienticum, libri III. C: Francofurti, Egenolph, 271 p.

Faujas de Saint-Fond, B. [1798–1799], Histoire naturelle de la Montagne de Saint-Pierre de Maestricht: Paris, H.J. Jansen, 340 p., 52 plates.

Gessner, C., 1565, De Rerum Fossilivm, Lapidvm et Gemmarvm maximè, figuris & similitudinibus Liber: Tiguri, Non solùm Medicis, sed omnibus rerum Naturae ac Philologiae studiosis, vtilis & iucundus futurus, 338 p.

Geyer, G., 1893, Die mittelliasische Cephalopoden-Fauna des Hinter-Schafberges in Oberösterreich: Wien, Hölder, 76 p., 9 plates.

Goldsborough, A., 1919, Samuel Hubbard Scudder 1837–1911: National Academy of Sciences Biographical Memoirs, v. 17, p. 81–104.

Grabau, A.W., 1922, Ordovician fossils of north China: Paleontologia Sinica, Series B, v. 1, p. 1–127.

Grabau, A.W., and Shimer, H.W., 1909–1910, North American Index Fossils: Cambridge, Massachusetts Institute of Technology Press, v. 1, 853 p.; v. 2, 909 p.

Heer, O., 1865, Die Urwelt der Schweiz: Zurich, Friedrich Schulthess, 622 p., 11 plates.

Hooke, R., 1705, The Posthumous Works of Robert Hooke … Containing His Cutlerian Lectures, and Other Discourses, Read at the Meetings of the Illustrious Royal Society … Illustrated with Sculptures. To These Discourses Is Prefixt the Author's Life, Giving an Account of His Studies and Employments, with an Enumeration of the Many Experiments, Instruments, Contrivances and Inventions, by Him Made and Produc'd as Curator of Experiments to the Royal Society: London, Sam. Smith and Benj. Walford (Printers to the Royal Society), 28 p., p. 1–209, p. 279–572, 13 plates.

Knorr, G.W., 1755, Sammlung von Merckwürdigkeiten der Natur und Alterthümer des Erdbodens, welche petrificirte Cörper enthält aufgewiesen und beschrieben: Nuremberg, Andreas Bieling, 36 p.

Koch, C.L., and Berendt, G.C., 1854, Die im Bernstein befindlichen Crustaceen, Myriapoden, Arachniden und Apteren der Vorwelt, *in* Berendt, G.C., ed., Die im Bernstein befindlichen organischen Reste der Vorwelt, Volumen 1 (part II): Berlin, Nicholaischen Buchhandlung, 125 p., 8 plates.

Kruta, I., Landman, N.H., and Cochran, J.K., 2014, A new approach for the determination of ammonite and nautilid habitats: PLoS ONE, v. 9, e87479, https://doi.org/10.1371/journal.pone.0087479.

Lamsdell, J.C., Briggs, D.E.G., Liu, H., Witzke, B.J., and McKay, R.M., 2015, The oldest described eurypterid: A giant Middle Ordovician (Darriwilian) megalograptid from the Winneshiek Lagerstätte of Iowa: BMC Evolutionary Biology, v. 15, p. 169, https://doi.org/10.1186/s12862-015-0443-9.

Lang, K.N, 1708, Caroli Nicolai Langii Lucernens. Helvet. Phil. & Medic. Acad. Caes. Leopold. Nat. Curios. German. & Physio.-Crit. Senens. Historia lapidum figuratorum Helvetiae: Ejusque viciniae, in quâ non solùm enarrantur omnia eorum genera, species et vires aeneisque tabulis repraesentantur. Sed insuper adducuntur eorum loca nativa, in quibus reperiri solent, ut cuilibet facile sit eos colligere, modo adducta loca adire libeat: Venetis, Sumptibus Autoris, 165 p., 52 plates.

Lehmann, U., 1981, The Ammonites: Their Life and Their World: Cambridge, Massachusetts, Cambridge University Press, 246 p.

Levéillé, C., 1837, Description de quelques nouvelles coquilles fossiles du Département des Basses-Alpes: Mémoires de la Société Géologique de France, v. 12, p. 313–315, plates 22–23.

Lhwyd, E., 1699, Eduardi Luidii apud oxonienses climeliarchae ashmoleani; Lithophylacii Britannici Ichnographia. Siue, Lapidum aliorumque fossilium Britannicorum singulari figura insignium; quotquot hactenus vel ipse invenit vel ab amicis accepit, distributio classica, scrinii sui lapidarii repertorium cum locis singulorum natalibus exhibens: Londini, Ex officina M.C., 139 p., 23 plates.

Mantell, G., 1822, The Fossils of the South Downs, or, Illustrations of the Geology of Sussex: London, L. Relfe, 327 p., 42 plates.

Mantell G., 1850, A Pictorial Atlas of Fossil Remains, Consisting of Coloured Illustrations Selected from Parkinson's "Organic remains of a former world" and Artis's "Antediluvian phytology" with Descriptions: London, H. G. Bohn, 207 p., 74 plates.

Mercati, M., 1717, Michaelis Mercati Samminiatensis Metallotheca. Opus posthumum, auctoritate, & munificentia Clementis undecemi Pontificis Maximi e` tenebris in lucem eductum Opera autem, & studio Joannis Mariae Lancisii; archiatri pontificii illustratum. Cui accessit appendix cum XIX. Recens inventis iconibus: Mariam Salvioni typographum Vaticanum in Archigymnasio sapientiae, 64 p. + 378 p. + 53 p.

Montfort, D., 1799, Mémoire sur une nouvelle espèce de corne-d'ammon: Journal de physique, de chimie, d'histoire naturelle et des arts, v. 49, p. 141–147.

Parkinson, J., 1811, Organic Remains of a Former World Examination of the Mineralized Remains of the Vegetables and Animals of the Antediluvian World; Generally Termed Extraneous Fossils, Volume 3, The Fossil Starfish, Echini, Shells, Insects, Amphibia, Mammalia, & C.: London, Sherwood, Neely, and Jones, Paternoster-Row, 479 p., 22 plates.

Phillips, J., 1829, Illustrations of the Geology of Yorkshire; or, a Description of the Strata and Organic Remains of the Yorkshire Coast Accompanied by a Geological Map, Sections, and Plates of the Fossil Plants and Animals (Part 1): York, England, Th. Wilson and Sons, 185 p., 14 plates.

Roemer, F., 1876, Lethaea geognostica, oder Beschreibung und Abbildung der für die Gebirgs-Formationen bezeichnendsten Versteinerungen. Herausgegeben von einer Vereinigung von Paläeontologen. I Theil. Lethaea palaeozoica. Atlas Mit zweiundsechzig Tafeln: Stuttgart, E. Scweizerbart'sche Verlagshandlung, 62 plates.

Scilla, A., 1670, La vana speculazione disingannata dal senso: Lettera risponsiua circa i corpi marini, che petrificati si trouano in varij luoghi terrestre. Di Agostini Scilla pittore accedemico della fucina detto lo scolorito. Dedicata all'illustrissimo signore, il signor D. Carlo Gregori Marchese di Poggio Gregorio, cavaliero della stella: Napoli, Appresso Andrea Colicchia, 168 p., 29 plates.

Selden, P.A., and Penney, D., 2017, Imaging techniques in the study of fossil spiders: Earth-Science Reviews, v. 166, p. 111–131, https://doi.org/10.1016/j.earscirev.2017.01.007.

Shu, D., Vannier, J., Luo, H., Chen, L., Zhang, X., and Hu, S., 1999, Anatomy and lifestyle of *Kunmingella* (Arthropoda, Bradoriida) from the Chengjiang fossil Lagerstätte (lower Cambrian; Southwest China): Lethaia, v. 32, p. 279–298, https://doi.org/10.1111/j.1502-3931.1999.tb00547.x.

Smith, M.H., 1845, Catalogue of Fossil Organic Remains in the Cabinet of Mrs. M.H. Smith. [Manuscript list by S.P. Woodward, with water-colour drawings of some of the specimens by him, G.A. Mantell, W.H. Bensted, J. Delves, & T. Merritt.]: Tunbridge Wells, Natural History Museum, London, 115 p.

Soldani, A., 1780, Saggio orittografico ovvero osservazioni sopra le terre nautilitiche ed ammonitiche della Toscana. Con appendice o indice latino ragionato de' piccoli testacei, e d'altri fossili d'origin marina per schiarimento dell'opera: Siena, Nella stamperia di V. Pazzini Carli, 146 p., 25 plates.

Sowerby, J., 1815, The Mineral Conchology of Great Britain; or, Coloured Figures and Descriptions of Those Remains of Testaceous Animals or Shells, Which Have Been Preserved at Various Times and Depths in the Earth, Volume 1: London, Meredith, 234 p., 102 plates.

Sowerby, J., and Sowerby, J.D.C., 1829, The Mineral Conchology of Great Britain; or, Coloured Figures and Descriptions of Those Remains of Testaceous Animals or Shells, Which Have Been Preserved at Various Times and Depths in the Ear, Volume 6: London, R. Taylor, 230 p.

Sowerby, J.C., 1837, [Notes and drawings of ammonites from Speeton], Unpublished manuscript C111 The Sowerby Collection (1739–1985) at the Natural History Museum, London.

Sowerby, J.C., 1840, Letter from Mr. James de Carle Sowerby to the Secretary, on the Genus *Crioceratites* and on *Scaphites Gigas*: Transactions of the Geological Society of London, Series 2, v. 5, p. 409–411, https://doi.org/10.1144/transgslb.5.2.409.

Walch, J.E.I., 1768, Die Naturgeschichte der Versteinerungen zur Erläuterung der Knorrischen Sammlung von Merckwürdigkeiten der Natur, Volume 1: Nuremberg, P.J. Felssecker, 184 p., 81 plates.

Walch, J.E.I., 1769, Die Naturgeschichte der Versteinerungen zur Erläuterung der Knorrischen Sammlung von Merckwürdigkeiten der Natur, Volume 2: Nuremberg, P.J. Felssecker, 303 p., 51 plates.

Walch, J.E.I., 1771, Die Naturgeschichte der Versteinerungen zur Erläuterung der Knorrischen Sammlung von Merckwürdigkeiten der Natur, Volume 3: Nuremberg, P.J. Felssecker, 235 p., 84 plates.

Walcott, C.D., 1912, Cambrian Geology and Paleontology. II. No. 6—Middle Cambrian Branchiopoda, Malacostraca, Trilobita, and Merostomata: Smithsonian Miscellaneous Collections, v. 57, p. 146–228.

Manuscript Accepted by the Society 13 January 2021
Manuscript Published Online 11 June 2021

The Geological Society of America
Memoir 218

Development of paleontological art in Poland

Piotr Krzywiec*
Institute of Geological Sciences, Polish Academy of Sciences, 51/55 Twarda Street, 00-818 Warsaw, Poland

Aleksandra Arndt*
Adam Mickiewicz University in Poznań, Faculty of Polish and Classical Studies, Institute of Classical Philology, Aleksander Fredro Street, 61-701 Poznań, Poland

ABSTRACT

The first illustrations of geo-objects—different crystals of salt—from Poland were included by U. Aldrovandi in his *Musaeum Metallicum* (1648). The first publications containing paleontological sketches of fossil remains of animals and plants appeared in the early eighteenth century. G.A. Helwing, in his *Lithographia Angerburgica* (1717) and *Lithographiae Angerburgicae Pars II* (1720), included drawings of fossils of various ages from the Peri-Baltic area. G.A. Volkmann's *Silesia Subterranea* (1720) was extensively illustrated by elaborate sketches of fossils including Carboniferous plants from the Lower Silesia region. In 1764, J.-É. Guettard published an important paper on the geology of Poland that contained detailed illustrations of fossils from various parts of the country. S. Staszic, in his two seminal books published in 1805 and 1815, provided detailed illustrations of animal remains, mainly bones of large, extinct mammals. This "pioneering era" of development of paleontological art came to an end with publications by two geologists that laid the foundations of modern paleontology in Poland: *Polens Paläontologie* by G.G. Pusch (1836) and *Paleontologia Polska* (1846) by L. Zejszner. In less than 150 years, paleontological art evolved from simple illustrations of "curious objects" from the subsurface to scientific drawings that marked the birth of modern paleontology.

FOSSIL ORGANIC REMAINS AS NATURAL "CURIOSITIES FROM THE SUBSURFACE"

Subsurface objects attracting people's attention included minerals, rocks, and fossils. The progressive understanding of natural processes operating at depth and on the Earth's surface, which developed from analysis of these subsurface objects, eventually led to the birth and quick development of the modern Earth sciences: geology, mineralogy, and paleontology. The first book that contained illustration of geo-objects from Poland was published by Italian naturalist Ulisse Aldrovandi, who, in his *Musaeum Metallicum*, showed different crystals of salt, most probably from the world-known salt mines in Wieliczka near Kraków (Aldrovandi, 1648).

The first books containing illustrations of fossil remains of animals and plants were published by Georg Andreas Helwing (1666–1748), a Lutheran pastor in Węgorzewo in northeastern Poland, which was then Angerburg in the Duchy of Prussia, fief of the Crown of Poland. Helwing's main field of interest was botany, but he was also a keen collector of minerals and fossils.

*E-mails: piotr.krzywiec@twarda.pan.pl; a_arndt@amu.edu.pl.

Krzywiec, P., and Arndt, A., 2022, Development of paleontological art in Poland, *in* Clary, R.M., Rosenberg, G.D., and Evans, D.C., eds., The Evolution of Paleontological Art: Geological Society of America Memoir 218, p. 91–100, https://doi.org/10.1130/2021.1218(11).

Helwing published two books, *Lithographia Angerburgica* and *Lithographiae Angerburgicae Pars II* (Helwing, 1717, 1720). His first book was the very first one published with paleontological illustrations from the territory of Poland. It is divided into seven chapters, with the first two chapters containing general information about Węgorzewo and its surroundings and various types of rocks and soils (i.e., "earths" [*De Terris*]); these are followed by chapters devoted to various "stones" (*De lapidibus*). Helwing's classification of these objects depended on their external character and visual characteristics: he distinguished "Shapeless stones" (*lapides certa figura carentes*; chapter III), "Translucent stones" (*lapides Diaphani*; chapter IV), and "Figured stones" (*lapides certa figura praedati*; chapter V). Chapter VI is devoted to "Stones representing natural objects" (*De Lapidus res naturales repraesentantibus*) and is further subdivided into three parts on the "Plant Kingdom" (*Ex Regno Vegetabili*), "Animal Kingdom" (*Ex Regno Animali*), and "Mineral Kingdom" (*Ex Regno Minerali*). Part 1 consists of four sections: "Petrified fruits and seeds" (*Lapideos fructus & Semina exhibit*), "Plants, fungi, leaves and roots" (*Plantas, Fungos, folia, ligna & radices offert*), "Carbonate incrustations" (*osteocollae generationem examinat*), and finally "Fossil corals" (*corallia fossilia recenset*).

Helwing collected his specimens in the Warmia–Mazury region, usually in close vicinity to Węgorzewo, e.g., in Okartowo (Eckersberg) or in Kal (Kehlen). This region, located above the southwestern edge of the East European Craton, is covered by mostly flat-lying, Phanerozoic sedimentary succession. It is devoid of any large outcrops, and in many instances collected fossils could have included both locally derived Cretaceous or Cenozoic fossils or much older fossils transported from Scandinavia by glaciers. This was, of course, not known to Helwing, but he was aware that objects he had been collecting could be classified as fossil organic remains, as is clearly stated in the section on fossil corals (Helwing, 1717, p. 47–54). Figure 1 shows two lithographed plates that illustrate corals, either their fragments called astroites ("starstones") or fully preserved specimens. They were produced with a high level of detail and are comparable to illustrations from other much better known contemporary works by Lhuyd (1699), Scheuchzer (1702), Lang (1708), and Mylius (1709) that are all cited by Helwing.

Helwing's books, despite their content and high-quality illustrations, have been somewhat forgotten. The opposite was true for Helwing's contemporary Georg Anton Volkmann (1663–1721) of the Silesia region (presently SW Poland). Volkmann

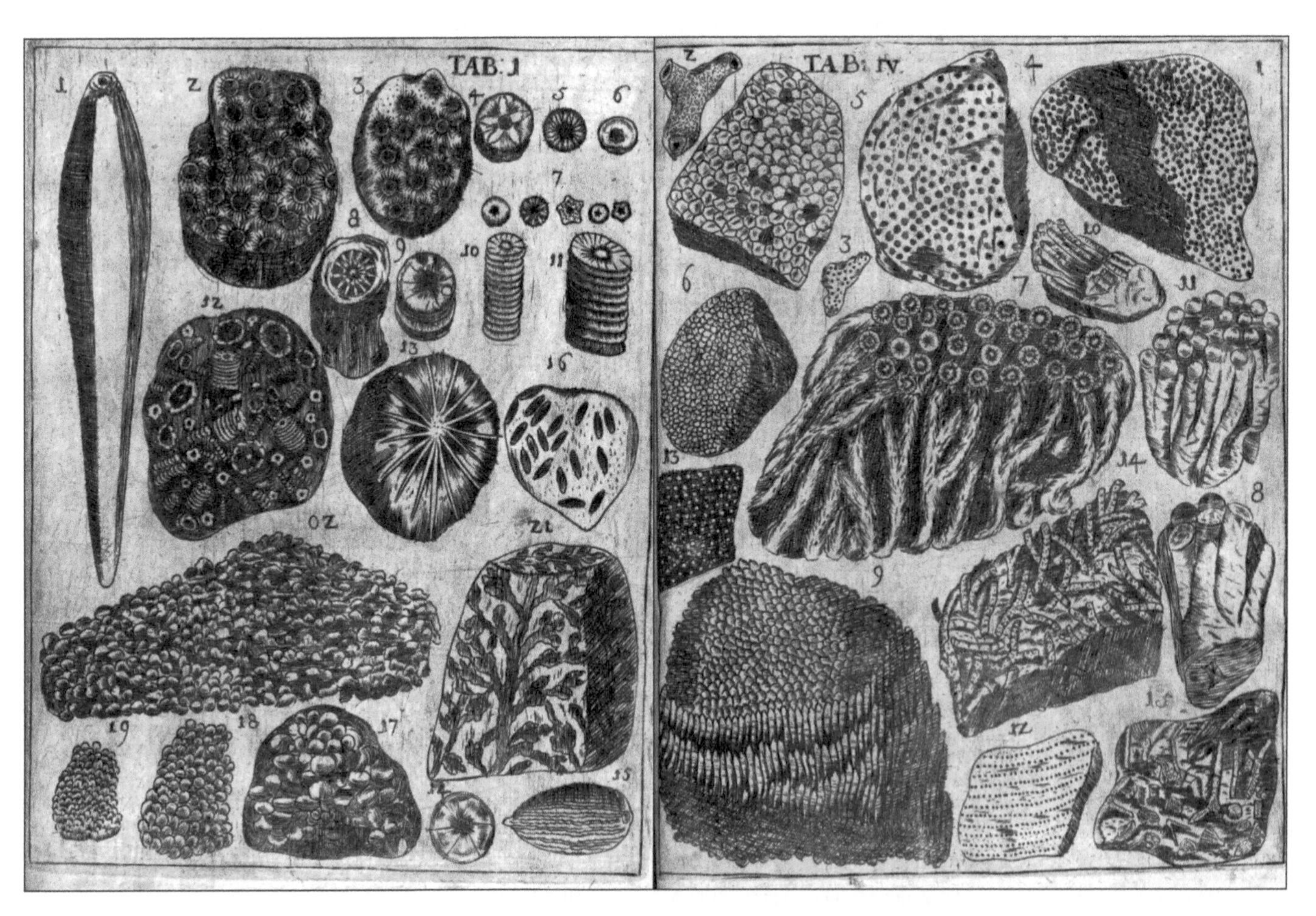

Figure 1. Plates from Helwing (1717) show illustrations of fossil corals. (Piotr Krzywiec private collection.)

studied in Padua, Italy, and upon returning home embarked on studies of Silesia flora and fauna and then fossils, minerals, and rock (Rzymełka, 1988; Syniawa, 2006). His *Silesia Subterranea* (1720) was widely read and remained the key source of information about the Silesia region for more than a century (e.g., Parkinson, 1808). The first part of this book, richly illustrated by numerous copperplates, is partly devoted to petrified organic remains of plants and animals. Silesia has been known for centuries for its rich, Carboniferous coal deposits that contain various fossil plants. Some of those thick coal seams were accessible to Volkmann either at the surface or in the shallow subsurface, in particular in the Wałbrzych (Waldenburg) area, where coal mining began in the fifteenth century. Volkmann identified numerous locations where he retrieved specimens used in his book such as Biały Kamień (Weisstein), Boguszów (Gottesberg), Kamienna Góra (Landeshut), Męcinka (Hermannsdorf), and Stary Zdrój (Altwasser). His illustrations are very detailed (Fig. 2) and are precisely described in the accompanying text. His descriptions often include comparative analysis of fossils with recent plants such as fern, pines, willows, and reeds. For example, in Figure 2, Volkmann's specimen no. 1 was compared to *Myrrhis silvestris*, specimen no. 2 to *Filix querna*, specimen no. 3 to *Tithymalus cyparissias*, specimen no. 4 to *Apium montanum*, specimen no. 5 *to Filicula petraea*, and specimen no. 6 to *Pinus silvestris*. Volkmann clearly understood that objects he was describing represented petrified plant remains from the "old times." To honor Volkmann's achievements, subsequent researchers named two Carboniferous plant remains after him: *Lepidodendron volkmannianum* and *Volkmannia* (e.g., Hooker, 1854; Pacyna, 2012).

TRANSITIONAL PERIOD: FROM "CURIOSITIES" TO SCIENTIFIC SPECIMENS

Paleontology was established in the eighteenth century, and it fully developed in the nineteenth century (Adams, 1938; Rudwick, 2014). One of the important naturalists who contributed to its development during the early days was Jean-Étienne Guettard (1715–1786) (Geikie, 1905). In 1760, he arrived in Poland and spent two years as a doctor for the French ambassador (Daszkiewicz and Tarkowski, 2009). Upon his return to France, Guettard published a treatise on various aspects of the geology of Poland (Guettard, 1764a, 1764b) based on his own observations and information derived from other sources, mainly from works by Gabriel Rzączyński (1721, 1742). He also relied

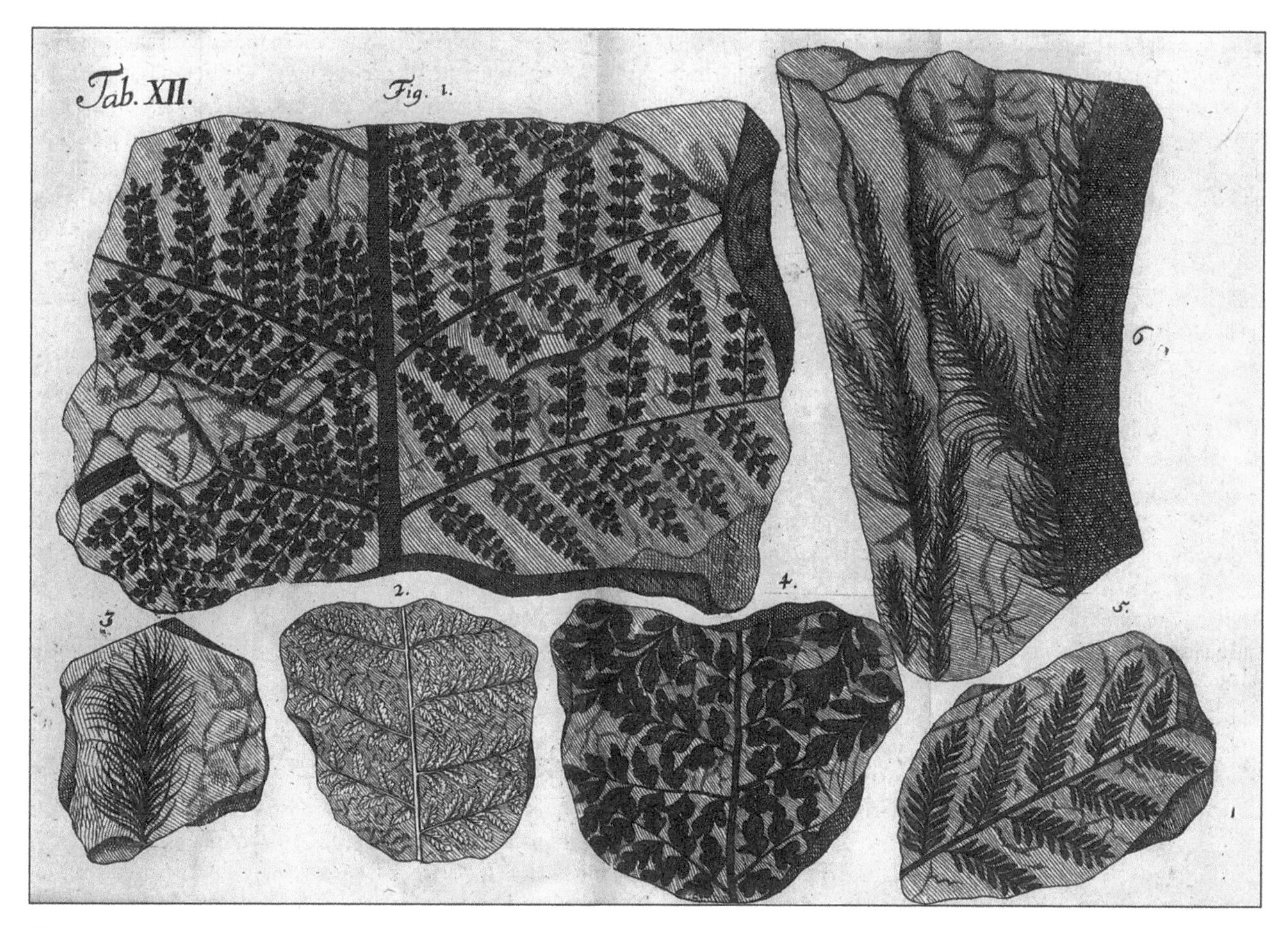

Figure 2. Plates from Volkmann (1720) show Carboniferous fossil plants from the Lower Silesia region, SW Poland. (Piotr Krzywiec private collection.)

on personal contacts with scholars residing in different parts of Poland who supplied him with specimens of rocks, minerals, and fossils. Guettard's treatise (1764b) contains six aquatint plates with elaborate illustrations of various fossils and rock specimens (Fig. 3; cf. Daszkiewicz and Tarkowski, 2009). Plates I and II (shown in Figs. 3A–3B) contain drawings of shells found in the vicinity of Kraków, Puławy, and Kazimierz (southern Poland) and Lviv (currently located in western Ukraine); plates III and IV (Figs. 3C–3D) contain, apart from shells, shark teeth, brachiopods, ammonites, urchins, corals, stromatoporoids, and rock specimens such as jasper and limestone, which were collected in various locations including the Kraków region, the Carpathians, and eastern parts of the Kingdom of Poland and Grand Duchy of Lithuania (vicinity of Nieśwież, currently located in Belarus). Guettard correctly recognized the true nature of fossil remains of marine organisms and associated them with ancient seas that must have existed on the territories he had visited or had been informed about (Daszkiewicz and Tarkowski, 2009). Clearly, they were not treated as "curiosities" anymore; Guettard was looking at these fossils as specimens that could be used, e.g., for geological cartography. In his treatise, he described four zones (belts) of different lithological characteristics in Poland: sandy belt (*bande sableuse*) in the north, marly belt (*bande marneuse*) in the central part, and salty belt (*bande saline*) and schist ore belt (*bande schisteuse ou métalique*) in the south. He associated most of the fossils described in his treatises with the marly belt, within which numerous outcrops of fossil-bearing Jurassic, Cretaceous, and Miocene rocks are located (Daszkiewicz and Tarkowski, 2009). Guettard's descriptions of fossils are similar to those given by Helwing and Volkmann; he focused on their external shapes and made some comparisons with living marine organisms such as scallops and oysters. Without a doubt, however, Guettard's publications define the breaking point in modern geological and paleontological studies in Poland, and all of the outcrops that provided specimens for him were studied in much more detail in future decades and centuries.

The late eighteenth century and early nineteenth century witnessed increased interest in the geology of the territory of Poland and its surroundings. These were very turbulent times: Poland, in 1772–1795, was partitioned between Russia, Prussia, and Austria, and eventually disappeared from the map as an independent country; it regained its independence in 1918. During those times, an increasing number of naturalists/geologists worked in Poland and published their results (e.g., Carosi, 1781–1784; Ferber, 1804; Hacquet, 1796). Among them, the prime position is held by Stanisław Staszic (1755–1826), Polish priest, philosopher, statesman, geologist, scholar, poet and writer, and leader of the Polish Enlightenment (Wójcik, 2008).

Staszic graduated from a Jesuit school in Poznań, and studied in France and Germany under the supervision of, among others, Georges-Louis Leclerc, Comte de Buffon. Staszic advocated the industrial development of Poland as a vehicle for regaining the country's independence; he organized the Mining Academy in Kielce and served as president of the Society of Friends of Sciences (*Towarzystwo Przyjaciół Nauk*). His first geological publication, "O Ziemiorodztwie gór dawney Sarmacyi a późniey Polski" ("On the Earth-formation of the Ancient Sarmatia, Later Poland," Staszic, 1805), was compiled with several other essays in Staszic's major geological book, *O Ziemiorodztwie Karpatów i innych gor i rownin Polski* (*On the Earth-formation of the Carpathians and Other Mountains and Lowlands of Poland*; Staszic, 1815). This book was accompanied by four sheets of an impressive geological map entitled *Carta geologica totius Poloniae, Moldaviae, Transylvaniae, et partis Hungariae, et Valachiae*, which illustrated the surface geology of a vast area between the Baltic Sea and the Black Sea (Grigelis et al., 2011; Krzywiec, 2016, 2018; Wołkowicz and Wołkowicz, 2014). Staszic's work also included two aquatint plates with illustrations of fossils (Fig. 4).

Unlike his predecessors Helwing, Volkmann, and Guettard, Staszic focused his interest in paleontological illustrations on the bones of large mammals. He referred to these animal remains as remnants of "marine monsters." This is very understandable considering the great impact that the contemporary works of Georges Cuvier (1769–1832) had on the development of paleontology. Cuvier, whose great achievements included his contribution toward the establishment of the scientific discipline of stratigraphy (Cuvier and Brongniart, 1811), was also a proponent of comparative anatomy; he studied fossil bones of large mammals in Europe and in the United States, and this allowed him to formulate the theory of large, extinct quadrupeds such as mammoths and mastodons (Cuvier, 1812), which was met with great public interest and provided stimulus for the rapid advancement of paleontology in the first half of the nineteenth century. Staszic was aware of those achievements and compared one of the bones excavated in Czersk, near Warsaw, to bones of Cuvier's "*l'animal de l'Ohio*," i.e., *Mammut americanum* (Staszic, 1815, p. 9). Staszic, in his description of a large fossil skull excavated in Kamieńczyk nad Bugiem, directly referenced the principles of Cuvier's comparative anatomy (Staszic, 1815, p. 369) and concluded that the skull must have belonged to *Rhinoceros unicornis*. Analyzing a fossil tooth, he proposed that this animal, which he called the "huge beast from the other world," was not carnivorous and must have fed on plants despite its large size. Apart from illustrations of various bones, Staszic also included three illustrations of fossil Carboniferous plants he retrieved from the coal mines in the Upper Silesia region in Dąbrowa Górnicza and Jaworzyna (Fig. 4). He concluded that this was a fossil fern and compared it to a similar specimen described by Scheuchzer (1723).

BEGINNINGS OF MODERN PALEONTOLOGY

The establishment of modern paleontology in Poland is related to the life and work of two prominent geologists: Georg Gottlieb Pusch (1790–1846) and Ludwik Zejszner (1805–1871).

Georg Gottlieb Pusch was Abraham Gottlob Werner's student in the Mining Academy in Freiberg (Kleczkowski, 1970, 1972, 1974). Following an invitation from Stanisław Staszic, he

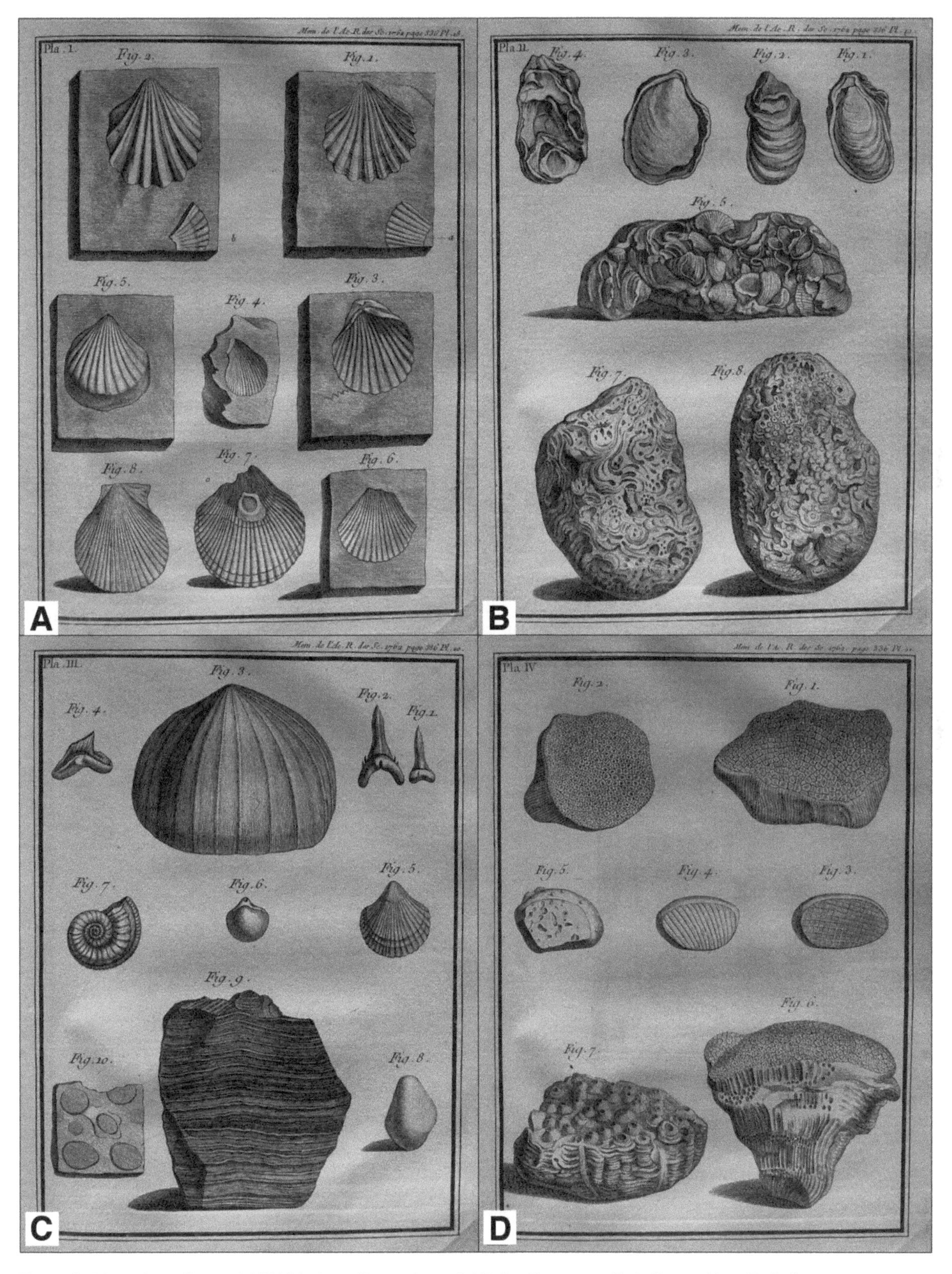

Figure 3. Plates from Guettard (1764b) show illustrations of (A) fossil pectens, (B 1–4) ostreidae, (B 5) limestone encrusted by bivalves, (B 7–8) organodetritic limestone, (C 1, 2, 4) fossil shark's tooth, (C 3) echinoids, (C 5) fossil bivalve, (C 6, 8) brachiopods, (C 7) ammonite, (C 9) jasper, (C 10) limestone with belemnite fragments, and (D 1–7) fossil corals. (Piotr Krzywiec private collection.)

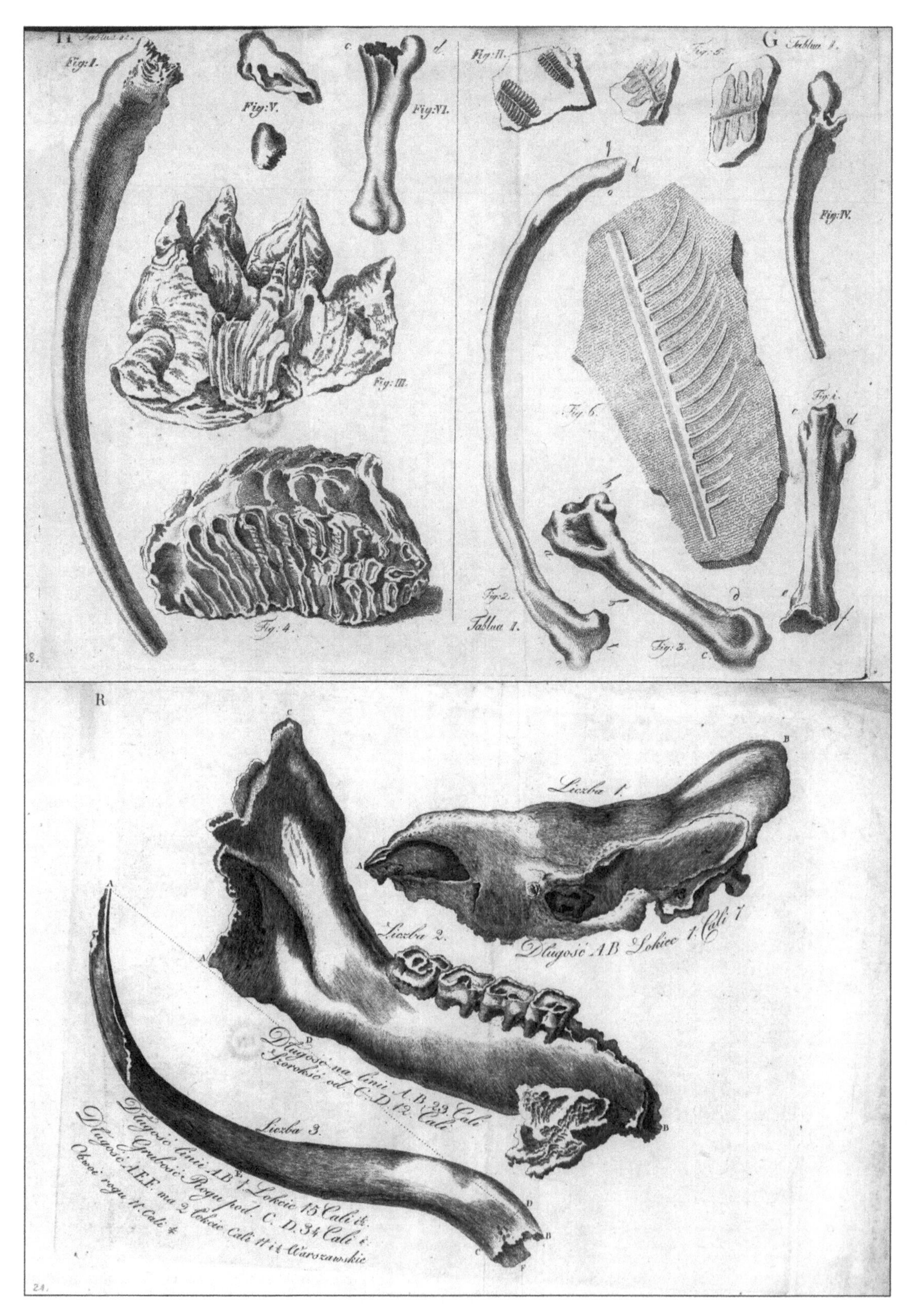

Figure 4. Plates from Staszic (1815) show Carboniferous plants and fossil bones and teeth of large mammals. (Public domain, https://polona.pl/.)

came to Poland in 1816 to join the staff of the newly established Mining Academy in Kielce. He was deeply involved in field studies, which were first focused on the Holy Cross Mountains (*Góry Świętokrzyskie*) and then also on the Carpathians and Silesia region. In 1827, after the Mining Academy in Kielce was liquidated, Pusch moved to Warsaw, where he held several positions at the mining administration and remained until his death. He was a very prolific author, and some of his publications should be regarded as milestones for the geology of Poland. Among other works, he published an extensive treatise on geology and mining potential of the Northern Carpathians (Pusch, 1824) and a two-volume treatise on the geology of Poland (Pusch, 1833–1836) that was accompanied by a large geological atlas (Pusch, 1836b; cf. Wołkowicz and Wołkowicz, 2014; Krzywiec, 2018). One of his most important achievements was a large volume on the paleontology of Poland illustrated with 16 lithographed plates (Pusch, 1836a). In this work, Pusch described organic remains of plants and animals of various ages collected in different parts of Poland. The book was published only two decades after Staszic's treatise was printed, but Pusch's approach to fossils was considerably different. To him, organic remains were not just "curiosities" excavated from the subsurface; he understood principles of stratigraphy and the role of fossils in determining the order of rock strata. Pusch was aware of the latest developments in this field, and his *Polens Paläontologie* (1836b) clearly illustrates this. Fossils described in this book are pictured with high-quality, precise lithographic plates that even today could be used for stratigraphic studies (Fig. 5). Descriptions of those plates are systematic and detailed and clearly prove that Pusch was using fossils for proper stratigraphic studies and not just to illustrate some "interesting objects" found within rocks. In his structured descriptions, he often refers to paleontological works of other contemporary researchers in this field such as Brongniart, von Buch, Parkinson, Eichwald, and Sowerby. Figure 5 provides insight into a wide spectrum of fossils described and illustrated by Pusch, including Carboniferous plants, Jurassic brachiopods and ammonites, Cretaceous corals, and Cenozoic vertebrates. Pusch clearly indicated the inferred stratigraphic ages of fossils he analyzed and, in many cases, provided localities where they were collected. Pusch's descriptions and illustrations were used as a reference point for stratigraphic studies for many decades (see translator's preface in Pusch, 1903).

Ludwik Zejszner was educated in Germany and obtained his doctorate in 1826 in Göttingen, and in 1829 he relocated to Poland, where he remained until his death (Graniczny et al., 2007). He shared his very active professional life between Kraków and Warsaw, where he held various positions in academia and in other, mostly mining, establishments. Zejszner was an extremely prolific author; his scientific output includes over 300 treatises and articles published in Polish, German, Austrian, French, Russian, Czech, and Hungarian periodicals that describe the geology of the key geological provinces of Poland. His studies dealt with Paleozoic, Mesozoic, and Cenozoic rocks. It is also worth noting that Zejszner was the research associate of Roderick Murchison, one of the preeminent scientists of the nineteenth century (Narkiewicz et al., 2012).

Paleontology was a key research area for Zejszner, and he published several important treatises chiefly devoted to this subject (e.g., Zejszner, 1846a, 1846b). Zejszner fully recognized the importance of fossil remains of plants and organisms to studies of sedimentary rocks, their ages, and structures. Zejszner's (1846a) *Paleontologia polska* contains detailed descriptions of various fossils that were prepared using state-of-the-art taxonomic nomenclature; descriptions were accompanied by elaborate illustrations of the fossils analyzed. An example is shown in Figure 6, which consists of three plates of Jurassic ammonites and brachiopods. Zejszner's intent was to provide comprehensive and systematic treatment of all fossils found in Poland. Due to various but mostly financial obstacles, he did not finalize his research on Polish paleontology. His published works cover mostly Jurassic fossils; some Carboniferous, Cretaceous, and Miocene fossils are also described and illustrated. Zejszner's paleontological studies laid a solid foundation for future stratigraphic and paleontological studies in Poland.

SUMMARY AND CONCLUSIONS

Human interest in subsurface treasures has been longstanding and provided stimulus for studies of "subsurface objects" including paleontological specimens. The earliest studies were mere compilations of descriptions of all objects that could be excavated from the subsurface and included archaeological artifacts as well as minerals, rocks, and fossils. In time, separate branches of science evolved from those early studies, including paleontology and stratigraphy, which relied on fossil remains of plants and animals. The evolution of printing techniques allowed for the production of images of fossils to accompany their descriptions; this provided an additional important stimulus for the development of paleontology.

The first illustrations of fossils from the territory of Poland were published at the very beginning of the eighteenth century. Their quality was rather high, although understanding of the true meaning of fossils was still in its infancy. Fossil remains of plants and animals were treated as "curiosities" from the subsurface and not as paleontological specimens telling stories about ancient geological epochs, past oceans, climates, depositional environments, and the evolution of life. This, however, quickly changed as late-eighteenth-century understanding of fossil remains of plants and animals prevailed. Consequently, illustrations depicting paleontological specimens also changed. They became more accurate, and in the early nineteenth century, they started to include certain details that could be used in rigorous taxonomic studies. The evolution of paleontological illustration can be well traced in publications by the authors mentioned in this chapter: from Helwing and Volkmann as representatives of the early period; to Guettard and Staszic, whose work clearly belongs to the transitional period; and, finally, to Pusch and Zejszner, who can be regarded as pioneers of modern paleontology and stratigraphy.

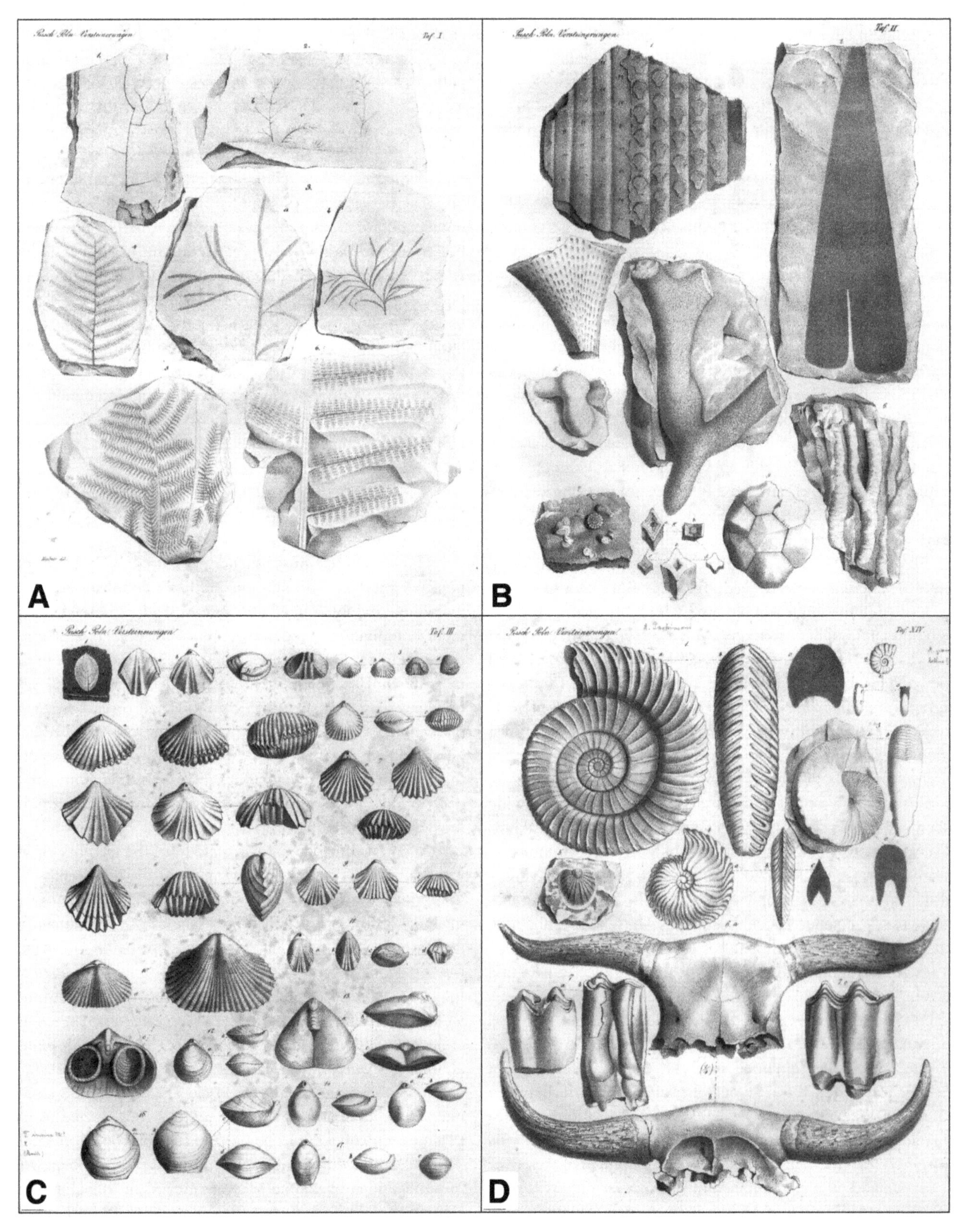

Figure 5. Plates from Pusch (1836b) show illustrations of (A 1–3) *Fucoides*; (A 4–6) *Pecopteris* i.e., leaves of Carboniferous plants; (B 1) Carboniferous plants *Sigillaria*; (B 2) Carboniferous leaf; (B 3–4) Cretaceous *Spongiae*; (B 5–8) fossil corals; (C 1–17) brachiopods; (D 1–4) ammonites; and (D 6–7) remnants of fossil vertebrates. (Piotr Krzywiec private collection.)

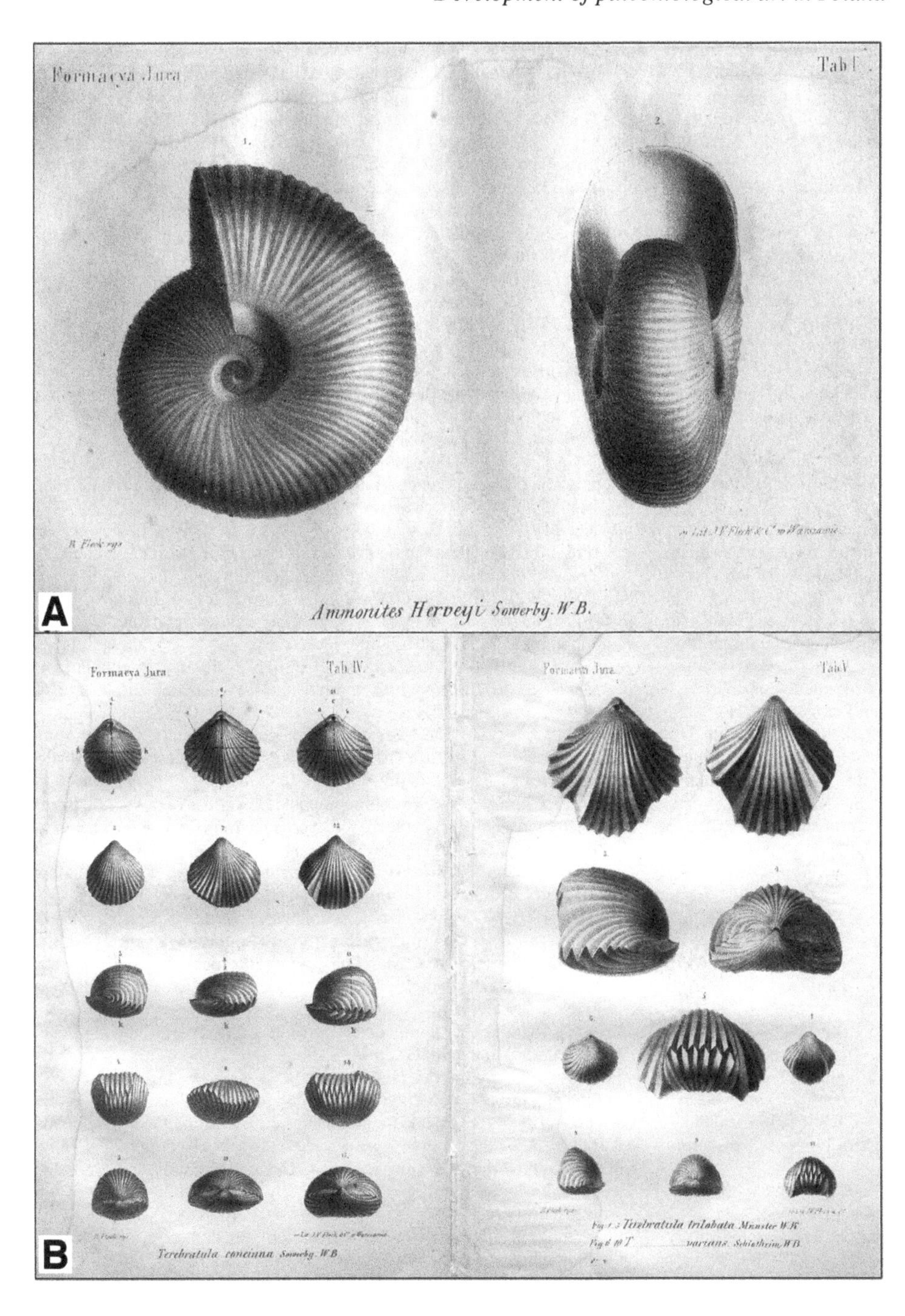

Figure 6. Plates from Zejszner (1846a) with illustrations of Jurassic (A) ammonites and (B) brachiopods. (Public domain, https://polona.pl/.)

ACKNOWLEDGMENTS

Two anonymous reviewers and editor Renee Clary are thanked for numerous suggestions that helped to shape this paper. Justyna and Wojtek Dołhun are thanked for their help with recognition of various printing techniques.

REFERENCES CITED

Adams, F.D., 1938, The Birth and Development of the Geological Sciences: Baltimore, Maryland, The Williams and Wilkins Company, 506 p.

Aldrovandi, U., 1648, Musaeum Metallicum in libros IIII: Bologna, Io. Baptistæ Ferronij, 979 p.

Carosi, J.P., 1781–1784, Reisen Durch Verschiedene Polnische Provinzen, Mineralischen und Andern Inhalts: Leipzig, Johann Gottlob Immanuel Breitkopf, 2 vols., v. 1, 166 p.; v. 2, 280 p.

Cuvier, G., 1812, Recherches sur les ossemens fossiles de quadrupèdes, où l'on rétablit les caractères de plusieurs espèces d'animaux que les révolutions du globe paroissent avoir détruites: Paris, Deterville Libraire, 278 p., 23 plates.

Cuvier, G., and Brongniart, A., 1811, Essais sur la géographie minéralogique des environs de Paris, avec une carte géognostique et des coupes de terrain: Paris, Baudin, 278 p.

Daszkiewicz, P., and Tarkowski, R., 2009, Pobyt i badania przyrodnicze Jeana-Etienne'a Guettarda w Rzeczpospolitej (1760–1762) wraz z tłumaczeniem tekstu Rozprawy o naturze ziem Polski i minerałach w nich zawartych: Kraków, Uniwersytet Pedagogiczny im. Komisji Edukacji Narodowej, Prace Monograficzne, 190 p.

Ferber, J.J., 1804, Relation von der ihm aufgetragenen mineralogischen, berg- und hüttenmännischen Reise durch einige polnische Provinzen: Arnstadt und Rudolfstadt, Langbein und Kluger, 140 p.

Geikie, A., 1905, The Founders of Geology: London, Macmillan and Co., Ltd., 486 p.

Graniczny, M., Kacprzak, J., Urban, H., and Krzywiec, P., 2007, Ludwik Zejszner–wybitny człowiek i przyrodnik, jeden z pionierów kartografii geologicznej w Polsce: Przegląd Geologiczny, v. 55, no. 11, p. 925–932.

Grigelis, A., Wójcik, Z., Narębski, W., Gelumbauskaite, L.Z., and Kozák, J., 2011, Stanisław Staszic: An early surveyor of the geology of central and Eastern Europe: Annals of Science, v. 68, p. 199–228, https://doi.org/10.1080/00033790.2010.511263.

Guettard, J.-É., 1764a, Mémoire sur la Nature du terrain de la Pologne et des Minéraux qu'il renferme. Première partie: Mémoires de l'Académie Royale des Sciences de Paris 64, p. 234–257.

Guettard, J.-É., 1764b, Mémoire sur la Nature du terrain de la Pologne et des Minéraux qu'il renferme. Seconde partie: Mémoires de l'Académie Royale des Sciences de Paris 64, p. 293–336.

Hacquet, B., 1796, Hacquet's neueste physikalisch-politische Reise in den Jahren 1788, 89 und 90 durch die Dacischen und Sarmatischen oder Nördlichen Karpathen, Vierter Theil: Nürnberg, Raspischen Buchhandlung, 256 p.

Helwing, G.A., 1717, Lithographia Angerburgica sive Lapidum et Fossilium In Districtu Angerburgensi & ejus vicinia, ad trium vel quatuor millarium spatium, *in* Montibus, Agris, Arenosodinis & in primis circa lacuum littora & fluviorum ripas, collectorum brevis et succincta Consideratio, Additis rariorum aliquot figuris aeris incisis com Praesatione Autoris & Indicibus necessariis: Regiomonti, Johannis Stelteri, 96 p.

Helwing, G.A., 1720, Lithographiae Angerburgicae pars II, in qua de lapidibus figuratis ad triplex regnum minerale, vegetabile et animale redactis alissque fosilibus in districtu Angerburgensi ejusque vicinia noviter detectis, et in specie de origine lapidum literas exprimentium, occasione lapidis cujusduam resaviensis, literas Latinas L. V. R. representantis, succincte disseritur; additis iconibus rariorum: Lipsiae, Immanuelis Titil, 132 p.

Hooker, J.D., 1854, On a new species of Volkmannia: Quarterly Journal of the Geological Society, v. 10, p. 199–202, https://doi.org/10.1144/GSL.JGS.1854.010.01-02.14.

Kleczkowski, A.S., 1970, Z lat młodzieńczych G. G. Puscha (1790–1816): Prace Muzeum Ziemi, v. 15, p. 95–111.

Kleczkowski, A.S., 1972, Jerzy Bogumił Pusch—His life and work in the period of the Kingdom of Poland (1816–1831) (in Polish with English summary): Studia i materiały z dziejów Nauki Polskiej, v. 17, p. 123–150.

Kleczkowski, A.S., 1974, Jerzy Bogumił Pusch–ostatni okres życia i działalności 1830–1846: Prace Muzeum Ziemi, v. 21, p. 65–104.

Krzywiec, P., 2016, The First Geological Map of Eastern Europe: GeoExpro, v. 12, p. 68.

Krzywiec, P., 2018, Birth and development of oil and gas industry in the Northern Carpathians (until 1939), *in* Craig, J., Gerali, F., MacAulay, F., and Sorkhabi, R., eds., History of the European Oil and Gas Industry: Geological Society, London, Special Publication 465, p. 165–189, https://doi.org/10.1144/SP465.24.

Lang, C.N., 1708, Historia Lapidum Figuratorum Helvetiæ: Venetiis, Typis Jacobi Tomasini, 165 p.

Lhuyd, E., 1699, Lithophylacii Britannici ichnographia: Londini, Ex Officina M. C., 150 p.

Mylius, G.F., 1709, Memorabilium Saxoniaæ Subterraneæ: Lepizig, Friedrich Groschussen, 89 p.

Narkiewicz, M., Krzywiec, P., and Diemer, J., 2012, Geology of the Holy Cross Mts. in the eyes of Roderick Murchison—visit in June of 1843 and its echoes (in Polish with English summary): Przegląd Geologiczny, v. 60, p. 220–225.

Pacyna, G., 2012, Critical review of studies of Carboniferous and Lower Permian plant reproductive organs in Poland with complete list of so far published taxa: Acta Palaeobotanica, v. 52, no. 2, p. 271–301.

Parkinson, J., 1808, Organic Remains of a Former World; An Examination of the Mineralized Remains of the Vegetables and Animals of the Antediluvian World; Generally Termed Extraneous Fossils. Volume 2: The Fossil Zoophytes: London, Nornaville and Fell, 283 p.

Pusch, G.G., 1824, Geognostisch—bergmännische Reise durch einen Theil der Karpathen, Ober- und Nieder-Ungarn ausgestellt im Jahre 1821, Erster Theil: Leipzig, Johann Ambrosius Barth, 386 p.

Pusch, G.G., 1833–1836, Geognostische Beschreibung von Polen so wie der übrigen Nordkarpathen-Länder: Stuttgart und Tübingen, J.G. Cotta'schen Buchhandlung, 338 p.

Pusch, G.G., 1836a, Geognostischer Atlas von Polen: Stuttgart und Tübingen, Cotta, maps.

Pusch, G.G., 1836b, Polens Paläontologie oder Abbildung und Beschreibung der vorzüglichsten und der noch unbeschriebenen Petrefakten aus den Gebirgsformationen in Polen, Volhynien und den Karpathen, nebst einigen algemeinen Beiträgen zur Petrefaktenkunde und einem Versuch zur Vervollständigung der Geschichte des Europäischen Auer-Ochsen: Stuttgart, E. Schweizerbart's Verlagshandlung, 214 p.

Pusch, J.B., 1903, Geologiczny opis Polski oraz innych krajów na północ położonych, przez Jerzego Bogumiła Puscha. Stuttgart i Tybinga 1833–1836: Dąbrowa, Drukarnia St. Święcickiego, 221 p.

Rudwick, M.J.S., 2014, Earth's Deep History: How It Was Discovered and Why It Matters: Chicago, University of Chicago Press, 392 p., https://doi.org/10.7208/chicago/9780226204093.001.0001.

Rzączyński, G., 1721, Historia naturalis curiosa Regni Poloniae, Magni Ducatus Lituaniae, annexarumq; provinciarum in tractatus XX divisa: Sandomirae, Typis Collegii Soc. Jesu, 456 p.

Rzączyński, G., 1742, Auctuarium Historiae Naturalis Regni Poloniae Magnique Ducatus Lithuniae Annexarumque Provinciarum in Puncta XII: Gedani, Soc. Jesu., 504 p.

Rzymełka, J.A., 1988, The History of Geological Exploration of the Upper Silesian Coalfield up to 1870 (in Polish with English summary): Katowice, Uniwersytet Śląski, 261 p.

Scheuchzer, J.J., 1702, Specimen lithographiae Helveticae curiosae quo lapides ex figuratis helveticis selectissimi aeri incisi sistuntur & describuntur: Tiguri, Typis Davidis Gesneri, 67 p.

Scheuchzer, J.J., 1723, Herbarium Diluvianum. Editio Novissima duplo Auctior: Lugduni Batavorum, Petri Vander, 119 p.

Staszic, S., 1805, O Ziemiorodztwie gór dawniey Sarmacyi a późniey Polski. Pierwsza rozprawa o równinach tey krainy; o pasmie Łysogór; o części Bieskidów; i Bielaw. Czytana na posiedzeniu publicznem Tow. Warsz. Przyjaciół Nauk, dnia 13. Grudnia 1805: Warszawa, Drukarnia Xięży Piarów, 129 p.

Staszic, S., 1815, O Ziemiorodztwie Karpatów i innych gor i rownin Polski: Warszawa, Drukarnia Rządowa, 390 p.

Syniawa, M., 2006, Biograficzny słownik przyrodników śląskich: Katowice, Centrum Dziedzictwa Przyrody Górnego Śląska, 459 p.

Volkmann, G.A., 1720, Silesia Subterranea: Leipzig, Moriz Georg Weidmann, 344 p.

Wołkowicz, S., and Wołkowicz, K., 2014, Geological cartography in Poland in the 19th century: Geological Quarterly, v. 58, p. 623–658, https://doi.org/10.7306/gq.1198.

Wójcik, Z., 2008, Stanisław Staszic: Radom, Instytut Technologii Eksploatacji, Biblioteka Polskiej Nauki i Techniki, 476 p.

Zejszner, L., 1846a, Paleontologia polska. Opis zoologiczny, botaniczny i geologiczny wszystkich zwierząt i roślin skamieniałych polskich do poznania warstw Ziemi służący, wraz z wizerunkami wszystkich gatunków rysowanemi z natury: Warszawa, Nakładem Redakcyi Biblioteki Warszawskiej, 79 p.

Zejszner, L., 1846b, Nowe lub niedokładnie opisane gatunki skamieniałości Tatrowych: Warszawa, Stanisław Strąbski, 31 p.

Manuscript Accepted by the Society 15 January 2021
Manuscript Published Online 11 June 2021

The Geological Society of America
Memoir 218

George Victor Du Noyer's large format paintings: Nineteenth-century lecture slides

Matthew Alastair Parkes*
National Museum of Ireland—Natural History, Merrion Street, Dublin 2, D02 F627, Ireland

ABSTRACT

The National Museum of Ireland's natural history collections include a range of large format artworks, many of paleontological subjects, which were painted by George Victor Du Noyer, the celebrated nineteenth-century geologist, antiquarian, and artist who worked for both the Ordnance Survey of Ireland and the Geological Survey of Ireland (GSI). Letterbook references in the archives of GSI indicate that most, if not all of these, were commissioned by Joseph Beete Jukes, director of the GSI, for different public lecture series. The artistic qualities of the work suggest they were done at speed. However, they also are designed to be seen from a distance within a lecture hall, so an apparently crude technique is appropriate to the purpose. In effect, the watercolor paintings in this series are the PowerPoint presentation of the 1850s.

INTRODUCTION

The paleontological, or indeed any geological, student of today is empowered by the immense resources at their fingertips through the internet. Regardless of the content and quality of their research, it is extremely easy for students to create a polished and attractive presentation in software such as PowerPoint. The package allows text, graphs, images, videos, sound, and other effects to be utilized with great ease, and the internet contains uncountable images that can be searched for and copied for use in seconds.

It must be difficult for today's student to imagine the author in the late 1980s as a postgraduate student preparing a talk for an external meeting or even for an internal presentation within the department. The first computers in the department were shared and quite limited in their capacities. Most talks and lectures given by staff to students relied on two tools. One was the 35 mm slide projector and the other was the overhead projector. Both have become obsolete in recent decades, but if used well and with good preparation they could provide very professional presentations. However, preparing a diagram or a map and then photographing it with 35 mm slide film could take many hours and might involve drawing with ink on tracing paper, using Letraset lettering to provide annotations, and then photocopying the drawing film to get a white line illustration that could be photographed. Slide films generally had to be sent away to be processed, so several weeks of preparation might be required by a student for one short talk at a meeting.

Try to imagine, then, how much more difficult it must have been in the mid- to late 1800s for a professional geologist to provide illustrations of their ideas for an audience. Their ideas must have largely been communicated verbally or perhaps by every member of the audience having access to the same printed maps or texts, perhaps with woodcut illustrations within the books. Of course, the practicalities and costs of printing specialized

*published posthumously (1961–2020); send correspondence to Nigel Monaghan: naturalhistory@museum.ie

Parkes, M.A., 2022, George Victor Du Noyer's large format paintings: Nineteenth-century lecture slides, *in* Clary, R.M., Rosenberg, G.D., and Evans, D.C., eds., The Evolution of Paleontological Art: Geological Society of America Memoir 218, p. 101–108, https://doi.org/10.1130/2021.1218(12).

materials would have restricted access to a limited audience. For the purposes of a public lecture, it would have been impossible to cater to a large audience.

Such woodcut illustrations routinely appeared in daily and weekly newspapers and periodicals, but the woodblocks rarely survived as they were regarded as ephemeral items and discarded. The *Memoirs of the Geological Survey of Ireland* (GSI) during the 1850s–1880s were well illustrated using woodblock illustrations, including many fossil illustrations, but limitations of printing and the availability of box wood meant that illustrations of this sort were rarely larger than ~10 cm. The rare surviving collection of over 500 woodblocks in GSI (Parkes et al., 2000) does include a few larger blocks, but they are often composed of smaller blocks that are attached to each other. Many of these woodblocks were drawn and engraved by George Victor Du Noyer (1817–1869), geologist, artist, antiquarian, and focus of this study. They are highly artistic, skilled, and detailed illustrations to the extent that the director of GSI, Joseph Beete Jukes (1811–1869), was moved to suggest that Du Noyer should produce less detailed work in order not to delay publication of the *Memoirs* and to reduce costs of their production (*GSI Letterbooks*, 16 May 1868). It is clear that such small illustrations were only suitable for illustrating publications. They would not have worked at all in a lecture room setting unless they were made universally available to the audience. Most *Memoirs of the Geological Survey of Ireland* were printed in quite modest numbers and at a cost that would have prohibited their mass use in public lectures.

Du Noyer's artistic talents were commissioned to create works that form the central subject of this contribution. Jukes clearly recognized the abilities of one of his staff.

THE LIFE AND WORK OF GEORGE VICTOR DU NOYER (1817–1869)

Du Noyer's undoubted talents as an artist may have been acknowledged by his colleagues in his lifetime, but remained largely unrecognized for well over a century after his death. His story was first documented by Petra Coffey (1993), but in 1995 he received the acclaim of an exhibition of his works in the National Gallery of Ireland entitled *Hidden Landscapes* in celebration of 150 years of the Geological Survey of Ireland (Croke, 1995). An accompanying catalogue contained detailed appraisals of his work in different spheres such as geology, zoology, botany, antiquaries, and observation of everyday life. In that catalogue, Archer (1995), in describing his outdoor geological artistry, made brief mention of the lecture illustrations but largely refers to a series of watercolors each measuring 52 × 32 cm. For many years, paintings of this size were hanging on the walls of the Geology Department in University College Dublin (UCD) and in Geological Survey Ireland. Some of those from UCD have since transferred to the Natural History Museum. However, it is argued here that these were not painted specifically for lecture illustrations. Compared to the large format watercolors, the detail is much more developed, and they are best viewed within a short distance as with a typical artwork. Archer (1995) also discussed a large map of Killarney on which Du Noyer used the hill shading technique to illustrate relief, and which was possibly used by Jukes in his lecture series.

Aspects of Du Noyer's works have received additional or expanded attention subsequent to the *Hidden Landscapes* studies. Monaghan and Sides (1995) looked specifically at zoological and paleontological illustrations but expanded this in a wider context (Monaghan, 2001). Du Noyer has had a small renaissance in the last year or two with a large exhibition, *Stones, Slabs and Seascapes*, in the Crawford Art Gallery in Cork from November 2017 through February 2018. A smaller version of that exhibition subsequently exhibited in the National Museum of Ireland at Collins Barracks. A sumptuously illustrated catalogue accompanied the exhibition. In his essay, main curator Peter Murray did mention the "banner sized" lecture illustrations and showed one of the large format fossil illustrations in the National Museum of Ireland collections along with a watercolor *Near the Angle, Mer de Glace*. It was noted that Du Noyer used published sources and sometimes copied them for these works (Murray, 2017).

Subsequently, Susan Hegarty, one of the essay authors, published a detailed study of his geological career (Hegarty, 2018). In a further detailed work on an aspect of Du Noyer's wide interests, Manning (2017) examined his archaeological works within the Royal Society of Antiquaries of Ireland. Consequently, this brief study addresses one small aspect of his diverse portfolio that has not really been examined in any detail by other authors.

THE GSI LECTURE SERIES

Herries Davies (1995) best summarized the story of lecture courses given by the Geological Survey of Ireland in his chapter "Reaching Out." Of relevance to this study is the period from 1854 until 1867, when the Museum of Irish Industry at 51 St. Stephens Green enabled scientific collaboration with the creation of a lecture theater. Jukes, then director of the Geological Survey and a professor in the Department of Science and Art, was expected to deliver 54 lectures annually. Twenty-four were elementary lectures in the Royal Dublin Society. These were open to the public free of charge; dubbed the "Popular Lectures," some attracted audiences of more than 400 people. The remainder were the "Systematic Lectures" with a fee charged and optional exams at the end of the course. They were held in the Museum of Irish Industry in the evenings and continued until his death in 1869 and from then on with his successor, Edward Hull. It is unknown whether Jukes used the large format watercolors in only one or both of the lecture courses.

THE LARGE FORMAT WATERCOLORS

The National Museum of Ireland (NMI) collection of these large format works (mostly 95 × 130 cm) is clearly an incomplete series since there are 38 of them but numbers on the paintings go up to 149, and a very few do not have a number on them at all. Some were only found and recognized within the museum in 1992. The paintings are on paper backed with canvas. Small metal hoops sewn on the corners show they were hung for display. From either a full signature and date or initials in a bottom corner it is clear that the vast majority of those that survive, if not all of them, were painted by Du Noyer. Even when not signed or initialed, his style of work is recognizable.

There are three broad categories. The high numbers in the 120s and 130s are alpine scenes with glaciers and are either proven or suspected to be redrawn from illustrations in contemporary textbooks. Approximately another third are illustrative of Irish geological field sections, showing particular strata, rock types, or sections, and these are often versions of other Du Noyer sketches in smaller formats.

One "custom" painting is jointly credited to Jukes and Du Noyer in February 1859 through their dated initials in the bottom corner; it is a diagrammatic cross section through coal workings. There are also two unnumbered cross sections through cave excavations/explorations, which were very much in fashion at this time. One is *Bone Caves in Franconia* (a copy of the frontispiece of Cuvier, 1827) and the other *The Mouth of Kirkdale Cave* (a copy of a figure from Buckland, 1823). The third category, which is the focus here, is the paleontological illustrations listed in Table 1.

In trying to analyze these paintings, one finds that various sources are identified while others remain speculative. For some, reasonable assumptions can be made based on the style of the individual works with knowledge of the broad range of Du Noyer's artistic works. For the identified sources, the *Apiocrinites* in Bradford Clay (Fig. 1) seems to be a reworking in color of a figure in editions of Charles Lyell's *Elements of Geology*. *Anoplotherium* (Fig. 2) seems to be from Cuvier's (1816) *Le règne animal*, although there is an ink note on the bottom left-hand corner of the work indicating that it is "from Buckland's (1836) Bridgewater Treatise." The *Deinotherium* image (Fig. 3A) first appeared on the cover of the original monograph on this species by Kaup and Klipstein (1836). It was widely copied and appeared in several popular accounts in English from which Du Noyer could have sourced his inspiration. It is also reproduced by Wilson (1882), but again without attribution to the source that would have been available to Du Noyer. Two slightly smaller works (Fig. 4) that illustrate fossils plants are from an unknown source, but are perhaps drawn from specimens available to Du Noyer in the Geological Survey of Ireland fossil collections or as composite sketches from a variety of samples. Figure 4 especially has sufficient unique detail of the *Lepidodendron elegans* plant fossil to suggest that it may be from one specimen. No attempt has yet been made to compare the illustration to the GSI fossil collections, which would be a significant undertaking.

With the stratigraphical assemblages of fossils, it is quite a varied situation. On some panels there are no attributions, but on others there are small, penciled annotations as to a source. For example, on the Lias fossils watercolor almost all of the species are from monographs by Sowerby or Phillips with the individual

TABLE 1. PALEONTOLOGICAL ILLUSTRATIONS BY DU NOYER

No. on panel	Title	Date	Dimension (height x width in cm)	Signed/Unsigned	Figure no.	NMI* registered number
5	*Silurian Fossils*		94 x 130	Initialed?		GLM27
7	*Devonian Fossils*	January 1855	95 x 135	Signed	7	GLM28
8	*Carboniferous Fossils*	January 1855	94 x 135	Signed	6	GLM29
12	Lepidodendron elegans		65 x 98	Unsigned	4	GLM58
14	Sphenopteris *and* Odontopteris		66 x 99	Unsigned	11	GLM59
15	*Permian Fossils*	January 1855	94 x 130	Signed	5	GLM30
18	*Lias Fossils*	February 1855	95 x 130	Signed		GLM31
27	*Bath Oolite Fossils*		94 x 130	Unsigned		GLM32
28	Apiocrinites *in Bradford Clay*		89 x 130	Signed	1	GLM33
32	*Cretaceous Fossils*	1855	94 x 130	Signed	8	GLM34
33	*Eocene Fossils*	1855	94 x 130	Signed		GLM35
35	Anoplotherium commune		93 x 129	Unsigned	2	GLM36
36	*Crag Fossils*	1855	95 x 130	Signed	9	GLM37
37	Deinotherium	1855	94 x 130	Signed	3	GLM38
42	*Placoid/Ganoid/Cycloid/Ctenoid* types of fish scale]		68 x 95	Unsigned	12	GLM60
149	*Carboniferous Limestone* [all fossil illustrations]		107 x 138	Unsigned	10	GLM97

*NMI—National Museum of Ireland.

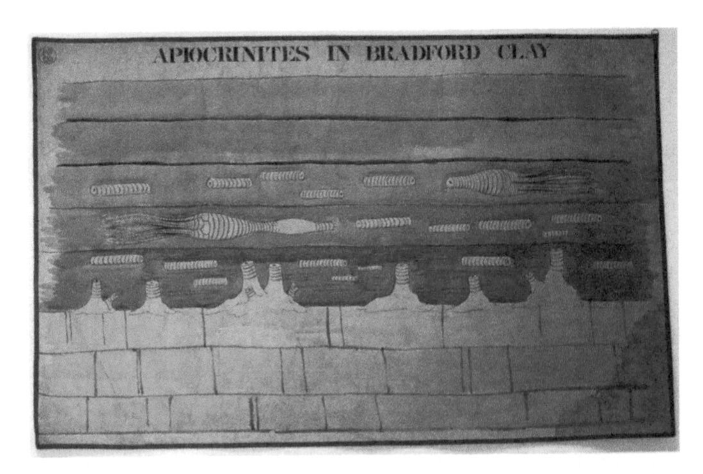

Figure 1. Large format (89 × 130 cm) watercolor of *Apiocrinites* in Bradford Clay, number 28 in the series. The painting appears to be a color version of a figure in editions of Charles Lyell's *Elements of Geology*.

Figure 2. Large format (93 × 129 cm) watercolor of *Anoplotherium commune*, number 35 in the series. The work is not signed or dated. The image, of a skeleton within an outline, seems to be from Cuvier's (1816) *Le Règne animal* (plate 82, figure 1), although there is a pencil note on the work indicating that it is from Buckland's *Bridgewater Treatise* (of 1836).

Figure 3. Large format (94 × 130 cm) watercolor of *Deinotherium*, number 37 in the series. The Miocene fossil elephant in a "lying down" posture is not named but is the species *Dinotherium giganteum* Kaup, 1829. (B) A clip art image shows remarkable similarity to the image in part A (credit: Patrick Guenette / Alamy Stock Vector). The lower jaw bone illustrated on the top left has detail of breaks and fragments, matching the original specimen of Kaup illustrated in 1836 and reproduced in many subsequent publications.

plate and figure numbers quoted. The *Gryphaea* is "from Nature." On the *Permian Fossils* watercolor (Fig. 5), there are individual table and figure numbers as annotations beside the fossils but no information other than "Palaeontographical Society Monograph 1848." This actually refers to *A Monograph of Permian Fossils* by William King, which was issued in 1850, and each animal is copied from it. King became professor in Queen's College Galway in the west of Ireland in 1849, so he was probably in communication with Survey geologists at this time.

The *Carboniferous Fossils* watercolor (Fig. 6) has plate and figure number annotations with no indication of the publication. On the *Devonian Fossils* watercolor (Fig. 7), the fossil fish *Pterichthys* is annotated as "from Miller's Old Red Sandstone," but others are unattributed. Du Noyer's paleontological (and somewhat artistic) colleague in the Geological Survey, William Hellier Baily (1819–1888), only commenced work as acting paleontologist in the Irish Survey in 1856, but may have been the person who later annotated the watercolors as his handwriting is very similar, and it is the act of a curatorial mind rather than an artistic one (Wyse Jackson and Parkes, 2009).

However, as a branch of the Geological Survey of the UK, the GSI received substantial collections of fossils of all ages from England, Scotland, and Wales for the GSI's Museum in Dublin and sent collections of representative Irish fossils to London, Edinburgh, and other provincial centers. These British fossils would have been available to Du Noyer to use for sketching. The detail on the Lias and younger watercolors (Figs. 8–9) suggests that most were copied from other illustrations. However,

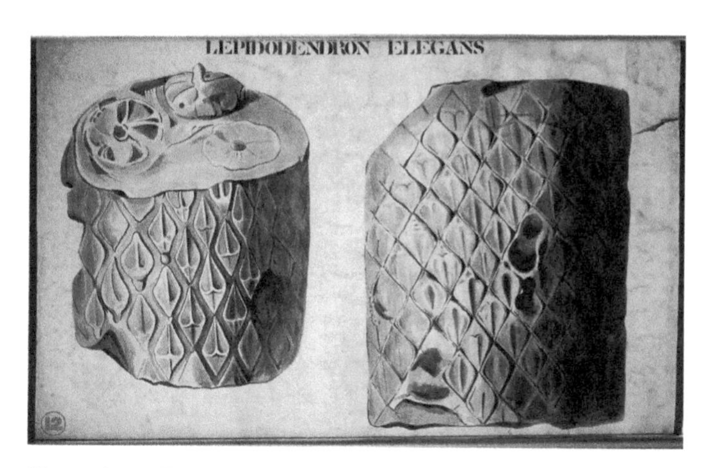

Figure 4. Medium-sized (65 × 98 cm) watercolor of *Lepidodendron elegans*, number 12 in the series. There is sufficient detail in the painting of a portion of the trunk of a Carboniferous lycopsid to suggest that it was painted from one or perhaps two real specimen(s), but none have yet been traced. The leaf scars indicate the left-hand image is "upside down" relative to life position, but it is not clear what the structures on the broken surface are meant to be.

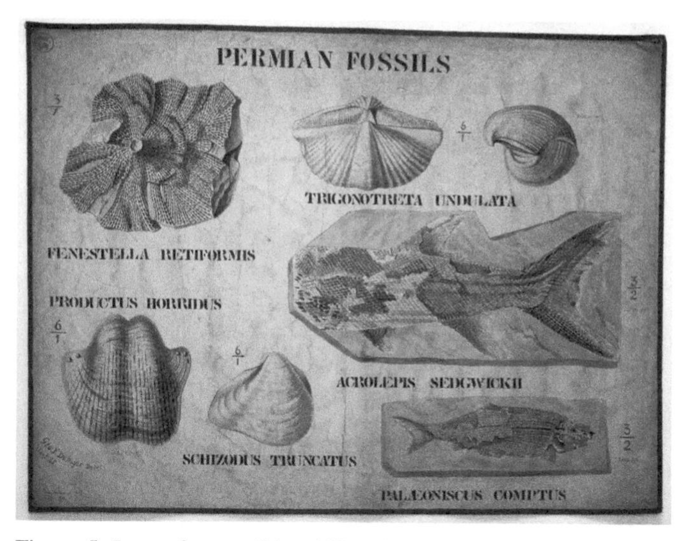

Figure 5. Large format (94 × 130 cm) watercolor *Permian Fossils*, number 15 in the series. Signed by George Victor Du Noyer, January 1855. On this panel there are individual table and figure numbers as small annotations beside the fossils but no information other than "Palaeontographical Society Monograph 1848" (see text for discussion).

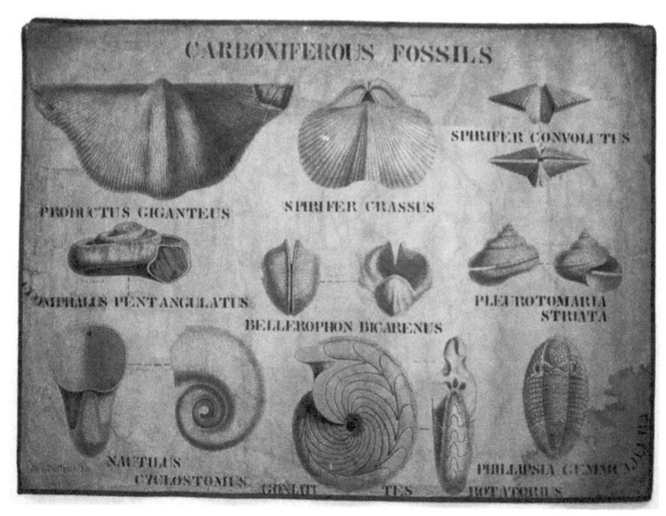

Figure 6. Large format (94 × 135 cm) watercolor *Carboniferous Fossils*, number 8 in the series. Signed by George Victor Du Noyer, January 1855.

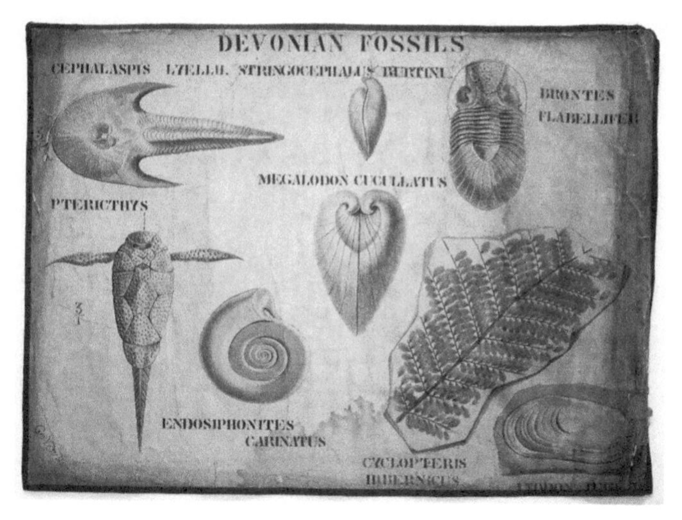

Figure 7. Large format (95 × 135 cm) watercolor *Devonian Fossils*, number 7 in the series. Signed by George Victor Du Noyer, January 1855. While the plant fossil and large freshwater bivalve are from the famous Kiltorcan locality in County Kilkenny, which had been first found and excavated in 1853, most of the other fossils are not found in Ireland and are probably drawn from specimens from Scottish or British localities, perhaps from specimens routinely transferred between branches of the Geological Survey of the UK during this period.

Carboniferous Limestone (Fig. 10A), the Devonian and Silurian panels especially, has adequate detail of imperfections and breaks and missing sections to suggest that they may have been, in fact, drawn from life using real specimens from the GSI collections. Given the enormous variety of specimens available in the GSI collections, this is not surprising.

For various practical reasons, it has not been possible to conduct thorough searches for individual specimens across the range of panels, but one distinctive specimen has been traced. The *Cardiomorpha* n.s. (Fig. 10B), illustrated on the left-hand side of the *Carboniferous Limestone* panel, is in fact GSI:F23477. It is *Cardiomorpha egertoni* (M'Coy, 1844), figured by Hind (1898, p. 274, plate XXIV, fig. 1), as recorded in Parkes and Sleeman (1997). On the same panel is a painting of *Conocardium koninckii* n.s. The species name of this rostroconch was in fact published by Baily in 1871. This was two years after Du Noyer died. The date, and also the style of the painting, plus the slightly different size of the panel than that of the standard Du Noyer works, are not proof but do generate a suspicion that this last panel, numbered 149, was in fact the work of Baily rather than Du Noyer.

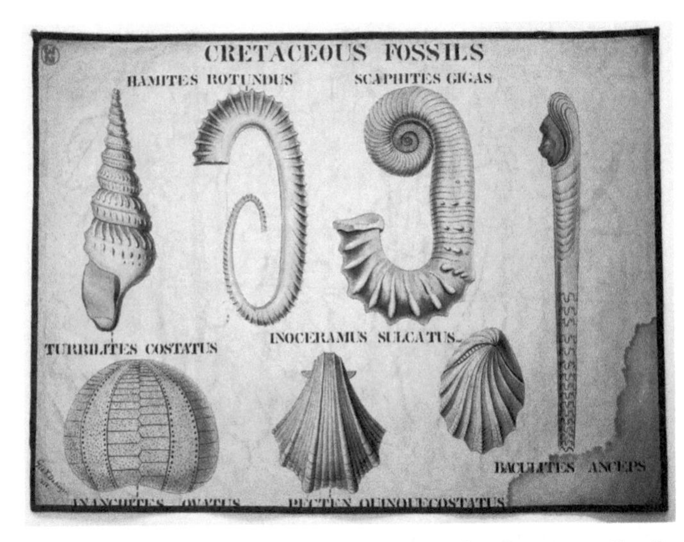

Figure 8. Large format (94 × 130 cm) watercolor *Cretaceous Fossils*, number 32 in the series. Signed by George Victor Du Noyer, 1855.

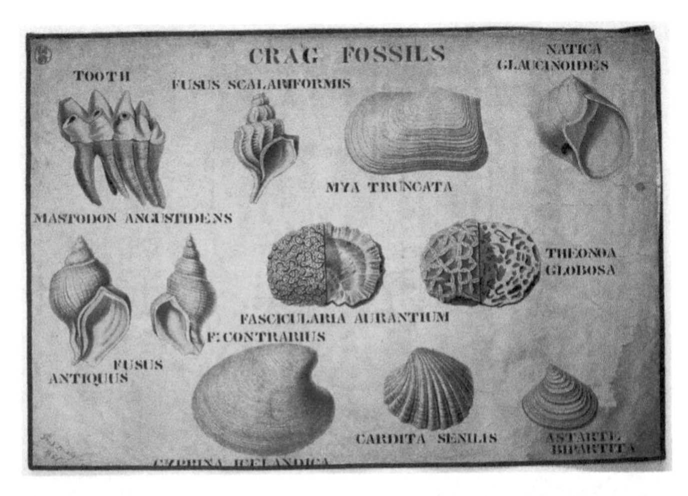

Figure 9. Large format (95 × 130 cm) watercolor *Crag Fossils*, number 36 in the series. Signed by George Victor Du Noyer, 1855.

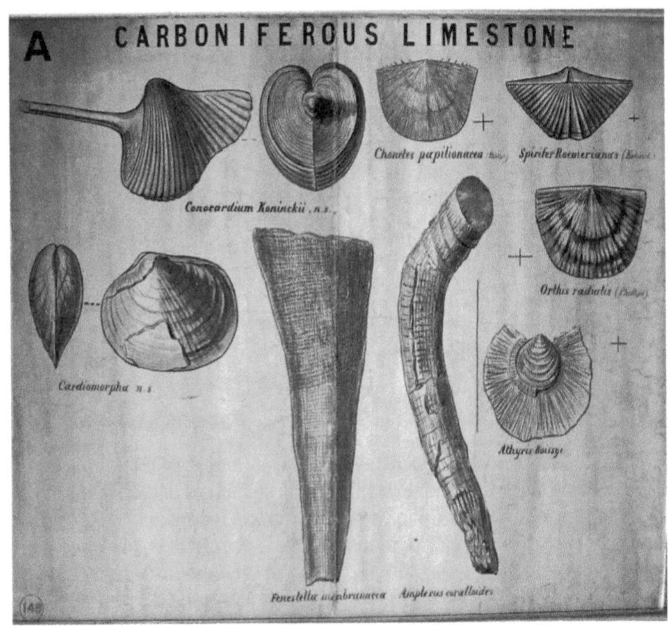

Figure 10. (A) Large format (107 × 138 cm) watercolor *Carboniferous Limestone*, number 149 in the series. The work is unsigned and was possibly painted by William Hellier Baily, acting paleontologist in the Geological Survey of Ireland, rather than by Du Noyer (see text). (B) *Cardiomorpha egertoni*, GSI:F23477 is the specimen illustrated in part A.

With the Silurian panel, it must be noted that this was created at a time when the Ordovician had not been defined (which was not until Charles Lapworth in 1879), and some of the fossils are now known to be Ordovician in age, while others are Silurian as it is understood today. Figure 11 is another plant fossil illustration, which is rather more generic than in Figure 4. Figure 12 illustrates the four different types of fish scales.

In addition, there are present four canvases in a loosely similar category, each ~62 cm high × 90 cm wide. Each portrays typical forms of foraminifera. From the very fine print label of "LONDON GEOLOGIST OFFICE 154 STRAND" and "GEOLOGICAL DIAGRAMS No 4," etc., and their appearance, it is believed they are a printed product of much more modern vintage than Du Noyer's works and are found with them by virtue of physical dimensions and materials rather than being directly connected to their creation.

PALEONTOLOGICAL IMPORTANCE

The fossil paintings by Du Noyer in the large format watercolors described here do not have a significant place in the development of paleontology, but they do record an important effort by the Geological Survey of Ireland at what would today be classed as "outreach." The public lecture series, run for many years in partnership with the Museum of Irish Industry, was part of a continuous effort over the 175 years of GSI (in 2020) to educate the

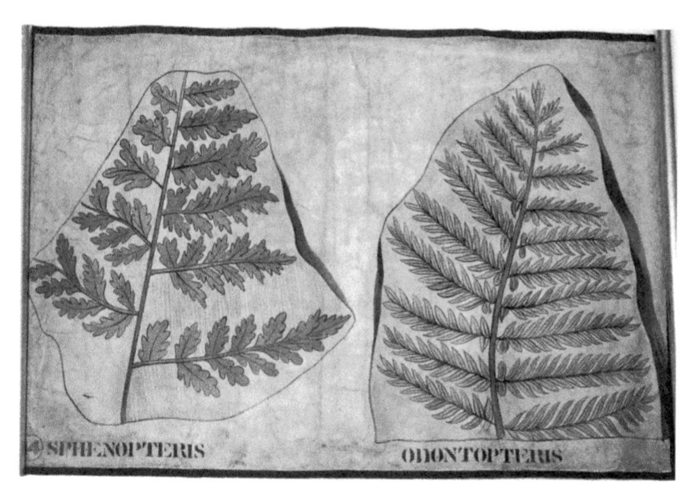

Figure 11. Medium-sized (66 × 99 cm) watercolor of *Sphenopteris* and *Odontopteris*, number 14 in the series. The work is unsigned.

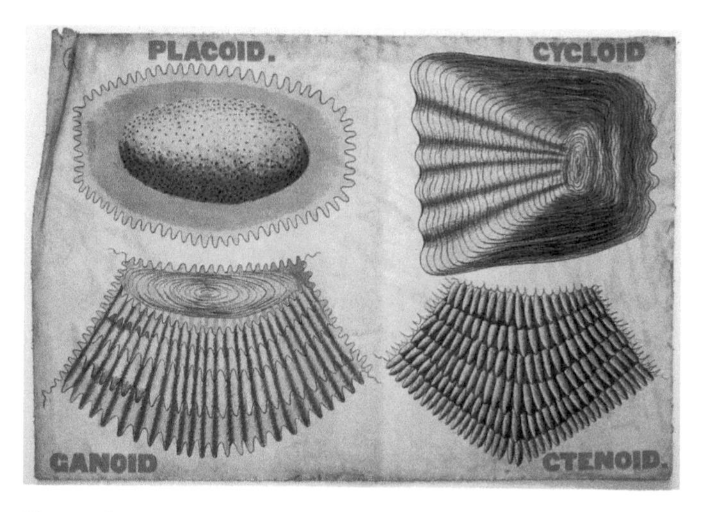

Figure 12. A medium-sized (68 × 95 cm) watercolor illustrates four types of fish scales, number 42 in the series. The work is unsigned.

wider public about geology. In the 1850s, as now, paleontology played a key role in being of great public interest compared to other areas of geology. Even if individual specimens within the 27,000 or so fossils in the GSI collection, largely curated by the author in 1994–1996, could be identified as those illustrated on these works, it would not raise their status as it would if they were published in a journal paper as type, figured, or cited material. Thus, the effort to make those detailed comparisons has not been attempted (other than the example of *Cardiomorpha* discussed earlier), especially since thousands of the Irish fossils were systematically sent to London and numerous provincial centers such as Edinburgh, Belfast, and Oxford as well as to individuals, and are thus not available without enormous effort and cost. The fossils illustrated are merely a small representation of the hundreds of species found and identified by the GSI. In addition, the numerous post-Carboniferous fossils illustrated are indicative of the position of the Geological Survey of Ireland as a branch of the Geological Survey of the UK, within the broader political context that Ireland was merely a provincial part of the British Empire. Although there are some rocks of this age in County Antrim in Northern Ireland, the Cretaceous, Eocene, Crag, and other works are mostly indicative of the geology of southeast England. The large format watercolors are likely to remain as an interesting footnote in paleontology, but one which shows the importance of the medium in the transmission of the message.

CONCLUSION

The many and varied geological and other artworks of George Victor Du Noyer have rightly garnered attention for the skill and often exquisite detail contained within them, especially in small size sketches, watercolors, and other works in notebooks or squeezed into blank space on a corner of a geological map. The large format watercolors described here, produced for educational lecture series, are equally skilled in delivering the detail of fossils and geological topics in a few bold brush strokes, which are entirely intended to be seen from the depths of a lecture room. Aside from the paleontological interest and the artistic merit on display, they are worthy of note as a historical equivalent of tools such as PowerPoint that we take for granted today.

ACKNOWLEDGMENTS

All images courtesy of the National Museum of Ireland.

REFERENCES CITED

Archer, J., 1995, Field folios: Du Noyer's outdoor geological artistry, *in* Croke, F., ed., Hidden Landscapes: George Victor Du Noyer 1817–1869: Dublin, National Gallery of Ireland, p. 48–63.

Buckland, W., 1823, Reliquiae Diluvianae; or, Observations on the Organic Remains Contained in Caves, Fissures, and Diluvial Gravel, and on Other Geological Phenomena, Attesting the Action of an Universal Deluge: London, Murray, viii + 303 p.

Buckland, W., 1836, Geology and Mineralogy Considered with Reference to Natural Theology, Volume 2, Bridgewater Treatise: London, Pickering, 128 p., https://doi.org/10.5962/bhl.title.125523.

Coffey, P., 1993, George Victor Du Noyer 1817–1869: Sheetlines, v. 35, p. 14–26.

Croke, F., ed., 1995, Hidden Landscapes George Victor Du Noyer 1817–1869: Dublin, National Gallery of Ireland, 88 p.

Cuvier, G., 1816, Le règne animal distribué d'après son organisation, pour servir de base à l'histoire naturelle des animaux et d'introduction à l'anatomie comparée. Tome 1. L'introduction, les mammifères et les oiseaux: Paris, Fortin, Masson et cie., 350 p., 100 pls.

Cuvier, G., 1827, Essay on the Theory of the Earth: Edinburgh, Blackwood, 550 p.

Hegarty, S., 2018, George Victor Du Noyer's career in the Ordnance and Geological Surveys (1835–69): Geologist by profession, artist by temperament: Proceedings of the Royal Irish Academy: Archaeology, Culture, History, Literature, v. 118C, p. 271–298.

Herries Davies, G.L., 1995, North from the Hook: 150 Years of the Geological Survey of Ireland: Dublin, Geological Survey of Ireland, 342 p.

Hind, W., 1898, The Carboniferous Lamellibranchiate, Part 3: Monographs of the Palaeontographical Society, v. 52, p. 209–276, https://doi.org/10.1080/02693445.1898.12035482.

Kaup, J.J., and Klipstein, A. von, 1836, Beschreibung und Abbildungen von dem in Rheinhessen aufgefundenen colossalen Schedel des Dinotherii gigantei mit geognostischen Mitteilungen über die knochenführenden

Bildungen des mittelrheinischen Tertiärbeckens: Darmstadt, Christian Friedrich Will, 53 p.
King, W., 1850, The Permian fossils of England [pls. i–xxviii.]: Monographs of the Palaeontographical Society, v. 3, no. 2, p. 1–258.
Manning, C., 2017, The Du Noyer Collection and its archaeological importance: Journal of the Royal Society of Antiquaries of Ireland, v. 147, p. 65–90.
Monaghan, N.T., 2001, Irish palaeontological illustrations of the 19th century, *in* Rushton, B.S., Hackney, P., and Tyrie, C.R., eds., Proceedings of the Systematics and Biological Collections Conference, Belfast, August 1996: Otley, West Yorkshire, Westbury Academic and Scientific Publishing, Linnean Society Occasional Publications 3, p. 83–91.
Monaghan, N.T., and Sides, E., 1995, Of fossils and fish: The palaeontological and zoological illustrations of George Victor Du Noyer, *in* Croke, F., ed., Hidden Landscapes: George Victor Du Noyer 1817–1869: Dublin, National Gallery of Ireland, p. 75–84.
Murray, P., ed., 2017, Stones, Slabs and Seascapes: George Victor Du Noyer's Images of Ireland: Cork, Crawford Art Gallery, 83 p.
Parkes, M.A., and Sleeman, A.G., 1997, Catalogue of type, figured and cited fossils in the Geological Survey of Ireland: Dublin, Geological Survey of Ireland, 124 p.
Parkes, M.A., Coffey, P., and Connaughton, P., 2000, The printing wood block collection of the Geological Survey of Ireland: The Geological Curator, v. 7, no. 4, p. 149–156.
Vaughan, L.B., ed., 1906, Hill's Practical Reference Library of General Knowledge: New York, Dickson, Hanson and Co., 4 vols.
Wilson, A., 1882, Elephants: Belgravia, v. 47, March–June, p. 420–441.
Wyse Jackson, P.N., and Parkes, M.A., 2009, William Hellier Baily (1819–1888): Forever an acting palaeontologist with the Geological Survey of Ireland: The Geological Curator, v. 9, no. 2, p. 57–84.

Manuscript Accepted by the Society 15 January 2021
Manuscript Published Online 28 October 2021

Printed in the USA

The Geological Society of America
Memoir 218

Nineteenth-century paleontological art in the Natural History Museum Vienna, Austria: Between demystification and mythologization

Stefanie Jovanovic-Kruspel*
Natural History Museum Vienna, History and Architecture, Burgring 7, 1010 Vienna, Austria

Mathias Harzhauser*
Natural History Museum Vienna, Geological-Paleontological Department, Burgring 7, 1010 Vienna, Austria

ABSTRACT

The nineteenth century was the dawn of scientific and systematic paleontology. The foundation of Natural History Museums—built as microcosmic "Books of Nature"—not only contributed to the establishment of this new discipline but also to its visual dissemination. This paper will take the metaphor of the "book" as a starting point for an examination of the paleontological exhibition at the Natural History Museum in Vienna. In keeping with "Natural Theology," the earliest natural science museums in Britain were designed as expressions of the medieval idea of the "Holy Book of Nature." Contrary to this, the Natural History Museum Vienna, opened in 1889, wanted to be a nonreligious museum of evolution. Nevertheless, the idea of the "book" was also influential for its design. According to the architects and the first director, it should be a modern "walk-in textbook" instructive for everyone. The most prominent exhibition hall in the museum is dedicated to paleontology. The hall's decorative scheme forms a unique "Paleo-Gesamtkunstwerk" (Gesamtkunstwerk: total piece of art). The use of grotesque and mythological elements is a particularly striking feature of the hall's decoration and raises the question of how this relates to the museum's claim to be a hard-core science institution. As it was paleontology's task to demystify the monsters and riddles of Earth history systematically, it seems odd that the decorative program connected explicitly to this world. This chapter sheds light on the cultural traditions that led to the creation of this ambiguous program that oscillates between science and imagination.

Looking at the results of the research on the nature of the earth, one looks into a book that contains the oldest history we humans know. With amazement, we see the wonders of the first epochs of the earth arising before our mind's eyes, and what until recently have been incomprehensible hieroglyphs is now almost completely clear to us. How many fables may have been created by the sudden appearance of prehistoric structures in the form of animals and plants? No fairy tales, no fantasies, tangible reality now stands before us and yet no less wonderful, even more wonderful, and this miracle has been achieved by science, the restless seeker.

—J. Hoffmann (undated, ca. 1885, p. 1; translation from German)

*stefanie.jovanovic@nhm-wien.ac.at; mathias.harzhauser@nhm-wien.ac.at

Jovanovic-Kruspel, S., and Harzhauser, M., 2022, Nineteenth-century paleontological art in the Natural History Museum Vienna, Austria: Between demystification and mythologization, *in* Clary, R.M., Rosenberg, G.D., and Evans, D.C., eds., The Evolution of Paleontological Art: Geological Society of America Memoir 218, p. 109–116, https://doi.org/10.1130/2021.1218(13).

INTRODUCTION

The "Book of Nature"

Over centuries, knowledge had been treasured in books, so it is not surprising that the newly established museums drew in their architecture on the intellectual concepts developed by literate culture dating back to medieval times (Holmes and Rogers, 2019). According to the medieval metaphor of the "Book of Nature," the natural world was interpreted as a book, which could be read to gain knowledge about God's creation. With the establishment of the first Natural History Museums (hereafter NHMs) around mid-century, this idea experienced a new interpretation. Consistent with the concept of Natural Theology, many Victorian natural science museums should be a microcosmic expression of the "Holy Book of Nature" (Holmes and Rogers, 2019; Yanni, 1999). The Oxford University Museum (1855–1860) became extremely influential as an architectural role model, and later NHMs followed exactly this idea. The carved angel holding a book in one hand and a living cell in the other by John Hungerford Pollen (1820–1902) over the entrance of the Oxford Museum is the visual expression of this concept. The museum's architecture and design—like the layout and binding of a book—was supposed to work as a "visual device," giving the visitor clear instruction on how to "read" the museum. This approach corresponded well with the concept of the "Gesamtkunstwerk" (total piece of art) of the architect Gottfried Semper (1803–1879), and the NHM Vienna took this idea to a climax.

The museum's first director, geologist Ferdinand von Hochstetter (1829–1884), was—in addition to his reputation as top geologist—also a very important proponent of public education. When Hochstetter was appointed director of the museum in 1876, he was already a renowned author of textbooks (e.g., *Allgemeine Erdkunde*, 1872, and *Geologische Bilder*, 1873). His textbook of 1873 was especially designed in the spirit of the idea of "visual education" (German: Anschauungsunterricht), which at that time was gaining acceptance as a teaching method. Hochstetter's clear mission was to make the new NHM Vienna not only a leading scientific research institute, but also an important public educational institution (Hochstetter, 1884).

In keeping with the ideas of the "Gesamtkunstwerk" and "Anschauungsunterricht," Hochstetter worked together with the architects Gottfried Semper (1803–1879) and Carl Freiherr von Hasenauer (1833–1894) to make the NHM Vienna a modern "walk-in textbook of nature" instructive for everyone. The architectural scheme in the museum's upper ground floor follows a general pattern: while the walls of the exhibition rooms were kept monochrome as not to distract from the objects on display, the frieze zone (under the ceiling) was used to didactically expand on the collections. This was done with the aid of paintings and, in some rooms, with the aid of sculptures. Despite the decorations' restriction to the margins of the rooms, their importance must not be underestimated. On the contrary, it seems that the decorative schemes were designed to act like a "visual foreword" to the exhibition. This is also emphasized by the fact that in the first guidebook of the museum, which was published for the museum's opening in 1889, the presentation of the exhibitions in each room was preceded by a thorough description of the decorative program (Hauer, 1889). Hochstetter became responsible for the content of the decorations, which left him to decide on the topics and with the task of providing the artists with possible templates (Jovanovic-Kruspel and Schumacher, 2014).

PALEONTOLOGY IN THE NHM VIENNA

When the construction work for the NHM Vienna started in 1871, it was not yet decided which topics this "walk-in textbook of nature" was to contain in detail. With Hochstetter's assignment as director (1876), Emperor Franz Joseph I (1830–1916) also approved a new organizational plan designed by Hochstetter. According to this plan, the new scientific disciplines of paleontology, ethnography, anthropology, and prehistory were integrated into the museum, thus making the NHM Vienna a consequent museum of evolution (Jovanovic-Kruspel and Schumacher, 2014; Jovanovic-Kruspel, 2018). In this evolutionary museum concept, the presentation of the historicity of nature attained special significance. Already in 1858–1859, during his exploration of New Zealand, on the occasion of the expedition of the SMS *Novara*, Ferdinand von Hochstetter had started to focus on paleontology (Unger et al., 1864). Hochstetter dedicated five entire rooms to the newly established Department of Paleontology in the new museum. Among them was also the largest and by far the most prominent exhibition hall in the museum. Hall X, located in the very center of the museum behind the main stairwell, was to present the collection of fossil birds and mammals. A collection of fossil plants was displayed on the back wall (Hauer, 1889). In terms of content, Hall X also stood in an intermediate position. In the museum's overarching exhibition narrative, it marked the border between Earth and cultural history. The presentation of the fossil contemporaries of the European Stone Age man created the transition to prehistory: the adjoining rooms on the one side (Hall XI) displayed human prehistory and, on the other side (Hall IX), the rocks and fauna of the Cenozoic Era.

THE BOOK OF EARTH HISTORY

Through the discoveries of the Earth sciences, the analogy of the "Book of Nature" gained new significance. Hochstetter wrote: "Just as the stone slabs of rock lie over one another, layer by layer, a thousand feet high, so he [the geologist; author's note] reads from the same, as from the pages of a book, the history of the individual periods of the earth's formation…" [translation from German] (Hochstetter, 1873, p. 1). When the furnishing of Hall X began in the 1880s, Hochstetter designed the hall as a "total work of paleontological art" by incorporating sculptures and paintings, which were aligned with the collections. Realizing that "reading the book of Earth's history" solely by stratigraphy and by interpreting fossils and rocks was only possible for a small elite of experts, he wanted the hall to follow the concept of "visual education." Hochstetter's experience in writing scientific textbooks for schools and also for children inspired many aspects of the hall's decorative scheme.

The "Paleo-Gesamtkunstwerk"

According to the general architectural concept, the corner halls and the central hall of the upper ground floor were decorated by both paintings and sculptures. This combination of sculptures and paintings adapted to paleontology makes the furnishing of Hall X a "Paleo-Gesamtkunstwerk," which is unique in its kind. Both decorative elements, the paintings and the sculptures, complement and at the same time contrast with the collections displayed. Each is inspired—albeit in different ways—by the idea of the book. An individual examination first of the pictures and then of the sculptures will illuminate the differences and also the similarities of the components as well as their interplay.

Paleo-Paintings

Hall X was decorated with a total of 17 paintings (Fig. 1) by three different Austrian painters: Josef Hoffmann (1831–1904), Heinrich Otto (1832–1902), and Robert Russ (1847–1922). One of the artists, Hoffmann, published a description of the decorative concept of Hall X in a booklet titled "Erläuterungen zu den Gemälden. Die Bildungs-Epochen der Erde und Charakterbilder für Asien und Central-Afrika":

> The plan drawn up by the late Director, Ferdinand von Hochstetter, was to present characteristic pictures of the five continents of the world: Central Africa, South Asia, South America and South Australia should each be in one of the four corners of the room, while Europe should be represented on the main wall of the room through the portrayal of the various eras of the Earth with "The marine fauna and flora of the Silurian and Devonian periods," "The animal world of the Carboniferous period," "Characteristic picture of the Carboniferous period in Bohemia," "Characteristic picture of the Triassic period," combining the Northern and the Southern Limestone Alps, "The marine fauna and flora of the Jura in south-west Germany," "The Cretaceous period in Lower Austria at the Hohe Wand near Wiener Neustadt" and "The Miocene period [*sic*]." On the opposite wall, the main types of today's

Figure 1. *Ideal Landscape of the Upper Cretaceous, Lower Austrian Alps*, Josef Hoffmann, ca. 1885, in Hall X; photo courtesy of A. Schumacher.

world of plants are to be symbolised by examples of cactus, lilies, orchids and aroids. The last four pictures and the paintings of America and Australia are not yet to be executed." [translation from German] (Hoffmann, undated, ca. 1885, p. 3 and 4)

The described combination of recent "character-pictures" and paleontological reconstructions had its forerunner in Hochstetter's (1873) picture book *Geologische Bilder* (*Geological Pictures*). Whereas this book presented primeval landscapes combined with modern geological formations, the decorative concept of the paintings in the hall showed a juxtaposition of European primeval landscape reconstructions with recent vegetation images from other parts of the world. Like in his picture book, Hochstetter wanted the visitor to realize that Earth's history had not come to an end. While the picture book should illustrate that the same forces that "dominated the course of development of Earth's history in primeval times" were also the "effective causes of change in the present" (Hochstetter, 1873, p. 15), the paintings in Hall X were intended to create a link between fossil and contemporary plant life. In this way, it also mirrored the working method of paleobotany in the nineteenth century, in which detailed morphological comparisons with recent plants were used to determine fossil remains (e.g., Ettingshausen, 1861).

In particular, the seven paintings created by Josef Hoffmann can be considered important works of paleontological art and, therefore, deserve closer examination. Three of the seven paintings are landscapes and four are still lifes. Hoffmann's series of paleo-paintings is the first in Europe to be integrated into a museum context. The incorporation of primeval paintings as didactic enhancement in a museum has only one predecessor in the United States. In 1875, Benjamin Waterhouse Hawkins (1807–1894), who is renowned for the creation of the first 3-D models of dinosaurs for the Crystal Palace (1854), was commissioned with a series of 17 huge panoramic paintings of geological eras, which were also located in the frieze zone of the new Elizabeth Marsh Museum of Geology and Archaeology at the College of New Jersey (now Princeton University). As Gosse (2010, p. 3) states, with this a new museum tradition was started: "Hawkins' murals are the first paintings illustrating this theme, setting a precedent for natural history museums in the decades to come." It is quite possible that Hochstetter knew about these paintings and was encouraged by them for his own plan for Hall X. Hoffmann's three paleo-landscapes stand in a tradition of primeval visualization reaching back to the first half of the nineteenth century. The first attempt to reconstruct a whole habitat of the primeval world stems from the English geologist Henry De la Beche (1796–1855). His watercolor *Dura antiquior*, dated 1830, is considered the first published depiction of primeval life that is really based on fossil evidence (Rudwick, 1992). Compared to Hoffmann's paintings in the NHM Vienna, De la Beche's watercolor was only a singular flashback in time.

The first attempt to reconstruct a succession of geological periods in ideal landscapes took place in Austria. In 1851, the Austrian paleobotanist Franz Xaver Unger (1800–1870) published his book *Die Urwelt in ihren verschiedenen Bildungsepochen*, which visualized the primeval periods in Earth history in 14 landscape pictures (Unger, 1851, 1863 [English version]). Unger found a partner in Josef Kuwasseg (1799–1859), a renowned Styrian landscape painter and lithographer. Supervised by Unger, Kuwasseg created an atlas of 14 lithographs of primeval landscapes with special focus on the paleontological flora. The project of creating this atlas of primeval landscapes was clearly seen by Unger as an educational endeavor (Stoffel, 2018). The illustrations of Unger's book hit the nerve of time and became the epitome of how to imagine Earth's history. Through lanternslides, these images found the widest distribution (Jovanovic-Kruspel and Olivares, 2017; Stoffel, 2018). For the paleontological landscapes, Kuwasseg defined the point of view as if the beholder were standing in the middle of the reconstructed landscape. By this, Kuwasseg took the observer on an imaginary, but at the same time fact-based, journey back in time (Hubmann and Moser, 2006).

A very similar approach was taken by Hoffmann in his museum landscapes. Just as Kuwasseg, he wanted the spectator to really have the impression of being in the scene. All three landscape paintings feature ideal areas located in the Austro-Hungarian Empire. In the *Ideal Landscape of the Cretaceous Period Lower Austrian Alps*, Hoffmann even used the topographically well-known landscape of the Hohe Wand mountain range close to Emmersberg and transferred it to the Cretaceous Period (Fig. 1). In the description of this painting, Hoffmann gives the impression that he really thought the landscape looked like this in Cretaceous time. However, at that time geologists already knew that this specific topographic formation had formed much later. This inconsistency raises the question of how much accuracy was really required or whether other intentions also played a role. One possible reason for this inaccuracy could be that using a well-known landscape would grip the visitor's attention, thus opening his imagination for a deeper engagement with paleontology.

Nevertheless, Hoffmann stated that his paintings were created "conscientiously and strictly according to all the results of science" (Hoffmann, undated, ca. 1885). In a newspaper article, Hoffmann remarked that he could not have completed the pictures without the richness of the collections of the Imperial Geological Survey in Vienna, and the famous geologist Dionýs Štúr (1817–1893), at that time head of this institution, supervised Hoffmann (Ranzoni, 1885).

However, looking more closely at Hoffmann's other paintings in the hall, especially at the still lifes, it is obvious that Hoffmann was given considerable artistic freedom in his compositions. The four still lifes represent ornamentally arranged reconstructions of stratigraphically characteristic fossils (Fig. 2), which already hint stylistically in the direction of Art Nouveau (Jovanovic-Kruspel and Olivares, 2017). To achieve better artistic results, Hoffmann even gave up using the exact proportions (Hoffmann, undated, ca. 1885), and this was obviously tolerated by his scientific advisers. Despite this, the paintings' main purpose still was to instruct wide audiences.

Figure 2. *Marine Fauna and Flora, Silurian and Devonian Periods* and *Marine Fauna and Flora, Jura*, both by Josef Hoffmann, ca. 1885, in Hall X, Natural History Museum Vienna; photo courtesy of A. Schumacher.

Soon after their completion (May/June 1885), Josef Hoffmann exhibited his paintings at the "Österreichischer Kunstverein," and Hoffmann held talks about the paintings' content for the interested public (3 June 1885; see Ranzoni, 1885). The paintings' didactic function as educative illustrations in the walk-in textbook museum was considered successful as a report on the exhibition states: "Whoever takes the trouble to read the catalogue and to look at the paintings would learn more in one hour's time about the evolution of earth than by sitting for half a day over a geological book" (Ranzoni, 1885, p. 4). The paintings in the hall, however, are only part of the "total work of art." The sculptural program of Hall X was at least as important, if not even more formative, for the general impression.

Paleo-Sculptures

In addition to the 17 paintings, a series of 24 figures by the Austrian sculptor Rudolf Weyr (1847–1914) decorates the hall. Weyr's sculptures are to this day the determining element in this room (Fig. 3). Although due to the white overpainting that covers their original partially bright colorings, the figures appear considerably more discreet than at the time of the museum's opening (Jovanovic-Kruspel and Hoffmann, 2019). Their peculiar moment of the "grotesque" is nevertheless dominant and deserves special attention. Weyr's series of "caryatides" had the general task of illustrating the evolution of plants and animals during Earth's history in the last 500 million years. (The term "caryatides" is historically incorrect, as the figures had no load-bearing function but were only pilasters with a human upper body. We will stick to this term as it was used when the sculptures were created [Nossig, 1889].) The first guidebook of the museum describes the program:

> On the long wall to the left of the entrance door they represent in the row from left to right: algae, lepidodendrons, Paleozoic ferns, cycads,

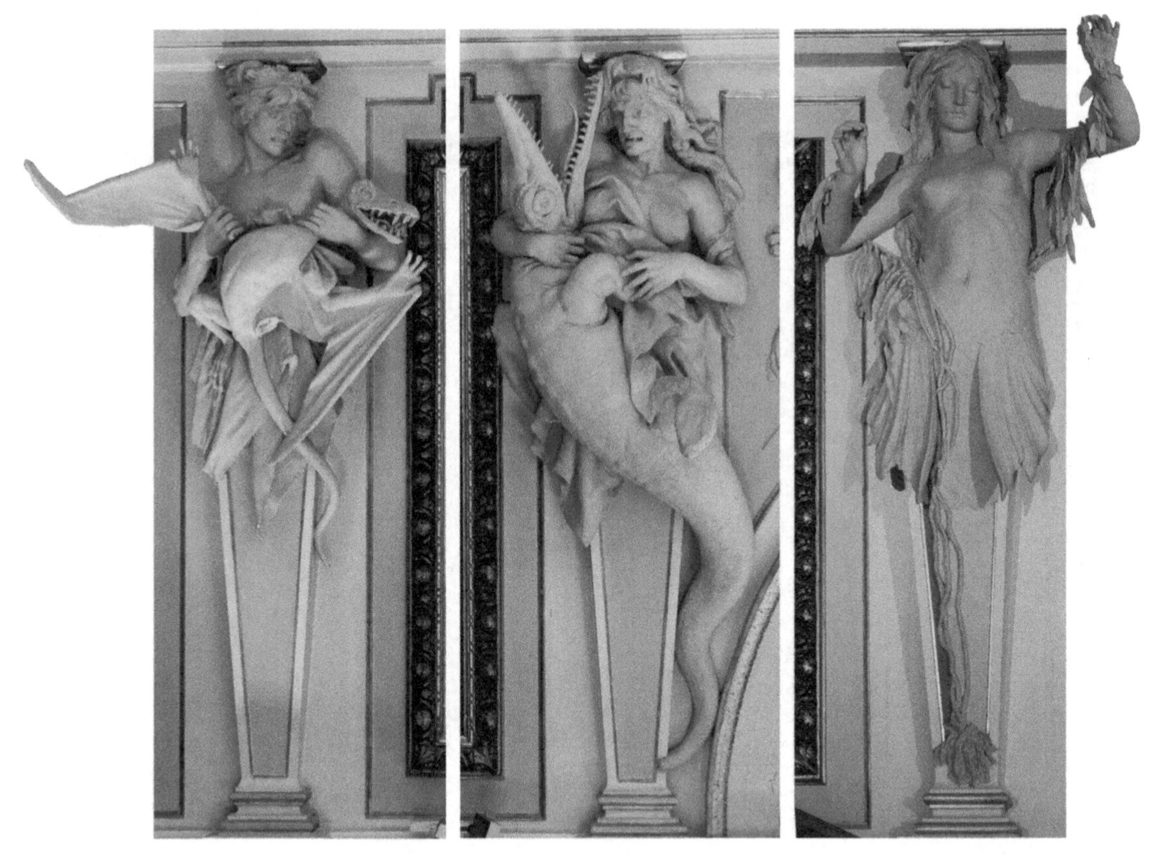

Figure 3. Caryatides representing *Rhamphorhynchus,* an ichthyosaur and algae by Rudolf Weyr, 1884/1885, in Hall X, Natural History Museum Vienna; photo courtesy of A. Schumacher.

Mesozoic palms, and oak, beech and flower-bearing Cenozoic plants. On the other three walls, beginning to the right of the entrance door and proceeding from right to left: Graptolites, crinoids, *Paradoxides* (a trilobite genus) and *Phragmoceras* (belonging to the nautiloids) as representatives of the Paleozoic period; further at the window wall sponges and corals, sea urchins, crabs, Turrilites, ammonites, *Plesiosaurus*, *Ichthyosaurus* and *Pterodactylus*, all from the Mesozoic period [*sic*], finally at the wall above the exit door: *Dinoceras*, *Dinotherium*, *Sivatherium* and Irish Giant Deer from the Cenozoic era. [translation from German] (Hauer, 1889, p. 122)

However, any attempt to read the series as a visualization of a specific scientific theory of development (formulated by Lamarck or Darwin) fails. Weyr did not want to illustrate any scientific theory, but sought his own artistic and poetic approach (Nossig, 1889). The figures' grotesque features pay tribute to their late baroque predecessors, such as the herms on the *Wallpavillion* by the sculptors Balthasar Permoser and Paul Egell (from around 1718) at the Zwinger in Dresden, Germany. Weyr's caryatides are in many ways the embodiment of what the word "grotesque" means. Not only were his figures hybrids between static elements (the pilasters) and human figures, but even their humanity was questioned by references to mythological, fantastic, and monstrous creatures. The original meaning of the word "grotesque" derives from the ornamental decorations of antique palaces and thermal baths that were discovered at the end of the fifteenth century below ground and mistakenly interpreted as decorations of caves (le grotte). Characteristic of these decorations was the fusion of contrasts, through tendrils, architectural elements, and ornaments. Although monstrous and hybrid figures were rare in the antique grotesques, in its sixteenth-century revival, the frescoes abounded with hybrids and monsters (Hansen and Skovbjerg Paldam, 2015, p. 86). In antiquity, monstrosities or grotesque creatures were believed to inhabit the margins of the world (Pliny the Elder, *Historia Naturalis*, 77 CE). This marginalization in their believed place of existence was also mirrored in their place in art. In medieval times, monsters increasingly appear in the margins of illuminated books or in the sculptural decorations of cathedrals or cloisters (Hansen and Skovbjerg Paldam, 2015). The concept of the medieval manuscript with its marginal designs containing monsters and hybrids not only found its reflection in medieval architecture, but also in the "cathedrals of modern times," the museums (Holmes and Rogers, 2019).

Like the paintings in Hall X, which have been interpreted above as illustrations in the "walk-in textbook," the caryatides also seem to reference to the idea of the book. Whereas the paintings are connected to the idea of the modern school book, the caryatides tie in with a much older concept of book: the medieval manuscript. Similar to marginal designs in an illuminated medieval book, which often contained grotesque monsters and hybrids that "could reinforce the meaning of the primary text, or they could work against it" (Holmes and Rogers, 2019; Rogers, 2018), the grotesque decorations of the hall—located under its ceiling—can be interpreted as a visual subtext to the exhibition. Read like this, the sculptures by Rudolf Weyr had the task of somewhat thwarting the primary scientific narrative of the exhibition by opening the visitor's imagination to the world of ambiguity between science and mythology. Three of the caryatids present, in their attributes, the reconstructions of "living" Mesozoic animals, such as a *Rhamphorhynchus* (erroneously listed as *Pterodactylus* by Hauer, 1889) and an ichthyosaur. The figures seem to struggle and even fight to control the beasts they are holding. The attempt to show these creatures, which date from the early 1880s, as living and breathing beasts makes them the first scientifically reconstructed 3-D models created in Austria and probably in the whole of the European mainland. The idea for this came from England, where such reconstructions were carried out almost 30 years earlier for the purposes of exhibitions and for the decorative furnishing of the Natural History Museum in London. The *Antediluvian Monsters* of London's Crystal Palace by Benjamin Waterhouse Hawkins (1807–1894) are surely the first and most influential predecessors of Weyr's sculptures. Hawkins, who worked closely with geologist Richard Owen (1804–1892), saw his reconstructions as a form of "visual education." Also, the figures of extinct animals by architect Alfred Waterhouse (1830–1905) on the NHM London's facade were—despite being based on Owen's scientific papers—criticized by contemporaries as "incorrect and grotesque" (Stearn, 2001, p. 49).

The example of the ichthyosaur-caryatide illustrates impressively that Weyr's figure is an ambiguous combination of scientific accuracy and free artistic representation. The fact that the ichthyosaur features large scleral rings in the eye sockets corresponds to the knowledge of the time (Hochstetter, 1873, p. 11 and fig. 4). In the 1880s, these rings were still erroneously believed to have been visible on the living animal. In contrast, the ichthyosaur's tail was already generally accepted to have had some kind of fin, even though its exact form was not known before 1892, when a complete ichthyosaur with a tail fin was found (Fraas, 1892). Despite this, Weyr's ichthyosaur was represented with a pointed lizard-type tail, which made it look more like a dragon than a dinosaur. This inaccuracy raises the question: why? Crossing the border between scientific reconstruction and fantastic compensation of scientific flaws is certainly a general hallmark of paleontological art that makes it vulnerable to being outdated. Paleontological art always has to struggle with the problem of becoming anachronistic as science progresses. The architectural integration of paleontological art in the NHM Vienna made this problem even more acute as the decorations were not removable when outdated. Weyr's decision to promote historicism and a conscious mythologization could be interpreted as one possible way out of the conundrums of anachronism (Jovanovic-Kruspel, 2019). All of the other caryatides feature fossil plants and animals without the reconstruction of soft tissue. Most animals from the Cenozoic Era, such as the elephantid *Deinotherium* and the giant deer *Megaloceros,* have not been restored and are represented by skulls held by figures resembling Ice Age hunters in fur clothes. Only the head of the giraffid *Sivatherium* was reconstructed to be life-like. Many of the caryatids—especially those that represent sea organisms—are hybrids of nature and humanity, like mermaids, mermen, and green men.

With careful scrutiny, beards made of leaves and algae sprouting on breasts and arms can be found in many figures as well as scaled fish tails and fins, which eventually merge into the pilasters. As Laurent (2017) pointed out, creatures such as the mermaid not only fit neatly with the concept of missing links in the context of evolution, but they were also a visual rendering of the process of fish coming out of the water to become mammals. The figures' hybridity reminds us of the idea of the metamorphism, which related artistically to some aspects of the evolutionist variability of species. Looking more closely at the caryatides, it is also striking to see that many of the mermaids have lowered their gazes; their eyes are only half open. They seem to look into themselves or even to dream. The caryatides stand on the border between nature and humanity, between interior and exterior, between dream and reality. Their introspection makes them a mirror image of the visitor. Like the figure, the visitor should open his or her inner eye to the imagination of the past.

CONCLUSION

The paleo-Gesamtkunstwerk of Hall X was intended to make the history of the Earth readable. However, the "book" being opened here for the visitor was not a strict scientific textbook but rather an example of "scientific fiction." It tells of fairy tales and wonders, of history as well as of scientific facts and eventual historical realities. The grotesque sculptures especially—originally partly brightly colored—must have been much more dominant in their expression. As marginal designs, they artistically counteract the scientific narrative of the exhibition. The sculptural program's emphasis on the grotesque and hybridity can be interpreted as an artistic answer to the concept of changeability connected to evolutionary species variability. The idea that everything is in constant flux was one of the disturbing realizations of the nineteenth century. The associated feeling of insecurity led to a new desire for mythology, which found its expression in the art of symbolism. Rudolf Weyr's caryatids can be seen as a first indication of this trend, paving the way to a hitherto unknown subjectivism that became the basis for modernism.

ACKNOWLEDGMENTS

We thank Alice Schumacher (Natural History Museum Vienna) for taking the pictures of the paintings and sculptures. We are also grateful for the inspirational conversations with Janine Rogers (Mount Allison University, Canada) and John Holmes (University of Birmingham, UK).

REFERENCES CITED

Ettingshausen, C.v., 1861, Die Blattskelette der Dikotyledonen. Mit besonderer Rücksicht auf die Untersuchung und Bestimmung der fossilen Pflanzenreste: Wien, k. k. Hof- und Staatsdruckerei, 308 p.

Fraas, E., 1892, Ueber einen neuen Fund von Ichthyosaurus in Württemberg: Neues Jahrbuch für Mineralogie, Geognosie: Geologie und Petrefaktenkunde, v. 3, p. 87–90.

Gosse, A., 2010, The Victorians' Dinosaurs: GardenStateLegacy.com, v. 10, p. 1–6, http://gardenstatelegacy.com/files/The_Victorians_Dinosaurs_Gossen_GSL103.pdf (accessed December 2019).

Hann, J., Hochstetter, F.v., and Pokorny, A., 1872, Allgemeine Erdkunde. Ein Leitfaden der astronomischen Geographie, Meterologie, Geologie und Biologie: Prag, Tempsky, 372 p.

Hansen, M.F., and Skovbjerg Paldam, C., 2015, Grotesque! Strategies of figurative genesis in the sixteenth century and in the Surrealism of the 1920s and 1930s, *in* Skovbjerg Paldam, C., and Wamberg, J., eds., Art, Technology and Nature: Renaissance to Postmodernity: London and New York, Routledge Taylor & Francis Group, p. 81–102.

Hauer, F.v., 1889, Allgemeiner Führer durch das k. k. naturhistorische Hofmuseum: Wien, Naturhistorisches Museum Wien, 368 p.

Hochstetter, F.v., 1873, Geologische Bilder der Vorwelt und der Jetztwelt. Zum Anschauungs-Unterricht und zur Belehrung in Schule und Familie: Esslingen, Schreiber, 37 p.

Hochstetter F. v., 1884, Das k. k. Hof-Mineraliencabinet in Wien, die Geschichte seiner Sammlungen und die Pläne für die Neuaufstellung derselben in dem k. k. naturhistorischen Hofmuseum. Zwei Vorträge, gehalten in den Sitzungen der geol. Reichsanstalt am 5. und 19. Februar 1884: Jahrbuch der kaiserlich-königlichen Geologischen Reichsanstalt, v. 34, p. 263–298.

Hoffmann, J., undated, ca. 1885, Erläuterungen zu den Gemälden. Die Bildungs-Epochen der Erde und Charakterbilder für Asien und Central-Afrika: Wien, J.B. Wallishauser, 13 p.

Holmes, J., and Rogers, J., 2019, Monkey business: The Victorian natural history museum, evolution, and the medieval manuscript: Romanticism on the Net, v. 70, p. 3357, https://research.birmingham.ac.uk/portal/files/58941499/RoN70_03_RogersHolmes.pdf (accessed December 2019).

Hubmann, B., and Moser, B., 2006, "Biedermeierliche" Rekonstruktionen geologischer Ökosysteme durch Joseph Kuwasseg und Franz Unger: Berichte des Institutes für Erdwissenschaften, Graz: Karl Franzens Universität, v. 12, p. 32–34.

Jovanovic-Kruspel, S., 2018, Das Wiener Naturhistorische Museum und die Rezeption von Darwin(ismus) aus kunsthistorischer Perspektive, *in* Mathis, H., and Reiter, W.L., eds., Darwin in Zentraleuropa. Die wissenschaftliche, weltanschauliche und populäre Rezeption im 19. und frühen 20. Jahrhundert: Wien, LIT Verlag, p. 427–445.

Jovanovic-Kruspel, S., 2019, 'Visual histories' science visualization in nineteenth-century natural history museums: Museum and Society, v. 17, no. 3, p. 404–421, https://doi.org/10.29311/mas.v17i3.3234.

Jovanovic-Kruspel, S., and Hoffmann, H., 2019, Buntes Lehrbuch der Natur? Zur Farbigkeit der Stuckplastiken in den Schausälen des Naturhistorischen Museums in Wien: Annalen des Naturhistorischen Museums in Wien, v. A121, p. 327–351.

Jovanovic-Kruspel, S., and Olivares, O., 2017, The primeval world by the Austrian painter Josef Hoffmann (1831–1904)—A cross over between art and science and its export to Mexico: Jahrbuch der Geologischen Bundesanstalt, Wien, v. 157, p. 269–299.

Jovanovic-Kruspel, S., and Schumacher, A., 2014, Das Naturhistorische Museum. Baugeschichte, Konzeption & Architektur: Wien, Naturhistorisches Museum Wien, 264 p.

Laurent, B., 2017, Monster or missing link? The mermaid and the Victorian imagination: Cahiers Victoriens & Edouardiens, v. 85, p. 1–17, https://doi.org/10.4000/cve.3188.

Nossig, A., 1889, Die Schausäle des naturhistorischen Hofmuseums: Allgemeine Kunst-Chronik, v. 17, p. 479–482.

Ranzoni, E., 1885, Kunstblatt: Malerei: Neue Freie Presse, v. 1885, p. 4.

Rogers, J., 2018, Graffiti and the Medieval margin, *in* Frood, E., Harmanşah, Ö., Ragazzoli, C., and Salvador, C., eds., Scribbling Through History: Graffiti, Places and People from Antiquity to Modernity: London, Bloomsbury, p. 175–188.

Rudwick, M.J.S., 1992, Scenes from Deep Time. Early Pictorial Representations of the Prehistoric World: Chicago, The University of Chicago Press, 280 p., https://doi.org/10.7208/chicago/9780226149035.001.0001.

Stearn, W.T., 2001, The Natural History Museum at South Kensington. A History of the Museum 1753–1980: London, Natural History Museum, 414 p.

Stoffel, P., 2018, Prähistorische Landschaften. Die Inszenierung der Tiefenzeit, *in* Balke, F., Siegert, B., and Vogl, J., eds., Mikrozeit und Tiefenzeit, Archiv für Mediengeschichte: Leiden, Boston, Paderborn, Wilhelm Fink Verlag, p. 35–46, https://doi.org/10.30965/9783846764176_005.

Unger, F., 1851, Die Urwelt in ihren verschiedenen Bildungsperioden. 14 landschaftliche Darstellungen mit erläuterndem Texte: Gratz, Minsinger, 40 p.

Unger, F., 1863, Ideal Views of the Primitive World in Its Geological and Palaeontological Phases (English edition): London, S. Highley, 32 p.

Unger, F., Zittel, K., Suess, E., Karrer, F., Stoliczka, F., Stache, G., and Jaeger, G., 1864, Paläontologie von Neu-Seeland, Beiträge zur Kenntniss der fossilen Flora und Fauna der Provinzen Auckland und Nelson, Redigirt von Dr. Ferdinand von Hochstetter, Dr. Moritz Hörnes, and Franz Ritter von Hauer. Novara-Expedition: Geologischer Theil I. Band, 2. Abtheilung, with 26 plates, Vienna, Kaiserlich-Königliche Hof- und Staatsdruckerei; in Commission bei K. Gerold's Sohn, 318 p.

Yanni, C., 1999, Nature's Museums: Victorian Science and the Architecture of Display: Baltimore, Maryland, Johns Hopkins University Press, 220 p.

Manuscript Accepted by the Society 15 January 2021
Manuscript Published Online 22 September 2021

Printed in the USA

The Geological Society of America
Memoir 218

The use of artwork to document geologic systems in The Geology of Russia *(1845)*

John Diemer
Department of Geography and Earth Sciences, University of North Carolina at Charlotte, 9201 University City Boulevard, Charlotte, North Carolina 28223, USA

Lydia Diemer
Center for the Book, University of Iowa, 216 North Hall, Iowa City, Iowa 52242, USA

ABSTRACT

Artwork in *The Geology of Russia* (1845) documents the extent and fossil content of several Paleozoic systems in Europe and large tracts of Russia. That artwork conveys a sense of landscape, portrays the distribution of strata both at and below the surface, and documents the fossil evidence for identifying several Paleozoic geologic systems. The artwork includes wood engravings, lithographs, zincographs, and copper plate engravings. The choice of technique was governed by the content and desired character of the images and the logistics of printing. Roderick Murchison was a master of organization who commissioned, assembled, and oversaw the production of artwork that was crucial to presenting the evidence for the Paleozoic systems documented in *The Geology of Russia* (1845).

INTRODUCTION

The use of artwork to visually record observations and present interpretations has been essential to the development of geology as a science as illustrations are powerful tools for transmitting geologic information (Betz, 1963; Oldroyd, 1990, 1996, 2013; Rudwick, 1992, 2005; Secord, 1986). In this chapter the importance of artwork to the scientific output of a leading geologist of his day, Roderick Murchison (1792–1871), is discussed. Throughout his career, artwork was an integral part of Murchison's research methodology (Collie and Diemer, 2004; Diemer, 1996, 2008, 2016, 2018; Geikie, 1875). He used artwork to convey a sense of landscape, portray the distribution of strata both at and below the surface, and document the fossil evidence for establishing geologic systems (Murchison, 1839, 1854; Murchison et al., 1845). Murchison used many kinds of artwork in his publications including wood engravings, lithographs, zincographs, and copper plate engravings (Thackray, 1972, 1978a, 1978b; Torrens, 1990).

In examining *The Geology of Russia* (1845) it is apparent that Murchison's use of artwork was sophisticated and met his objectives. The artwork provided an efficient way to integrate stratigraphic and paleontological observations to document changing fossil assemblages throughout much of the Paleozoic. Thus, in this chapter, we will not limit the discussion to depictions of fossils alone, but will introduce the full range of artwork used by Murchison and his co-authors in *The Geology of Russia* (1845), whereby they placed the fossil evidence in its stratigraphic and geologic context. By engaging in an integrative approach, Murchison was able to convincingly document not only the Silurian System but also the Devonian and Permian Systems (Murchison, 1842; Rudwick, 1985).

Diemer, J., and Diemer, L., 2022, The use of artwork to document geologic systems in *The Geology of Russia* (1845), *in* Clary, R.M., Rosenberg, G.D., and Evans, D.C., eds., The Evolution of Paleontological Art: Geological Society of America Memoir 218, p. 117–126, https://doi.org/10.1130/2021.1218(14).

THE GEOLOGY OF RUSSIA (1845) VOLUME 1

The Geology of Russia is a large format quarto two-volume book published by John Murray and Paul Bertrand in 1845. Volume 1 (662 numbered pages) was mainly written by Murchison and focuses on "geology," and Volume 2 (512 pages) was written in French by Edouard de Verneuil and focuses on "paleontology." When examining the book, the question that immediately comes to mind is, why publish a large format book? After all, such books were expensive to produce and to acquire and required sustained effort over the course of many years to publish. One reason could be that the number and size of pages available in a large format book allowed Murchison and his co-authors to fully develop their ideas and present their data in the most effective manner. In particular, a large format book would allow them to use a variety of illustrations, both large and small, to present their ideas.

Another reason may have to do with the financing of such a book. In the early nineteenth century, it was possible, with advanced notice, to persuade interested people to subscribe to a yet-to-be-written book (Torrens, 1983). Such large format books would, for example, be suitable for display in personal libraries, including those of large country estates. In the case of *The Geology of Russia*, the Russian government subsidized the production of the book, an arrangement that no doubt pleased John Murray, the publisher of Volume 1. Also, Murchison's financial status had improved upon the death of his mother-in-law in 1838, when his wife received a substantial inheritance (Geikie, 1875).

Volume 1 of *The Geology of Russia* (1845) includes 83 wood engravings, 12 scenic lithographs, and seven copper plate engravings. In the case of the wood engravings, the height of the block was the same as that of the text blocks being assembled by the printer, and both could therefore be run through the press together when printing (Gascoigne, 1986). Murchison referred to this form of illustration as "woodcuts"; however, that medium was largely replaced by "wood engravings" by the middle of the eighteenth century (Gascoigne, 1986). The basic difference is that linework for woodcuts is cut away from the plank edge of the wood, while wood engravings rely on reducing and creating the imagery on the end grain, which is a much stronger portion of the wood that can hold up longer in the printing process and provides finer image quality.

An example of one of the wood engravings in *The Geology of Russia* (1845, p. 13) that was later redrafted for *Siluria* (1854) appears in Figure 1. The key section at Krok-kleiva in Norway first appeared in Murchison's field notebook (M/N 100, p. 19, Geological Society of London archives). The section links the topography along the transect with the attitude of the stratigraphy labeled below the ground surface. As was his practice, Murchison used simple graphic patterns suitable for wood engravings and labeled the strata using letters that were explained in a legend. The original field book sketch clearly captured the moment when Murchison discovered evidence of both Silurian and Devonian strata at this key section (see Diemer, 2008).

In the case of lithographs, the original field sketches were converted by professional lithographers into "scenic" landscapes and printed at a lithography firm for insertion into the final book (e.g., Fig. 2). The scenic plates were used to convey a sense of the landscape and its underlying geology that is more "painterly" in style than either wood or copper engravings (Antreasian and Adams, 1971). The linework for the lithographs has tonal qualities that are suggestive of rapid handwork, and the width of the lines could be manipulated to depict the variation in land surfaces and vegetation. The lithograph printing process was less time-consuming, and therefore lithographs were cheaper to produce than copper plate engravings. The original sketch for Figure 2 was made by Murchison, and the lithograph was prepared by Louis Haghe, a partner in the firm Day and Haghe, Lithographers to the Queen. Murchison clearly was fascinated by the new sights and cultures that he encountered during his expedition to the Urals, and this lithograph captures an evocative scene at a Bashkir camp.

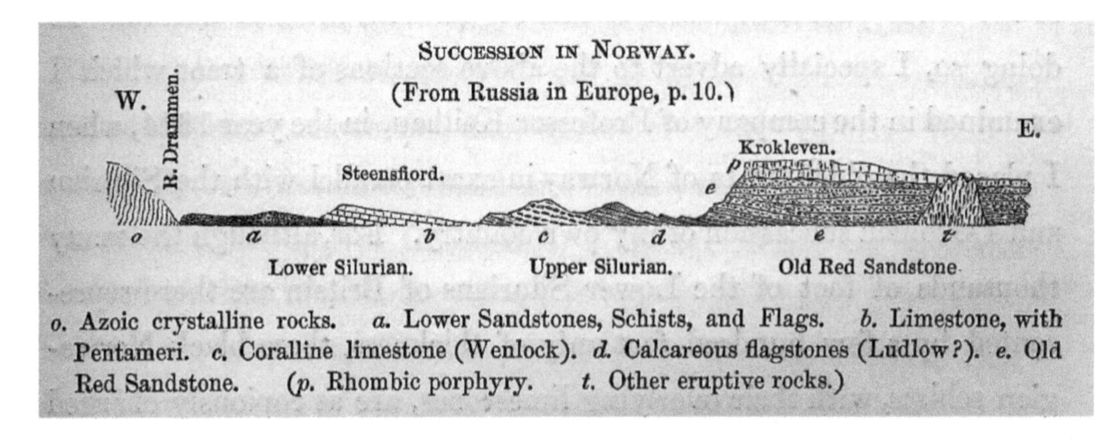

Figure 1. The Krok-Kleiva cross-section is shown as it appears in *Siluria* (1854, p. 319), modified from figure 1 in *The Geology of Russia* (1845, p. 13). Note that Murchison habitually used a lettering scheme to label units, and that scheme was explained in the legend.

Figure 2 is an example of a stone lithograph. Close examination reveals that the image is sitting on the surface of the paper, and there is no embossment or raised ink. The flat nature of the image is typical of a planographic process like lithography (Antreasian and Adams, 1971; Gascoigne, 1986; Hullmandel, 1982). Essentially the matrix (in this case stone) was completely flat, and all of the image-making was derived from a chemical transformation of the stone. This contrasts with prints in relief, such as wood engravings, or even intaglio methods such as copper plate engravings, where there is a physical alteration of the substrate. During the lithographic printing process, an even pressure is applied that transfers the inked image on the stone to the paper, so the paper remains fairly flat aside from some minor stretching. The lithographic renderings throughout both volumes of *The Geology of Russia* likely were done with grease-based litho crayons on fine-grained stones. Some of the scenic plates by Louis Haghe appear to have been completed with two print runs, one with a tonal imagery (usually created by applying grease to the stone, often tusche paste diluted in turpentine, which was then reduced with coarse tools for tonal variation), followed by a key image using the more traditional crayon-drawn layer printed in black. The pinpricks that are evident on the scenic plates are registration artifacts of this multi-layered process.

Murchison used copper plate engravings in Volume 1 of *The Geology of Russia* to present both cross-sectional (Fig. 3) and map information (Fig. 4). The engraved copper plates permitted higher resolution linework than either wood engravings or lithographs and were therefore preferred for those illustrations containing abundant detailed text and linework. The copper engravings were typically folded and hand colored to depict the range of lithologies being portrayed. Figure 3 contains a portion of Plate 1, where the occurrence and attitudes of coal seams in the Donetz region are

Figure 2. The twelfth scenic lithograph from *The Geology of Russia* (1845), facing p. 453, entitled *Bashkir Camp in the Irendyk Ridge, S. Urel*. The artist was Roderick Murchison, the lithographer was Louis Haghe, and the printer was Day and Haghe.

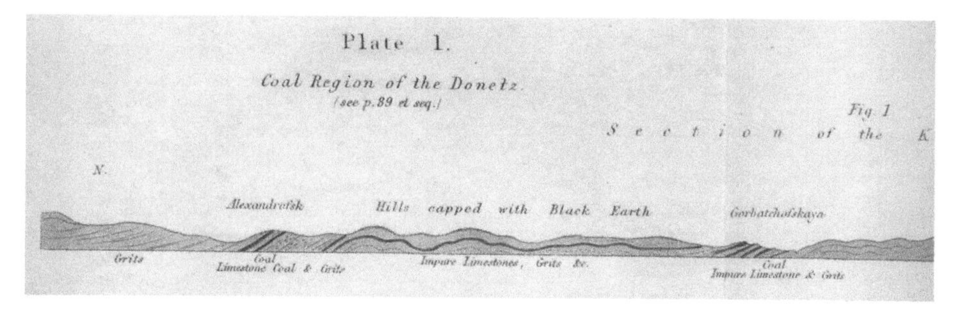

Figure 3. A portion of Plate 1, *Coal Region of the Donetz*, a hand-colored copper plate engraving from *The Geology of Russia* (1845). The full plate contains nine cross-sections documenting the distribution of coal beds in the Donetz region.

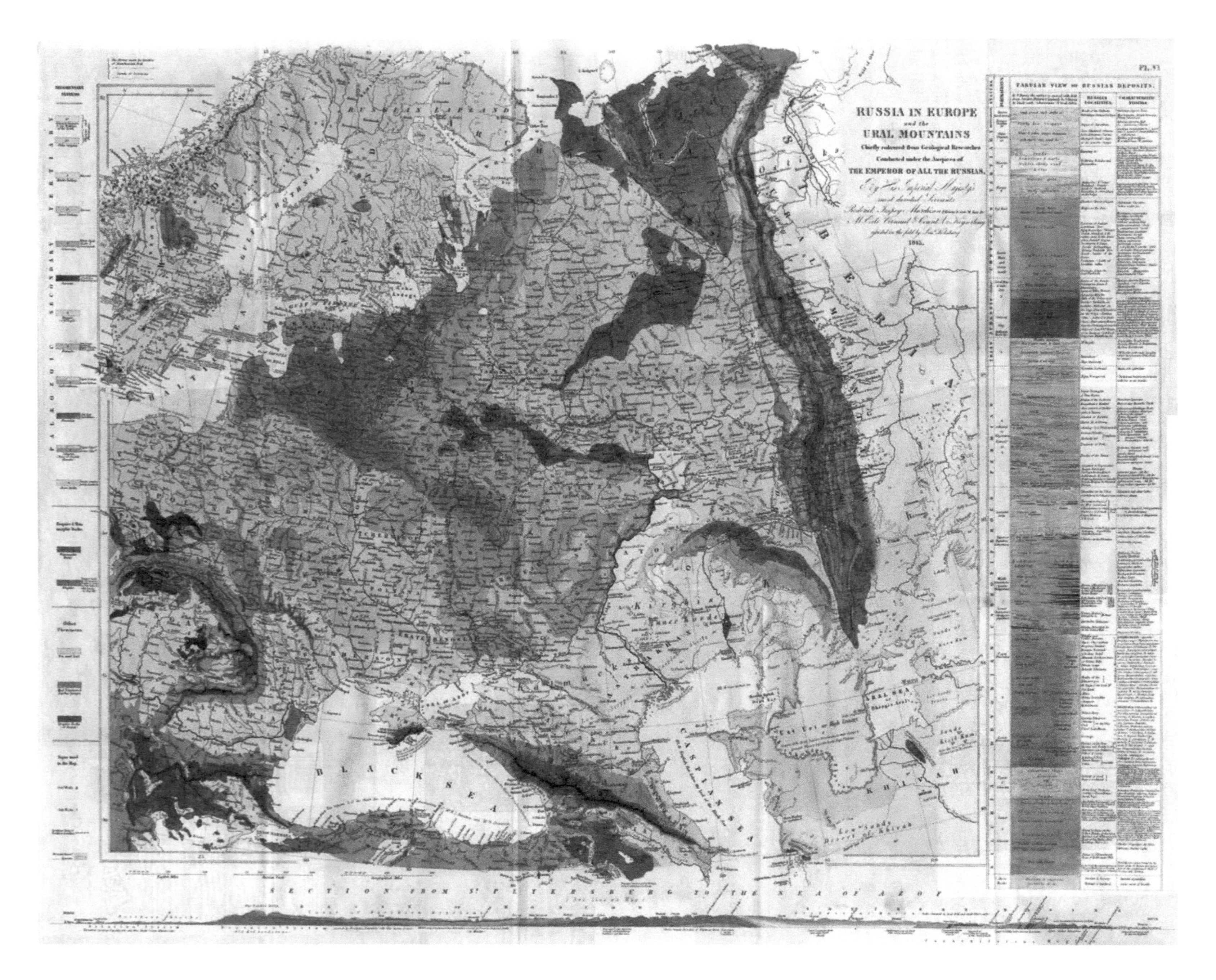
RUSSIA IN EUROPE
and the
URAL MOUNTAINS
Chiefly coloured from Geological Researches
Conducted under the Auspices of
THE EMPEROR OF ALL THE RUSSIAS,
1845.
TABULAR VIEW OF RUSSIAN DEPOSITS.
Pl. VI
BLACK SEA
CASPIAN SEA
KHIVAH
SECTION FROM ST PETERSBURG TO THE SEA OF AZOF

Figure 4.

Figure 4. Plate 6, the geologic map of Russia in Europe and the Ural Mountains from Volume 1 of *The Geology of Russia* (1845). This hand-colored copper plate engraving was prepared at a scale of ~1:5,000,000 and printed on a sheet of paper that was 84 cm wide × 68 cm tall. It has a long cross-section along the bottom margin and a stratigraphic column on the right-hand margin of the map that summarizes the Russian fossil and lithologic data. The locations of the cross-sections in Plates 1–5 are indicated on the map. This version of Plate 6 is from Edition 1, state 3 of Plate 6, printed in December 1845 (Thackray, 1978a).

documented. Figure 4 reproduces Plate 6 from *The Geology of Russia*, which is the geologic map of Russia in Europe.

All seven of the plates in Volume 1 of *The Geology of Russia* (1845) show clear signs that they are copper plate engravings, which are examples of an intaglio method. The first sign is the plate mark: the slightly embossed rectilinear form outside of each image. Any intaglio method would involve a printing process that requires enough pressure and a sheet of moist, malleable paper, so that the ink applied to the plate would be transferred onto the paper. During the printing process, these presses would roll onto and off of the plate, leaving a mark on the paper indicating the physical location of the plate's edge. If the printer did a good job of applying the ink and wiping the excess away, the plate mark would be free of any sign of ink and less noticeable to the viewer. Each of the seven plates in Volume 1 of *The Geology of Russia*, including the geologic maps (Plates VI and VII), have plate marks.

The linear components of each image also correlate with engraved work. Since the artists would primarily use a burin to strip metal out of the plate, each line begins in a slightly narrower and more delicate fashion and is followed by a wider central passage. The line tapers again at the end, as the tool would gradually have been lifted to the tip, which is the smallest point of the triangular-shaped burin. This clearly can be seen in the text on the plates but also throughout more elongated lines. There are also examples where tonal effects, to describe ridges or mountains, occur with repetitive lines. Again, this is typical of many engravings where, in addition to burins, there were other tools at hand such as roulettes that could produce parallel lines in tandem or impress particular marks/patterns into the plate.

Finally, there is also the evidence from the ink itself. Intaglio methods, including copper engraving, require ink to be driven into the newly incised marks and lines in the plate. Any excess ink is then removed from the surface of the plate, leaving behind an inked image that is ready for printing. The inked plate and dampened printing paper, sandwiched together, are run through the press, which transfers the image to the sheet. Similar to the plate mark, this process leaves slightly raised lines of ink across the resulting image. The distinctiveness of these lines has a lot to do with who created and printed the image. For example, it is evident that Plates A–D in Volume 2 of *The Geology of Russia*, created by George Brettingham Sowerby, Jr., have almost a textured quality (see Fig. 5). The lines are thicker and bolder, with more ink transferred in the printing process, as compared to Plates 1–7 of Volume 1 of *The Geology of Russia*, which are more precise and controlled (compare Figs. 3 and 4 to Fig. 5). In Figures 3 and 4, the ink layer is very fine and not very dimensional; in fact, it is relatively flat.

Figure 5. Examples of Paleozoic plant remains from Russia sketched by Morris and engraved by George B. Sowerby, Jr., under the supervision of Adolphe Brongniart are shown. From Volume 2 of *The Geology of Russia* (1845), Plate A. Note the plate mark (white band) along the bottom edge of the image, below the text, which indicates that this is a copper plate engraving.

FOSSIL ILLUSTRATIONS IN *THE GEOLOGY OF RUSSIA* (1845) VOLUMES 1 AND 2

The general views and definitions of the systems developed by Murchison and his colleagues appear in Volume 1 of *The Geology of Russia* (1845). They argued that changes in fossil species demarcated the boundaries between the systems. That argument is also cogently made in the foreword to Volume 2 (p. v–vi) by Edouard de Verneuil, in which he describes the organization of Volumes 1 and 2 of *The Geology of Russia* (1845):

The first [volume], divided into two parts, one on European Russia and the other on the Urals, includes all the geology as well as general paleontological considerations directly connected with it; the second [volume] contains the detailed description of species. Our general views resulting from the study of each large system of layers and their fossils were to be placed in the first volume, for in a country where the deposits of different ages succeed each other without pronounced disruption, superposition is not always sufficient to mark the limits of those natural groupings to which we have given the name of systems and terrains, and it is necessary to use the succession of organised bodies (*corps organisés*). In this endeavour, everything depends on an exact knowledge of species, and it is therefore essential to study them in the depth and with the care they deserve, and this is the reason the description of the fossils and the third part of the work needed a volume to itself. In some way, this volume [Volume 2] gives the evidence upon which the main results in the first volume are based. The major part has been dedicated to Paleozoic fossils, most of our work having been to do with the layers which contain them. In fact, as already mentioned, our first aim in coming to Russia was to seek to apply to the ancient deposits of this country the principal divisions that one of us had already established in England, in Germany, in Belgium and in the *Boulonnais*.

Some of the fossil evidence used by Murchison and de Verneuil appeared in Volume 1, in particular in Appendix A by William Lonsdale (*The Geology of Russia*, Volume 1, p. 591–634), which described some characteristic Paleozoic "corals" of Russia. That appendix included a lithograph prepared by J. de Carle Sowerby and printed by Hullmandel and Walton Lithographers (Fig. 6). According to the explanation (*The Geology of Russia*, p. 633), "The Plate was lithographed by Mr. J. de Carle Sowerby with his habitual attention to truthfulness of character." A number

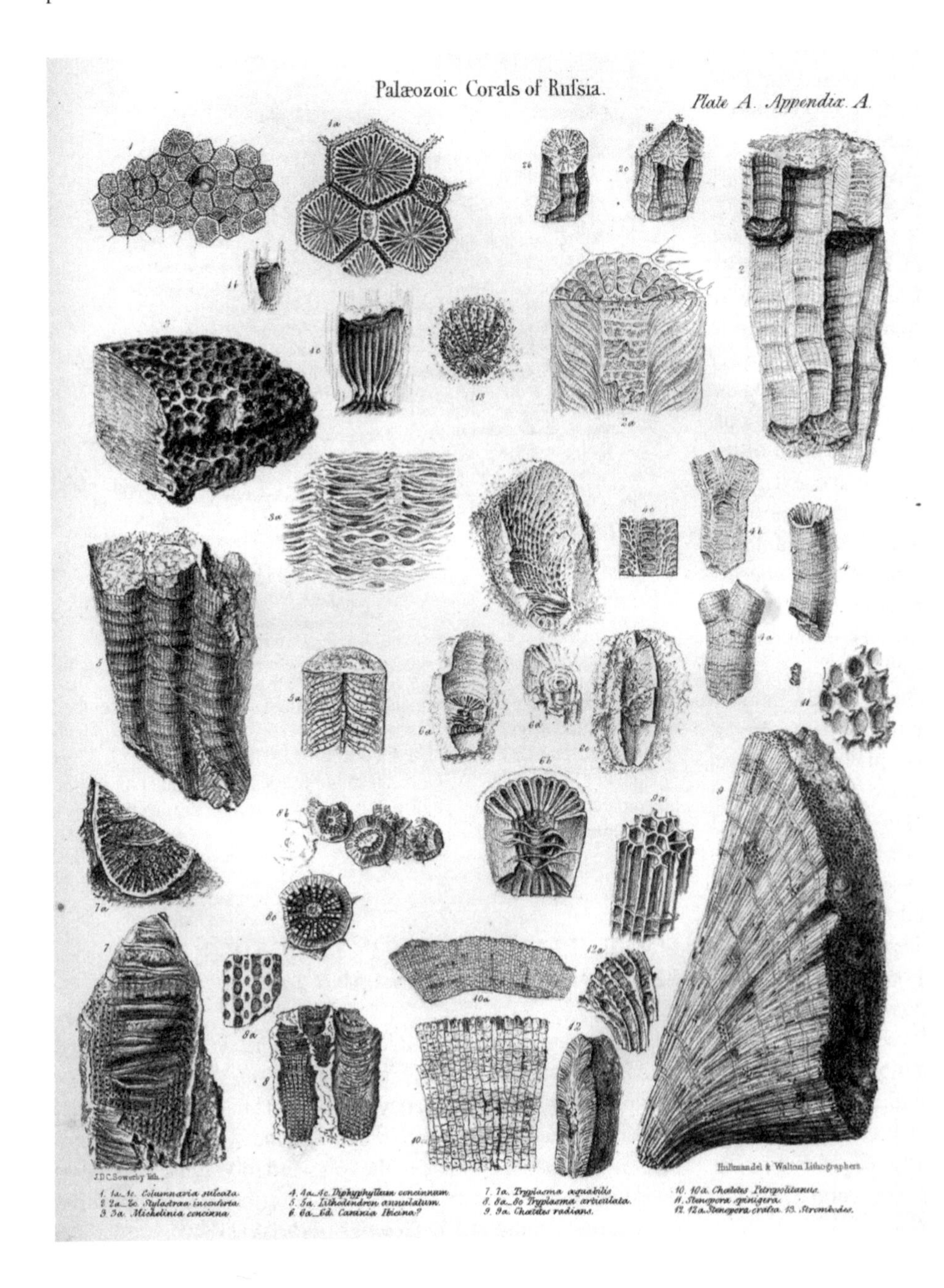

Figure 6. Paleozoic corals of Russia were described by William Lonsdale, illustrated by J. de Carle Sowerby (lithographer), and printed by Hullmandel and Walton Lithographers. Plate A from Appendix A of Volume 1 of *The Geology of Russia* (1845), inserted between p. 632 and 633.

of these "corals" are in fact bryozoans. One, "*Chaetetes Petropolitanus*" [now *Diplotrypa petropolitana* Nicholson, 1879] was illustrated in thin-section (Plate A, figure 10; herein Fig. 6). This was the first time that the interior skeleton of a bryozoan was so figured (see Wyse Jackson, 2008).

Volume 1 also contains Appendix B (p. 635–636 with one zincographic plate), in which Richard Owen (1804–1892) compared a tooth found near Riga, Latvia, and given to Murchison by Christian Heinrich Pander (1794–1865) during his visit in 1841, that is similar in form and internal structure to a tooth recovered from the Old Red Sandstone at Scat-Crag near Elgin, Morayshire, Scotland (see Fig. 7). Owen described and named the Latvian tooth (*Dendrodus Murchisoni* (Owen)), illustrated the internal structure in microscopic view, and compared it to the Scottish tooth (*Dendrodus biporcatus* (Owen)). Owen pointed out the similarities in the vascular canals and sinuses of the Latvian and Scottish teeth and assigned them to the genus *Dendrodus* of Sauroid fishes. He also pointed out that the internal structure of the Sauroid teeth differs markedly from the internal structure of reptile teeth. In Appendix B, Owen confirmed Murchison's interpretation that the strata that contained the Latvian tooth belonged to the Devonian Old Red Sandstone. Owen may have chosen to use zincography, an early form of lithography, for this plate because the zinc plate would have been cheaper than limestone. Zinc plates were nonporous and would have required graining to give it "tooth" so it could be used instead of limestone to print the plate.

Volume 2 of *The Geology of Russia* was written and illustrated by Edouard de Verneuil. The full title in French is: *Géologie de la Russie d'Europe et des Montagnes de l'Oural, Vol. II, Troisième Partie. Paléontologie*. It was published in 1845 in Paris by P. Bertrand of rue Saint-André-des-Arts, Number 38. After his experience organizing the fossil descriptions and illustrations for *The Silurian System* (1839), it seems likely that Murchison would have been quite content to let de Verneuil manage the task of describing and illustrating the Russian fossils. Nearly all of the fossils collected during their joint fieldwork in Russia were described in Volume 2 in stratigraphic order from Paleozoic to Tertiary fossils. The 50 plates illustrating the fossils, both fauna and flora, are found at the end of Volume 2. Table 1 provides a summary of the content, artists, and lithographers of the 50 plates that accompany Volume 2 of *The Geology of Russia*. All but four of the plates were lithographs printed by Lemercier of Paris (for example, see Fig. 8). The other four were the previously mentioned engravings of plants sketched by Mr. Morris, engraved

Figure 7. The zincograph entitled *Teeth of Devonian Ichthyolites* is Plate B of Appendix B and was prepared by Richard Owen. The artist and zincographer was Lens Aldous. From Volume 1 of *The Geology of Russia* (1845), inserted between p. 636 and 637.

TABLE 1. ILLUSTRATIONS IN VOLUME 2 OF *THE GEOLOGY OF RUSSIA* (1845) COMPILED BY EDOUARD DE VERNEUIL

Plates	Fossil type	Section	Artist	Printer
1–27	Shells	"Russie Terrain Paléozoique"	Thiolat	Lemercier
28–42	Shells	"Russie Terrain Secondaire" (Système Jurassique)	Delarue	Lemercier
43	Shells	"Russie Terrain Crétace"	Delarue	Lemercier
A–D	Plants	"Russie Terrain Paléozoique"	Morris	G.B. Sowerby
E–F	Plants	"Russie Terrain Paléozoique"	Thiolat	Lemercier
G	Plants	"Russie Terrain Paléozoique, Secondaire et Tertiare"	Thiolat	Lemercier

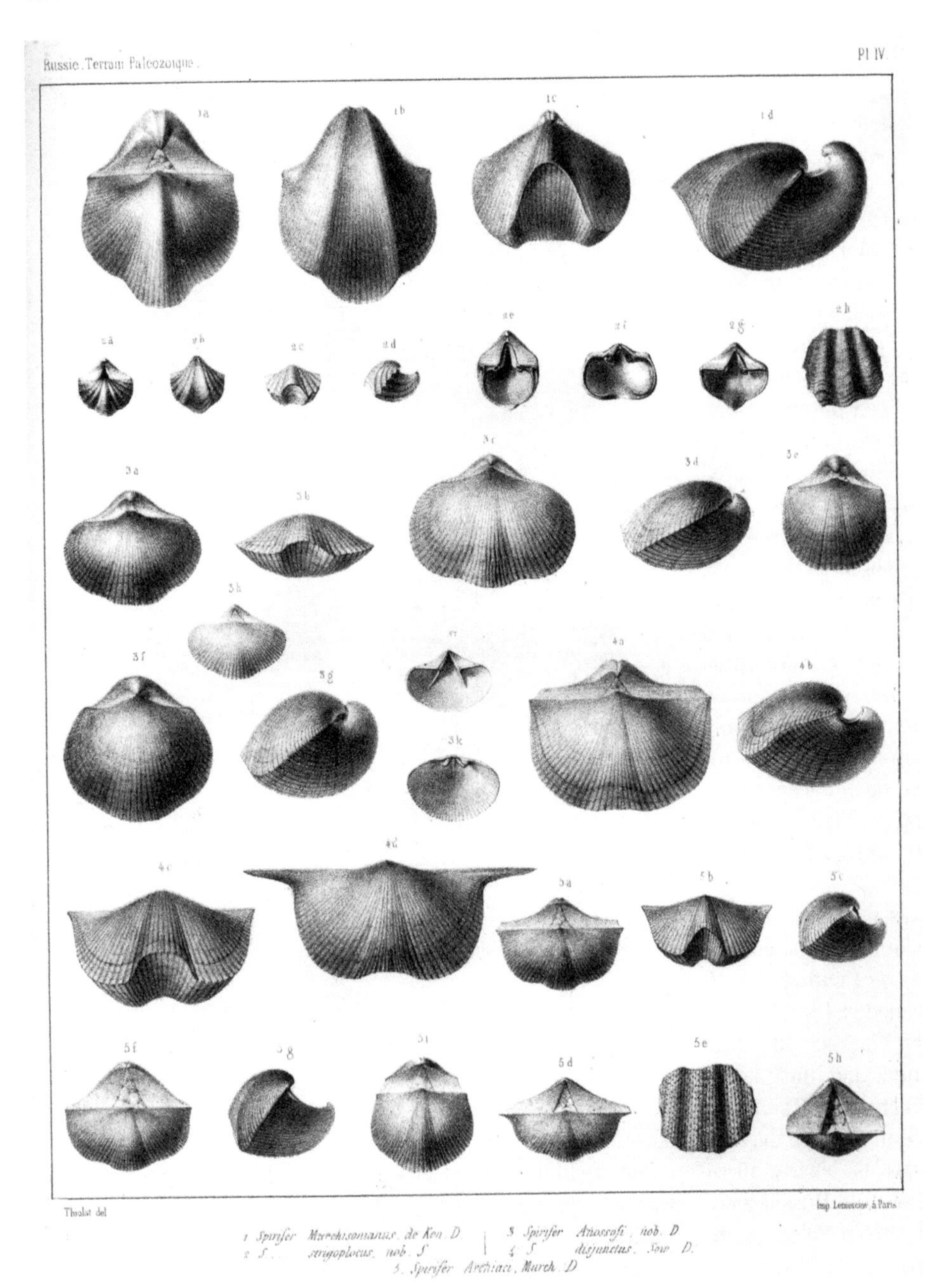

Figure 8. Examples of Paleozoic brachiopods from Russia are shown, including *Spirifer Murchisonianus*, which was described by Edouard de Verneuil, illustrated in a lithograph prepared by Thiolat, and printed by Lemercier of Paris. From Volume 2 of *The Geology of Russia* (1845), Plate 4.

by G.B. Sowerby, and identified by Adolphe Brongniart (e.g., Fig. 5).

While de Verneuil was responsible for describing and illustrating many of the fossils, especially crinoids, molluscs, and crustaceans (for example, see Fig. 8), he also received assistance from Lonsdale with the corals (Fig. 6), from Mr. Morris and Adolphe Brongniart with plants, and from d'Orbigny with Jurassic and Cretaceous fossils. As previously mentioned, the 46 lithographs in Volume 2 of *The Geology of Russia* (1845) were printed by Lemercier of Paris. Figure 9 captures the activity in that printing house, including the 30 printing presses, the storage racks for the lithographic stones on side walls of the ground floor, and the mezzanine galleries where the artists worked together with the lithographers to prepare the stones. No doubt de Verneuil spent considerable time in the galleries finalizing the fossil plates and had ample opportunity to observe lithography in action.

CONCLUSIONS

Murchison used wood engravings, lithographs, zincographs, and copper plate engravings to great effect in Volume 1 of *The Geology of Russia* (1845). It is likely that Murchison was happy to let Edouard de Verneuil manage the production of the fossil plates for Volume 2 of *The Geology of Russia* (1845) following his experience assembling *The Silurian System* (1839). De Verneuil was clearly well-positioned to make use of skilled lithog-

Figure 9. Interior of Lemercier lithographic printing house, ca. 1846, is shown. The artist was Victor Adam (1801–1866), and the lithographer was Charles Villemin. From the Art Institute of Chicago, Creative Commons Zero (CCO) collection.

raphers at Lemercier, a reputable lithography house, to produce the fossil plates. Murchison's strategy of presenting landscape scenes, stratigraphic sections, cross-sections, and geologic maps to place the fossils in their geologic and stratigraphic contexts was instrumental in documenting the existence and characteristics of several Paleozoic systems including the Silurian, Devonian, and Permian Systems.

ACKNOWLEDGMENTS

Access to the archives of the British Geological Survey, Geological Society of London, National Library of Austria, and the National Library of Wales is gratefully acknowledged. Assistance from Wendy Cawthorne, Paul Johnson, and Caroline Lam of the Library of the Geological Society is much appreciated. Thanks go as well to Marianne Klemun of the University of Wien for arranging access to archives in Vienna and to Joanne Collie for translating the foreword to Volume 2 of *The Geology of Russia*. Many thanks go to John Henry and Patrick Wyse Jackson for their insightful reviews.

REFERENCES CITED

Antreasian, G.Z., and Adams, C., 1971, The Tamarind Book of Lithography: Art and Techniques: Los Angeles, California, Tamarind Lithography Workshop, 463 p.

Betz, F., Jr., 1963, Geological communication, *in* Albritton, C.C., Jr., ed., The Fabric of Geology: Boulder, Colorado, Geological Society of America, p. 193–217.

Collie, M., and Diemer, J.A., 2004, Murchison's Wanderings in Russia: Keyworth, UK, British Geological Survey, 474 p.

Diemer, J.A., 1996, Old or New Red Sandstone? Evolution of a nineteenth century stratigraphic debate, northern Scotland: Earth Sciences History, v. 15, p. 151–166, https://doi.org/10.17704/eshi.15.2.uq461282n11qkg61.

Diemer, J.A., 2008, Murchison's research method: An example from southern Norway: Earth Sciences History, v. 27, p. 31–58, https://doi.org/10.17704/eshi.27.1.e876055751500655.

Diemer, J.A., 2016, Murchison in Sweden: Consolidating Lower Silurian stratigraphy in the summer of 1844, *in* Mayer, W., Clary, R.M., Azuela, L.F., Mota, T.S., and Wolkowicz, S., eds., History of Geoscience: Celebrating 50 Years of INHIGEO: Geological Society, London, Special Publication 442, p. 353–366.

Diemer, J.A., 2018, Fossil collections and mapping the Silurian: An example from Scandinavia, *in* Rosenberg, G.D., and Clary, R.M., eds., Museums at the Forefront of the History and Philosophy of Geology: History Made, History in the Making: Geological Society of America Special Paper 535, p. 91–116, https://doi.org/10.1130/2018.2535(07).

Gascoigne, B., 1986, How to Identify Prints: A Complete Guide to Manual and Mechanical Processes from Woodcut to Ink Jet: London, Thames and Hudson, 208 p.

Geikie, A., 1875, Life of Sir Roderick I. Murchison, Based on His Journals and Letters, with Notices of His Scientific Contemporaries and a Sketch of the Rise and Growth of Palaeozoic Geology in Britain: London, John Murray, 2 vols., v. 1, 387 p.; v. 2, 385 p.

Hullmandel, C., 1982, The Art of Drawing on Stone (with a new introduction by Joan M. Friedman): New York, Garland Publishing., 125 p.

Murchison, R.I., 1839, The Silurian System, Founded on Geological Researches in the Counties of Salop, Hereford, Radnor, Montgomery, Caermarthen, Brecon, Pembroke, Monmouth, Gloucester, Worcester and Stafford; With Descriptions of the Coal-fields and Overlying Formations: London, John Murray, 2 vols., v. 1, 576 p.; v. 2, 768 p., https://doi.org/10.5962/bhl.title.88029.

Murchison, R.I., 1842, Letter to M. Fischer de Waldheim … containing some of the results of his second geological survey of Russia: Edinburgh New: The Philosophical Journal, v. 32, p. 99–103.

Murchison, R.I., 1854, Siluria. The History of the Oldest Known Rocks Containing Organic Remains, with a Brief Sketch of the Distribution of Gold over the Earth: London, John Murray, 532 p.

Murchison, R.I., de Verneuil, E., and von Keyserling, A., 1845, The Geology of Russia in Europe and the Ural Mountains, Volume 1, Geology: London, John Murray, 700 p.; Volume 2, Paléontologie: Paris, P. Bertrand, 512 p.

Oldroyd, D.R., 1990, The Highlands Controversy: Constructing Geological Knowledge through Fieldwork in Nineteenth-Century Britain: Chicago, Chicago University Press, 448 p.

Oldroyd, D.R., 1996, Thinking about the Earth: A History of Ideas in Geology: London, Athlone, and Boston, Harvard University Press, 410 p.

Oldroyd, D.R., 2013, Maps as pictures or diagrams: The early development of geological maps, *in* Baker, V.R., ed., Rethinking the Fabric of Geology: Geological Society of America Special Paper 502, p. 41–101, https://doi.org/10.1130/2013.2502(04).

Rudwick, M.J.S., 1985, The Great Devonian Controversy: The Shaping of Scientific Knowledge among Gentlemanly Specialists: Chicago, University of Chicago Press, 494 p., https://doi.org/10.7208/chicago/9780226731001.001.0001.

Rudwick, M.J.S., 1992, Scenes from Deep Time: Early Pictorial Representations of the Prehistoric World: Chicago, University of Chicago Press, 280 p., https://doi.org/10.7208/chicago/9780226149035.001.0001.

Rudwick, M.J.S., 2005, Bursting the Limits of Time: The Reconstruction of Geohistory in the Age of Revolution: Chicago, University of Chicago Press, 708 p., https://doi.org/10.7208/chicago/9780226731148.001.0001.

Secord, J.A., 1986, Controversy in Victorian Geology: The Cambrian-Silurian Dispute: Princeton, New Jersey, Princeton University Press, 386 p.

Thackray, J.C., 1972, Essential source-material of Roderick Murchison: Journal of the Society of Bibliography of Natural History, v. 6, no. 3, p. 162–170, https://doi.org/10.3366/jsbnh.1972.6.3.162.

Thackray, J.C., 1978a, R.I. Murchison's *Geology of Russia* (1845): Journal of the Society of Bibliography of Natural History, v. 8, p. 421–433, https://doi.org/10.3366/jsbnh.1978.8.4.421.

Thackray, J.C., 1978b, R.I. Murchison's *Silurian System* (1839): Journal of the Society of Bibliography of Natural History, v. 9, no. 1, p. 61–73, https://doi.org/10.3366/jsbnh.1978.9.1.61.

Torrens, H.S., 1983, Arthur Aikin's mineralogical survey of Shropshire 1796–1816 and the contemporary audience for geological publications: British Journal for the History of Science, v. 16, p. 111–153, https://doi.org/10.1017/S0007087400026777.

Torrens, H.S., 1990, The scientific ancestry and historiography of *The Silurian System*: Journal of the Geological Society, v. 147, p. 657–662, https://doi.org/10.1144/gsjgs.147.4.0657.

Wyse Jackson, P.N., 2008, William Lonsdale and the first thin-section of a fossil bryozoan, *in* Wyse Jackson, P.N., and Spencer Jones, M.E., eds., Annals of Bryozoology 2: Aspects of the History of Research on Bryozoans: Dublin, International Bryozoology Association, p. 435–442.

Manuscript Accepted by the Society 14 January 2021
Manuscript Published Online 21 September 2021

Printed in the USA

The Geological Society of America
Memoir 218

Fossil illustrations in three dimensions: Ward's models at Cornell University

William R. Brice*
116 Luna Lane, Johnstown, Pennsylvania 15904, USA

ABSTRACT

Some fossil examples are rare, but the educational value of such samples is undeniable. One way around this dilemma, and one that was popular in the late 1800s and early 1900s, was to have students study 3-D models; this solution was used by many universities, among them Cornell University. One of the main, but not the only, suppliers of such models was Ward's Natural Science Establishment of Rochester, New York, USA, which was founded in 1862 by Henry Augustus Ward (1834–1906). Even today the use of virtual, computer-generated 3-D models in classroom laboratories indicates how important 3-D visualization continues to be. But a computer image cannot be held in one's hands, so the use of 3-D printer technology allows students to create their own physical models. However, none of these technologies can totally replace seeing and working with actual specimens or life-sized reproductions. Thus, museum displays are still an important aspect of educational activity for both students and the general public. This chapter explores how Cornell University made use of the models purchased from Ward's in the late 1800s and the fate of some of these replicas.

INTRODUCTION

Perhaps as long as we have been on this planet, humans have been expressing themselves through some kind of art. Often the subjects of the art were the animals around them, but the drawings were only in two dimensions as was most ancient art. Three-dimensional art was a concept of the future, and the drawings were only of objects seen in daily life. Fossils, if known at all, were simply not used as subjects. That, too, would come in the future[1]. De Chadarevian and Hopwood (2004) provide a detailed look at the use of 3-D modeling in science that appears to have begun in earnest, at least in Europe and England, in the middle of the eighteenth century. But much of this work was in medicine, architecture, ship building, etc., and not in paleontology. Most of the restoration work in paleontology was done in two dimensions (Allmon, 2017).

What appears to be one of the first major moves into 3-D representation of fossil organisms[2] came in the 1850s, when the paleontologist Richard Owen (1804–1892) helped Benjamin Waterhouse Hawkins (1807–1894) create large 3-D, life-size models for exhibit at the Crystal Palace during what was called the "Great Exhibition" (Secord, 2004; Cantor, 2012), which ran from 1 May to 15 October 1851. These life-size, 3-D models created considerable public interest because the idea and meaning of extinction was just beginning to be understood by the scientific community. The general public had its own explanation as to why these animals no longer existed, as explained in a

*wbrice@pitt.edu

[1]For a good description of the early work in two-dimensional fossil reproduction, see Allmon (2017).

[2]Note that only macrofossils are discussed in this paper. Microfossils, such as foraminifera, are also modeled in three dimensions. For a discussion of microfossil illustrations, see Chapter 22 by J.H. Lipps (this volume).

Brice, W.R., 2022, Fossil illustrations in three dimensions: Ward's models at Cornell University, *in* Clary, R.M., Rosenberg, G.D., and Evans, D.C., eds., The Evolution of Paleontological Art: Geological Society of America Memoir 218, p. 127–137, https://doi.org/10.1130/2021.1218(15).

contemporary quotation: "Because they were too large to go into the ark; and therefore they were all drowned" (quoted in Secord, 2004, p. 138). In 1854, after the exhibition had closed, the models were moved to Penge Place atop Sydenham Hill in South London (Secord, 2004; O'Connor, 2007). Accordingly, over the next 50 years or so over a million people a year came to see the reproductions[3] of these "drowned" creatures. The models were so large that Hawkins actually held a dinner party inside one of the reproductions (Fig. 1), and they can be seen now in Crystal Palace Park (Fig. 2) in the London borough of Bromley.

In the mid- to late 1800s, another approach became popular, especially for vertebrates, in which, based on the bones that were uncovered, the full skeleton was reconstructed. Museums went to great expense in these re-articulations (Rieppel, 2012). For example, in the early 1900s, Earl Douglas (1862–1931), a geologist with the Carnegie Museum of Natural History in Pittsburgh, opened a large dig in Utah that yielded many famous skeletons, including one that Mr. Douglas named *Diplodocus carnegii*, after Andrew Carnegie, who helped finance the excavation work. This so pleased Carnegie that he paid to have plaster casts made of each bone, all 300 of them, and then the model went on a tour of the world's major museums, and a copy was presented to each museum where the model was displayed (Colbert, 1968), including the British Museum (Fig. 3; Desmond, 1975). The original still resides at the Carnegie Museum of Natural History in Pittsburgh, Pennsylvania.

THE MASTER MODEL MAKER/SELLER

Henry Augustus Ward (1834–1906) (Fig. 4) was born in Rochester, New York, studied first at Williams College, and then became an assistant to Louis Agassiz at the Lawrence Scientific School at Harvard University. As a young man, Ward traveled in the Middle East and studied at the Sorbonne, the School of Mines in Paris, and at the Universities of Munich and Freiberg. He continued his travels in West Africa and the West Indies and made natural history collections. He was a professor at the University

Figure 2. One of Benjamin Waterhouse Hawkins' reconstructions as it stands today in Crystal Palace Park. Note: Refer to Figure 1 and the foreground plants for the scale (Wikimedia Commons; https://en.wikipedia.org/wiki/Crystal_Palace_Dinosaurs#/media/File:Mantellodon_in_Crystal_Palace_Park.jpg).

Figure 1. A sketch of the dinner held inside the Iguanodon model before it was displayed at the Crystal Palace Exhibition. Richard Owen is proposing the toast (inside far left, next to the head). (*Illustrated London News*, 7 January 1854, p. 22; Desmond, 1975, fig. 5; Wikimedia Commons; https://commons.wikimedia.org/wiki/File:Crystal_palace_iguanodon.jpg).

Figure 3. The *Diplodocus carnegii* model in the British Museum, which was presented to the museum on 12 May 1905 (image appeared in Desmond, 1975) (this photo by W.R. Brice).

[3]Further details behind these reconstructions are found in Chapter 17 by R.M. Peck and S.M. Rowland (this volume).

Figure 4. Henry Augustus Ward (1834–1906) in 1906 with the Santa Rosa meteorite (https://en.wikipedia.org/wiki/Henry_Augustus_Ward; accessed July 2020; public domain).

REPTILES. 31

Nos. 56–62. [302–308] **Restorations of Fossil Reptiles.**

Pterodactyle, Megalosaurus, Iguanodon, Labyrinthodon, Ichthyosaurus, Plesiosaurus dolichodeirus and *P. macrocephalus.* They are reduced (one inch to the foot) from the gigantic models in the Crystal Palace, London; constructed to

No. 56. [302] PTERODACTYLE. No. 57. [303] MEGALOSAURUS.

a scale by B. Waterhouse Hawkins, F. G. S., from the form and proportions of the fossil remains, and in strict accordance with the scientific deductions of

No 58. [304.[IGUANODON. No. 59. [305] LABYRINTHODON.

Professor Owen. Preliminary drawings, with careful measurements of the originals in the Royal College of Surgeons, British Museum and Geological Society,

Nos. 60–62. [306–308] ICHTHYOSAURUS WITH PLESIOSAURI.

were prepared, and sketch models made at a fraction of the natural size, and submitted to the above high authority. Clay models were then made of the natural size.

Figure 5. Ward's 1870 catalog listing for the models of the Crystal Palace restorations (Ward, 1870, p. 31).

of Rochester from 1860 until 1865 when he established Ward's Scientific, a unique enterprise through which he collected and sold rock, mineral, fossil samples, and fossil models from around the world. Unfortunately, in 1906 he was struck and killed by an automobile while walking, thus becoming the first auto-related fatality in Buffalo, New York (Davidson, 2008).

In the beginning, Mr. Ward supplied real rocks and fossils from his extensive collections, but in the mid-1860s he began supplying plaster models as well. Given the rarity of many fossil specimens, Mr. Ward said that the only way to provide completeness to geological collections "…was by the introduction of *Plaster Copies* of these fossils, the originals of which are either unique specimens or are so rare that it is quite impossible to obtain them" (Ward, 1870, p. v; original emphasis). His 1866 catalog listed 1207 fossil models and casts of both vertebrates and invertebrates (Davidson, 2008). And Mr. Ward also included his own models of Mr. Hawkins' models from the Crystal Palace Exhibition, albeit at a different scale (Fig. 5). In 1868, as Cornell University and a new geology department were about to open, Ward's Scientific had just begun selling these models.

CORNELL UNIVERSITY—AN EARLY EXAMPLE OF THE MODELS IN USE

In the fall of 1868, Cornell University opened its doors to students for the first time, and as part of this new university, Charles F. Hartt (1840–1878)[4] (Fig. 6; Brice, 1994; Brice and Figueirôa, 1994, 2001, 2003) began the geological studies at Cornell, which

Figure 6. Charles Frederick Hartt (1840–1878) (courtesy of Division of Rare and Manuscript Collections, Cornell University Library).

[4]There is an interesting connection here as both Henry A. Ward and Charles F. Hartt studied with Agassiz at Harvard but at different times.

continue to the present day. Almost from the first day of classes, Hartt, and those who followed him, recognized the importance of using 3-D models when the actual samples were not available. Initially, Hartt held his classes in the basement of South Hall (now Morrill Hall) as that was the only space available. Among the early purchases made by Ezra Cornell for his new university were geological collections (Brice, 1989), for it was important then, as it is now, to have samples and specimens for students to study. It was obvious that the department had to have more space, so in 1869 ground was broken for McGraw Hall, a new building erected between South Hall and North Hall[5] (Brice, 1989). McGraw Hall opened in 1873 (Fig. 7) and was the home of the Cornell Geology Department for almost 100 years.

To illustrate the interest in 3-D models in the late 1800s, in March of 1873, Hartt wrote to Ezra Cornell, the university's founder, about a scheme to possibly produce some income:

> If you have occasion to visit the University during the coming week, would you have the kindness to drop into the Geol. Laboratory? I have a proposition to make you relative to the manufacture of some new kinds of geological models. I should like to talk with you where we can have access to books & specimens, for that reason I do not go to your house. I think that at a very small cost we can make for ourselves an exceedingly useful set of models as illustrations of structural geology, topography, & physical geography. When once the models are made, by employing student labor, casts could be multiplied ad infinitum. These could be used for exchange to great advantage, and set might be sold to pay expenses of making.[6] [emphasis in the original]

Figure 7. McGraw Hall, Cornell University, which was the home of the Geology Department from 1873 until 1971 (courtesy of W.R. Brice).

Hartt must have sensed that there was great interest in 3-D models, and he felt it was possible to make some money by making and selling them. At the time, however, nothing came of Hartt's request to Mr. Cornell, but several years later things did happen. In the early 1900s at Cornell University, Gilbert D. Harris (Brice, 1996) and Ralph S. Tarr (Brice, 1985, 1999) both saw the need for 3-D model building, although this time fossils were added to the mix: fossil models for Harris and his students and landscape models for Tarr and his students. As a result of this interest, a model-making class was created by Tarr, and it was still taught in the department as late as 1945 (Brice, 1989). Unfortunately, no other details of the class have been found, and few of the student models have survived. Of those that have survived, the main material used in making the models was some form of plaster or plaster of Paris, which, of course, makes them very fragile, easily damaged, and hard to conserve.

As Hartt and his successors expanded the various departmental collections, many of Ward's fossil models[7] were among the purchases. Figure 8A is an example of one such purchase, a model of *Ammonites gigas*, and Figure 8B is the original label for the model, indicating that it was part of Ward's Scientific series of 3-D fossil models. In the 1866 edition of Ward's Scientific catalog, the *Ammonites gigas* is listed to sell at $1.75 (Fig. 9), not a bad price for such a model.[8] Another example from the 1866 catalog became part of the Cornell collection (Fig. 10). This is a trackway of *Chirotherium barthi*, a Triassic trace fossil consisting of five-fingered (pentadactyle) footprints. Many of Ward's fossil models were of vertebrates, e.g., the skull of *Ursus spelæus* (Fig. 11).

MARY ANNING: "THE GREATEST FOSSILIST THE WORLD EVER KNEW"

One of the most famous discoverers of fossil vertebrates was Mary Anning (1799–1847) (Fig. 12A; Torrens, 1995). Some people (Appleby, 1979), but not all,[9] say Mary Anning may have been the basis of Terry Sullivan's lyrics to the 1908 song that became the popular tongue twister, "She Sells Seashells":

She sells seashells on the seashore,
The shells she sells are seashells, I'm sure.
So if she sells seashells on the seashore,
Then I'm sure she sells seashore shells.

And Ward's Scientific did not overlook her work, for replicas of several of her fossil finds are found among Ward's Scientific models and in the Cornell collection. For example, in 1830, Mary

[5]Today South Hall is called Morrill Hall, named for Justin S. Morrill, who introduced the "Land Grant Act" signed in 1862 that allowed the formation of many universities and colleges, including Cornell University. Likewise, North Hall today is called White Hall in honor of the first Cornell President, Andrew D. White.

[6]Hartt to Ezra Cornell, 28 March 1873. Ezra Cornell Papers, Collection # 1/1/1; Kroch Library/Dept. Rare & Manuscript Collections, Cornell University.

[7]Note that all of the existing models illustrated in this paper are now housed and some are displayed at the Paleontological Research Institution in Ithaca, New York, and are shown here with permission.

[8]That would be about US$28.44 in 2021 dollars. (Currency conversions from https://futureboy.us/fsp/dollar.fsp; accessed April 2021.)

[9]Thomas Goodhue, author of *Fossil Hunter: The Life and Times of Mary Anning* (Goodhue, 2004), wrote: "It is sometimes claimed she inspired Terry Sullivan's famous tongue twister of 1908: 'She sells sea-shells on the sea-shore ...'"

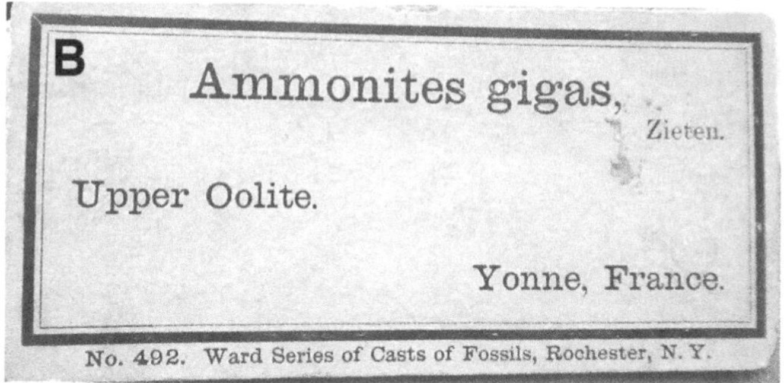

Figure 8. (A) The full-sized replica of *Ammonites gigas* from Ward's Scientific. (B) The original label authenticating the replica as Ward's model number 492 (photos courtesy of W.R. Brice).

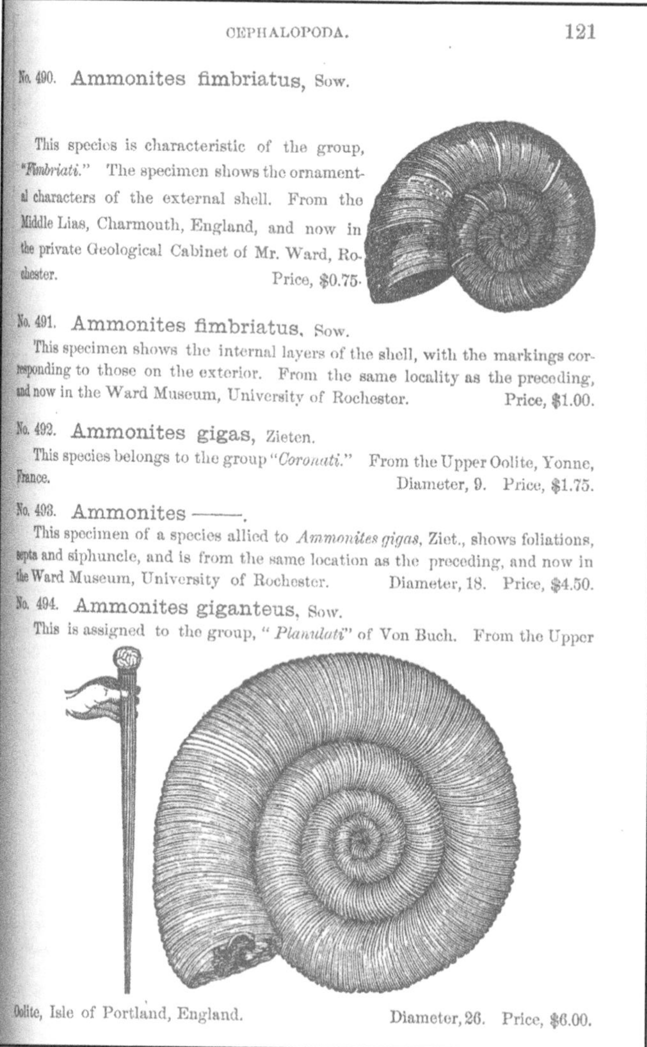

CEPHALOPODA. 121

No. 490. Ammonites fimbriatus, Sow.

This species is characteristic of the group, "*Fimbriati*." The specimen shows the ornamental characters of the external shell. From the Middle Lias, Charmouth, England, and now in the private Geological Cabinet of Mr. Ward, Rochester. Price, $0.75.

No. 491. Ammonites fimbriatus, Sow.

This specimen shows the internal layers of the shell, with the markings corresponding to those on the exterior. From the same locality as the preceding, and now in the Ward Museum, University of Rochester. Price, $1.00.

No. 492. Ammonites gigas, Zieten.

This species belongs to the group "*Coronati*." From the Upper Oolite, Yonne, France. Diameter, 9. Price, $1.75.

No. 493. Ammonites ——.

This specimen of a species allied to *Ammonites gigas*, Ziet., shows foliations, septa and siphuncle, and is from the same location as the preceding, and now in the Ward Museum, University of Rochester. Diameter, 18. Price, $4.50.

No. 494. Ammonites giganteus, Sow.

This is assigned to the group, "*Planulati*" of Von Buch. From the Upper Oolite, Isle of Portland, England. Diameter, 26. Price, $6.00.

Figure 9. A page from Ward's Scientific catalog of 1866 listing the *Ammonites gigas* (*Ward's Catalogue of Casts of Fossils*, 1866, p. 121; Davidson, 2008, p. 67).

Anning discovered a small *Plesiosaurus macrocephalus*, which was named by Buckland in 1836 (Fig. 13A) and which Richard Owen, who was introduced earlier, eventually described in 1840 (Torrens, 1995, p. 267). In 1831, Mary Anning sold the original fossil to Mr. William Willoughby (also known as Viscount Cole and later Earl of Enniskillen), a Fellow of the Geological Society (London), for the then-massive sum of 200 guineas, which in today's currency would be almost US$39,000.[10] The specimen is now housed at the Natural History Museum in London[11] (Fig. 13B). Figure 13C is the drawing and listing in Ward's 1870 catalog.

One of the casts Ward's Scientific made of this *Plesiosaurus macrocephalus* became part of the Cornell collection (Fig. 14). No doubt the same model could be found in many other universities as well. Cornell was certainly not the only university to have these reproductions as they were commonly acquired by other universities across the country.[12] Most of these models from Ward's were made well before Mr. Ward's death in 1906, so no doubt he had a hand in selecting the samples to be modeled and possibly even in the making of the models.

CORNELL MUSEUM

By the late 1800s, the Cornell Geology Department had established an extensive natural history/geology museum in McGraw Hall that was open to both students and the general public (Brice, 1989), and many of Ward's fossil models were displayed in this museum (Fig. 15). The museum also housed another of Ward's models that appears to be based on another fossil found by Mary Anning. In December 1823, Ms. Anning came across a large fossil Plesiosaur (Fig. 16), which was later described at the Geological Society (London) meeting on 20 February 1824 (Torrens, 1995). The model from Ward's 1866

[10] https://futureboy.us/fsp/dollar.fsp (accessed 10 April 2021)

[11] https://gslpicturelibrary.org.uk/plesiosaurus-macrocephalus-lyme/ (accessed August 2020)

[12] For example, see the listing of universities with Ward's casts in an addendum by F.W.P. to Morse (Morse, 1873, p. 253).

A

VERTEBRATA.

No. 294. Cheirotherium Barthi, Kaup.

T
rem
rese
hum
title
are
five
in ad
of t
four
The
in p
apar
scrib
ed t
been
sum
rupe
side
rema
have
Laby
in th
print
that t
those
This

New Red Sandstone (Lower Trias) at Jena, German
seum in the University of Rochester. Size, 6 ft.

Figure 10. (A) A page from the 1866 catalog (Ward's *Catalogue of Casts of Fossils*, 1866, p. 7; also in Davidson, 2008, p. 57); (B) the full-sized replica from the Cornell Collection (courtesy of W.R. Brice).

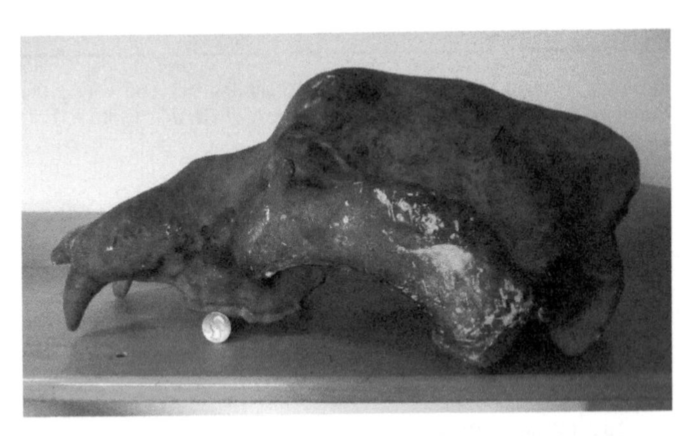

Figure 11. *Ursus spelæus,* a vertebrate fossil cast from Ward's Scientific, number 16, p. 8 (1870 catalog); note the U.S. 25 cent piece for scale (courtesy of W.R. Brice).

catalog became part of the Cornell Museum collection, but with a strange mounting arrangement: on the ceiling (Fig. 17). After the museum was dismantled and the atrium closed off, the Plesiosaur was mounted in the stairway of McGraw Hall (Fig. 18A). It moved again in 1971 to the department's new home in the College of Engineering, and the Ward's model can be seen today (2021) on the wall of the atrium of Snee Hall on the Cornell University campus (Fig. 18B).

SOME MODELS DO GET AROUND

Several of the models from the Cornell collection did a little traveling in their later life. In 1971, the Cornell Geology Department[13] changed colleges, from Arts and Sciences to Engineering, and changed buildings, first from McGraw Hall to Kimball Hall, and in 1984, from Kimball to its present location in Snee Hall. As a result of these moves, there was not always room or a home for the models. At the time of these moves, I was a graduate student (1967–1971) at Cornell and then a member of the department's summer faculty (1976–2002), and I managed to save a few of them for display and study at the University of Pittsburgh at Johnstown, Johnstown, Pennsylvania (UPJ), where I was a member of the faculty. Then, in 2012, due to renovations at UPJ,

[13] At this time, the department was known as the Department of Geological Sciences; currently it is the Department of Earth & Atmospheric Sciences.

Figure 12. (A) Mary Anning is the subject of a painting attributed to William Grey (Wikimedia Commons; https://commons.wikimedia.org/wiki/File:Mary_Anning_painting.jpg). (B) This painting is exhibited in the Natural History Museum, London next to a large plesiosaur that she discovered (courtesy of W.R. Brice).

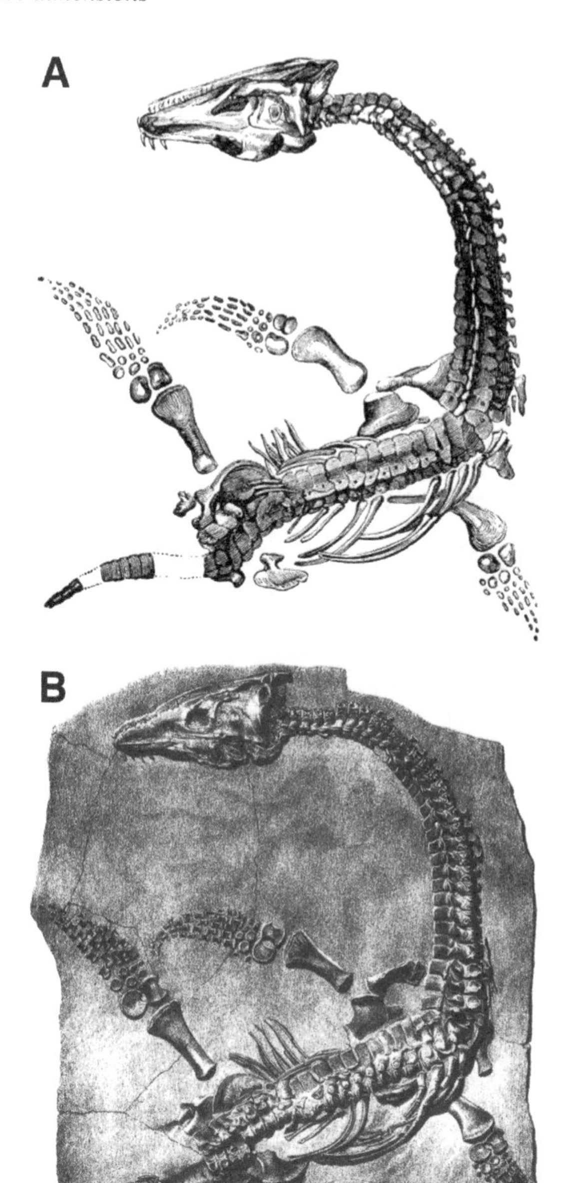

No. 43. [227] Plesiosaurus macrocephalus, Conyb.

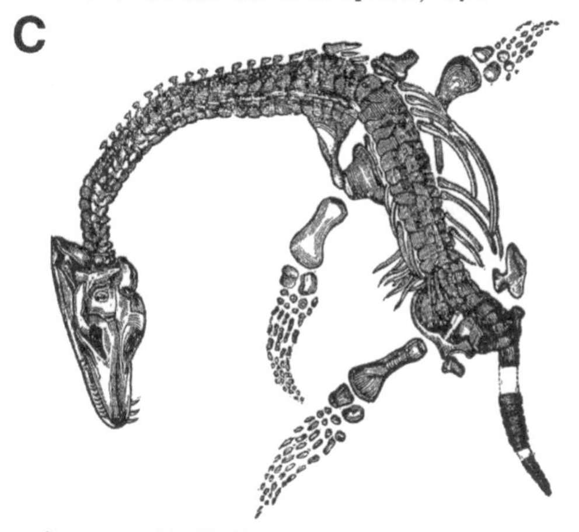

SKELETON on slab. The Plesiosaurus was first discovered in 1823, by Conybeare and De la Beche. Cuvier thought "its structure the most singular, and its characters the most anomalous that had been found amid the ruins of a former

Figure 13. (A) A sketch of the juvenile *Plesiosaurus macrocephalus* that appeared in a book by William Buckland (http://laelaps.files.wordpress.com/2007/06/21a.jpg, public domain, https://commons.wikimedia.org/w/index.php?curid=4338128; accessed August 2020); (B) the sample in the Natural History Museum in London (Wikimedia Commons; https://commons.wikimedia.org/wiki/File:Plesiosaurus_macrocephalus.JPG; accessed August 2020); (C) the listing of the cast from Ward's Scientific 1870 catalog (Ward, 1870, p. 24).

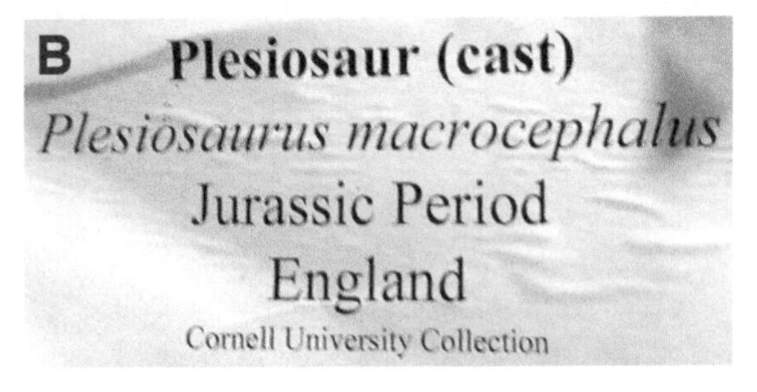

Figure 14. (A) Ward's model of Mary Anning's find (courtesy of W.R. Brice); (B) the label attached to it.

Figure 15. Two views of the Geological Museum housed in McGraw Hall at Cornell University, ca. 1890 (courtesy of Division of Rare and Manuscript Collections, Cornell University).

the models had to move again, but with this move they essentially went back home.

In 1932, when Gilbert D. Harris retired from Cornell, he founded the Paleontological Research Institution (PRI) literally in his backyard, for it was there that the first building was constructed (Brice, 1996). Over the years, the institution survived and eventually outgrew its space in Harris' backyard, and in the 1960s the institution moved to its present site on West Hill overlooking Cayuga Lake near Ithaca, New York. In 2003, the Museum of the Earth opened to further expand PRI's mission of educating the public about the Earth.

So, when the models had to move again in 2012, they were returned to the institution founded by Gilbert Harris, one of the people originally responsible for some of them being at Cornell. They were taken back to PRI (Fig. 19), where they, along with many others from the old department museum, now reside and continue to generate interest and excitement in those who see and work with them.

CONCLUSION

Three-dimensional modeling of fossils has been around for over 100 years, and by using and studying these models, students get to work with fossils that would otherwise be seen only in pictures or not at all. The use of 3-D models as study aids for students was especially popular in the late 1800s and early 1900s. Many of these same models were used for museum displays as well. In this way, these models are important to paleoart because they make this part of geology available for education both formally in college classrooms and informally in museums. They offer a way to educate the next generation of scientists and engage the public.

Starting in the mid-nineteenth century, Ward's Scientific of Rochester, New York, became a major, but not sole, source of these models, and the Geology Department at Cornell University, just one of many academic institutions, purchased many of

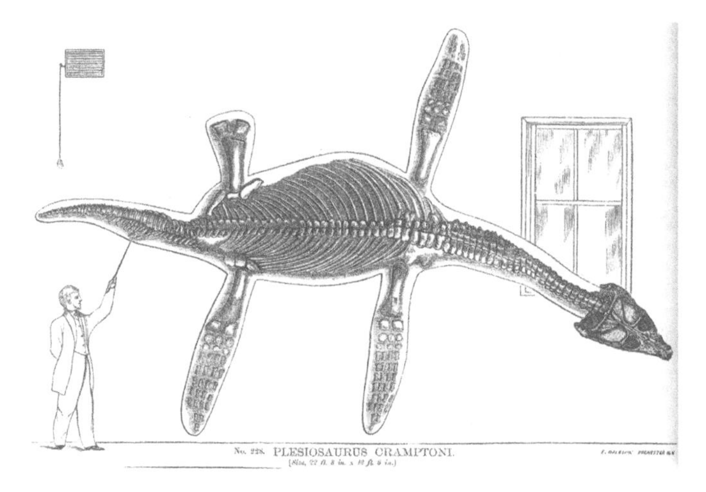

Figure 16. The illustration of the large, more complete Plesiosaurus in Ward's Scientific 1866 catalog (*Ward's Catalogue of Casts of Fossils*, 1866; also in Davidson, 2008, p. 68).

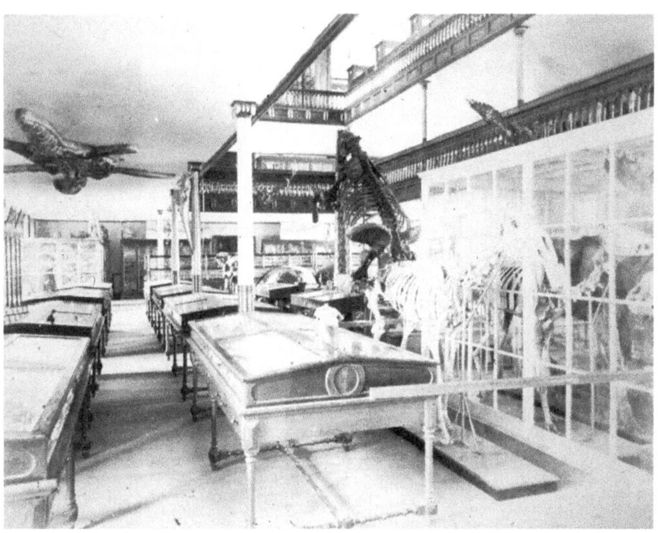

Figure 17. Another view of the Geological Museum at Cornell University ca. 1890; note the location of the mounted Plesiosaur (upper left) (courtesy of Division of Rare and Manuscript Collections, Cornell University Library).

Figure 18. (A) The location of the Plesiosaur in the stairway of McGraw Hall until 1971; (B) where it now resides in the atrium of Snee Hall, the home of the Earth and Atmospheric Sciences at Cornell University (photos by W.R. Brice).

Figure 19. The fossil models being delivered to the Paleontological Research Institution (PRI) on 1 May 2012. Accepting the return from William R. Brice (kneeling) are members of the PRI staff, including Director Dr. Warren Allmon (far right in black coat; courtesy of PRI).

them for study and display. And even today, 3-D models can be purchased from Ward's Scientific, but the prices are somewhat higher than in 1866. For example, a *Paradoxides harlani* (Cambrian), catalog number 470237–642, now costs US$79.95[14] and an *Archaeopteryx* reproduction, catalog number 470226–630, costs US$194.95[15]. Now, with modern computer technology, 3-D digital models can be easily created as computer images. For example, the British Museum has a project[16] to develop a single database of the type specimens held in British collections, and a selection of them will have 3-D digital models available. In addition, individuals using a 3-D printer can print their own 3-D model,[17] at whatever scale the printer allows, but these techniques do have technological limitations depending on what equipment is available. So, we have come quite a long way from the days of mixing plaster, making the model, and waiting for it to dry before finally painting it.

[14]*Paradoxides harlani* (Cambrian): https://www.wardsci.com/store/search?label=Invertebrates&navSearch=WardsSci000404 (accessed July 2020).

[15]*Archaeopteryx*: https://www.wardsci.com/store/product?keyword=Archaeopteryx (accessed July 2020).

[16]GB3D Type Fossils Online: http://www.3d-fossils.ac.uk/home.html (accessed July 2020).

[17]Build your own dinosaur: Fossil models arrive for 3-D printers; Thousands of ancient relics, quite literally at your fingertips. By Katie Drummond: https://www.theverge.com/2013/8/30/4671828/3d-print-your-own-fossils-new-online-database (accessed July 2020).

ACKNOWLEDGMENTS

I thank the Paleontological Research Institution of Ithaca, New York, and Director Warren D. Allmon for allowing me access to the fossil models housed at that facility. I also thank that institution for preserving these models when so many similar ones have been lost. My expression of appreciation goes to the Department of Earth & Atmospheric Sciences, Cornell University, also in Ithaca, New York, for access to its departmental history archive, and to Eisha Neely, Research Services Librarian, Carl A. Kroch Library, Cornell University, for her assistance with the early images of the Geology Department. I very much appreciate the assistance provided by Robert A. Miller (AM Labs–Science Education, West Henrietta, New York) for pointing me to the 1870 Ward's Scientific catalog and for his help in researching the images from the 1866 catalog. And to my friends and colleagues Renee Clary and Gary Rosenberg, a big thank you for your help and support with this project and many others over the years.

REFERENCES CITED

Allmon, W.D., 2017, Life-restorations of ammonites and the challenges of taxonomic uniformitarianism: Earth Sciences History, v. 36, no. 1, p. 1–29, https://doi.org/10.17704/1944-6178-36.1.1.

Appleby, V., 1979, Ladies with hammers: New Scientist, v. 84, no. 1183, p. 714–715.

Brice, W.R., 1985, Ralph Stockman Tarr; scientist-writer-teacher, *in* Drake, E.T., and Jordan, W., eds., Geological Ideas—A History of North American Geology: Boulder, Colorado, Geological Society of America, Centennial Special Volume 1, p. 215–235.

Brice, W.R., 1989, Cornell Geology through the Years: Ithaca, New York, College of Engineering, Cornell University, 230 p.

Brice, W.R., 1994, Charles Frederick Hartt (1840–1878); the early years: Earth Sciences History, v. 13, no. 2, p. 160–167, https://doi.org/10.17704/eshi.13.2.u817h0538w40p3v0.

Brice, W.R., 1996, Gilbert Dennison Harris; a Life with Fossils: Ithaca, New York, Paleontological Research Institution, Bulletins of American Paleontology, 154 p.

Brice, W.R., 1999, Tarr, Ralph Stockman, *in* Garraty, J., ed., American National Biography: New York, Oxford University Press, v. 21, p. 238–329.

Brice, W.R., and Figueirôa, S.F. de M., 1994, Charles Frederic Hartt and nineteenth century geological exploration in Brazil—The human cost, *in* Figueirôa, S.F. de M., and Lopes, M., eds., Geological Sciences in Latin America—Scientific Relations and Exchanges (INHEGEO Meeting July 1993): Campinas, SP, Brazil, Instituto de Geociências, Universidade Estadual de Campinas, p. 109–126.

Brice, W.R., and Figueirôa, S.F. de M., 2001, Charles Hartt, Louis Agassiz, and the controversy over Pleistocene glaciation in Brazil: History of Science, v. 39, p. 161–184, https://doi.org/10.1177/007327530103900202.

Brice, W.R., and Figueirôa, S.F. de M., 2003, Charles Frederick Hartt—A pioneer of Brazilian Geology: GSA Today, v. 13, no. 3, p. 18–19, https://doi.org/10.1130/1052-5173(2003)013<0018:RSCFHA>2.0.CO;2.

Cantor, G., 2012, Science, providence, and progress at the Great Exhibition: Isis, v. 103, no. 3, p. 439–459, https://doi.org/10.1086/667968.

de Chadarevian, S., and Hopwood, N., eds., 2004, Models; the Third Dimension of Science: Stanford, California, Stanford University Press, 464 p.

Colbert, E.H., 1968, Men and Dinosaurs; the Search in Field and Laboratory: New York, E.P. Dutton & Co., Inc., 283 p.

Davidson, J.P., 2008, A History of Paleontology Illustration: Bloomington & Indianapolis, Indiana, Indiana University Press, 217 p.

Desmond, A.J., 1975, Hot-Blooded Dinosaurs; a Revolution in Paleontology: New York, Dial Press, 288 p.

Goodhue, T., 2004, Fossil Hunter; the Life and Times of Mary Anning (1799–1847): Cambridge, Massachusetts, Academic Press, 202 p.

Lipps, J.H., 2022, this volume, Foraminiferal art through the ages, *in* Clary, R.M., Rosenberg, G.D., and Evans, D.C., eds., The Evolution of Paleontological Art: Geological Society of America Memoir 218, Chapter 22, https://doi.org/10.1130/2021.1218(22).

Morse, E.S., 1873, Notes: American Naturalist, v. 7, no. 4, p. 249–256, https://doi.org/10.1086/271134.

O'Connor, R., 2007, The Earth on Show; Fossils and the Poetics of Popular Science, 1802–1856: Chicago, The University of Chicago Press, 541 p., https://doi.org/10.7208/chicago/9780226616704.001.0001.

Peck, R.M., and Rowland, S.M., 2022, this volume, Benjamin Waterhouse Hawkins and the early history of 3-D paleontological art, *in* Clary, R.M., Rosenberg, G.D., and Evans, D.C., eds., The Evolution of Paleontological Art: Geological Society of America Memoir 218, Chapter 17, https://doi.org/10.1130/2021.1218(17).

Rieppel, L., 2012, Bringing dinosaurs back to life; exhibiting prehistory at the American Museum of Natural History: Isis, v. 103, no. 3, p. 460–490, https://doi.org/10.1086/667969.

Secord, J., 2004, Monsters at the Crystal Palace, *in* de Chadarevian, S., and Hopwood, N., eds., 2004, Models; the Third Dimension of Science: Stanford, California, Stanford University Press, p. 138–169.

Torrens, H.S., 1995, Mary Anning (1799–1847) of Lyme; the greatest fossilist the world ever knew: British Journal for the History of Science, v. 28, p. 257–284, https://doi.org/10.1017/S0007087400033161.

Ward, H.A., 1866, Catalogue of Casts of Fossils from the Principal Museums of Europe and America with Short Descriptions and Illustrations: Rochester, New York, Benton and Andrews, 228 p.

Ward, H.A., 1870, Catalogue of the Academy Series of Casts of Fossils, from the Principal Museums of Europe and America, with Short Descriptions and Illustrations: Rochester, New York, Ezra R. Andrews, 80 p., https://hdl.handle.net/2027/miun.ajp9107.0001.001.

Manuscript Accepted by the Society 14 January 2021
Manuscript Published Online 28 October 2021

Printed in the USA

The Geological Society of America
Memoir 218

The illustration of dinosaur tracks through time

Donald H. Goldstein
University of Connecticut, Department of Geosciences, Beach Hall Room 207, 354 Mansfield Road–Unit 1045, Storrs, Connecticut 06269, USA

Patrick Getty
Collin College, Plano Campus, Department of Geology, 2800 East Spring Parkway, J-246, Plano, Texas 75074, USA

ABSTRACT

Dinosaur tracks have been illustrated since they were first found. The earliest illustrations depicted dinosaur tracks as the work of mythical beings. With the advent of scientific inquiry into dinosaur tracks in the nineteenth century, natural explanations were sought for the fossil tracks. Illustrations of the period were relatively realistic but were influenced by then-current beliefs and were constrained by the artists' skills and by what scientists considered salient. In the mid-nineteenth century, the first photographs were used for the scientific study of fossil tracks. Photography eliminated some limitations of artistic talent and showed complete specimens, not just aspects that were deemed salient. The ability to compare and name similar tracks from disparate authors and places became easier. Advances in photography, laser scanning, optical scanning and lidar, and the ability to manipulate images with computers, have enabled the modern synthesis of illustrating dinosaur tracks, which combines many types of images. With each advance and the adoption of newer technologies, the older methods have not been retired. Rather, we have continued to see new uses for old methods and an integration of illustrative styles.

For Patrick. *Your friendship and your vision will be so deeply missed.*

INTRODUCTION

Dinosaur track illustration has evolved over time. The earliest works on the traces were influenced by supernatural interpretations that are called ichnoheirophanies (Baucon et al., 2012). Naturalistic depictions became common with the advent of scientific inquiry, but the technologies used have changed. Current scientific illustrations connect our knowledge of dating and sedimentology and the anatomy of dinosaurs with metadata available through novel means of imaging and manipulating the data from original tracks into meaningful displays.

Folktales abound throughout the world regarding dinosaur tracks. The fascination with dinosaur tracks is evident in pictographs and ancient cave art in the vicinity of trackways (Helm, 2013; Helm and Benoit, 2019; Lockley et al., 2006; Ellenberger et al., 2005). Early explanations of the tracks included tales of Marala, the Emu Man in Australia (Baucon et al., 2012; Mayor and Sarjeant, 2001; Salisbury et al., 2016), Feng Huang, and Tian Ji, mythical birds in Chinese folklore (Xing et al., 2011), the Thunderbird in ancient America (Mayor, 2005; Lockley et al., 2006), the tracks of Heracles in Greco-Roman times (Mayor and Sarjeant, 2001; Baucon et al., 2012), and tales of a giant mule

Goldstein, D.H., and Getty, P., 2022, The illustration of dinosaur tracks through time, *in* Clary, R.M., Rosenberg, G.D., and Evans, D.C., eds., The Evolution of Paleontological Art: Geological Society of America Memoir 218, p. 139–150, https://doi.org/10.1130/2021.1218(16).

in Portugal (Antunes, 1976; Antunes and Mateus, 2003; Baucon et al., 2012). The naturalists of seventeenth-century Europe purporting to illustrate trace fossils were sometimes prone to "poetic license" (Pemberton and Pemberton, 2018). Although ancient ideas of the tracks' origins do not comport to our scientific understanding, the depictions of the tracks themselves were often accurate representations of what the artists considered salient.

Scientific inquiries into fossil tracks in the early 1800s focused on identifying their makers among the ancestors of living animals. These were carried over from folk explanations such as the quarrymen declaring the tridactyl tracks of the Deerfield Basin (Massachusetts, USA) to be "turkey tracks" (Hitchcock, 1843). One early explanation by Edward Hitchcock stated that the tracks "could not have been made by any other known biped except birds" (Hitchcock, 1836, p. 313). This understanding evolved with the discovery of tridactyl, bipedal dinosaurs in 1858 (Leidy, 1858) and culminated when tracks were found with dinosaur skeletal remains in the Wealdon Formation of England (Beckles, 1862). Drawings and engravings of the time were meant to be accurate representations of the prints. The earliest use of photography, which quickly became established as the most accurate way to illustrate tracks, also began during this period.

In the twentieth century, improvements in photography and new methods of scanning and recording tracks opened up a world of data beyond the simple image. Accurate measurements could now be made from photographs and scans. From the late twentieth century to today, advances in computer processing have allowed us to generate dimensional and enhanced color images from photographs or laser scans. Using computer algorithms, we have also gained the ability to reconstruct "lost" images (Helm, 2013). If photography could be considered the advent of realism in depicting dinosaur tracks, then this new age can be considered the age of hyper-realism.

Advances in depicting dinosaur tracks have not resulted in earlier methods becoming obsolete; rather, each advance added a level of imagery, which resulted in an amalgam of techniques that give both a visceral connection to the original tracks and an understanding of the information that can be extracted from the tracks.

THE AGE OF THE SUPERNATURAL (HEIROPHANIC)

Supernatural explanations (heirophanic interpretations) of dinosaur tracks were common in the pre-scientific world (Baucon et al., 2012). Those who first illustrated the tracks might have considered the sites where they were found to be sacred. The artworks themselves may have been inspired by the tracks, but it is often difficult to establish a direct connection between the art and the fossils. An early depiction of a tridactyl print can be found on the wall in Moenkapi cave, Lesotho (Helm, 2013; Helm and Benoit, 2019). Unfortunately, the pictograph has faded in the 75 years since its discovery. It was painted red and lined in black and resembles tracks found elsewhere in the country. The painting measured ~7 cm long × 10 cm wide; the digits divaricated ~100° (Ellenberger et al., 2005). Its proportions are similar to those of ornithopod tracks. The footprint design is accompanied by pictures of two upright creatures resembling large birds. An enhanced illustration published by Charles Helm (2013) used the panoramic photography technique and computer toolset Capture, Process, Enhance and Display (CPED) (Hollmann and Crause, 2011), which recovered the original black outline. Estimates of when the pictograph was made range from 1810 to 1820, which is at least a decade before the first illustration of a dinosaur track in a scientific publication (Ellenberger et al., 2005).

The Chinese have been aware of fossil tracks since antiquity. Theropod tracks have been incorporated into stones as decorative elements in various buildings (Xing et al., 2015) and tales tell of revered Jin Ji, "Golden Chicken" tracks (Xing et al., 2011). Herders in Inner Mongolia in the 1950s named theropod tracks "Shen Niao," Divine Bird tracks. They believed that they represented beautiful wishes. These tracks were only discovered by scientists in 1979 (Xing et al., 2011). Hadrosaur tracks in Qijang County, China, were once interpreted as Lotus blossoms. An inscription, discovered in 2007–2008, described a shelter erected near hadrosaur tracks during the Song Dynasty in 1256 CE. Another inscription was added in 1839, and in 1862, the site was named "The Mountain Stronghold Protected by Lotus" (Xing et al., 2011, p. 217).

Australian Aboriginal folklore tells of Marala, the giant Emu Man, wandering the Earth in Dreamtime (Baucon et al., 2012; Mayor and Sarjeant, 2001; Salisbury et al., 2016). The rock art of Australia includes numerous depictions of emu trackways (Basedow, 1914). These may be interpretations of Australia's dinosaur tracks (Salisbury et al., 2016), some of which are from the vicinity where rock paintings are found. Since Aborigines are excellent trackers, however, it is unclear if these are truly depictions of the fossils or skillful renderings of modern emu tracks.

Native American and post-colonial explanations for tracks are wide-ranging. The Abenaki and Iroquois invoked the "Great Elk" with an extra prehensile limb, which was an interpretation of mastodon skeletal remains. Peruvian legends speak of extinct giants (Mayor, 2005). Native Americans in the American Southwest attributed three-toed fossil prints to giant birds (Mayor, 2005, p. 139), although the beliefs of pictograph painters near Flag Point, Utah, are unknown. The pictograph includes a three-pronged image (Fig. 1) identified as a dinosaur footprint like that of *Kayentapus*, which is found nearby (Lockley et al., 2006). It is estimated to have been painted between 900 CE and 1150 CE during the Pueblo II phase. Other three-pronged carvings of "Ancestral Peubloan" age (1–1300 CE) (Staker, 2006) are located near a set of tracks in Zion National Park. Mayor and Sarjeant (2001) note carvings at Paraiba, northeastern Brazil, that the local people interpreted as prints of giant running birds. In the nineteenth century, quarrymen from the Connecticut Valley said that the tracks they found were those of large birds and often attributed them to turkeys (E. Hitchcock, letter to Charles Lyell, 1843).

Folktales of the Devil have been associated with dinosaur tracks in Europe (Mayor and Sarjeant, 2001). For example,

Figure 1. Pictograph shows a tridactyl track (center) resembling those of the ichnogenus *Kayentapus* nearby in Flag Point, Utah, USA. Courtesy of Bureau of Land Management, Grand Staircase-Escalante National Monument.

undated petroglyphs from Poland depicting devils are thought to be connected to the known dinosaur tracks at the site (Gierlinski and Kowalski, 2006). In other parts of Europe, the fossil tracks are thought to be those of ancient heroes or saints (Mayor and Sarjeant, 2001).

An example of trackways and heirophanic interpretations leading to art works of enduring beauty can be seen at Cabo Espichel, Portugal. Fishermen interpreted sauropod prints as those of a giant mule that carried the Virgin Mary up the cliff (Antunes, 1976). A chapel (Fig. 2B), which quickly became a national pilgrimage site, was built at the top of the cliff in 1410 (Antunes and Mateus, 2003). The cliff has at least 38 sauropod trackways and two theropod trackways on its face (Lockley et al., 1994; Santos et al., 2008). In the eighteenth century, a series of tile panels was placed in the chapel to illustrate the legend of Our Lady of the Mule Stone (Santos et al., 2008; Baucon et al., 2012). Prints are depicted in the tiles ascending the cliff at an angle similar to those of the dinosaur trackways (Fig. 2A).

In this pre-scientific world, the representations of fossil tracks could be relatively accurate, but explanations were varied and sometimes culturally specific. This is similar to the distinction between representation and reality and the use of poetic license that was common in early scientific illustrations (Pemberton and Pemberton, 2018). The artworks were meant for public consumption and, sometimes, for veneration.

EARLY SCIENTIFIC DEPICTIONS OF DINOSAUR TRACKS

The scientific depiction of fossil tracks began in Scotland with the publication of Reverend Henry Duncan's work on prints from a Dumfriesshire quarry (Duncan, 1831). The slab containing the tracks was given to Duncan in 1824. After a series of exchanges with William Buckland, Duncan wrote an account of the fossil footmarks (Pemberton and Gingras, 2003). Duncan's work was first reported by James Grierson to the Literary and Antiquarian Society of Perth, Australia, on 22 November 1827. Duncan presented the work to the Royal Society of Edinburgh on 7 January 1828 (Duncan, 1831). The first publication of the report, without illustrations, was in the October edition of *The American Journal of Science and Arts* (Duncan, 1828). The complete report, released in 1831, included the first scientific illustration of a fossil vertebrate track (Fig. 3).

For the next 23 years, various methods of drawing, sketching, and engraving were used in the scientific illustration of fossil tracks. Most illustrators sought accuracy in their renditions of the specimens, but what was created depended upon the skills of the artists and on what was considered salient. Scientific illustrations in this period stressed proportions, angles, and measurements to discriminate between species, size, and gait. The major purposes of the drawings were study, comparison, and public consumption.

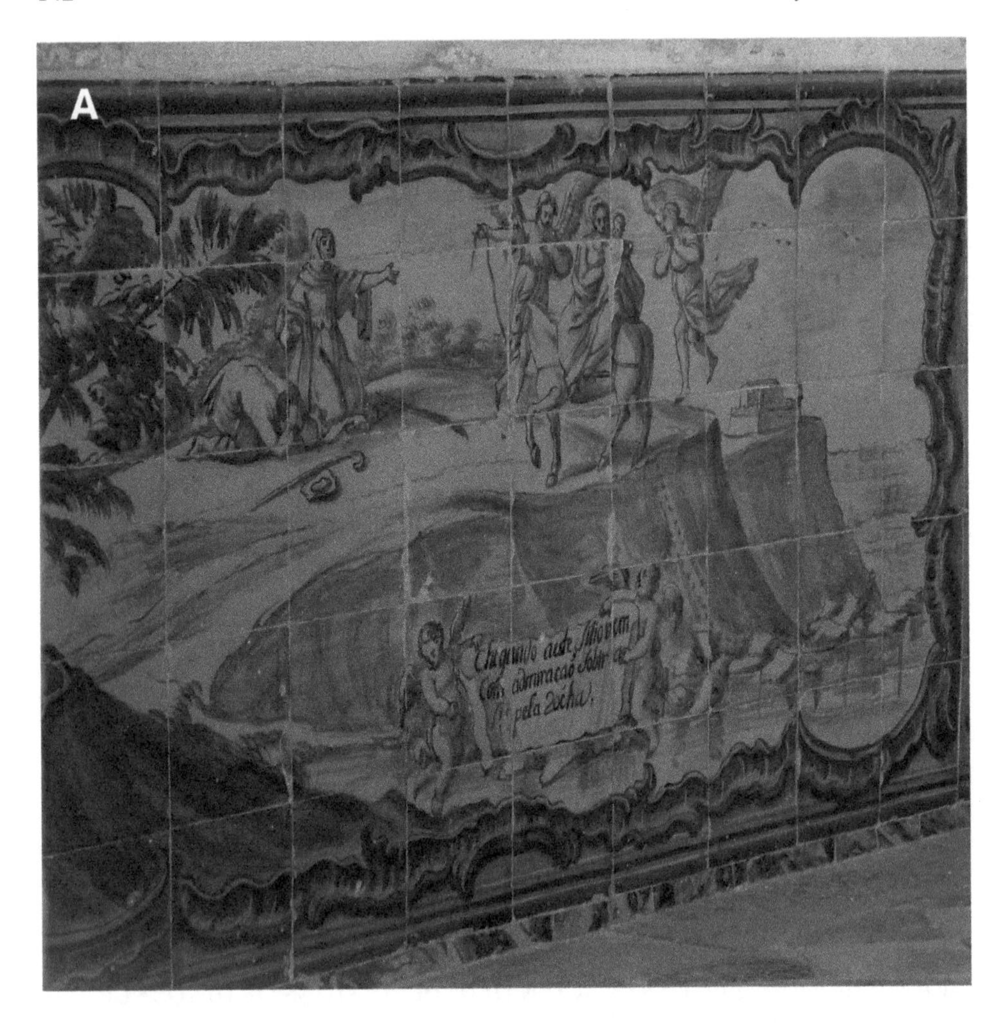

Figure 2. (A) Tile depiction shows the donkey with the Virgin Mary in the Ermida da Memoria, Cabo Espichel, Portugal. Note the trail on the cliff depicting the dinosaur footprints. Photo credit: Silvério Figueiredo, Centro Português de Geo-História e Pré-História. (B) The tracksite at Lagosteiras Bay, Cabo Espichel, Portugal. The chapel is on the top of the cliff. Sauropod footprints appear as dark spots against the cliff face. Photo credit: Silvério Figueiredo, Centro Português de Geo-História e Pré-História.

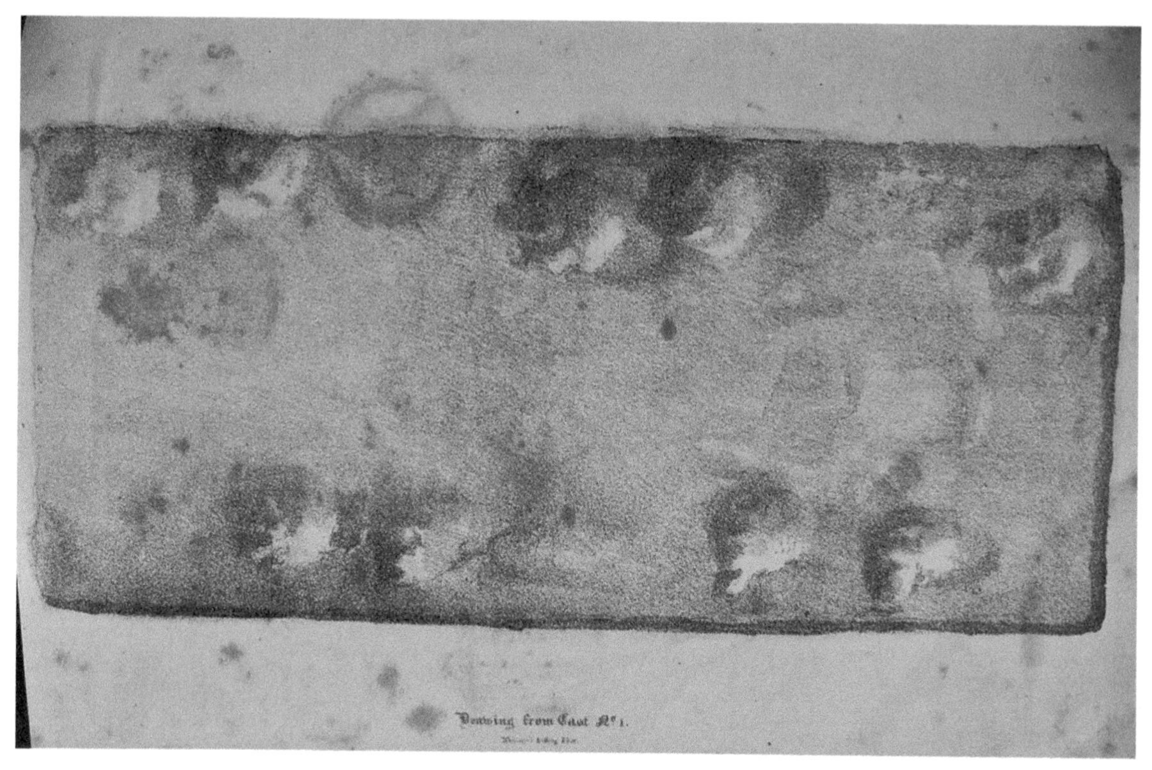

Figure 3. Rev. Henry Duncan (1831), *Drawing from Cast no. 1*. The tracks, *Chelichnus duncani* Owen 1842, were described as those of a tortoise by Duncan. Courtesy of Yale University Library. Photo credit: Goldstein.

Sketches, such as those appearing in Edward Hitchcock's papers, were used as field studies. His sketch in Figure 4A shows the early scientific approach to measuring prints and differentiating trackways. Hitchcock considered himself a poor artist (Hitchcock, 1858b, p. 163; Goldstein et al., 2017); thus, many of his illustrations (e.g., Fig. 4B, plate 39 in Hitchcock, 1841) were executed by others. Among her many contributions his wife, Orra White Hitchcock, created a series of large drawings of fossil tracks (Fig. 4C) for his classroom (Hitchcock, 1863, p. 294) as well as two plates of modern tracks for his *The Final Report on the Geology of Massachusetts* (Hitchcock, 1841). Based on elements of style, she may have also created other unsigned footprint figures for Edward Hitchcock (Herbert and D'Arienzo, 2011). In Hitchcock's early works, some of the illustrations were more artistic than accurate. By the time that his definitive 1858 work was published, his representations were more reliably detailed and included many photographs (see following section). The lovely engraving called *The Moody Foot Mark Quarry, South Hadley*, figure 1 of *Ichnology of New England*, is a prime example of an evocative illustration meant for public display (Fig. 5).

PHOTOGRAPHIC REALISM

The mid-nineteenth century was an age of photographic invention. Dr. John Warren's 1854 book *Remarks on Some Fossil Impressions in the Sandstone Rocks of Connecticut River* was the first American scientific publication of any kind to feature a photograph of a specimen (Steinbock, 1989; Pemberton and Pemberton, 2018). This photograph, included as the frontispiece of Warren's book (Fig. 6A), was illustrated by Silsbee and Case of Boston in the salt print method that utilized paper, a solution of salt and a solution of silver nitrate. The paper darkened upon exposure, and when the photographer judged that it was sufficiently exposed, the process was stopped. An application of an additional strong solution of salt stabilized the image and rendered it only slightly sensitive to further exposure (Pemberton and Pemberton, 2018). Time has not been kind to these salt print images. Almost all of the copies that we have seen, or have seen photographs of, are faded. The photograph here is from a copy presented to the Yale Library by Dr. Warren and has been kept in comparatively excellent condition.

The illustrated slab was quarried at Turners Falls, Massachusetts. Dr. Warren noted two sets of "chelonian (turtle) tracks," four sets of "bird tracks," and "footsteps of an unknown animal." The collection, including the slab, was auctioned in 1852 with specimens going to various colleges and scientific institutions (Warren, 1854), and it is currently missing.

Fortunately, the counterpart to the Warren specimen is housed in the Beneski Museum at Amherst College as specimen 26/10. The 114 × 110 cm slab is figured as plate 40, no. 1,

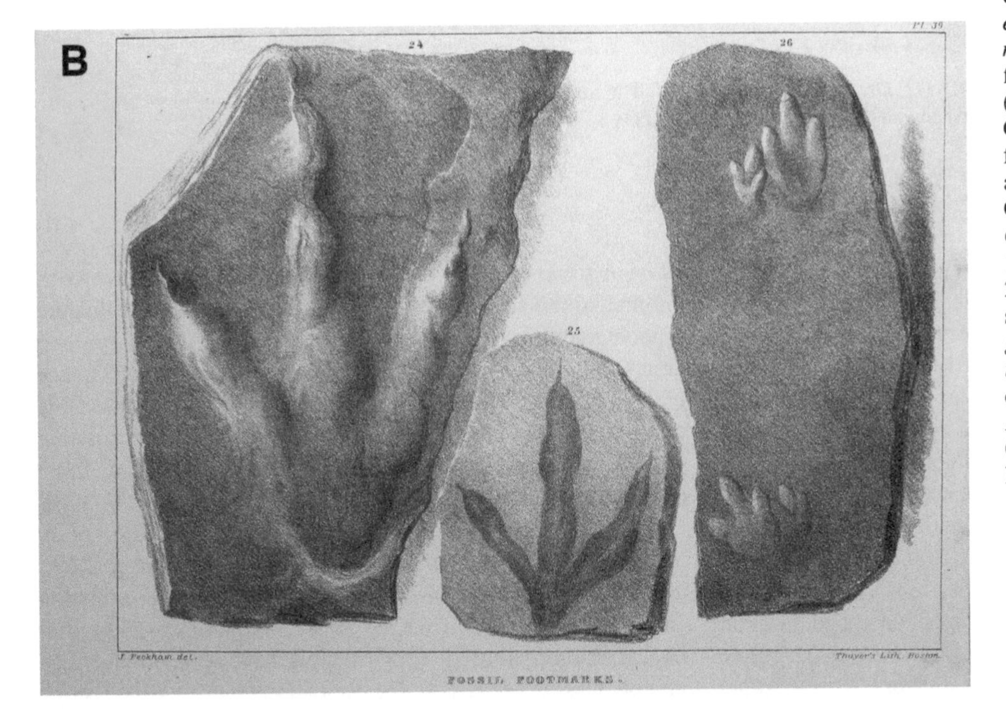

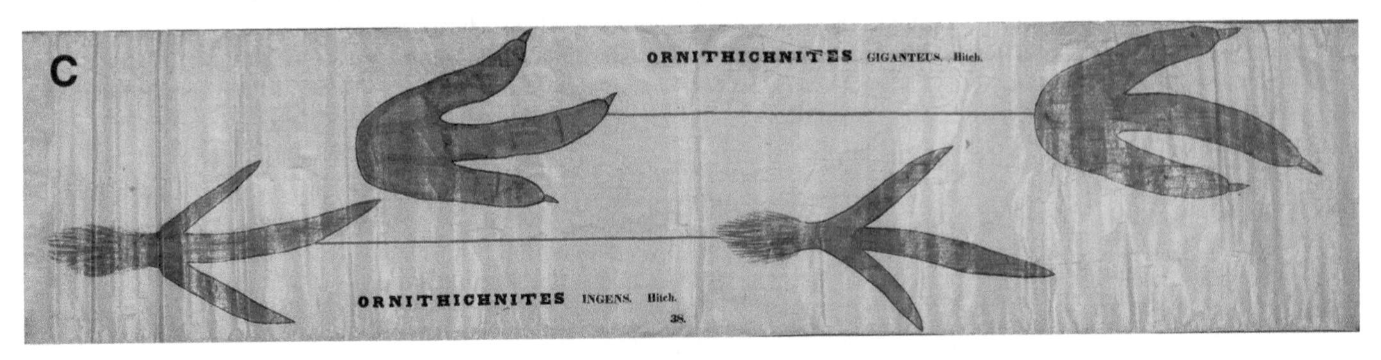

Figure 4. (A) Edward Hitchcock's pencil sketches of fossil tracks from Middletown, Connecticut, USA, ca. the middle to late 1830s are shown. The tracks identified in the sketch as *O. tuberosus* (*Eubrontes tuberosus*) include measurements in inches of track length, claw length, and stride. Edward and Orra White Hitchcock Papers [Box 20, folder 5], Amherst College Archives and Special Collections. Photo credit: Goldstein. (B) Sketch of several tracks. J. Peckham. Thayer Lithography. Plate 39, Hitchcock 1841, Final Report on the Geology of Massachusetts. Figure 24: *Ornithoidichnites expansus* (*Eubrontes expansus*); figure 25: *Ornithoidichnites cuneatus* (*Eubrontes cuneatus*); figure 26: *Ornithoidichnites parvulus* (*Eubrontes parvulus*). Edward and Orra White Hitchcock Papers [Box 11, folder 22]. Amherst College Archives and Special Collections. Photo credit: Goldstein. (C) Ora White Hitchcock's *Classroom Drawing Number 38,* ca. 1838–1840. Pen and ink on linen, 49 × 218 cm. Two lines of ornithichnites fossil footprints: *O. giganteus* (*Eubrontes giganteus*) and *O. ingens* (*Steropoides ingens*). Edward and Orra White Hitchcock Papers [Map case 3, Drawer 14]. Amherst College Archives and Special Collections. Photo courtesy of Amherst Digital Collections.

Figure 5. Engraving of the Pliny Moody Quarry is shown. Lithography, J.H. Bradford and Co. Plate 1 from Hitchcock's 1858 *Ichnology of New England*. The central track was identified by E. Hitchcock in 1836 as *Ornithichnites diversus* (*Eubrontes diversus*). Amherst College Archives and Special Collections, Amherst College Library. Photo credit: Goldstein.

by Hitchcock (1858b) (Fig. 6B) and contains trails identified by Hitchcock (1858a, 1858b) as tortoise and *Brontozoum isodactlylum* (*Anomoepus scambus*) trails. The plate was produced by the ambrotype method, made "on a glass plate coated with a wet, light sensitive substance" (Pemberton and Pemberton, 2018, p. 73). The exposed image was then dried and made into a negative that was mounted against a dark background or coated with a dark varnish. Hitchcock considered the specimen to be the "gem" of the collection and wrote that "the engraving is intended to be … more perfect than the specimen" (1858a, p. 236). This seems to indicate that Hitchcock intended the plate to not only reproduce the appearance of the specimen, but also to captivate a wider audience with its artistic quality than just the scientific community.

Various methods of photographing specimens became commonplace from the mid-nineteenth century onward. In the United States, the posthumous 1861 publication of James Deane's memoir *Ichnographs from the Sandstone of Connecticut River* included nine photo-lithographs, 22 salt prints, and numerous engravings (Deane, 1861; Pemberton and Pemberton, 2018).

From the nineteenth century until today, photographs have become standard in illustrating and interpreting dinosaur tracks. As a link to the wider public, the sight of a child dwarfed by a sauropod track provides an instant sense of scale in human terms. As a means to communicate scientific descriptions of new ichnospecies, photographic accuracy has eliminated some of the confusion in coordinating scientific names deriving from the weaknesses of older pictorial methods.

BEYOND REALISM

Advances in photography and computing in the twentieth and twenty-first centuries have enabled the use of high-resolution digital images that can be edited, combined, measured, and manipulated by powerful computer programs. The acuity of digital photography has increased steadily since its introduction, and it is common to work with images of 4000 × 6000 pixels. These images can be corrected for lighting, color balance, sharpness, image size, and other parameters using computer programs such as Adobe Photoshop. Measurements can

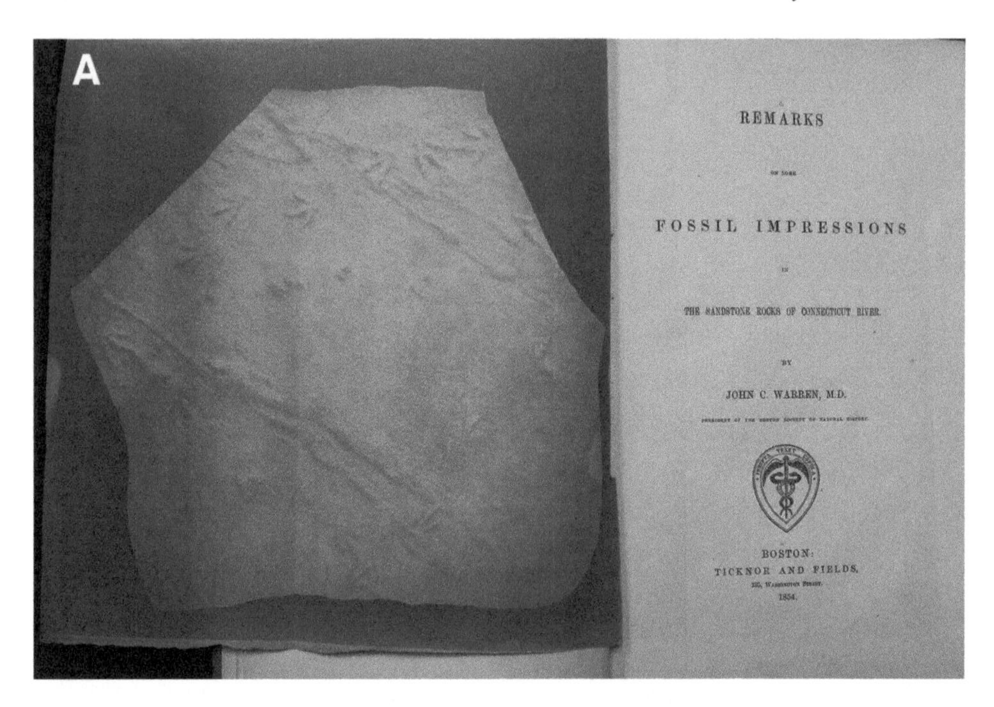

REMARKS

FOSSIL IMPRESSIONS

THE SANDSTONE ROCKS OF CONNECTICUT RIVER.

BY

JOHN C. WARREN, M.D.

BOSTON:
TICKNOR AND FIELDS,
1854.

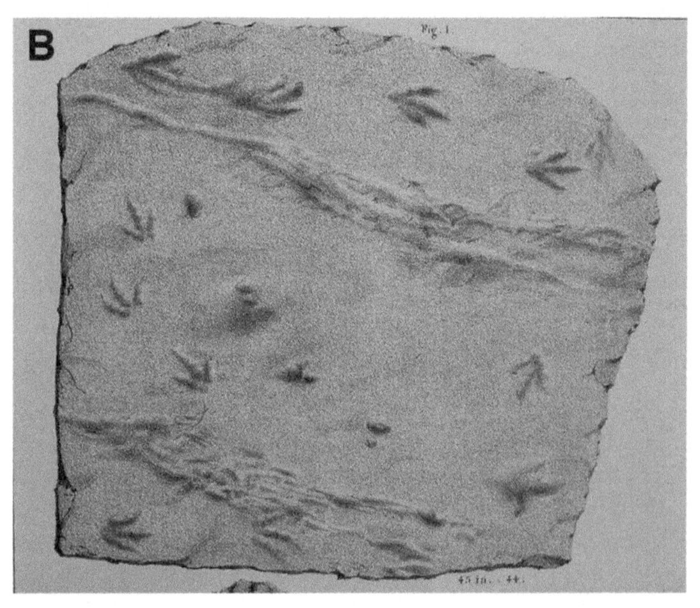

Figure 6. (A) Frontispiece and title page of Warren 1854 is shown. Silver Salt print of *Chelonian Tracks, Bird Tracks, and the Tracks of an Unknown Animal*. Courtesy of Yale University Library. Photo credit: Goldstein. (B) The counterpart image from Hitchcock 1858 (plate 40, figure 1). Specimen ACM 26/10. Ambrotype. Amherst College Archives and Special Collections, Amherst College Library. Photo credit: Goldstein.

be taken using photo editing programs such as Image J. Scale bars, symbols, and labels can be added to digital photographs in many programs.

Extended Depth of Field (EDF) techniques, which combine several partially focused photographic images into one in-focus image, have helped in visualizing deep prints or those with uneven surfaces. Photogrammetry combines six or more shots taken with a single focal length lens of an object at specific angles, and at the same distance where possible, along with low angle and overhead views. All of the shots need sufficient overlap and an included target of known size (Matthews et al., 2016). Structured light scanning and hand-held laser scanners (Pruitt et al., 2017) can both output three-dimensional data. Images created by many scanning techniques can be rotated to present different perspectives of a single data set (Figueiredo et al., 2017). This enables the computer to assemble an image or series of images as a depth map or contour map to emphasize structure or as an orthophoto to give the illusion of three-dimensionality (Fig. 7).

These developments have taken us to a realm where we can manipulate images and gain information about the parameters of the specimen that can be used to create a sense of hyper-reality. The specimen has become the basis of a reality reconstructed from the information gained by new data-gathering methods. In many cases, structures that are difficult to discern in a traditional

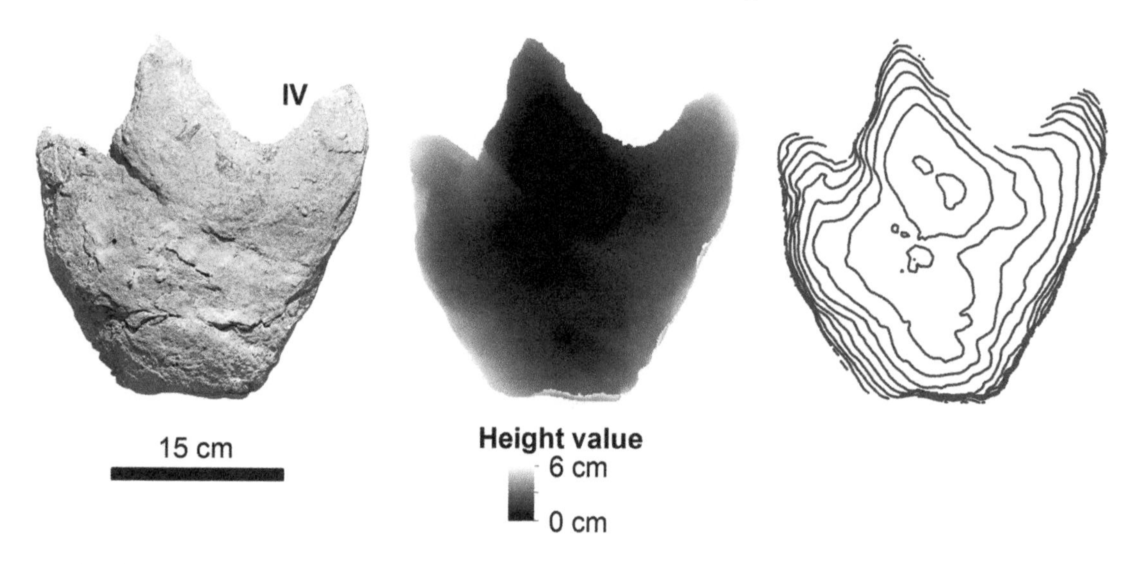

Figure 7. Three images of a possible ornithopod track from Cabo Espichel, prepared from photogrammetric data, are shown. (A) Three-dimensional orthophoto, (B) digital surface model, and (C) visual contour model. (From Figueiredo et al., 2017, figure 5, p. 223; used with permission from *Bollettino della Società Paleontologica Italiana.*)

photo, and which might have been clear only on the best of specimens, become apparent when analyzing the dimensional data available with the new methods (Figueiredo et al., 2017).

AN INTEGRATED FUTURE

Older illustration methods will supplement modern ones. Museum exhibits, book cover art and paintings will still make the connection to the public, incorporating knowledge gained by years of scientific research, as in this display from the Beneski Museum of Natural History at Amherst College, where tracks can be seen behind a model dinosaur (Fig. 8).

Scientific studies will have more details assembled to present multiple interpretations within a single work. A study by Razzolini et al. (2017) defining the ichnospecies *Megalosauripus transjuranicus* exemplifies this approach (Fig. 9). This series of images illustrates a contour map, the photograph, an outline sketch prepared based on digital information, and a false color depth map. Above those panels is a representation of the trackway. Information was gathered for these images by mapping in the field using laser, orthophotography, and photogrammetric and optical scans. The computer manipulation of the data included generating outline and high-resolution photogrammetric models. The integration of techniques can be expected to continue. What is hinted at in Pruitt et al. (2017), that the three-dimensional data can be used to print 3-D models, is already being used to print solid paleontological models for museums and classrooms. The Perot Museum of Nature and Science exhibited 3-D printed models of *Eubrontes glenrosensis* in their discovery center (Fig. 10). They were created in 2011 from the laser data files of Adams et al. (2010) (Ronald Tykoski, Perot Museum, 2020, personal commun.).

The product of modern techniques can be put to use in novel ways. A granulometric 3-D image (Fig. 11), a project of the Centro Portugués de Geo-História e Pré-Historia, was made of tracks at Parede Beach for the municipality of Cascais, Portugal. The image was created by João Belo using digital photogrammetry enhanced to clarify the microrelief. Images were converted from 2-D to 3-D using the program *Structure from Motion* (Silvério Figueiredo, 2019, personal commun.). Three sets of tracks are shown with their direction of travel indicated by arrows. Santos et al. (2015) identified the tracks as those of narrow-gauge sauropods. Identification of the ornithopod track and other sauropod tracks on the surface was facilitated by the use of the new enhanced image. The municipality wanted to garner attention for their geo-heritage and to attract visitors through the use of the image in posters and web pages.

As new methods of visualization come into use we expect that this age of hyper-realism will see a deeper integration of old and new. Paintings, sketches, photographs, and computer-generated images and models will continue to improve our ability to analyze tracks and to convey to the public their importance to our understanding of evolution.

ACKNOWLEDGMENTS

This study could not have been completed without the help of many people and institutions. Margaret Dakin, Rachel Jirka, and Mariah Leavitt of the Amherst College Archives and Special Collections gave access to rare documents. Hayley Singleton and Alfred Venne allowed long hours of work at the Beneski Museum of Natural History. The Yale University Library is thanked for their stewardship of rare volumes. Some of the photographs in this work are provided through the courtesy of

Figure 8. "Otozoum *Tracks by an Ancient Lakeshore*" is shown. Diorama of track maker and tracks, 2005. Background mural, "*Jurassic Landscape in the Connecticut Valley,*" William Sillin. Foreground model, Gary Staub, 8 ft high × 14 ft wide × 5 ft deep. Beneski Museum of Natural History, Amherst College. Photo credit: Goldstein.

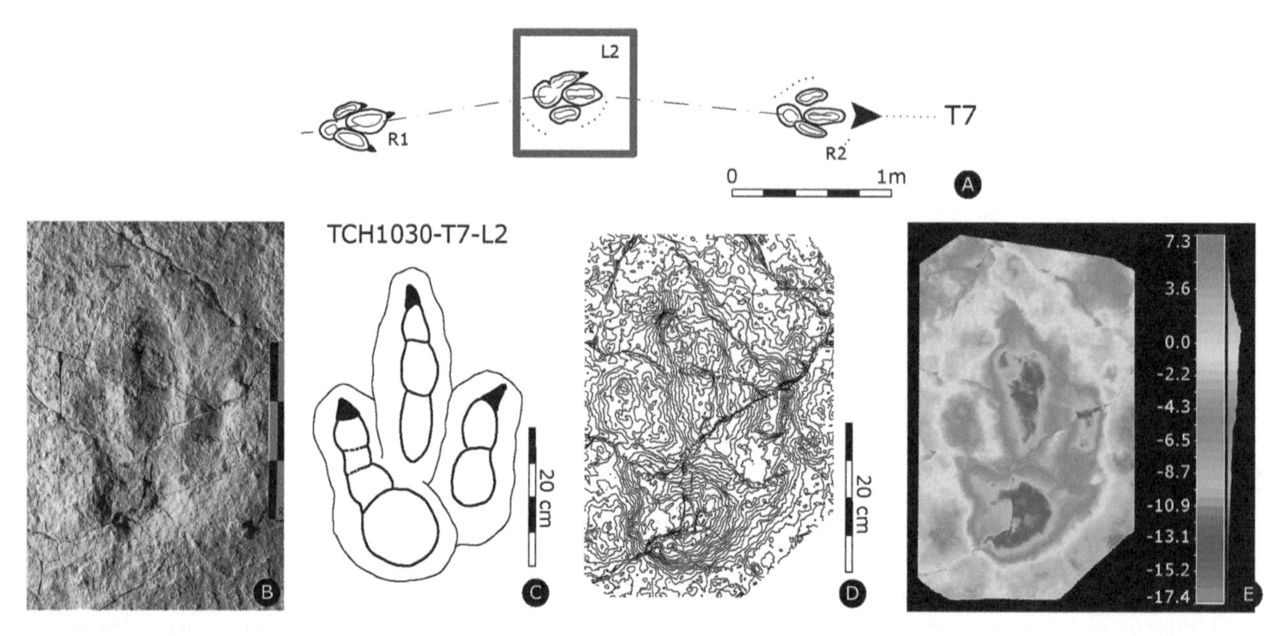

Figure 9. Five representations are shown of a single track, the paratype of *Megalosauripus transjuranicus* and its associated trackway, prepared from photogrammetric data (Razzolini et al., 2017, figure 6). The elements of this series are: (A) The trackway representation. (B) Color photograph of the specimen. (C) Interpretive outline drawing. (D) Contour lines rendered at 1 mm intervals. (E) A false-color depth map at millimeter scale.

Figure 10. Three-dimensional printed tracks of *Eubrontes glenrosensis* in the Perot Museum of Nature and Science are shown. Reproduced with permission, Renee Clary/EarthScholars Research Group, © December 2012.

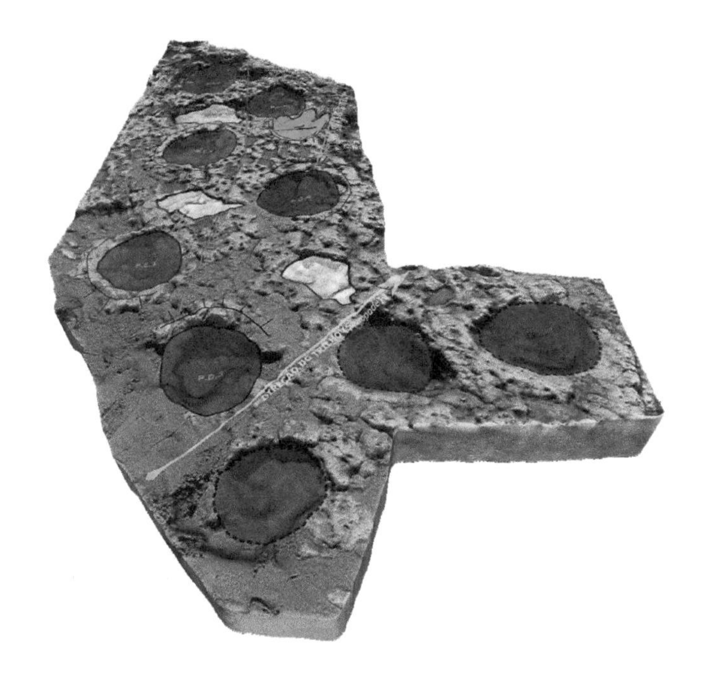

Figure 11. Granulometric 3-D image of three dinosaur trackways made for the municipality of Cascais, Portugal, is shown. One ornithopod track and rounded sauropod tracks are seen. Arrows point in the direction of travel. Courtesy of the Centro Portugués de Geo-História e Pré-Historia. Image credit: João Belo.

Silvério Figueiredo of the Centro Português de Geo-História e Pré-História; David Hercher, Nicole Lohman, and Valerie Russell of the Bureau of Land Management; and Bears Ears National Monument, Utah. To these individuals, the authors of the books and articles cited, and our editors and reviewers, we give our thanks.

REFERENCES CITED

Adams, T.L., Strganac, C., Polcyn, R.M., and Jacobs, L.L., 2010, High resolution three-dimensional laser scanning of the type specimen of *Eubrontes (?) glenrosensis* Shuler, 1935, from the Comanchean (Lower Cretaceous) of Texas: Implications for digital archiving and preservation: Paleontologia Electronica, v. 13, no. 13.31T, 11 p., https://palaeo-electronica.org/2010_3/226/index.html.

Antunes, M.T., 1976, Dinossáurios Eocretácicos de Lagosteiros: Lisboa, Portugal, Universidade Nova De Lisboa, 35 p.

Antunes, M.T., and Mateus, O., 2003, Dinosaurs of Portugal: Comptes Rendus Palevol, v. 2, no. 1, p. 77–95, https://doi.org/10.1016/S1631-0683(03)00003-4.

Basedow, H., 1914, Aboriginal rock carvings of great antiquity in South Australia: The Journal of the Royal Anthropological Institute of Great Britain and Ireland, v. 44, p. 195–211, https://doi.org/10.2307/2843536.

Baucon, A., Bordy, E., Bruster, T., Buatois, L.A., Cunningham, T., De, C., Duffin, C., Felletti, F., Gaillard, C., Hu, B., Hu, L., Jensen, S., Knaust, D., Lockley, M., Lowe, P., Mayor, A., Mayoral, E., Mikulas, R., Muttoni, G., Neto de Carvalho, C., Pemberton, S.G., Pollard, J., Rindsberg, A.K., Santos, A., Seike, K., Song, H., Turner, S., Uchman, A., Wang, Y., Yi-ming, G., Zhang, L., and Zhang, W., 2012, A history of ideas in Ichnology, *in* Knaust, D., and Bromley, R.G., eds., Trace Fossils as Indicators of Sedimentary Environments: Amsterdam, Elsevier, Developments in Sedimentology, v. 64. p. 3–43.

Beckles, S.H., 1862, On some natural casts of reptilian footprints in the Wealden Beds of the Isle of Wight and of Swanage: Quarterly Journal of the Geological Society of London, v. 18, no. 1–2, p. 443–447, https://doi.org/10.1144/GSL.JGS.1862.018.01-02.60.

Deane, J., 1861, Ichnographs From the Sandstone of Connecticut River: Boston, Little Brown and Co., 61 p., https://doi.org/10.5962/bhl.title.61934.

Duncan, H., 1828, An account of the tracks of footmarks of animals found impressed on sandstone in the quarry of Cornockle Muir, in Dumfriesshire: The American Journal of Science and Arts, v. 15, no. 1, p. 84–89.

Duncan, H., 1831, An account of the tracks of footmarks of animals found impressed on sandstone in the quarry of Cornockle Muir, in Dumfriesshire: Transactions of the Royal Society of Edinburgh, v. 11, p. 194–209.

Ellenberger, P., Mossman, D.J., Mossman, A.D., and Lockley, M.G., 2005, Bushmen cave paintings of Ornithopod Dinosaurs: Paleolithic trackers interpret Early Jurassic footprints: Ichnos, v. 12, no. 3, p. 223–226, https://doi.org/10.1080/10420940591008971.

Figueiredo, S., Dinis, P., Belo, J., Rosini, P., and Strantzali, J.B., 2017, A new record of a possible ornithopod footprint from the Lower Cretaceous of Cabo Espichel (Sesimbra, Portugal): Bollettino della Società Paleontologica Italiana, v. 56, no. 2, p. 217–231.

Gierlinski, G.D., and Kowalski, K.Z., 2006, Footprint of a large, Early Jurassic ornithischian from the ancient sacred site of Kontrewers, Poland, *in* Harris, J.D., Lucas, S.G., Spielmann, J.A., Lockley, M.G., Milner, A.R.C., and Kirkland, J.I., eds., The Triassic-Jurassic Terrestrial Transition: Albuquerque, New Mexico, New Mexico Museum of Natural History Bulletin 37, p. 217–220.

Goldstein, D.H., Getty, P.R., and Bush, A.M., 2017, Hitchcock's treptichnid trace fossils (Jurassic, Massachusetts, USA): Conflicting interpretations in the "Age of Fucoids": Bollettino della Società Paleontologica Italiana, v. 56, no. 2, p. 106–116.

Helm, C.W., 2013, Preliminary evidence for an indigenous paleontology in southern Africa: The Digging Stick, v. 30, no. 2, p. 15–18.

Helm, C.W., and Benoit, J., 2019, Geomythology in southern Africa: The Digging Stick, v. 36, no. 1, p. 15–18.

Herbert, R.L., and D'Arienzo, D., 2011, Ora White Hitchcock (1796–1863): An Amherst Woman of Art and Science: Amherst, Massachusetts, Mead Art Museum, Amherst College, 111 p.

Hitchcock, E., 1836, Ornithichnology. Description of the foot marks of Birds, (Ornithichnites) on new red sandstone in Massachusetts: The American Journal of Science and Arts, v. 29, p. 307–340.

Hitchcock, E., 1841, Final Report on the Geology of Massachusetts: Northampton, Massachusetts, J.H. Butler, 831 p.

Hitchcock, E., 1843 (17 Dec.), Letter to Charles Lyell, copy of the original from Edinburgh University: Amherst College Archives and Special Collections, Edward and Orra White Hitchcock papers, Box 5, folder 17.

Hitchcock, E., 1858a, Ichnology of New England, a Report on the Sandstone of the Connecticut Valley, Especially Its Fossil Footmarks: Unpublished manuscript draft, Amherst College Archives and Special Collections, Box 12, folder 9–17, 725 p.

Hitchcock, E., 1858b, Ichnology of New England, a Report on the Sandstone of the Connecticut Valley, Especially Its Fossil Footmarks: Boston, William White, 327 p.

Hitchcock, E., 1863, Reminiscences of Amherst College, Historical Scientific, Biographical and Autobiographical: Also of Other and Wider Life Experiences: Northampton, Massachusetts, Bridgman and Childs, 407 p.

Hollmann, J.C., and Crause, K., 2011, Digital imaging and the revelation of 'hidden' rock art: Valekop Shelter, KwaZulu-Natal: Southern African Humanities, v. 23, p. 55–76.

Leidy, J., 1858, Remarks concerning Hadrosaurus: Proceedings of the Academy of Natural Sciences of Philadelphia, v. 10, p. 215–218.

Lockley, M.G., Meyer, C.A., and Santos, V.F., 1994, Trackway evidence of a herd of juvenile sauropods from the Late Jurassic of Portugal: GAIA, v. 10, p. 27–35.

Lockley, M.G., Gierlinski, G.D., Titus, A.L., and Albright, B., 2006, An introduction to Thunderbird footprints at the Flag Point pictograph track site: Preliminary observations on Lower Jurassic Theropod tracks from the Vermillion Cliffs area, southwestern Utah, *in* Harris, J.D., Lucas, S.G., Spielmann, J.A., Lockley, M.G., Milner, A.R.C., and Kirkland, J.I., eds., The Triassic-Jurassic Terrestrial Transition: Albuquerque, New Mexico, New Mexico Museum of Natural History Bulletin 37, p. 310–314.

Matthews, N., Noble, T., and Breithaupt, B., 2016, Close range photogrammetry for 3-D ichnology: The basics of photogrammetric ichnology, *in* Falkingham, P.L., Marty, D., and Richter, A., eds., Dinosaur Tracks: The Next Steps: Bloomington, Indiana, Indiana University Press, p. 28–55.

Mayor, A., 2005, Fossil Legends of the First Americans: Princeton, New Jersey, Princeton University Press, 446 p.

Mayor, A., and Sarjeant, W.A.S., 2001, The folklore of footprints in stone: From classical antiquity to the present: Ichnos, v. 8, no. 2, p. 143–163, https://doi.org/10.1080/10420940109380182.

Pemberton, S.G., and Gingras, M.K., 2003, The Reverend Henry Duncan (1774–1846) and the discovery of the first fossil footprints: Ichnos, v. 10, no. 2–4, p. 69–75, https://doi.org/10.1080/10420940390255574.

Pemberton, S.G., and Pemberton, E.A., 2018, Role of ichnology in the history of photography: Earth Sciences History, v. 37, no. 1, p. 63–87, https://doi.org/10.17704/1944-6178-37.1.63.

Pruitt, J.B., Clement, G.C., and Tapanila, L., 2017, Laser and structured light scanning to acquire 3-D morphology: The Paleontological Society Papers, v. 22, p. 57–69, https://doi.org/10.1017/scs.2017.8.

Razzolini, N.L., Belvedere, M., Marty, D., Paratte, G., Lovis, C., Cattin, M., and Mayer, C., 2017, *Megalosauripus transjuranicus* ichnosp. nov. A new Late Jurassic theropod ichnotaxon from NW Switzerland and implications for tridactyl dinosaur ichnology and ichnotaxonomy: PLoS One, v. 12, no. 7, no. e0180289, https://doi.org/10.1371/journal.pone.0180289.

Salisbury, S.W., Romilio, A., Herne, M.C., Tucker, R.t., and Nair, J.P., 2016, The dinosaurian ichnofauna of the Lower Cretaceous (Valanginian-Barremian) Broome Sandstone of the Walmadany area (James Price Point), Dampier Peninsula, Western Australia: Journal of Vertebrate Paleontology, v. 36, supplement to no. 6, p. 1–152.

Santos, V.F., Marques da Silva, C., and Rodrigues, L.A., 2008, Dinosaur tracksites from Portugal: Scientific and cultural significance: Oryctos, v. 8, p. 77–87.

Santos, V.F., Callapez, P.M., Castanera, D., Barroso-Barcenilla, F., Rodrigues, N.P.C., and Cupeto, C.A., 2015, Dinosaur tracks from the Early Cretaceous (Albian) of Parede (Cascais, Portugal): New contributions for the sauropod paleobiology of the Iberian Peninsula: Journal of Iberian Geology, v. 41, no. 1, p. 155–166, https://doi.org/10.5209/rev_JIGE.2015.v41.n1.48662.

Staker, A.R., 2006, The earliest known dinosaur trackers of Zion National Park, Utah, *in* Harris, J.D., Lucas, S.G., Spielman J.A., Lockley, M.G., Milner, A.R.C., and Kirkland, J.I., eds., The Triassic–Jurassic Terrestrial Transition: Albuquerque, New Mexico, New Mexico Museum of Natural History Bulletin 37, p. 137–139.

Steinbock, R.T., 1989, Ichnology of the Connecticut Valley: A vignette of American science in the early nineteenth century, *in* Gillette, D.D., and Lockley, M.G. eds., Dinosaur Tracks and Traces: Cambridge, UK, Cambridge University Press, p. 27–36.

Warren, J.C., 1854, Remarks on Some Fossil Impressions in the Sandstone Rocks of Connecticut River: Boston, Ticknor and Fields, 54 p., https://doi.org/10.5962/bhl.title.13968.

Xing, L., Mayor, A., Chen, Y., Harris, J.D., and Burns, M.E., 2011, The folklore of dinosaur trackways in China: Impact on paleontology: Ichnos, v. 18, no. 4, p. 213–220, https://doi.org/10.1080/10420940.2011.634038.

Xing, L., Zhang, J., Klein, H., Mayor, A., Chen, Y., Dai, H., Burns, M.E., Gao, J., Tang, Y., and Dong, S., 2015, Dinosaur tracks, myths and buildings: The Jin Ji (Golden Chicken) stones from Zizhou area, northern Shaanxi, China: Ichnos, v. 22, p. 227–234, https://doi.org/10.1080/10420940.2015.1059334.

Manuscript Accepted by the Society 14 January 2021
Manuscript Published Online 14 April 2021

The Geological Society of America
Memoir 218

Benjamin Waterhouse Hawkins and the early history of three-dimensional paleontological art

Robert M. Peck
The Academy of Natural Sciences of Philadelphia, Drexel University, 1900 Benjamin Franklin Parkway, Philadelphia, Pennsylvania 19103, USA

Stephen M. Rowland
Department of Geoscience, University of Nevada Las Vegas, 4505 S. Maryland Parkway, Las Vegas, Nevada 89154, USA

ABSTRACT

Benjamin Waterhouse Hawkins (1807–1894) was a British scientific illustrator and sculptor who illustrated many British exploration reports in the 1830s and 1840s. In the early 1850s, Hawkins was commissioned to create life-size, concrete sculptures of *Iguanodon*, ichthyosaurs, and other extinct animals for a permanent exhibition in south London. They were the first large sculptures of extinct vertebrates ever made, and they are still on view today.

Inspired by his success in England, Hawkins launched a lecture tour and working trip to North America in 1868. Soon after his arrival, he was commissioned to "undertake the resuscitation of a group of animals of the former periods of the American continent" for public display in New York City. Had it been built, this would have been the first paleontological museum in the world.

As part of this ambitious project, with the assistance of the American paleontologist Joseph Leidy, Hawkins cast the bones of a recently discovered *Hadrosaurus* specimen and used them to construct the first articulated dinosaur skeleton ever put on display in a museum. It was unveiled at the Academy of Natural Sciences of Philadelphia in November 1868.

Hawkins worked tirelessly on New York's proposed "Paleozoic Museum" for two years, until his funding was cut by William "Boss" Tweed, the corrupt leader of the Tammany Hall political machine, who grew hostile to the project and abolished the Central Park Commission that had made it possible. When Hawkins defiantly continued to work, without funding, Tweed dispatched a gang of thugs to break into his studio and smash all of the sculptures and molds. Although Hawkins would create several copies of his articulated *Hadrosaurus* skeleton for other institutions, the prospect of building a grand museum of paleontology in America was forever destroyed by Tweed's actions.

Peck, R.M., and Rowland, S.M., 2022, Benjamin Waterhouse Hawkins and the early history of three-dimensional paleontological art, *in* Clary, R.M., Rosenberg, G.D., and Evans, D.C., eds., The Evolution of Paleontological Art: Geological Society of America Memoir 218, p. 151–159, https://doi.org/10.1130/2021.1218(17).

INTRODUCTION

Life-size models and articulated skeletons of dinosaurs and other extinct creatures are now commonplace in natural history museums the world over. They often serve as the primary draw for young visitors and the most memorable part of a museum experience for older ones. This was not always so. Until the British artist Benjamin Waterhouse Hawkins (1807–1894) (Fig. 1) pioneered the making of such displays in the second half of the nineteenth century, dinosaurs and their kin were rarely seen in museums. Prehistoric life of any kind was poorly understood and of little interest to all but a handful of professional paleontologists. Hawkins would change that through his enormously popular displays in Great Britain and the United States.

THE EARLY YEARS

Hawkins' enthusiasm and talent for artistically capturing the anatomy of animals must have begun with a deeply rooted love of natural history, but the circumstances under which this passion developed are not known. His baptismal entry reveals that his father, Thomas Hawkins, who died when Benjamin was just four years old, had been an artist (Bramwell and Peck, 2008), so his artistic talent presumably was inherited from his father. Nor is it known whether he received formal training as his talents were developing. Surviving drawings from the 1820s and 1830s, when Hawkins was in his twenties, suggest that, in addition to family portraits, the central focus of his artistic attention was mammals and birds. They remained so throughout his career.

Figure 1. Benjamin Waterhouse Hawkins by his wife, Frances Louisa Hawkins, 1855. Academy of Natural Sciences of Drexel University, ANS Archives, Coll. 803; used with permission.

While in his early twenties, Hawkins began making contacts at the Zoological Society of London, the Hunterian Museum of Comparative Anatomy (owned by the Royal College of Surgeons), and the British Museum (whose natural history section had not yet been turned into its own separate museum). He was able to gain access to living animals as well as the sketches and preserved skins of a wide range of animals that all three institutions had in their collections. Hawkins used these to hone his drafting skills and build knowledge of anatomy. In this early stage of his career, he also established a network of mentors, friends, and associates with whom he would collaborate in the years to come.

Hawkins' first artistic commission was to prepare 200 lithographic plates based on watercolors made by other artists for a book entitled *Illustrations of Indian Zoology* with text by John Edward Gray. The success of this publication led to subsequent commissions, including the illustrations for John Richardson's landmark book *Fauna Boreali-Americane; Or the Zoology of the Northern Parts of British America* (1829–1837), for a multi-authored book entitled *The Zoology of Captain Beechey's Voyage* (1839)[1], and for the official report of the zoological discoveries made by travelers on HMS *Beagle* during its famous expedition charting the coast of South America from 1832 to 1836. Edited by Charles Darwin, the *Beagle* report was published in five parts in 1842 and 1843. The last two sections contained 49 illustrations of fish and reptiles that were made by Hawkins. His plates of birds and mammals for *The Zoology of the Voyage of HMS Sulfur* (1844), and his emu plate for John Gould's *The Birds of Australia* (1840–1848), further added to Hawkins' reputation as an artist who could capture the essence of preserved specimens and bring them to life (Bramwell and Peck, 2008).

Whether in London or Liverpool, working from life or from skins and "pickled" specimens, the 1830s and 1840s must have been heady years for Hawkins. Through his own initiative, one commission at a time, he had established a place for himself at the heart of scientific illustration in Great Britain. Without the academic credentials of most of his peers, he was building a lasting legacy in science and working with some of the most influential thinkers of the age.

THE CRYSTAL PALACE SCULPTURES: REVIVIFYING ANCIENT LIFE IN THREE DIMENSIONS

Hawkins' lifelong interest in capturing the three-dimensional qualities of the organisms he depicted led naturally to his experimentation with sculpture. He studied with a prominent sculptor named William Behnes, presumably in the mid-1840s, but

[1]In the Beechey volume, Hawkins' name does not appear on the title page and George Sowerby is credited as the book's artist, but an examination of the plates reveals that they were, in fact, drawn and lithographed by Hawkins. One of the Hawkins fish plates is reproduced in Bramwell and Peck (2008, p. 63).

details of this tutelage are unknown (Bramwell and Peck, 2008). Hawkins' earliest known sculpture was created in 1847 and depicted a live pair of rare European bison that had been presented to the Zoological Society by Tsar Nicholas I of Russia (Blunt, 1976). Hawkins was sufficiently pleased with the result that he had it cast in bronze and exhibited at the Royal Academy of Arts the following year.

Hawkins' biggest sculptural commission, and the one for which he is best known today, came in September 1852, at age 45, when he was asked to create a group of life-size sculptures of "antediluvian monsters" for the Crystal Palace in south London. Although technically placed in Penge and Anerley, the area was promoted as Sydenham by the Crystal Palace Company to give it wider appeal. It was a commercially owned and operated exhibition ground to which some of the contents of London's Great Exhibition of 1851 were being moved for permanent display. The park was to include extensive landscape features including lakes, fountains, and a series of islands on which England's geological and paleontological history would be recreated for the public to enjoy (Fig. 2).

Working under the direction of Sir Joseph Paxton, the innovative engineer and architect who had master-minded the original Crystal Palace in Hyde Park, and who was overseeing its recreation and expansion on Sydenham Hill, Hawkins was given a prime location and a substantial budget to, in Hawkins' words, "for the first time illustrate and realize—the revivifying of the ancient world." Through his own artistry, and with scientific guidance from naturalist Richard Owen (1804–1892), he was asked "to call up from the abyss of time and from the depths of the earth, those vast forms and gigantic beasts which the Almighty Creator designed with fitness to inhabit and precede us in possession of this part of the earth called Great Britain" (quoted in Bramwell and Peck, 2008, p. 69).

Hawkins went about his recreation of the prehistoric world with diligence, carefully researching the current understanding of geology, stratigraphy, geography, and paleontology, and examining fossils at the British Museum, the Royal College of Surgeons, the Geological Society, and in other collections around England. Using these as the foundation for his speculative reconstructions, Hawkins created clay models of dinosaurs, other extinct reptiles,

Figure 2. Lithograph of Crystal Palace Park by George Baxter, ca. 1854, with Hawkins' sculptures in the foreground and the Crystal Palace in the distance. The building was destroyed by fire in 1936 and not rebuilt. The sculptures are still on view today (Bramwell and Peck, 2008, fig. 30, p. 27; used with permission).

and early mammals. He worked to scale, one-sixth to one-twelfth the natural size, "designing such attitudes as my long acquaintance with the recent and living forms of the animal kingdom enabled me to adapt to the extinct species I was endeavouring to restore" (quoted in McCarthy and Gilbert, 1994, p. 89–92). He submitted these "sketch models" to Owen for comment and criticism.

Once his models were approved by Britain's most knowledgeable anatomist, Hawkins began turning them into full-sized sculptures. He worked in a large studio on the Crystal Palace grounds (Fig. 3), which Hawkins (quoted in McCarthy and Gilbert, 1994, p. 89–92) described as "a rude and temporary wooden building almost inaccessible for deep ruts and acres of swamps and mud," seamlessly shifting his role from that of scientific artist to sculptural engineer and builder. In an address to the Royal Society of Arts, he explained the enormous scale of the project:

> Some of these models contained 30 tons of clay, which had to be supported on four legs, as their natural history characteristics would not allow of my having recourse to any of the expedienta for support allowed to sculptors in an ordinary case. I could have no trees, nor rocks, nor foliage to support those great bodies, which, to be natural, must be built fairly on their four legs. In the instance of the *Iguanodon*,

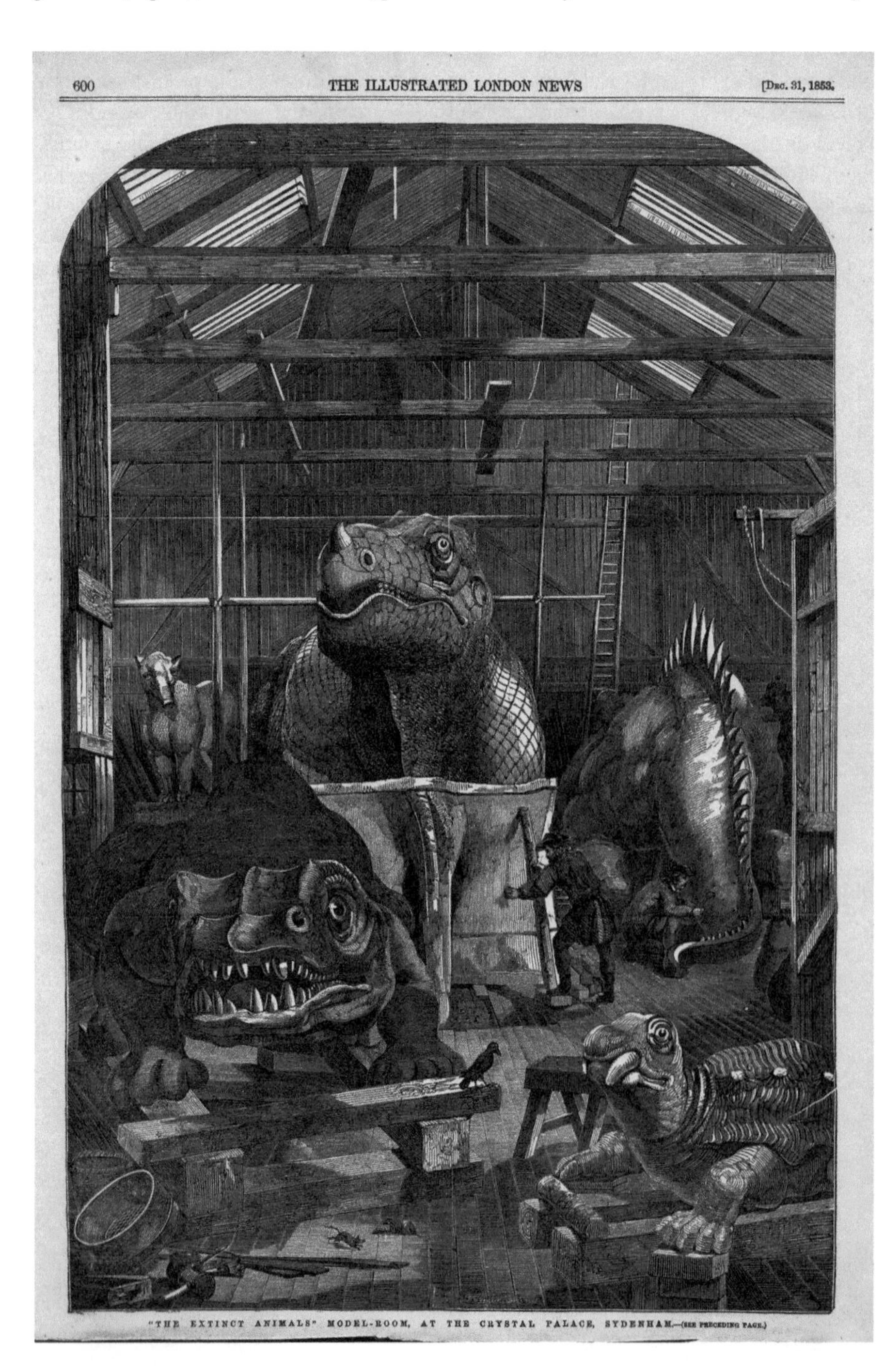
600 THE ILLUSTRATED LONDON NEWS [Dec. 31, 1853.

"THE EXTINCT ANIMALS" MODEL-ROOM, AT THE CRYSTAL PALACE, SYDENHAM.—(SEE PRECEDING PAGE.)

Figure 3. Hawkins' "model room" on the grounds of the Crystal Palace from *The Illustrated London News*, 31 December 1853. Academy of Natural Sciences of Drexel University, ANS Archives, Coll. 2012-061 (all rights reserved); used with permission.

it is not less than building a house upon four columns, as the quantities of material of which the standing *Iguanodon* is composed, consist of 4 iron columns 9 feet long by 7 inches diameter, 600 bricks, 650 5-inch half-round drain tiles, 900 plain tiles, 38 casks of cement, 90 casks of broken stone making a total of 640 bushels of artificial stone. These, with 100 feet of iron hooping and 20 feet of cube inch bar, constitute the bones, sinews, and muscles of this large model, the largest of which there is any record of a casting being made. (quoted in McCarthy and Gilbert, 1994, p. 89–92)

Although Hawkins tried to recreate extinct animals "of which the entire, or nearly entire, skeleton had been exhumed in a fossil state" (i.e., *Iguanodon*, *Plesiosaurus*, and *Megatherium*) (Fig. 4), there were some, such as *Mosasaurus*, "of which only the fossil skull and a few detached bones of the skeleton" had been discovered (Owen, 1854, quoted in McCarthy and Gilbert, 1994, p. 16–17). These Hawkins only partially represented, obscuring their unknown body parts in the water that surrounded his island display. Other species, such as *Labyrinthodon* and *Dicynodon*, he tried to creatively reconstruct. Though plausible by mid-nineteenth-century standards, and totally convincing to the public, these sculptures were, in Owen's words, "more or less conjectural" (Owen, 1854, quoted in McCarthy and Gilbert, 1994, p. 51; on the question of accuracy, see also Naish, 2016).

While the accuracy of Hawkins' reconstructions could—and would—be debated among the scientific cognoscenti, the life-size sculptures he created made an enormous impression upon the many people who saw them. Hundreds of thousands of visitors flocked to the new Crystal Palace and its beautiful grounds as soon as the exhibition was opened by Queen Victoria in October 1854. Forty thousand people attended the opening ceremonies alone (Piggott, 2004; Rudwick, 1992). Hawkins' taxonomic mélange, known today as the "Crystal Palace Dinosaurs," continues to be a popular attraction. It is lovingly promoted and protected by the Friends of Crystal Palace Dinosaurs (cpdinosaurs.org; accessed February 2021).

Figure 4. Hawkins' recently conserved *Iguanodon* sculpture in Crystal Palace Park. Photo courtesy of Lynn Hilton; used with permission.

Hawkins' work at the park and the publicity associated with his monumental constructions (including his famous dinner party inside the mold for his *Iguanodon* on New Year's Eve, 1853) firmly established his reputation as the master of fossil reconstructions. No one else had ever combined an artistic interpretation of the fossil evidence with the complex engineering and construction skills needed to create creatures on such a large (life-size) scale. Criticisms that were leveled at the sculptures by Hawkins' former friend and colleague John Edward Gray, among others, were really thinly veiled criticisms of Richard Owen, whose imperious personality and conservative (and later anti-evolutionary) views made him a popular target for younger scientists.

In a quickly emerging field such as paleontology, new discoveries and interpretations were certain to reveal errors in some of Hawkins' speculative reconstructions. The Crystal Palace sculptures document the mid-nineteenth-century view of at least one leading researcher—Richard Owen—regarding the anatomy and posture of dinosaurs and other extinct animals. In time, many of them were found to be almost completely inaccurate, but such findings did little to undermine Hawkins' reputation as an artist, or diminish his achievement of creating the first life-size creations of prehistoric life. Academic criticism of the anatomical accuracy of his creations, now as then, misses the real significance of his contribution. By creating life-size sculptures of extinct animals and putting them on permanent display in a venue as visible as the Crystal Palace Park, Hawkins fundamentally shifted the public's perception of time and life on Earth. While a small number of scholarly publications had been discussing, and even illustrating "Deep Time" for a century or more, it was Hawkins' installations that brought the concepts into the public eye and, unknowingly, began to prepare the public for the contentious debates about evolution that would emerge within just a few years (Rudwick, 1992).

HAWKINS IN AMERICA

Buoyed by the popular success of his Crystal Palace sculptures, and the commercial success of miniature models and sets of teaching charts of prehistoric scenes that were sold to schools and other educational institutions following the Crystal Palace project, Hawkins embarked on a lecture tour in America in 1868. He was 61 years old.

Hawkins arrived in New York on 14 March 1868, apparently with no prearranged speaking engagements. But he wasted no time in launching his lecture tour. Two days off the boat, on 16 March, he spoke before the Lyceum of Natural History (later the New York Academy of Sciences). This was followed two weeks later by a lecture to an audience reportedly approaching 3000 at the Cooper Union (Bramwell and Peck, 2008). By all accounts, Hawkins was an engaging speaker. He charmed his audiences by drawing sketches of dinosaurs and other extinct animals as he spoke (Kerley, 2001). A story in the *New York Times* following his Cooper Union lecture emphasized two points that Hawkins had made in his lecture. The first was a surprisingly environmentalist argument for "educating the masses" about natural history. "Nothing was more important than a knowledge of natural history," Hawkins had asserted, "for want of that knowledge England had already destroyed her salmon and was rapidly destroying her oyster fisheries" (quoted in Bramwell and Peck, 2008, p. 36).

The second point made by Hawkins in his Cooper Union lecture concerned his views on Darwinism. Darwin's *On the Origin of Species* had been published just nine years earlier, in 1859, and Hawkins' artistic renderings of large, extinct animals placed him unavoidably in the center of the public maelstrom concerning Darwin's provocative views on "descent with modification" driven by natural selection. Hawkins did not shy away from addressing this topic. According to the *Times* report, Hawkins had opined that "the Darwinian theory of the development of the species could not be believed by any comparative anatomist," and that "the unity of design in nature showed the hand of God himself" (quoted in Bramwell and Peck, 2008, p. 36).

Hawkins' rejection of the Darwinian paradigm was a recurring theme in his lectures throughout his ten-year sojourn in America. The reference to "any comparative anatomist" in the *New York Times* article quoted above strongly hints at the influence of comparative anatomist Owen in Hawkins' views on this question. Owen, who famously and aggressively rejected the concept of evolution, had been Hawkins' mentor on the Crystal Palace sculptures project. As mentioned above, Hawkins had also worked with Charles Darwin on the illustrations for *Zoology of the Voyage of H.M.S. Beagle*, which were published in the early 1840s, many years before Darwin's views on evolution were published. In spite of their contrasting views on evolution by natural selection, Darwin and Hawkins had an amiable professional relationship. Darwin, among others, provided a letter of reference to Hawkins, which Hawkins used when applying for a job at the British Museum in 1845 and also appears to have brought with him to America (Bramwell and Peck, 2008, Appendix).

The second half of the 1860s was a propitious time for Hawkins to market his oratorical and artistic talents in New York City. The post–Civil War economy was strong, and a mood of optimism and growth prevailed in this rapidly growing city. The city's leaders had agreed on a general plan for Central Park, and a commission had been established to flesh out the details. The Central Park Commission was actively seeking bold ideas that promoted culture and education in association with the nascent park. Two museums that sprang from this nexus of available open space, financial expansion, civic pride, and cultural optimism were—using their modern names—the Metropolitan Museum of Art and the American Museum of Natural History. A third museum, displaying sculptures by Waterhouse Hawkins of prehistoric American creatures in a spectacular, Crystal Palace–type building came very close to joining the other two. Tragically, the planned "Paleozoic Museum" slipped through the proverbial cracks of history.

The Ill-Fated Paleozoic Museum of Central Park

Through his lectures, Hawkins' sculptures of extinct animals in south London became well known to influential New Yorkers. On 2 May 1868, six weeks after Hawkins' arrival, the Central Park Commission proposed that he "undertake the resuscitation of a group of animals of the former periods of the American continent" (quoted in Colbert and Beneker, 1959, p. 140).

Hawkins quickly accepted the proposal, at a salary of US$5000 (equivalent to approximately US$130,000 today) (Bramwell and Peck, 2008), and he went to work planning what became known as the Paleozoic Museum. Of course, the term "Paleozoic" was used in the general sense of "prehistoric life" and not in the more restricted modern sense of the Paleozoic Era.

In the 16 years that had passed since Hawkins began to construct his Crystal Palace dinosaurs and other extinct animals, significant developments in vertebrate paleontology had occurred. Not only had Darwin's revolutionary book been published, stimulating an interest in extinct animals among the general public, but new fossil discoveries, especially in America, had been made. The new fossils and new anatomical studies had shown that the Owen-Hawkins reconstructions of dinosaurs in England had been excessively modeled on mammalian anatomy and posture. Dinosaur anatomy, it turned out, was quite different.

Hawkins was excited to get to work on the new project. He spent the summer and fall of 1868 examining fossils in the collections of several museums, including the U.S. National Museum in Washington, D.C. (Smithsonian Institution), the Academy of Natural Sciences of Philadelphia (ANSP), and the Peabody Museum at Yale University. This work involved measuring and sketching fossil bones, making casts, and modeling missing bones. Many of the bones were still encased in rock matrix, which Hawkins needed to remove to examine the relevant portions. It was a frenzy of museum work over a period of many months.

Reconstructing the First Dinosaur Skeleton

The American museum that proved to be most useful for Hawkins was the Academy of Natural Sciences of Philadelphia. Joseph Leidy, one of the curators at the academy's museum and a professor at the University of Pennsylvania, facilitated Hawkins' work and advised him on anatomical matters. Richard Owen probably provided the introduction [of Hawkins and Owen], for Leidy and Owen had met 20 years earlier when Leidy visited London (Bramwell and Peck, 2008). Although they embraced contrasting views about Darwinism—Leidy was a strong Darwinist, while Hawkins was a creationist—they were apparently able to work together amiably on questions of dinosaur anatomy.

Of special importance to Hawkins' Paleozoic Museum project was the presence in the ANSP collection of the bones of a large, duck-billed dinosaur that Leidy had excavated near Haddonfield, New Jersey, in 1858. Leidy had named the species *Hadrosaurus foulkii*. He had not found the animal's skull, but much of the post-cranial skeleton was present; it was the most complete, large dinosaur skeleton recovered in America at that time, so Hawkins decided to use it as a centerpiece of his prehistoric tableau in Central Park. In September of 1868 Hawkins began the painstaking process of constructing molds of each of the *Hadrosaurus* bones (Peck, 2008; Bramwell and Peck, 2008). Once the molds were made, he was able to produce multiple plaster casts of each bone, allowing him to make duplicate skeleton mounts. These mounts eventually ended up at the Smithsonian Institution, Princeton University, the Field Museum in Chicago, and the Edinburgh Museum of Science and Art.

Although the skeleton of a giant ground sloth from South America had been reconstructed and displayed in a museum in Madrid 80 years earlier (Rowland, 2009), and Charles Willson Peale had articulated the skeleton of a mastodon in his Philadelphia museum in the early nineteenth century, no dinosaur skeleton had yet been reassembled and placed on public display. One reason was the extreme rarity of complete skeletons. Due to the ravages of post-mortem processes, the bones of a dead animal are usually scattered and destroyed. A paleontologist may find a few bones but often not enough to reconstruct the animal. In the case of Leidy's *Hadrosaurus* bone assemblage, although the skull was missing, enough of the post-cranial bones were present for Hawkins to accomplish this. Leidy worked closely with the sculptor on this three-dimensional, anatomical project. Edward Drinker Cope, Leidy's younger colleague, also contributed to the effort (Peck and Stroud, 2012). Hawkins solved the problem of the missing skull by creating a plaster skull *ex nihilo* that was modeled loosely on the skull of a modern iguana (Fig. 5). Hawkins suspended each of the plaster bones in its proper anatomical position from a metal armature (Bramwell and Peck, 2008). The resulting skeleton was 12 m (39 ft) long and positioned in a standing posture with an artificial tree for support (Fig. 6).

Figure 5. Head sculpted from plaster and iron in 1868 by Hawkins for the reconstruction of Leidy's *Hadrosaurus* skeleton. Length is 77 cm (30 in). Academy of Natural Sciences of Drexel University, Department of Vertebrate Paleontology; used with permission.

In November of 1868, just six months after receiving the commission from the Central Park Commission, Hawkins had surveyed the fossil collections at key American museums, familiarized himself with the accumulated record of the continent's extinct fauna, and—with Leidy's help—constructed the first fully articulated skeleton of a dinosaur. It was an extraordinary accomplishment.

Hawkins presented this first mounted *Hadrosaurus* skeleton to the ANSP, and the towering skeleton was put on display in the Academy's museum, generating great public excitement. Although the museum was open only two afternoons a week, nearly 100,000 visitors came through the door in 1869, nearly doubling the previous year's attendance (Bramwell and Peck, 2008). The museum, which had previously been open to the public without charge, instituted a 10-cent admission fee to moderate

Figure 6. Photograph of Hawkins standing under his reconstruction of *Hadrosaurus foulkii* at the Academy of Natural Sciences of Philadelphia, circa 1869. Academy of Natural Sciences of Drexel University, ANS Archives Coll. 803; used with permission.

the size of the crowds (Peck and Stroud, 2012). Having launched "dinomania" in England 15 years earlier, Hawkins had successfully transported this cultural phenomenon to the New World. And it continues unabated today, more than a century and a half later (Bramwell and Peck, 2008). Unfortunately, Hawkins' ANSP *Hadrosaurus* skeleton has not survived the ravages of time and museum redesign. At one point it was apparently moved outdoors, where it eventually crumbled beyond repair. Only its real bones and fabricated skull survive (Bramwell and Peck, 2008). The four other casts he made of the bipedal dinosaur have similarly been lost to deterioration over time.

The Central Park Paleozoic Museum Fiasco

The Central Park commissioners developed a grandiose plan to house Hawkins' reconstructions in a large Crystal Palace–like, cast iron-frame, glass building with an arched glass ceiling. The museum was to be located on the edge of the park, facing Eighth Avenue (now Central Park West), directly opposite Sixty-third Street (Colbert and Beneker, 1959). Hawkins and his assistants began making the sculptures for it in a workshop housed in a nearby armory building. His plan was to construct models of an assemblage of Cretaceous and Pleistocene animals. The Cretaceous taxa were to include *Laelaps*, *Hadrosaurus*, plesiosaurs, and mosasaurs. The planned Pleistocene taxa included at least one of each of the following: mammoth, mastodon, glyptodont (a large, armadillo-like herbivore), two genera of giant ground sloths (*Megatherium* and *Megalonyx*), and unspecified additional taxa, including carnivores (Colbert and Beneker, 1959). One of the few surviving sketches of the planned museum, now in the Hawkins collection at ANSP, is reproduced in Figure 7.

The project proceeded as planned for about two years, but then William "Boss" Tweed, controller of the Tammany Hall political machine, abolished the Central Park Commission in order to replace it with a new Public Parks Board stacked with his own political appointees. Funding for the Paleozoic Museum project was cut from the budget (Colbert and Beneker, 1959; Kerley, 2001; Bramwell and Peck, 2008).

Refusing to abandon the project, Hawkins doggedly continued to work on his sculptures, hoping to regain the city's support or to find another home for them. He was not shy in publicly expressing his displeasure about what had happened. In March of 1871, in a speech at the New York Lyceum of Natural History, he publicly lambasted Tweed for stifling science and art in New York City. Hawkins' speech, and the angry comments of members of the audience, were reported in *The New York Times*, infuriating Tweed

Figure 7. Hawkins' sketch of the proposed Paleozoic Museum in New York City's Central Park, circa 1869. Academy of Natural Sciences of Drexel University, ANS Archives Coll. 803; used with permission.

(Kerley, 2001). A few weeks later, vandals—presumably "Boss" Tweed's goons—broke into Hawkins' workshop and destroyed all of his sculptures and molds. Two years of work were ruined (Kerley, 2001; Peck, 2008). Tweed was eventually convicted of embezzling tens of millions of dollars from New York City taxpayers, and he died in jail, but the Paleozoic Museum and Hawkins' Central Park sculptures were permanent casualties of his corrupt hegemony over New York politics in the late 1860s and early 1870s. Fragments of Hawkins' molds and casts, along with the foundation of the Paleozoic Museum, lie buried in Central Park today—archaeological remnants of the nearly forgotten, almost successful, world's first paleontological museum (Colbert and Beneker, 1959; Kerley, 2001).

CONCLUSION

Benjamin Waterhouse Hawkins had the skill and talent to transform piles of dry bones into three-dimensional, life-like reconstructions of animals from a "former world." His contribution to the evolution of paleontological art was enormous. His Crystal Palace sculptures, with his reconstruction of Leidy's *Hadrosaurus* skeleton, not only launched "dinomania" on both sides of the Atlantic, they kick-started the entire genre of three-dimensional paleontological art. Through his sculptures, his skeletal articulations, and his art, Hawkins made paleontology and the history of life on Earth accessible and relevant to the general public and paved new ways of thinking about the world that existed before the appearance of humankind.

ACKNOWLEDGMENTS

Thanks to reviewers Ellinor Michel and Thomas D. Carr and also to Renee Clary for detailed comments that improved the manuscript. Unfortunately, due to space limitations, there were many excellent suggestions by the reviewers that we were unable to follow. Thanks to Ellinor Michel for providing photographs of the Crystal Palace Dinosaurs and especially to Lynn Hilton for permission to use her photograph of the Crystal Palace *Iguanodon* in Figure 4. And thanks to the editors of this volume, Renee Clary, Dallas Evans, and Gary Rosenberg, for undertaking this important and challenging project.

REFERENCES CITED

Blunt, W., 1976, The Ark in the Park: London, Hamish Hamilton in association with Tryon Gallery, 256 p.

Bramwell, V., and Peck, R.M., 2008, All in the Bones: A Biography of Benjamin Waterhouse Hawkins: Philadelphia, The Academy of Natural Sciences of Philadelphia, 128 p.

Colbert, E.H., and Beneker, K., 1959, The Paleozoic Museum in Central Park, or the museum that never was: Curator: The Museum Journal, v. 2, p. 137–150, https://doi.org/10.1111/j.2151-6952.1959.tb01403.x.

Kerley, B., 2001, The Dinosaurs of Waterhouse Hawkins: New York, Scholastic Press, 43 p.

McCarthy, S., and Gilbert, M., 1994, The Crystal Palace Dinosaurs: London, Crystal Palace Foundation, 100 p.

Naish, D., 2016, The dinosaurs of Crystal Palace: Among the most accurate renditions of prehistoric life ever made: Scientific American, https://blogs.scientificamerican.com/tetrapod-zoology/the-dinosaurs-of-crystal-palace-among-the-most-accurate-renditions-of-prehistoric-life-ever-made.

Owen, R., 1854, Geology and Inhabitants of the Ancient World: London, Euston Grove Press, 2013 reprint, 50 p.

Peck, R.M., 2008, The art of bones: Natural History, v. 117, no. 10, p. 24–29.

Peck, R.M., and Stroud, P.T., 2012, A Glorious Enterprise: The Academy of Natural Sciences of Philadelphia and the Making of American Science: Philadelphia, University of Pennsylvania Press, 438 p.

Piggott, J.R., 2004, The Crystal Palace at Sydenham, 1854–1936: London, Hurst & Co, 230 p.

Rowland, S.M., 2009, Thomas Jefferson, extinction, and the evolving view of Earth history in the late eighteenth and early nineteenth centuries, *in* Rosenberg, G.D., ed., The Revolutions in Geology from the Renaissance to the Enlightenment: Geological Society of America Memoir 203, p. 225–246, https://doi.org/10.1130/2009.1203(16).

Rudwick, M.J.S., 1992, Scenes from Deep Time: Chicago, University of Chicago Press, 280 p., https://doi.org/10.7208/chicago/9780226149035.001.0001.

Manuscript Accepted by the Society 13 January 2021
Manuscript Published Online 6 December 2021

Printed in the USA

The Geological Society of America
Memoir 218

The present is the key to the paleo-past: Charles R. Knight's reconstruction of extinct beasts for the Field Museum, Chicago

Renee M. Clary*
Department of Geosciences, Mississippi State University, Box 5448, Mississippi State, Mississippi 39762, USA

ABSTRACT

Although he was legally blind, Charles R. Knight (1874–1953) established himself as the premier paleontological artist in the early 1900s. When the Field Museum, Chicago, commissioned a series of large paintings to document the evolution of life, Knight was the obvious choice. Knight considered himself an artist guided by science; he researched and illustrated living animals and modern landscapes to better understand and represent extinct life forms within their paleoecosystems. Knight began the process by examining fossil skeletons; he then constructed small models to recreate the animals' life anatomy and investigate lighting. Once details were finalized, Knight supervised assistants to transfer the study painting to the final mural. The Field Museum mural process, a monumental task of translating science into public art, was accompanied by a synergistic tension between Knight, who wanted full control over his artwork, and the museum's scientific staff; the correct position of an Eocene whale's tail—whether uplifted or not—documents a critical example. Although modern scientific understanding has rendered some of Knight's representations obsolete, the majority of his 28 murals remain on display in the Field Museum's *Evolving Planet* exhibit. Museum educators contrast these murals with contemporary paleontological knowledge, thereby demonstrating scientific progress for better public understanding of the nature of science.

INTRODUCTION

Charles Robert Knight (1874–1953) (Fig. 1) developed an early interest in animals, and his talent for drawing them emerged when he was a young boy. Through his father's employer, John Pierpont Morgan (1837–1918), Knight gained privileged, behind-the-scenes access to the American Museum of Natural History (AMNH)—even on Sundays (Knight, 2005). Tragically, he suffered damage to his left eye when struck by a rock thrown by a playmate; this would later seriously affect his vision. Shortly afterwards, in 1880, he lost his mother to pneumonia (Knight, 2005; Czerkas and Glut, 1982). When his father remarried, his stepmother, an artist herself, encouraged Knight's artistic talents and sent him to Froebel Academy in Brooklyn to receive his first formal art instruction (Czerkas and Glut, 1982; Milner, 2012). However, after a few years, his stepmother became competitive and jealous, which Knight attributed to "plain jealousy" (Knight, 2005, p. 10).

Knight's formal education continued at the Brooklyn Collegiate and Polytechnic Institute, and Metropolitan Art School, while his informal investigations of animals were nurtured through six summers at the farm of his parents' friends, the

*RClary@geosci.msstate.edu

Clary, R.M., 2022, The present is the key to the paleo-past: Charles R. Knight's reconstruction of extinct beasts for the Field Museum, Chicago, *in* Clary, R.M., Rosenberg, G.D., and Evans, D.C., eds., The Evolution of Paleontological Art: Geological Society of America Memoir 218, p. 161–170, https://doi.org/10.1130/2021.1218(18).

Figure 1. Charles R. Knight in 1914 (Wikimedia Commons; https://commons.wikimedia.org/wiki/File:Charles_Knight.jpg).

Hazells, and later at Peck Farm in Newton, and then through regular sketching sessions at the Central Park Zoo (Knight, 2005; Czerkas and Glut, 1982). Knight's first artistic employment was at age 16, with J & R Lamb, where he drew animal and plant designs for stained glass windows. Following his father's death in 1892, he moved to Manhattan and worked as a freelance illustrator for several publishing houses, including Harper's and McClure's (Knight, 2005). Knight continued to foster his interest in animals in his spare time, seeking out the taxidermy department at the American Museum of Natural History to examine and draw the specimens that passed through its doors. His friendship with taxidermist John Rowley led to an introduction to AMNH paleontologist Jacob Wortman (1856–1926) and the first Knight paleo-reconstruction of the pig-like *Elotherium* in 1894 (Czerkas and Glut, 1982). Wortman was pleased with Knight's attempt, and the watercolor was hung by the displayed specimen (Knight, 2005). It would be the beginning of a long, productive relationship between Knight and the American Museum of Natural History that would continue through 1934.

Knight's 1896 introduction to Henry Fairfield Osborn (1857–1935) is described as a pivotal event that changed the trajectory of his career (Milner, 2012). Osborn served as initial curator of AMNH's department of mammalian paleontology and later became the long-serving president of the AMNH Board of Trustees (1908–1933) (Gregory, 1937). Osborn recognized Knight's artistic skills and intended to utilize them for his grand design of the AMNH halls of paleontology, and it was through Osborn's vision that Knight's opportunities and successes as a paleoartist grew (Sommer, 2010). Osborn introduced Knight to his mentor, paleontologist Edward Drinker Cope (1847–1897) of Bone Wars fame. In 1897, Knight spent two weeks with Cope at his Philadelphia home shortly before Cope died. They discussed fossils excavated by Cope, and Cope crudely sketched his interpretations of extinct animals for Knight's future reference. Knight painted tyrannosaurs—including the famous leaping Laelaps (*Dryptosaurus*)—synapsids, a ceratopsid, ornithopods, a plesiosaur, and a mosasaur from Cope's insights (Czerkas and Glut, 1982).

Osborn's grand vision for Knight's large paintings at AMNH progressed incrementally, but the project never came to complete fruition (Milner, 2012). Knight preferred the freedom of freelance work, and Osborn's inconsistent fundraising resulted in Knight accepting projects elsewhere, including at the Smithsonian (1901), the Carnegie Museum of Natural History (1906), and the Natural History Museum of Los Angeles County (1925). However, another natural history museum, the Field Museum in Chicago[1], inaugurated a similar grand vision for Hall 38: the future Ernest R. Graham Hall.

THE FIELD MUSEUM COMMISSION

On 4 January 1926, Charles Knight wrote to George Kunz (1856–1932), mineralogist at Tiffany and Co. and a close friend of the Field Museum's first director, Frederick J.V. Skiff. Knight inquired about Field Museum possibilities since his AMNH "museum work has been practically discontinued." Knight marketed his skills in that letter: "I feel (between ourselves) that what our museums need <u>very badly</u> is a little art in their installations of exhibits." Kunz, a great admirer of Knight's paleontological reconstructions, then approached Field Museum Director D.C. Davies on 5 January 1926 to consider similar paintings for the Field Museum. On 17 February 1926, Kunz wrote, "I feel quite sure that if you had a full line of murals around the great hall painted by a biologist, paleontologist, and artist, who had over twenty-five years of experience, you would have something that does not exist in any museum in the world."[2]

Kunz's query was successful, and on 8 January 1926, Davies asked Kunz to reach out to Knight for a one-year, or permanent, association with the Field Museum. That same day, Knight contacted Davies. In a follow-up letter of 11 January 1926, Knight stated he preferred working by contract and described his method of observing living animals to recreate extinct ones:

> My work for the American Museum has always been done on contract, as I find that I can do better things in this way than on a salary basis. Under this plan I vary its prehistoric studies with paintings and models from living forms, and these in turn keep me fresh and inspired

[1]The museum was founded as the Columbian Museum of Chicago but changed its name several times during its history. It will be referenced here as the Field Museum since it was the Field Museum of Natural History during Knight's commission.

[2]All quoted material pertaining to Knight's Field Museum commission are from the Field Museum's archives unless otherwise noted. Archived correspondence examined includes G2691,G2693 Director's Papers General correspondence K-KU (140, 141, 142, 143, 144, 145); the Henry Field Near East Correspondence 1920–1950, Knabenshue-Langdon Folder 7; Man Correspondence Kennedy-Knight Folder 14, Box 2, Henry Field General Correspondence Volume 24; and Charles R. Knight-Knoeber Folder 3, Box 5.

> for its difficult task of putting life and acting into otherwise inanimate objects. You will realize that, in order to present anything really interesting along the lines of fossil restorations, one must be a close student of living things, and for this reason I have for many years painted and modeled all sorts of animals—birds, fish etc. not to mention of course the human figures which I studied very carefully in the art Schools, and was able to incorporate in my elaborate paintings of Prehistoric men for the museum here.

Davies notified curator of geology Oliver C. Farrington (1864–1933) on 25 January 1926 about the potential project, and Knight visited the Field Museum shortly afterwards. The original expensive proposition, which the Board of Trustees denied, involved extensive renovations that would include construction of false walls to mount the murals and a large studio space in Chicago. However, Knight was willing to compromise. Ultimately, he received a 1926 contract to paint 28 murals, at a total cost of US$140,000, for the Ernest R. Graham Hall. The project was to be completed by 1933. This consumed Knight's time for four years, with the murals painted within his New York studio and then shipped to Chicago, accompanied by Knight's specific telegraphed instructions for immediate stretching. The project was completed in 1930, and interim payments were issued to Knight as the Field Museum scientists approved each of his completed panels.

The agreed-upon mural topics documented a progression of Earth's history, from the Archean Eon (*The World Before Life*), through the Proterozoic (*The Beginnings of Life*), and then Paleozoic (five panels), Mesozoic—especially dinosaurs (eight panels), and Cenozoic (13 panels) eras (Table 1). Knight did not complete them in chronological order; Farrington reported that

TABLE 1. CHARLES R. KNIGHT MURALS AT THE FIELD MUSEUM, CHICAGO, ARRANGED BY GEOLOGIC TIME PROGRESSION

Painting title	Mural size	Date acquired
**World Before Life*	9 ft x 25 ft	1928
The Beginnings of Life	9 ft x 11 ft	1927
**A Sea Beach 500,000,000 Years Ago*	9 ft x 11 ft	1928
The Chicago Coral Reef	9 ft x 11 ft	1928
Forest of Devonian Time	9 ft x 25 ft	1930
Reptiles of Permian Time	9 ft x 25 ft	1930
African Reptiles of Permian Time	9 ft x 11 ft	1931
Flying Reptiles & Primitive Birds	9 ft x 11 ft	1931
Duck-billed & Crested Dinosaurs	9 ft x 25 ft	1931
Swimming Reptiles	9 ft x 25 ft	1930
Flying & Swimming Reptiles	9 ft x 25 ft	1929
Brontosaurs	9 ft x 25 ft	1929
Horned and Carnivorous Dinosaurs	9 ft x 25 ft	1928
Armored Dinosaurs	9 ft x 11 ft	1928
Egg-laying Dinosaurs	9 ft x 11 ft	1927
Zeuglodon—A Primitive Whale	9 ft x 11 ft	1929
Four-Toed Horse and Horned Mammals	9 ft x 11 ft	1931
Mammals of Lower Miocene Time	9 ft x 25 ft	1930
**Titanotheres*	9 ft x 25 ft	1931
Mammals of Upper Miocene Time	9 ft x 25 ft	1930
Giant Ground Sloth	9 ft x 25 ft	1929
Mastodons	9 ft x 11 ft	1928
Mammoths	9 ft x 25 ft	1929
Cave Bear	9 ft x 11 ft	1930
Prehistoric Scene at Rancho La Brea, California	9 ft x 25 ft	1930
Great Irish Deer	9 ft x 11 ft	1929
**Giant Kangaroos*	9 ft x 11 ft	1927
**Moas of New Zealand*	9 ft x 11 ft	1927

*Not currently on exhibit at the Field Museum, Chicago, Illinois.

the first four 11 ft × 9 ft panels received in July 1927 were "No. 1, Earliest Forms of Life; No. 8, Egg-laying Dinosaurs; No. 10, Giant Birds (New Zealand) and No. 11 Giant Marsupials (Australia)." In his correspondence with the Field Museum, Knight reiterated that he was "trying very hard to combine science and art in these panels" (1927, to Field[3]) and his "object is to make the Hall a work of art as well as correct scientifically" (27 July 1927, to Farrington).

THE PRESENT IS THE KEY TO THE PALEO-PAST

Knight had established his technique for recreating extinct organisms before he received the Field Museum commission. For Knight, the science first must be addressed through fossil investigation and paleo-landscape research, followed by the artistic license needed to breathe dynamism into prehistoric animals represented on a two-dimensional canvas. Encouraged by Osborn to make the process of mural creation transparent, Knight discussed his mural production steps with *Scribner's* in 1922 (Sommer, 2010; Knight, 1922). He described how he first examined the fossil evidence, established the appropriate paleo-landscape with its contemporary plants and animals, and then determined the prehistoric animals' appearances—including color, form, and attitudes (Sommer, 2010). When Knight understood the morphology of the extinct animal, he sculpted a model that he placed in various lighting conditions to authentically reproduce shadows in his paintings. Numerous sketches of the paleo-scene were drawn and approved by the scientists, with the finalized design carefully executed in a study painting that served as the mural's prototype (Fig. 2). The legally blind Knight supervised assistants as they scaled up the study painting to the full-size mural.

Knight stated, "One must realize that the animals pictured do not exist at the present day, and the artist is obliged, therefore, to use his knowledge and imagination to the fullest extent in the recreation of so many varying types" (Knight, 1922, p. 279). He also noted that the sketches consumed four-fifths of the time required for the entire work (Knight, 1922). During the construction of the Field Museum murals, Knight wrote that the entire mural collection's color palette required a "harmonious scheme throughout (a very difficult thing to do)" (Knight to Field, 1927). Ultimately, the success of Knight's prehistoric reproductions depended upon his understanding of *modern* animals and his considerable experience with them.

Vertebrate Studies: Fossil Bones and Extant Analogies

Knight claimed it was his intense love and interest in animal forms and attitudes that resulted in his success in portraying

Figure 2. Charles Knight's study painting for the Irish deer/Irish elk, *Megaloceros*, from which the Field Museum mural was painted. Study painting GEO85013c for Knight Mural CK1T GE 580, courtesy of Field Museum.

fossil organisms. He was critical of earlier paleoartists, stating that Benjamin Waterhouse Hawkins' "zeal far outstripped his knowledge of the material at hand" and that any artist who followed Hawkins could not animate the reconstructions since "no matter how great his scientific skill, was often totally lacking in knowledge of the lifelike appearance of even a modern animal"[4] (Knight, 1935, p. 16).

Knight's initial investigation of fossil bones was precise and detailed. For the Field Museum's *Protoceratops* reconstruction, Knight reported that his rendition was unique, "made from the newly mounted complete skeleton here[5], available for the first time. They are certainly queer looking customers and should prove interesting to the general public" (14 June 1927, Knight to Field). When Farrington requested, through Director Davies, that the "proportions of the legs more nearly resemble those in the restoration and leg bones which the Museum has on exhibition" in the Giant Moa mural, Knight responded, "I have assured myself that the <u>leg proportions</u> are correct for every large species which we agreed to do. But I found also that the smaller type shown in the Field Museum are <u>shorter</u> proportionately from the <u>angle drawn.</u> I shall look up the big skeletons in London and … available data on the subject" (Knight to Farrington, 22 July 1927).

After thorough investigations of the fossils, Knight called upon his experiences in the AMNH taxidermy department, his interactions with animals, and his observation and sketching sessions at the zoo to breathe life into extinct beasts. He was confident

[3]Field Museum policies required correspondence to be channeled through the Director. D.C. Davies died suddenly on 15 July 1928, and Stephen C. Simms was made Director by the Board of Trustees on 16 July 1928 according to the 1928 Field Museum Annual Report (Field Museum of Natural History, 1929). Field Museum President Stanley Field, nephew of founder Marshall Field, also served as Knight's contact.

[4]For additional information on Benjamin Waterhouse Hawkins, see Peck and Rowland (this volume).

[5]Knight's "here" references the American Museum of Natural History, since he continued to work from his studio in New York.

in his interpretation of the animals' physical reconstructions, and their attitudes, and questioned Field Museum scientists' criticism of his artistic interpretations. When writing to the museum director about the *Prehistoric Scene at Rancho La Brea, California* panel, Knight stated:

> I am rather amazed at some of the other criticisms contained in your letter, particularly the remarks about the Sabre-toothed tiger's attitude being canine instead of feline! It seems hardly necessary to remind me of the difference between these two families but I fail to see in any case how that could affect the position of the creature in question—as any one who has studied the large feline should know that they do gnaw bones or chew off pieces in precisely the manner shown in the picture. All one has to do is to look at the common house cat to see what I mean. I must ask that you have confidence in my knowledge of the character and psychology of animals as my particular specialty for thirty years has been the study of animal life under varying conditions and emotions. If therefore the attitude shown in the sketch gives the impression of gnawing or chewing I am perfectly willing to let it stand—as that was exactly the idea I intended it to convey. (Knight to Simms, 2 May 1929)

Later that month, Knight acknowledged that Farrington's geological and historical knowledge was superior, but "when it comes to the life-like attitudes and reconstructions of the animals that I should be left alone in this as it is my own particular specialty" (Knight to Simms, 14 May 1929).

Plant and Landscape Studies: Conformable Ecosystems

Since Knight's murals depicted prehistoric animals within their environments, the paleo-landscape was important. Knight recognized that organisms' colors were influenced by their environment, with monotone colors accompanying open landscapes and spotted or striped animals residing in heavily grassed or forested areas (Knight, 1935). Therefore, just as he studied living animals, he also invested time examining modern landscapes to better recreate paleoecosystems. During the Field Museum commission, Knight visited Florida to paint scenes and foliage studies; he wrote to Davies, "I'm in Florida making studies for my panels and the landscape is immensely valuable to me" (6 March 1927). He also spent time in "cave country" to "make some more sketches of the various environments" (Knight to Field, 31 July 1929).

When Knight was not able to travel directly to an appropriate location, he studied images of the sites. He remarked that, "The algal panel [*The Beginnings of Life*] I studied very carefully from some good posters of the Yellowstone park pools—but of course did not copy them exactly" (17 June 1917, Knight to Farrington). Knight's algal pool painting was not immediately accepted, since Field Museum scientists wrote "in the upper foreground the formation represented seems difficult of interpretation. In the middle foreground some source should be indicated for the water which appears in the upper central pool. The background and middle background seem to need more detail" (Field to Knight, 12 July 1927).

Knight's attentiveness to plants in the paleoecosystem may have been fostered by his mentor, Osborn, who recognized that plant life was key to herbivore evolution; Osborn provided descriptive treatment of paleoflora in his research (Osborn, 1910). Knight likewise demonstrated diligence in replicating the plants in his geologic scenes. In a rebuttal to the Field's scientific staff, he wrote:

> As to the Cycad Forest—I have taken great pains to reassure myself on this point from both Berry and Dr. Wieland[6] also—the latter, as you know, the world expert probably on CYCADS. These authorities say the forest is perfectly correct as the height and that, should I choose to include ARAUCARIAS, could grow much higher. It is possible that I may include some of these latter trees in the distance but not in the foreground. My original sketch shows tree-ferns as the tall trees in the fore-ground but I am substituting tall CYCADS instead, much like the modern Japanese forms, as being more typical of the period. Dr. Farrington is, I fear, mistaken in saying that the low CYCADS in the foreground are not typical of Jurassic Flora, as both Berry and Wieland assure me they are correct. Besides this form, however, in the finished panel I will include on Dr. Wieland's suggestion, the type shown in your Museum, with flowers on the trunk of the plant. This I'm sure will please Dr. Farrington and will add variety to the panel. (Knight to Simms, 18 April 1930)

SYNERGISTIC TENSION: THE CONTROLLING ARTIST

In accordance with Field Museum rules, all correspondence from Knight funneled through the director; Davies reminded Knight of this on 8 January 1927, when Knight wrote that he intended to send sketches directly to Farrington. The director received letters and sent internal queries to Farrington, who then responded to the director. The Field Museum correspondence documents disagreements between Charles Knight and the scientists who approved his study sketches, curator of geology O.C. Farrington (a petrologist) and his assistant curator Elmer S. Riggs, a skilled paleontologist (Brinkman, 2000). Often obsequious in their language, Knight's letters only thinly veil a passive-aggressive tension between *his* interpretation of extinct organisms and that of the Field Museum's scientific authorities.

There were differences over color, animal behavior depictions, and landscape representation. The Field Museum scientists found Knight's *Ordovician Beach* panel "most faulty, Mr. Knight never submitted a completed sketch" (Farrington to Simms, 28 February 1929). However, the debate over the position of the Zeuglodon (*Basilosaurus*) tail, which extended over multiple letters, appears the acridest and effectively demonstrates the synergistic tension between artistic representation and scientific consensus. In February 1929, Knight wrote:

> As you know I am trying to make something unique in this hall and naturally I am using all the means at my command to do so.

[6]George Weber Wieland (1865–1953), Yale University, of Fossil Cycad National Monument infamy, worked with Riggs on a collection of fossil cycads.

My particular business is to infuse some life into a mere collection of bones and so, when I draw an animal in a certain position you may rest assured that I have taken into account all the factors of weight—balance-perspective etc. much more minutely than any scientific man finds it necessary to do as he is not sufficiently concerned with the life appearance of the creature. Please do not infer from the preceding on the large panels remarks that I object to criticism, or do not wish to do all in my power to please all interested parties in the Museum. I merely wish to call your attention to points which might be overlooked and therefor [*sic*] cause no end of troubl [*sic*] and time if they are not considered before (not after) the large Murals are completed. In justice to myself allow me to say that the changes on the finished panels already in place which method you considered as unsatisfactory- were all after thoughts of Dr. Farringtons [*sic*] and while I was most happy to make them, they certainly could not be considered as any fault of mine. On the contrary they were made with the expenditure of musch [*sic*] time and labor to myself and for that very reason I am calling your attention so insistently to the fact that all changes should be made on the small sketches and not on the large panels. (Knight to Simms, 25 February 1929)

Simms quoted Farrington in his response to Knight: "Mr. Knight is incorrect in stating that he made changes in this panel which Mr. Riggs and I suggested when he submitted the sketch here. Both Mr. Riggs and myself distinctly remember requesting the elimination of the uplifted tail" (Simms to Knight, 4 March 1929).

Knight conceded (Fig. 3). He wrote that he would change the position of the tail: "I shall however be most happy to make this change for Dr. Farrington but personally I cannot agree with him as to the accuracy or desirability either scientifically or artistically":

I have ample precedent for the attitude of the raised tail in the ability of the living whale to do so. As Zeuglodon was very much longer and slimmer than any modern whale, it would have been even more possible for him to assume this position. I consulted Dr. Lucas (the acknowledged World's Expert on the subject) on this point and was pleased to find that my own ideas exactly coincided with his—I do not know the authority whose opinion Dr. Farrington quotes. (Knight to Simms, 14 March 1929)

Farrington responded via memorandum to Simms that:

The authorities referred to as informing the Museum that the anatomy of the Zeuglodon would not permit the raising of the tail as shown in Mr. Knight's picture are, besides Associate Curator Riggs, Remington Kellogg, Assistant Curator of Mammals in the U.S. National Museum and J.W. Gidley, Assistant Curator of Mammalian Fossils in the U.S. National Museum. Mr. Kellogg has specialized for years in the study of fossil Cetaceans and is recognized as the leading authority, in this country, in this line. Mr. Gidley assembled and mounted the Zeuglodon skeleton exhibited in the National Museum and described it fully in 1913. (Farrington to Simms, 10 April 1929)

Farrington then quoted Gidley's and Kellogg's extended responses. Kellogg cited his own published research and claimed the Zeuglodon "could hardly have had a powerful propelling tail operating in the same fashion, (i.e., like caudal flukes of whales). On the contrary these details indicate that the tail was adapted for lashing, and that in swimming the animal progressed by marked sinuous or serpentine movements." Gidley suggested, "As a possible improvement I would suggest dropping the end portion of the tail to the water-level and terminate it rather vaguely just

Figure 3. The position of the Zeuglodon tail—whether the animal could have raised it—was a rancorous dispute between Knight and the Field Museum scientists. Knight eventually eliminated the uplifted tail (Knight Mural CK26T GE 570, courtesy of Field Museum).

below the surface." In concluding his memorandum, Farrington remarked:

> It was stipulated in the contract that the paintings for Graham Hall should be "original in design." That of the Zeuglodon so closely resembles the one made for the American Museum and widely published, that it lacks the desired originality. The similarity can be seen by comparing the two accompanying prints. It is expected to have these paintings embody the latest researches and not be copies of earlier works. (Farrington to Simms, 10 April 1929)

The acrimony continued. Knight was incredulous over the Field Museum scientists' criticism for his saber tooth cat (see "Vertebrate Studies: Fossil Bones and Extant Analogies") and his Miocene *Moropus* scale. His irritation is palpable in his letter to Simms:

> I understood that the Field Museum wished me to do this work because it considered me the most competent man in the world for such a commission—that commission presupposed an ability on my part to produce these panels in a highly satisfactory manner—and for them I receive my usual price for work of this character. My part of the contract (as I understood it) was to be an artistic rendering of data supplied by the Museum authorities as to the types of creatures to be depicted—their supposed environment etc. I feel however that by some misunderstanding of the part of the museum authorities they have not clearly understood this very vital point and as a consequence are now asking me to make changes which I fear will lower the artistic as well as the scientific value of my work in a manner which seems to me rather unnecessary and one which would affect the production as a whole. (Knight to Simms, 2 May 1929)

Less than two weeks later, Knight wrote to Simms:

> In regard to the Elothere group and Rancho La Brea group: I am rather surprised that Dr. Farrington refuses to confer with me about them but simply issues a note which is in the nature of an ultimatum—an attitude quite outside my contract, he persistently ignores my remarks and apparently does not consider my opinions worthy of notice. (Knight to Simms, 14 May 1929)

The scientists continued to suggest modifications of Knight's sketches. On 6 November 1929, Simms communicated several changes recommended by Farrington for three murals that featured *Archaeopteryx* (*Flying Reptiles and Primitive Birds*), early horses (*Four-Toed Horse and Horned Mammals*), and mammoths. Farrington's communication provided detailed measurements and research references for the recommended changes. In July 1930, Farrington pointed out that Knight's billing statement included "Paleomastodon" instead of "Trilophodon," but admitted, "In conversations regarding the mural, the term 'Paleomastodon' has been used, but I assumed that this was a simply a general term for early mastodon," pointing out that Paleomastodon only occurs in Egypt and would be inappropriate for a prehistoric Nebraska scene (Simms to Knight, 13 July 1930). Knight admitted his error in a handwritten note to Simms (21 July 1930).

The artist-scientist dissension did not start with Zeuglodon, either. In 1927, Knight wrote to Stanley Field in what appears to be an attempt to reassure the Field Museum that it was only coincidental an AMNH scientist wrote to Farrington to correct him on Titanotheres:

> Shortly after I returned to New York I saw Gregory[7] who surprised me by saying that Blaschke[8] just consulted him on the proportions of the Titanother[e], and that he (Dr. Gregory) was writing a letter to Dr. Farrington urging Dr. F. not to use the creature in the position suggested as it would be misleading. This was exactly what I felt sure would happen, but the point I wish to make clear is that I had absolutely nothing to do with Gregory's part of the affair. (Knight to Field, 20 July 1927)

Was Charles Knight or Oliver Farrington the primary instigator of microaggressions documented within the Field Museum's archival correspondence? In a Geological Society of America memorial, Farrington was described as a man of "kindness, tolerance, and humility" (Roy, 1934, p. 193) whose "association with his colleagues was one of absolute equality, marked by unfailing courtesy" (Roy, 1934, p. 204). Additionally, another artist and engraver at the Field Museum, John Conrad Hansen (1869–1952), received a written endorsement from Field Museum paleontologist Bryan Patterson that discerningly stated, "A complete lack of artistic temperament of one of his [many] very commendable qualities" (Brinkman, 2018, p. 240). Considering that Hansen began work at the Field Museum in 1938, Patterson's statement may implicate Knight, as an earlier associated artist, as not of docile temperament. Modern biographical accounts discuss Knight's nervous disposition (with his wife, Annie, and daughter, Lucy, often serving as intermediaries in his commissions), poor money management skills, and a critical demeanor with his views readily unleashed within editorial letters (Czerkas and Glut, 1982; Milner, 2012). Further archival research may further illuminate tensions between Knight and the Field Museum scientists.

KNIGHT'S MURALS TODAY: INFORMAL EDUCATIONAL OPPORTUNITIES

Knight's 28 murals were originally hung in 1931 in the Ernest R. Graham Hall of the Field Museum. Although Knight painted the contemporary status of geologic research in his murals in the late 1920s, scientific progress rendered some scenes archaic. Interestingly, when constructing the murals, Knight presumed he was able to portray dinosaurs more accurately than Pleistocene fauna since reptiles were cold-blooded and had a scaly skin and no hair (Knight, 1935, p. 20)! More recent scientific research has revealed that some dinosaurs were feathered, and they did not drag their tails—but Knight's older illustrations still offer value in showcasing the evolving nature of science (Clary and Wandersee, 2011)[9].

---

[7]William King Gregory (1876–1970), American Museum of Natural History.

[8]Frederick Blaschke (1881–1938), Field Museum–commissioned sculptor.

[9]See also Allmon (this volume), for a thorough discussion on the evolution of dinosaur paleoart representation.

The Field Museum saw the value of Knight's murals, too, when they designed the *Evolving Planet* exhibit, which opened in 2006. The 27,000 ft^2 space showcased Earth's progression of life and featured 23 of Knight's original 28 murals—which held up extremely well in the light of new science according to William Simpson, now head of Geological Collections and Vertebrates Collection Manager Fossil Vertebrates (Mullen, 2005)[10].

Knight's murals are given prominent display throughout the exhibit, with a large sign featuring the artist and the "treasured Field Museum legacy." And while the restored murals help museum visitors visualize the paleo-past of the fossils on display, the exhibit developers did not ignore evolving scientific understanding of the paleoecosystems.[11] Bench placards, coded mural replicas, and informational Knight vignettes help visitors identify the prehistoric organisms, while transparently describing how some names and scientific understanding have changed. In the *Forests of Devonian Time* mural, visitors learn that the trunk of the progymnosperm *Aneurophyoton* that Knight drew "actually belongs to a completely different type of plant." Signage also alerts visitors that the *African Reptiles of Permian Time* includes Triassic, not Permian aged organisms, and that the landscape would have hosted more vegetation (Fig. 4). Other signs correct the once-presumed environment of duck-billed dinosaurs and question whether ichthyosaurs could leap out of the water as depicted (*Swimming Reptiles*). In a very balanced fashion, the *Evolving Planet* exhibit celebrates Knight's successes, such as how he accurately portrayed the alternating plates of *Stegosaurus* even when scientists debated their placement long after the mural was finished. The *Evolving Planet* signage also explicitly interprets Knight's murals within the scientific understanding of sea level and climate fluctuations in Earth's geologic past, which is an important construct in public understanding of the implications of climate change. Field Museum signage documents how fossil evidence from Kansas and the Great Plains provide evidence that the area was covered by an ocean 85 million years ago—a very different landscape than exists today.

KNIGHT'S PALEOART LEGACY

Knight wrote that the impetus for public paleoart came when scientists realized that the information they acquired "should be brought out, dusted off ... and spread before the fascinated gaze of a hitherto totally uninformed public" (Knight, 1935, p. vii). Considered by Osborn in 1934 as the "greatest genius in the line of prehistoric restoration of human and animal life that the science of paleontology has ever known" (Czerkas and Glut, 1982, p. 23), Knight's paleoart influenced not only how the public perceived Deep Time, but also how subsequent artists reinterpreted the Earth's prehistoric past[12]. Even if Charles Knight was

[10]With the move from Hall 38 to Halls 26 and 27, there was less exhibit space, and the Geology and Exhibits teams determined which murals would be excluded in the new exhibit: *World Before Life, A Sea Beach, Giant Kangaroos,* and *Moas of New Zealand.*

[11]Richard Kissel and Gretchen Baker, formerly of the Field Museum, were involved in the development of the *Evolving Planet* exhibit.

[12]Knight's art appeared on and influenced paleontological postage stamps; see Lipps et al. (this volume).

Figure 4. *The African Reptiles of Permian Time* mural (9 ft × 11 ft) was displayed within *The Evolving Planet* at the Field Museum. In the Field Museum's informative signage, visitors learned that Charles Knight depicted Triassic synapsids as "Permian reptiles" and included too little vegetation in his landscape (Knight Mural CK22T GE 561, courtesy of Field Museum).

not the only paleoartist of his time,[13] he certainly was the best known through his paleoart contributions to journals, museums, and books. The Field Museum murals, the largest collection of Knight paleoart, also represent the best of Knight's paleo-reconstructions; not only did each mural artistically document one snapshot of geologic time, but the entire series represents a "grand, sweeping statement about our world's prehistory" (Czerkas and Glut, 1982, p. 31).

Although Knight took great pride in artistically and scientifically portraying prehistoric life, it is interesting that his Field Museum murals illustrate marine fauna and flora through a viewpoint *above* the marine realm and not looking through the water. Henry De la Beche pioneered the aquarium viewpoint in graphic design a century earlier[14], and yet Knight's murals depict cephalopods and trilobites beached on a shore, and mosasaurs, plesiosaurs, and whales illustrated in a vantage point above the water's surface. None of Knight's 28 murals for the Field Museum included an aquarium viewpoint although it has become the default position for modern portrayal of marine organisms (Clary and Wandersee, 2005). Interestingly, Knight drew aquarium viewpoints within the AMNH *Elasmosaurus* (1827), *Tylosaurus* (1899), and *Carcharodon* paintings, and he later drew vivid aquarium views of Cambrian life and Devonian fishes for *National Geographic* (Knight, 1942). Further research may determine whether the absence of aquarium views in Field Museum murals resulted from Field Museum scientists' requests, Knight's personal choices, or Knight's concern for balanced color throughout the mural series.

As Knight's Field Museum murals approach their century mark, they continue to inspire and educate visitors within the *Evolving Planet* exhibit. Knight's iconic paleo-scenes remain entrenched as the public's view of Deep Time (Fig. 5). Even when inaccurate in their depictions—our modern understanding of *Tyrannosaurus rex* has its body parallel to the ground with an outstretched tail, as opposed to Knight's upright version—signage can harness the history of geology and paleontological art as an effective teaching tool to improve public understanding of the nature of science (Clary, 2017). Just as scientific knowledge is open to revision in light of new evidence (e.g., National Research Council, 2012 Nature of Science Matrix), so can Knight's murals be reinterpreted in the future to maintain their relevance to the visualization of Earth's geologic history.

[13]To learn more about Knight's contemporary paleoartists at AMNH, see Reitmeyer et al. (this volume).

[14]For detailed discussion of De la Beche's pioneering graphic *Duria antiquior*, see Sharpe and Clary (this volume).

ACKNOWLEDGMENTS

I am indebted to many at the Field Museum, especially Armand Esai, Museum Archivist; Gretchen Rings, Museum Librarian and Head of Library Collections; and Nina Cummings, Photography Archivist. My 2017 research at the Field Museum was aided by Paul Mayer, Collections Manager, Fossil Invertebrates; and William Simpson, Head of Geological Collections and Collections Manager, Fossil Vertebrates. My special thanks go to Paul Brinkman, Interim Director, Research Collections, and Head, History of Science Research Lab and Curator of Special Collections, North Carolina Museum of Natural Sciences, for his insights into the personality of O.C. Farrington; and Robert Bakker, Curator, Paleontology Department, Houston Museum of Natural Science, for introducing me to Henry Fairfield Osborn's "eloquent expression of Cenozoic paleoecology." I appreciate the comments and suggestions of Volume Editors Gary Rosenberg and Dallas Evans and reviewers Paul Brinkman and Andrew Farke (Curator, Raymond M. Alf Museum of Paleontology), which greatly strengthened the presentation of this research.

Figure 5. Described as Knight's most influential work (Czerkas and Glut, 1982), *Horned and Carnivorous Dinosaurs* (9 ft × 25 ft) remains influential in public perception of dinosaurs and Earth's Cretaceous past. Knight painted *Tyrannosaurus rex* in an upright position, but modern scientists agree that the body was parallel to the ground with the tail extended (Knight Mural CK9T GE 567, courtesy of Field Museum).

REFERENCES CITED

Allmon, W.D., 2022, this volume, "Extreme dinosaurs" and the continuing evolution of dinosaur paleoart, *in* Clary, R.M., Rosenberg, G.D., and Evans, D.C., eds., The Evolution of Paleontological Art: Geological Society of America Memoir 218, Chapter 23, https://doi.org/10.1130/2021.1218(23).

Brinkman, P.D., 2000, Establishing vertebrate paleontology at Chicago's Field Columbian Museum, 1893–1898: Archives of Natural History, v. 27, no. 1, p. 81–114, https://doi.org/10.3366/anh.2000.27.1.81.

Brinkman, P.D., 2018, John Conrad Hansen (1869–1952) and his scientific illustrations: Archives of Natural History, v. 45, no. 2, p. 233–244, https://doi.org/10.3366/anh.2018.0516.

Clary, R.M., 2017, Controversies in the history of geology and their educational importance for facilitating understanding of the nature of science, *in* Mayer, W., Clary, R., Azuela, L., Mota, T., and Wolkowicz, S., eds., History of Geoscience: Celebrating 50 Years of INHIGEO: Geological Society, London, Special Publication 442, p. 189–198.

Clary, R.M., and Wandersee, J.H., 2005, Through the looking glass: The history of aquarium views and their potential to improve learning in science classrooms: Science & Education, v. 14, p. 579–596, https://doi.org/10.1007/s11191-004-7691-1.

Clary, R.M., and Wandersee, J.H., 2011, DinoViz: The history and nature of science through the progression of dinosaur visualization: Science Scope, v. 34, no. 6, p. 14–21.

Czerkas, S.M., and Glut, D.F., 1982, Dinosaurs, Mammoths, and Cavemen: The Art of Charles R. Knight: Hong Kong, South China Printing Co., 120 p.

Field Museum of Natural History, 1929, Annual Report of the Director to the Board of Trustees for the Year 1928, v. VII, no 3: Chicago, Field Museum of Natural History; https://www.biodiversitylibrary.org/item/25533#page/9/mode/1up.

Gregory, W.K., 1937, Biographic Memoir of Henry Fairfield Osborn (1857–1938): National Academy of Sciences Biographical Memoirs XIX, 3rd Memoir, p. 52–119.

Knight, C.R., 1922, Mural paintings of prehistoric men and animals by Charles R. Knight [in the American Museum of Natural History, New York City]: Scribner's Magazine, v. LXXI, no. 3, p. 279–286.

Knight, C.R., 1935, Before the Dawn of History: New York, Whittlesey House McGraw Hill, 119 p.

Knight, C.R., 1942, Parade of life through the ages: National Geographic, v. 81, no. 2, p. 141–184.

Knight, C.R., 2005, Charles R. Knight: Autobiography of an Artist: Ann Arbor, Michigan, G.T. Labs, 112 p.

Lipps, J.H., Vartak, A., Van Eijden, T., Rajshekhar, C., Vaddadi, S., and Vartak, R., 2022, this volume, Paleontological postage stamps in art and education, *in* Clary, R.M., Rosenberg, G.D., and Evans, D.C., eds., The Evolution of Paleontological Art: Geological Society of America Memoir 218, Chapter 25, https://doi.org/10.1130/2021.1218(25).

Milner, R., 2012, Charles R. Knight: The Artist Who Saw through Time: New York, Abrams Books, 180 p.

Mullen, W., 2005 (28 April), Cleaning of Field murals shows off real dino might: Chicago Tribune, https://www.chicagotribune.com/news/ct-xpm-2005-04-28-0504280160-story.html.

National Research Council (NRC), 2012, A Framework for K–12 Science Education: Practices, Crosscutting Concepts, and Core Ideas: Washington, D.C., National Academies Press., 336 p.

Osborn, H.F., 1910, The Age of Mammals in Europe, Asia, and North America: New York, Macmillan Company, 635 p., https://doi.org/10.5962/bhl.title.102077.

Peck, R.M., and Rowland, S.M., 2022, this volume, Benjamin Waterhouse Hawkins and the early history of 3-D paleontological art, *in* Clary, R.M., Rosenberg, G.D., and Evans, D.C., eds., The Evolution of Paleontological Art: Geological Society of America Memoir 218, Chapter 17, https://doi.org/10.1130/2021.1218(17).

Reitmeyer, M., Morgan, R., and Baione, T., 2022, this volume, Beyond Charles Knight: Women paleo-artists at the American Museum of Natural History in the early twentieth century, *in* Clary, R.M., Rosenberg, G.D., and Evans, D.C., eds., The Evolution of Paleontological Art: Geological Society of America Memoir 218, Chapter 19, https://doi.org/10.1130/2021.1218(19).

Roy, S.K., 1934, Memorial of Oliver Cummings Farrington: Proceedings of the Geological Society of America for 1933, p. 192–209.

Sharpe, T., and Clary, R.M., 2022, this volume, Henry De la Beche's pioneering paleoecological illustration, *Duria antiquior*, *in* Clary, R.M., Rosenberg, G.D., and Evans, D.C., eds., The Evolution of Paleontological Art: Geological Society of America Memoir 218, Chapter 6, https://doi.org/10.1130/2021.1218(06).

Sommer, M., 2010, Seriality in the making: The Osborn-Knight restorations of evolutionary history: History of Science, v. xlvii, p. 461–482, https://doi.org/10.1177/007327531004800308.

Manuscript Accepted by the Society 2 February 2021
Manuscript Published Online 28 October 2021

The Geological Society of America
Memoir 218

Beyond Charles Knight: Women paleoartists at the American Museum of Natural History in the early twentieth century

Mai Reitmeyer
Rebecca Morgan
Tom Baione
American Museum of Natural History, Research Library, Central Park West at 79th Street, New York, New York 10024, USA

ABSTRACT

Under the direction of Henry Fairfield Osborn, Charles Knight helped shape popular images of the prehistoric past in the late nineteenth and early twentieth centuries. Although he was the most famous, Charles Knight was not the only paleoartist working at the American Museum of Natural History at this time. Behind the scenes, there were several women paleoartists who made significant contributions to museum displays and publications illustrating the prehistoric world. Often overlooked, this chapter highlights the contributions of Elisabeth Rungius Fulda, Helen Ziska, Lindsey Morris Sterling, and Margret Joy Flinsch Buba.

INTRODUCTION

"For the People, For Education, For Science"

At the American Museum of Natural History (AMNH) in the early twentieth century, this motto was widely applied, from annual reports and museum publications to logos and even the library's bookplates. On 9 April 1869, the act of incorporation established the AMNH as a scientific institution furthering the study of natural history, while also serving as a place of "popular instruction and recreation" (American Museum of Natural History, 1870, p. 10). The early administrators knew that to be successful, they would need to meet the needs of multiple audiences.

When Henry Fairfield Osborn was hired as curator of the newly created Department of Mammalian Palaeontology[1] in 1891, he too understood the importance of exhibitions in visually informing and engaging the public. He felt that the artistic interpretation of natural history furthered this goal (Hoagland, 1943). This was especially true in paleontological science because paleontologists observe the remains of long-dead organisms (Allmon, 2006), and there is a great deal of contested knowledge about their anatomy, life history, and behavior (Rieppel, 2012). It was rare to find a fossil specimen sufficiently complete to mount a full animal for exhibition. As a result, bones from different specimens, plaster casts, and sculpture were used to fill in the missing pieces (Rieppel, 2012). Osborn's desire was to depict animals known only from their fossil record as the living creatures they once were. In addition to mounting skeletons in dynamic poses, paintings provided visitors with details regarding the habits and environment of these animals, thereby providing the public with a window to past worlds (Rainger, 1991, p. 158).

[1]The Department's name would change multiple times between 1891 and 1950. From 1891 to 1941, the names were as follows: Department of Mammalian Palaeontology (1891–1895), Department of Vertebrate Palaeontology (1896–1937), and Department of Palaeontology (1938–1941). In 1942, the Museum discontinued the "segregation between the palaeontological departments, dealing with the life of the past, and those concerned with the living forms of today" so those that studied fossils became part of the Department of Mammals (American Museum of Natural History, 1943, p. 13). The Department was again reorganized in 1945 and became known as the Department of Geology and Paleontology (1945–1950). Today, it is the Division of Paleontology.

Reitmeyer, M., Morgan, R., and Baione, T., 2022, Beyond Charles Knight: Women paleoartists at the American Museum of Natural History in the early twentieth century, *in* Clary, R.M., Rosenberg, G.D., and Evans, D.C., eds., The Evolution of Paleontological Art: Geological Society of America Memoir 218, p. 171–180, https://doi.org/10.1130/2021.1218(19).

ART IN THE SERVICE OF SCIENCE

Beginning in the early 1890s, Osborn commissioned artists to create restorations, bringing ancient vertebrates to life and ultimately shaping the public perception and understanding of vertebrate paleontology (Cain, 2010). In an 1898 article in *Science*, Osborn (p. 841) wrote of the importance of these exhibits for public support.

There are certain obligations resting upon the curators of metropolitan museums from which curators of university museums should enjoy a grateful immunity. These mainly involve the difficult undertaking of arousing interest and spreading accurate information among a very large class of inquisitive but wholly uninformed people. If these obligations are unfulfilled the metropolitan museum fails in its purpose and deserves the withdrawal of public support.

Scientists and artists worked in close collaboration, but artists were "ultimately subordinated to the superior knowledge of the scientist, who ultimately claimed authorship" (Cain, 2010, p. 287). Scientists and artists went to great lengths to ensure that their restorations would be accurate. In the same article, Osborn (1898, p. 841–844) described this collaboration in detail:

… the Department of Vertebrate Paleontology at the American Museum have been making a special study of all the legitimate methods of attracting the attention and interest of visitors. Among these methods are the series of watercolor restorations of extinct vertebrates, executed by the animal painter, Mr. Charles Knight, with the aid of various scientific suggestions and criticisms. The preparation of these drawings involves a far more careful preliminary study than would generally be supposed. The artist begins by making a number of models in wax, based upon the actual proportions and muscular indications of the skeleton, and by a series of preliminary anatomical studies representing different attitudes and feeding habits. Thus in the restoration of an extinct animal the proportions and positions of all the joints and angles of the feet and limbs may be made true to life… Up to this point the animal may be considered a fairly correct representation of the original. On the other hand, the shape of the ears, the color and epidermic characters are largely imaginative, except in so far as they are suggested by relationship to modern allies…

Charles Knight was arguably the most famous of the artists hired by Osborn, and his paintings and murals adorn the walls of the AMNH and many other natural history museums to this day. However, many other iconic images produced by the AMNH in the early 1900s, including well-known illustrations of dinosaur eggs, titanotheres, and proboscideans, were created by female staff artists. Table 1 includes a list of the women working as artists in the Department of Paleontology in the first half of the twentieth century[2]. Many of these women contributed to the important output of the institution in its numerous scientific and popular publications and exhibitions. For example, according to the museum's Annual Report for 1937, the most important publication to appear in that year was a posthumous memoir by Dr. William D. Matthew, titled *Paleocene Faunas of the San Juan Basin, New Mexico*. This paper was described as "Dr. Matthew's greatest single

[2]Table 1 was compiled using personnel lists and biographical sketches found in the Departmental Records 1:7, Box 1, Folder 1, 4–6, AMNH Division of Paleontology Archives.

TABLE 1. WOMEN ARTISTS IN THE DEPARTMENT OF PALEONTOLOGY FROM 1900–1950

Name	Department of Paleontology tenure	Primary role
Dora F. Levett Bradley (1875–1957)	1933–1939	Artist, illustrating maps, charts, and drawings mostly for *Proboscidea* memoir
Margret Joy Flinsch Buba (1904–1998)	1928–1936	Artist, specializing in pen and ink illustrations and sculpture, mostly for *Proboscidea* memoir
Margarette Burchard McMullen (1891–1977)	1916–1917	Artist, illustrating for scientific articles
Mildred Clemans (1904–?)	1932–1936	Artist
Helen Morton Cox (1869–1946)	1921–1928	Artist, assisting Charles Knight with murals and coloring casts
Hazel De Berard (1884–1970)	1929–1958	Artist, specializing in pen and ink illustrations for the Frick Labs and later for the American Museum of Natural History
Elisabeth Rungius Fulda (1879–1968)	1917–1926	Artist and photographer
Elinor Gibson Graham (1901–1983)	1922–1923	Artist
Erna Kohlhaase (1882–1963)	1917–1920	Artist and preparator
Margaret Matthew Colbert (1911–2007)	1931–1933	Artist
Olive Otis (1895–1980)	1924–1925	Artist
Lindsey Morris Sterling (1876–1931)	1901–1931	Artist and head of Paleontology Department staff artists, specializing in pen and ink illustrations
Louise Waller Germann (1896–1957)	1924–1938	Artist, specializing in model restorations and pen and ink illustrations
Helen Ziska (1880–1951)	1917–1942	Artist, specializing in pen and ink illustrations and sculpture

contribution to Palaeontology" (American Museum of Natural History, 1937, p. 19). A book review in *Nature* (C.F.C., 1937, p. 47) described the volume as a "most important contribution to the early history of mammalian evolution … the descriptions of the various species, the eighty text figures and sixty-four quarto plates leave nothing to be desired." According to the acknowledgments, this publication's illustrations were prepared by multiple female artists including Lindsey Morris Sterling, Elisabeth Rungius Fulda, Louise Waller Germann, Mildred Clemens, and Margaret Matthew Colbert. Unfortunately, in the publication, not one of the illustrations is signed; the names of the artists only appear in the acknowledgments without specific attribution. As was often the case, many of these underpaid staff artists worked diligently behind the scenes, often late into the night and on weekends, leaving only fragments of their professional lives behind for modern scientists and historians to piece together.[3]

ELISABETH RUNGIUS FULDA—BRINGING PREHISTORIC FOSSIL VERTEBRATES FROM THE GOBI DESERT TO LIFE

Elisabeth Rungius Fulda (1879–1968) was one of these staff artists from 1917 to 1926. She also served as Department of Paleontology photographer from 1923 to 1926. Fulda was born in 1879 in Berlin, Germany, where at an early age she began studying painting and drawing of landscapes under the guidance of her older brother, Carl Rungius, an accomplished wildlife painter known for his moose paintings and for painting the moose diorama background in the AMNH's Hall of North American Mammals. Elisabeth came to New York in 1905 and continued her art studies at Cooper Union and the Art Students League in Woodstock, New York[4]. A short undated biography in the Division of Paleontology's archives simply states that "she came [to the Museum] as an artist" but does not indicate any details of how she learned of the position.[5] An employee payroll card in the library archives shows that she came recommended by William T. Hornaday, director of the New York Zoological Park. In the nine years that she was employed by the Department of Paleontology at the AMNH, Fulda would complete numerous illustrations for scientific publications, restorations of fossil animals, models of Mongolian animals, and a series of color sketches for an unrealized four-story mural for a museum staircase.

In the 1920s, the AMNH embarked on one of its largest natural scientific expeditions of the early twentieth century, the Central Asiatic Expedition (CAE) to northern China and Mongolia (1921–1930), under the leadership of Roy Chapman Andrews. The first important discovery of the CAE, a *Baluchitherium*, was made in the summer of 1922 (Manias, 2015). The specimen was quickly packed up and sent back to New York, where Osborn promptly published the find in the museum's scientific series, *American Museum Novitates* (Osborn, 1923a). The publication included a drawing "prepared under the direction of [Osborn] with the cooperation of Dr. W. K. Gregory and Mrs. L. M. Sterling" (p. 9) showing the size of the animal (Fig. 1). The scale of the animal would soon be revised by Granger and Gregory (1935b) and illustrated by Helen Ziska as discussed later in this chapter. After publication of the *Novitates*, Osborn made a push to unveil the specimen to the public (Manias, 2015). Under the direction of Osborn, Fulda completed a restoration of *Baluchitherium* (Fig. 2), which would appear in multiple articles for popular audiences by Osborn (1923b, 1923c). The restoration is credited to Fulda "under the direction of Osborn," further emphasizing the role of the scientist in the creation of the art.

In 1923, the Central Asiatic Expedition would again make history and captivate the public's attention when the team uncovered "twenty-five eggs, over seventy skulls and twelve complete skeletons of dinosaurs, of all ages from newly hatched to full-grown" (American Museum of Natural History, 1924, p. 87). Not only did the find capture the imagination of both the public and the press[6], it also proved important to science, settling the question of whether dinosaurs laid eggs and what the eggs looked like (American Museum of Natural History, 1924). Fulda would soon create two restoration drawings illustrating young dinosaurs coming out of their eggs (Fig. 3) and adult *Protoceratops* with

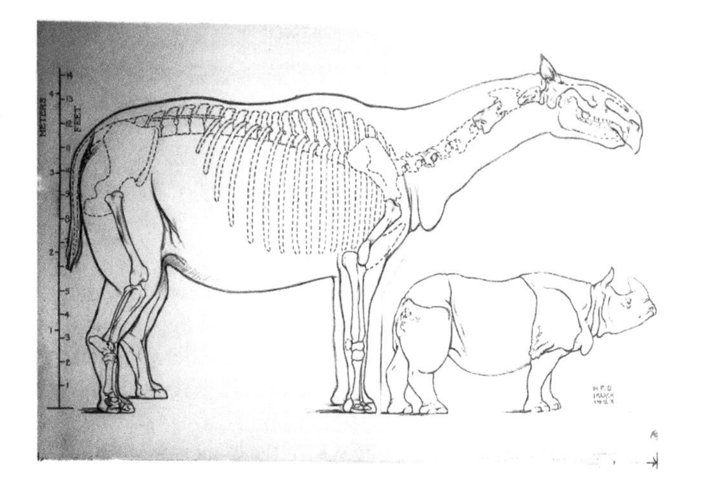

Figure 1. Size comparison of *Baluchitherium* with a black rhino prepared under the direction of Osborn with the cooperation of Lindsey Morris Sterling, 1923 (Image no. 410652, courtesy of American Museum of Natural History Library).

[3]Correspondence in the Central Archives shows that many artists negotiated for time and compensation for specific projects. For example, see Fulda to Gregory, 24 July 1926, Central Archives, 1262, AMNH Library.

[4]Burr Galleries Artist Biography, Elisabeth Rungius Fulda papers, 1895–1967, Archives of American Art, Smithsonian Institution, Microfilm reel N/695.

[5]Elisabeth Fulda Biographical Sketch (1942), Departmental Records 1:7, Box 1, Folder 4, AMNH Division of Paleontology Archives.

[6]In his 1932 publication, Andrews writes that he did "not realize what enormous popular interest had been aroused by our discovery of dinosaur eggs, until we arrived in Seattle. Newspaper representatives boarded the ship at Victoria, each one authorized to make a cash offer for the exclusive use of the egg photographs. Some of these reached thousands of dollars" (Andrews, 1932, p. 230).

Figure 2. Restoration drawing of *Baluchitherium* by Elisabeth Rungius Fulda, 1923 (Image no. 310386, courtesy of American Museum of Natural History Library).

Figure 3. *Young Dinosaurs Coming Out of Their Eggs* by Elisabeth Rungius Fulda, 1924 (Image no. 108581, courtesy of American Museum of Natural History Library).

young. These illustrations would appear in Andrews' (1926) book for popular audiences detailing the fieldwork of the CAE, *On the Trail of Ancient Man* (p. 202–203). Although there was also an *Oviraptor* (Latin for "egg robber") found with the eggs, they were presumed to belong to *Protoceratops* because it was the most common dinosaur at the locality where the eggs were found.[7]

In June 1925, at the request of Osborn, Museum Director George Sherwood wrote to Knight to commission a series of murals for the dinosaur exhibition halls. Osborn had suggested that Fulda could be one of two artists to assist Knight in creating these murals. Knight bristled at the prospect of cooperating with Fulda. He felt that her art was not on par with his so he wanted to complete the murals "entirely on [his] own."[8] As far as assistants were concerned, he would only choose those which would be "of help to [him] personally."[9] In a follow-up letter to Osborn, Knight emphasized that he did not collaborate with other artists throughout his career, and if he were to bring on assistants, it would be to "copy what I tell them to copy."[10] It was clear that Knight considered the other staff artists only as "museum workers," while he was an artist with proper training and practice.[11] However, Fulda's drawings appeared alongside Knight's in popular museum publications (Osborn, 1923c). It would appear that neither Osborn nor Andrews felt that her art was inferior or lacking as the art was created under their strict supervision. In 1924, when Fulda was also responsible for photography in the department, W.D. Matthew requested that she devote all her time to restorations, models, and drawings, except for necessary supervision of a newly hired photographer[12]. In a letter dated 18 March 1926, Frederic A. Lucas, honorary director of the museum, described Fulda as being "skillful with her brush and modeling tool… [She] has had a great deal of experience in drawing and modeling restorations of various kinds."[13] Perhaps Knight felt that collaborating with Fulda would somehow diminish his art, but we can't be certain.

In 1926, Childs Frick,[14] a longtime museum trustee, requested that Fulda work on sketches for a series of murals under the direction of William K. Gregory that would depict the "history of life."[15] The murals would take up an entire staircase from the first floor to the fifth floor. The sketches were completed by Fulda[16] (Fig. 4), but it appears that the murals were never executed. Perhaps if they had been finished, Fulda would be as famous a name as Knight in the halls of the AMNH.

In 1934, Fulda briefly returned to the museum, this time working on illustrations for publication in the Department of

[7]This was the prevailing thought until the 1990s, when museum expeditions to a locality in the same region discovered identical eggs, one of which contained the embryo of a close relative of *Oviraptor*. Additionally, the parent, also an *Oviraptor* relative, was found crouched atop a nest in a posture identical to the brooding position of chickens and pigeons possibly warming or protecting the eggs. This changed scientists' view of which animal laid these eggs and provided clues to the brooding behavior of these animals (Gorner, 1995).

[8]Knight to Osborn, 25 June 1925, Central Archives 1262, AMNH Library archives.

[9]Ibid.

[10]Knight to Osborn, [June 1925], Central Archives 1262, AMNH Library archives.

[11]Ibid.

[12]Matthew to Sherwood, 15 November 1924, Central Archives 456, AMNH Library archives.

[13]Frederic A. Lucas to Miss Gallup, Children's Museum, 18 March 1926, Central Archive 1131, AMNH Library.

[14]In 1916, the Department of Paleontology began a long association with Childs Frick, the son of steel magnate Henry Clay Frick. Childs Frick employed collectors and researchers to accumulate a collection of more than 200,000 fossil mammals, which was donated to the museum after his death in 1965 along with the financial assets of the Childs Frick Corporation in 1968 (American Museum of Natural History, n.d.).

[15]William K. Gregory to Acting Director Sherwood, 5 March 1926, Central Archives 1261, AMNH Library archives.

[16]Director [Sherwood] to Frick, 27 November 1931, Central Archives 1263, AMNH Library archives.

Figure 4. Sketch of one of the proposed stairway murals by Elisabeth Rungius Fulda (Image no. 314050, courtesy of American Museum of Natural History Library).

Mammalogy.[17] Funding was provided by The Public Works of Art Project, a Works Progress Administration (WPA) program paid for by the Civil Works Administration (CWA).[18] In the same year, the museum requested that funding for her work be continued as it was of "exceptional quality and greatly appreciated."[19] Unfortunately, New York had reached its quota for CWA jobs,[20] and Fulda would again leave the museum in 1934. Although she left the museum, she continued her art. By 1938, her works could be found at the Brooklyn Museum, the National Academy of Design, the National Arts Club, and the Gallery of Animal Paintings in the New York Zoological Park, and the Bird House of the National Zoological Park in Washington, D.C.[21] She would continue painting and exhibiting her art until her death in 1968.

HELEN ZISKA—RECONSTRUCTING GIANT RHINOCEROTOIDS

Helen Ziska (1880–1951) was a prolific illustrator whose career at the museum spanned from 1917 to 1942. Daughter of opera singer Josef Beck, she spent her childhood shuttling back and forth between New York and Vienna. Her artistic talents were recognized early and she attended art school in Munich and entered the College of Physicians and Surgeons at Columbia University to study anatomy and surgical drawing (Barton, 1938). Known as Madame Ziska, she was officially on staff of the museum's Comparative Anatomy Department. Her skills were highly valued, resulting in her frequently being "loaned out" to other museum departments—causing numerous rifts between scientific staff vying for her artistic attention. A 1929 letter to the museum's director reported her "...coming in on Sunday and working from home at night" to meet the numerous demands on her talent from her home department, the Paleontology Department, and an unidentified effort with a museum trustee.[22] Her long career resulted in an expansive portfolio of work that spanned paleontology and zoology, illustration and sculpture, under the scientific direction of numerous giants of their fields, including Henry Fairfield Osborn and paleontologists Walter Granger and William King Gregory.

What may be her best known and most enduring contribution was her collaboration with Gregory and Granger. Ziska was responsible for the important 1934 line-drawn, revised reconstructions depicting *Baluchitherium,* which was then thought to be the largest known terrestrial mammal (Fig. 5).[23] Ziska's line drawings continued to accompany papers by Gregory and Granger (Gregory, 1935; Granger and Gregory, 1935a, 1935b). The authors worked to scale up the overall animal's size from scant known remains of different individual specimens using a baseline of more complete fossil animals (such as a primitive rhinoceros), while Ziska worked through years of revisions to bring these beasts to life on paper. Despite the ongoing controversy over the author's "sizing up" methods, Ziska's illustrations were an influential reconstruction that was reproduced in the museum's scientific series and popular publication, *Natural History Magazine* (Gregory, 1935) (Fig. 6), and inspired a "life-sized" bas-relief sculpture that remained on exhibit in the museum's Hall of Mongolian Vertebrates for decades (Fig. 7).

LINDSEY MORRIS STERLING AND MARGRET JOY FLINSCH BUBA—ILLUSTRATING ELEPHANT EVOLUTION

Henry Fairfield Osborn's *Proboscidea* (1936–1942), his fifth and final book, was published posthumously after his death in 1935. The monograph, the result of more or less continuous work since 1907, was created with contributions from a large group of staff scientists, preparators, artists, and photographers in the Department of Paleontology (Osborn, 1930). For *Proboscidea*, as with his previous efforts, Osborn used the expertise

[17]Wayne Faunce (AMNH assistant director) to Public Works of Art Project New York Regional Committee, 10 May 1934, Central Archives 1283, AMNH Library archives.

[18]As part of New Deal initiatives, the WPA arts programs operated over a 10-year period from 1933 to 1943 to employ competent, unemployed artists during the Great Depression (U.S. Department of the Treasury, 2015).

[19]Museum memo, [4 May 1934], Central Archives 1283, AMNH Library archives.

[20]Grace Gosselin (Federal Civil Works Administration) to Wayne Faunce (AMNH assistant director), 5 March 1934, Central Archives 1283, AMNH Library archives.

[21]Recommendation letter from the N.Y. Zoological Park dated 4 March 1938, Elisabeth Rungius Fulda papers, 1895–1967, Archives of American Art, Smithsonian Institution, Microfilm reel 101.

[22]Clara P. Meadowcroft (comparative anatomy stenographer) to George Sherwood (museum director), 4 November 1929, Central Archives 1192, AMNH Library Archives.

[23]The name of this group of animals is famously confusing: *Baluchitherium* and *Indricotherium*, commonly referred to as Indricotheres, are now junior synonyms of the genus *Paraceratherium* (Witton, 2016).

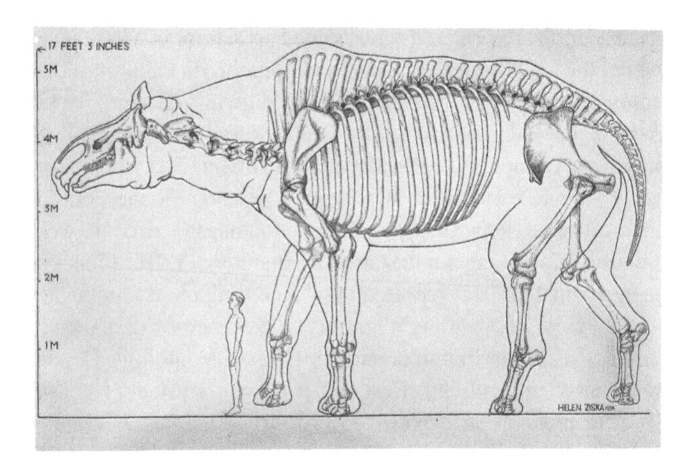

Figure 5. Helen Ziska's 1934 line drawing reconstruction on the *Baluchitherium*'s presumed size (Image no. 314519, courtesy of American Museum of Natural History Library).

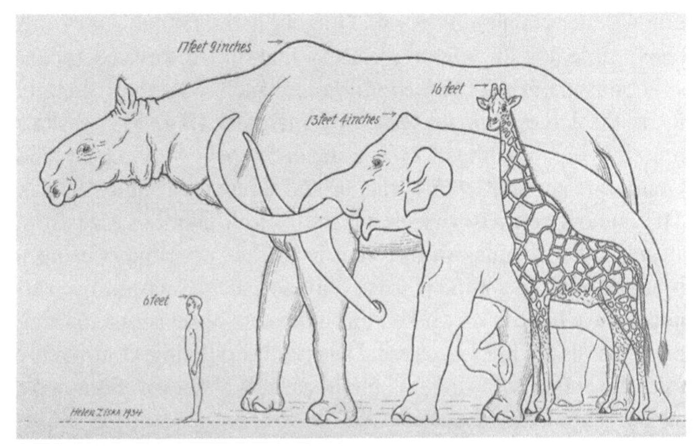

Figure 6. A late version of Helen Ziska's comparative sketch from *Natural History*, the museum's popular publication (Image no. 118353, courtesy of American Museum of Natural History Library).

of artists to help him resurrect fossil elephants and mastodonts from the past. Many staff artists contributed to this opus, but two, Lindsey Morris Sterling and Margret Joy Flinsch Buba, stand out and are acknowledged "with great generosity" by Osborn in the foreword.

Lindsey Morris Sterling (1876–1931) worked for Osborn during his time at Columbia University and followed him to the AMNH in 1901, where she would manage the Department of Paleontology's staff artists. Born in Pennsylvania, she studied art in New York at Cooper Union under George T. Brewster and at the Art Students League under renowned American sculptor James Earle Fraser. She also studied in Paris under Antoine Bourdelle and Paul Wayland Bartlett (National Sculpture Society, 1923). Although Sterling's training was in sculpture, most of her museum work was concentrated on creating skilled ink drawings and illustrations. Her two most notable contributions were her restorations in 1906 for Osborn's *Bulletin* (Osborn, 1906, plate XXXIX) on the first *Tyrannosaurus* discovered in

Figure 7. The Gregory/Ziska *Baluchitherium* reconstruction instructed museum sculptor John W. Hope's enormous bas relief in the museum's Hall of Mongolian Vertebrates, which is pictured here in 1936. Gregory (left) and Hope (right) flank Director Wayne Faunce, President Trubee Davison, and paleontologist Walter Granger (Image no. 314993, courtesy of American Museum of Natural History Library).

1905 by AMNH paleontologist Barnum Brown in Hell Creek, Montana (Fig. 8), and a series of drawings, begun in 1908 and ultimately numbering in the hundreds, of the osteology of the *Proboscidea* that chiefly depicted the crania of fossil and living forms (Osborn, 1931). In the introduction to his work, Osborn warmly writes of the impact Sterling had on the *Proboscidea* publication (1936–1942, p. xvii):

> Especially outstanding is the superb work of illustration rendered by Lindsey Morris Sterling from the year 1902 to the time of her death in 1931. Beginning with pen drawings of crania in the elephantoid branches, executed in imitation of wood engraving… Mrs. Sterling with rare intelligence, accuracy and contestant enthusiasm prepared the greater number of pen drawings and diagrams for this monograph and is thus entitled to an enduring rank among the leading scientific draughtsman of the present century…

Although Osborn was known for keeping tight scientific control over his projects, after many years of professional collaboration, Osborn clearly trusted Sterling's artistic interpretation explicitly, praising her for her "extraordinary accuracy, a fidelity to truth and an artistic finish" (Osborn, 1931, p. 563).

Sterling worked for Osborn on many projects throughout her professional life; however, she was not only defined by her work for the museum. She continued her artistic training, traveling to Paris in 1910 to further her sculpture studies.[24] Additionally, she actively exhibited her work outside the museum, notably winning a bronze medal while showing five pieces of sculpture in the Panama-Pacific Exhibition of 1915 in San Francisco (Panama-Pacific International Exposition, 1915). Sterling and many other

[24]Certificate of Registration of American Citizen. 1910, Vertical Files for Lindsey Morris Sterling, American Museum of Natural History Library.

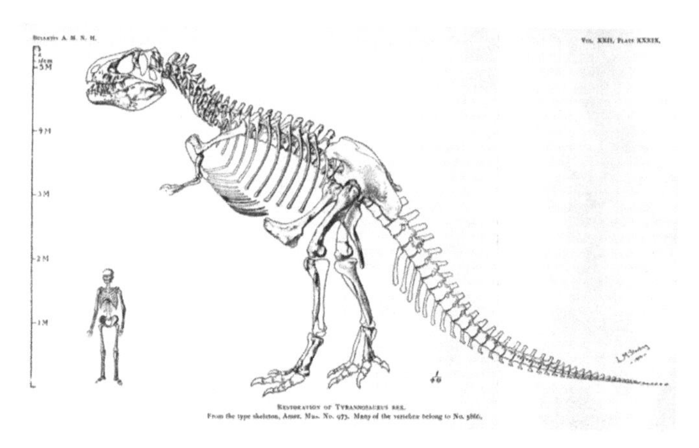

Figure 8. Restoration illustration by Lindsey Morris Sterling of a *Tyrannosaurus rex* skeleton with a human for scale from *American Museum of Natural History Bulletin*, Volume XXII (Image no. 46620, courtesy of American Museum of Natural History Library).

female artists from the Panama-Pacific Exhibition went on to participate later that same year in the New York City Exhibition of Painting and Sculpture by Women Artists for the Benefit of the Woman Suffrage Campaign (Dennison, 2003), which revealed her place in the New York art milieu.

In 1928, Margret Joy Flinsch Buba (1904–1998) joined the paleontology staff. Buba began her art studies at a young age in New York and continued her training in Europe, mainly Munich and Frankfurt, with a focus on sculpture and drawing living animals. She worked at the museum for seven years, from 1928 to 1936, and focused mainly on the *Proboscidea* monograph. For this publication, Osborn leveraged his international network of collaborators to solicit detailed information about specimens held across the world that he wanted to include in his monograph.[25] For information about living animals he used his connections with various zoos including the nearby New York Zoological Park. Osborn received a flood of data, including measurements, that were then utilized by Buba to create models and scaled reconstructions of the animals which then informed her restoration drawings. For example, Buba received photographs and measurements from F.D. Figgins[26], director of the Colorado Museum of Natural History, for their specimen of *Archidiskodon meridionalis nebrascensis*. Figures 9 and 10 show the series of reconstructions and the final restoration drawings of this animal that were created by Buba for publication. Osborn writes in the introduction to his work of the impact of Buba's contributions (Osborn, 1936–1942, p. xvii):

> Her work combines a fine sense of accuracy with rare artistic appreciation of the motions and adaptations of these remarkable animals. Beginning with the Moeritheres of the Fayum she has vigorously and freshly restored, under the author's direction, all the chief types of the proboscideans as members of the forty or more genera and twenty-odd subfamilies into which the order is now divided. The prolonged and very difficult undertaking of the last three years has been the outline restorations of most of the known fossil and living types for phylogenetic charts illustrating the adaptive radiation of the mastodonts and elephants, also the modeling in plaster of the outstanding mastodonts and elephants...

She was also a sculptor for various projects in the department.[27] Buba's skills as a sculptor brought a freshness to the reproductions, as exemplified in her work on the *Platybelodon* or shovel-tusker. Under the direction of Osborn, she created a sculpted model (Fig. 11) that also likely informed a series of lively restoration drawings of this animal for *Proboscidea* (Osborn, 1936–1942, figs. 284–285).

Buba left the museum in 1936 and went on to illustrate children's books but is internationally known for her sculptures found around the world, including New York, Washington, D.C., and across Europe, of well-known personalities such as John D. Rockefeller, H.F. Osborn, Pope Paul VI, John and Lucy Audubon, and Dr. Florence Sabin (Paid Notice: Deaths, 1998).

DOES ART INFLUENCE SCIENCE?

As previously stated, creating the detailed figures for scientific publication was a highly collaborative process. In 1935, William K. Gregory described his collaboration with artist Helen Ziska in detail (p. 343):

> For nearly a year we struggled with this problem of evolving a consistent restoration of the skeleton out of many odd lots of bones ... Literally scores of trials were made, checked back and forth against the available facts and then rejected or modified. In other words, the method of trial and error was followed through long and often discouraging months. A less willing and indefatigable artist than Mrs. Helen Ziska would have balked at filling many portfolios with trial drawings, while a less skillful artist could not have fitted together so convincingly the drawings of bones of originally different sizes.

In a 2003 article about visual representations of science, Anne R. Richards writes, "visual representations of nature always have been inseparable from science because they make it possible for scientists to interact with complex phenomena in an essential way" (Richards, 2003, p. 184). John K. Gilbert (2010) agrees, stating that "the full understanding of any phenomenon that falls within the remit of a science ... involves being able to produce visualizations of such types and being able to 'move' mentally between them" (p. 6). We know that the science was clearly informing the art, but we also wonder how much the art was used by scientists to then clarify or shape new ideas. We feel that this theoretical question is worthy of further investigation.

[25]In volume one of *Proscobidea*, Osborn lists over 124 collaborators (Osborn, 1936–1942, p. 13–15).

[26]Henry Fairfield Osborn Papers, Notes and Manuscripts, MSS 08352, Box 3, Folder 8, and Box 15 Oversized, American Museum of Natural History Library.

[27]After a visit to the museum in 1985, Buba writes to Director Dr. Tom Nicholson to offer her advice on the care of the bust of Osborn that she created and discusses her other work for the museum. Vertical File for Margret Joy Flinsch Buba, American Museum of Natural History Library.

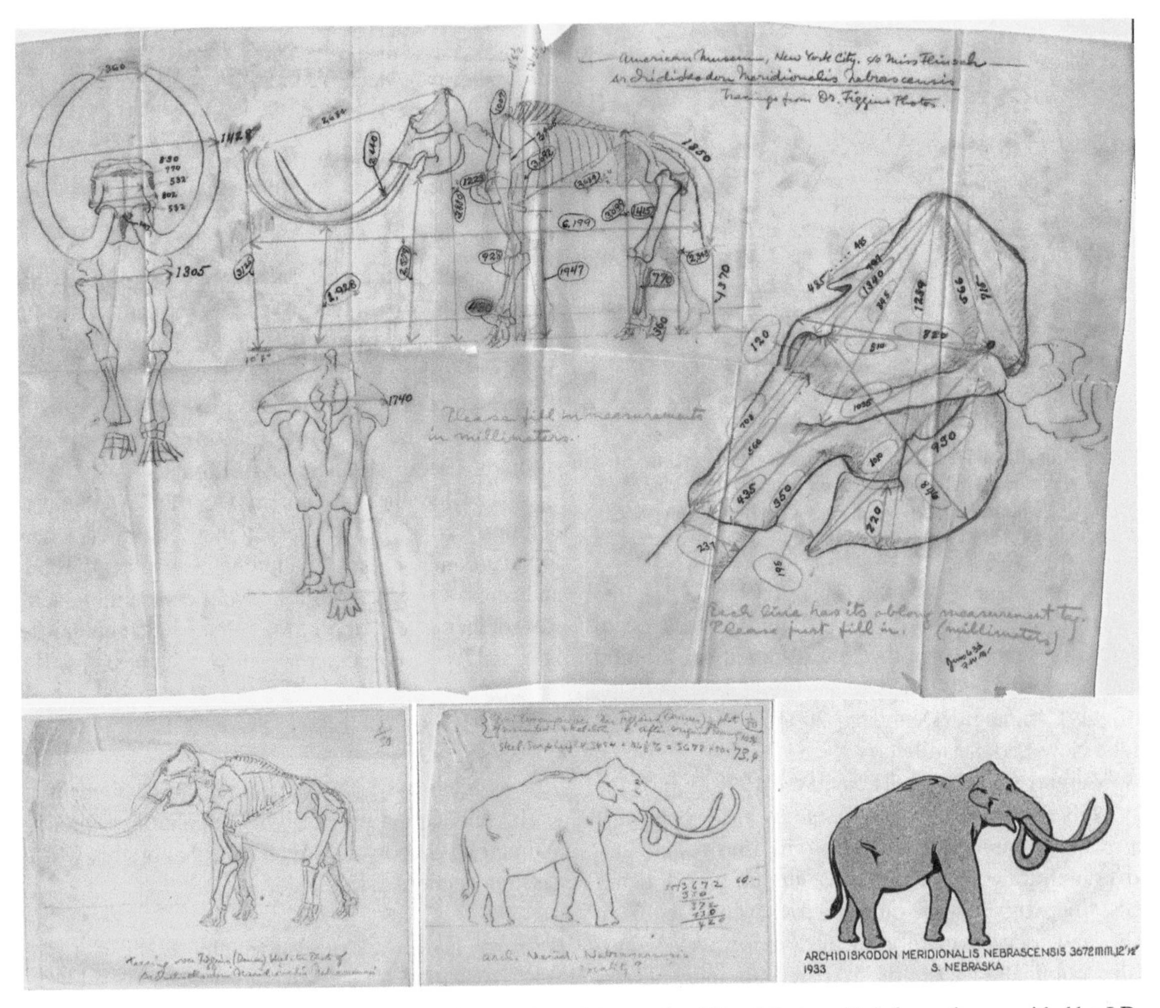

Figure 9. Reconstruction illustrations and drawings made by Margret Joy Flinsch Buba with information provided by J.D. Figgins, the director of the Colorado Natural History Museum (from Henry Fairfield Osborn Papers, Notes and Manuscripts, MSS 08352, Box 3, Folder 8, and Box 15 Oversized, courtesy of American Museum of Natural History Library). These illustrations were also used to create a restoration drawing of the same species (Fig. 10).

Figure 10. Restoration by Margret Joy Flinsch Buba of *Archidiskodon meridionalis nebrascensis* from complete skeleton and mandible with lower portion of the tusks lacking only the cranium (from Osborn, 1936–1942, p. 1036; used with permission).

Figure 11. *Platybelodon* sculpture by Margret Joy Flinsch Buba (Image no. 119048, courtesy of American Museum of Natural History Library).

CONCLUSION

Despite the fact that much of the paleoart created at the museum in the early twentieth century is no longer scientifically accurate, many of these images endure, perhaps because they are "convincingly alive" as Asher Elbein (2017, paragraph 1) writes, shaping the way humans imagine the distant past. "While paleo-art is a form of scientific art, its value doesn't always lie in its level of accuracy," especially since "paleontological accuracy is a moving target, constantly reshuffled by new discoveries and scientific arguments" (Elbein, 2017, paragraph 14). In the words of Emily Willoughby, a contemporary woman paleoartist, "'Evolution is a brush, not a ladder,'... so it's only fitting that the art depicting its sweep should be similarly difficult to pin down" (as cited in Elbein, 2017, paragraph 15).[28]

Although we were able to identify at least 14 women who worked in the Department of Paleontology in the early twentieth century, for the purposes of this chapter, we were only able to highlight a small selection of the contributions of a few of them. By identifying them in Table 1, we are hoping that this chapter provides others with a basis for further inquiry.

ACKNOWLEDGMENTS

We thank the editors of this publication for their invitation to participate in this volume. We also thank Susan K. Bell for access to the American Museum of Natural History (AMNH) Division of Vertebrate Paleontology archives; Carl Mehling, senior museum specialist, AMNH Department of Paleontology, for comments on the final draft version of our manuscript; and Kendra Meyer, AMNH Library, for the high-resolution images of the art appearing in this chapter.

REFERENCES CITED

Allmon, W., 2006, The Pre-Modern history of the Post-Modern dinosaur: Phases and causes in Post-Darwinian dinosaur art: Earth Sciences History, v. 25, no. 1, p. 5–35, https://doi.org/10.17704/eshi.25.1.g2687j050u3w1546.

American Museum of Natural History, n.d., History of the fossil mammal collection: https://www.amnh.org/research/paleontology/collections/fossil-mammals/history-of-the-fossil-mammal-collection (accessed December 2019).

American Museum of Natural History, 1870, The First Annual Report of the American Museum of Natural History: New York, American Museum of Natural History, 67 p.

American Museum of Natural History, 1924, The American Museum and the World: Fifty-Fifth Annual Report for the Year 1923: New York, American Museum of Natural History, 272 p.

American Museum of Natural History, 1937, Annual Report: New York, American Museum of Natural History, 131 p.

American Museum of Natural History, 1943, Seventy-Fourth Annual Report for the Year 1942: New York, American Museum of Natural History, 65 p.

Andrews, R.C., 1926, On the Trail of Ancient Man: New York, Putnam, 375 p.

Andrews, R.C., 1932, The New Conquest of Central Asia: A Narrative of the Explorations of the Central Asiatic Expeditions in Mongolia and China, 1921–1930: New York, American Museum of Natural History, 678 p.

[28]Quote from S. White, 2017, *Dinosaur Art II: The Cutting Edge of Paleoart*: London, Titan Books, 188 p., as cited in Elbein (2017).

Barton, D.H., 1938, The indoor explorer. Artist and animal trainer—The story of a double life: Natural History, v. 42, p. 379–380, 394.

C.F.C., 1937, Paleocene faunas of the San Juan Basin, New Mexico: Nature, v. 140, no. 3532, p. 46-47, https://doi.org/10.1038/140046a0.

Cain, V.E.M., 2010, 'The direct medium of the vision': Visual education, virtual witnessing and the prehistoric past at the American Museum of Natural History, 1890-1923: Journal of Visual Culture, v. 9, no. 3, p. 284–303, https://doi.org/10.1177/1470412910380334.

Dennison, M.C., 2003, Babies for suffrage: "The Exhibition of Painting and Sculpture by Women Artists for the Benefit of the Woman Suffrage Campaign": Woman's Art Journal, v. 24, no. 2, p. 24–30, https://doi.org/10.2307/1358783.

Elbein, A., 2017, The surprising evolution of dinosaur drawings: https://www.theatlantic.com/entertainment/archive/2017/11/paleoart-and-dinosaur-art-2/544505/ (accessed December 2019).

Gilbert, J.K., 2010, The role of visual representations in the learning and teaching of science: An introduction: Asia-Pacific Forum on Science Learning and Teaching, v. 11, no. 1, p. 1–19.

Gorner, P., 1995, Dinosaur fossil shows a good parent, https://www.chicagotribune.com/news/ct-xpm-1995-12-21-9512210183-story.html (accessed December 2019).

Granger, W., and Gregory, W.K., 1935a, Further notes on the gigantic extinct Rhinoceros, *Baluchitherium*, from the Oligocene of Mongolia: Bulletin of the American Museum of Natural History, v. 72, no. 1, p. 1–73.

Granger, W., and Gregory, W.K., 1935b, A revised restoration of the skeleton of *Baluchitherium*, gigantic fossil Rhinoceros of Central Asia: American Museum Novitates, no. 787, p. 1–3.

Gregory, W.K., 1935, Building a super-giant Rhinoceros: Natural History, v. 35, p. 340–343.

Hoagland, C., 1943, They gave life to bones: The Scientific Monthly, v. 56, no. 2, p. 114–133.

Manias, C., 2015, Building *Baluchitherium* and *Indricotherium*: Imperial and international networks in early-twentieth century paleontology: Journal of the History of Biology, v. 48, p. 237–278, https://doi.org/10.1007/s10739-014-9395-y.

National Sculpture Society, 1923, Exhibition of American Sculpture Catalogue: 156th Street West of Broadway, New York, April Fourteenth to August First, MCMXXIII: New York, National Sculpture Society, 372 p.

Osborn, H.F., 1898, Models of extinct vertebrates: Science: New Series, v. 7, no. 182, p. 841–845, https://doi.org/10.1126/science.7.182.841.

Osborn, H.F., 1906, *Tyrannosaurus*, upper Cretaceous carnivorous dinosaur (second communication): Bulletin of the American Museum of Natural History, v. 22, p. 281–296.

Osborn, H.F., 1923a, *Baluchitherium grangeri*, a giant hornless Rhinoceros from Mongolia: American Museum Novitates, no. 78, p. 1–15.

Osborn, H.F., 1923b, The extinct giant Rhinocerous *Baluchitherium* of western and central Asia: Natural History, v. 23, no. 3, p. 209–228.

Osborn, H.F., 1923c, Giant beasts of three million years ago: Asia and the Americas, v. 23, no. 9, p. 625–630.

Osborn, H.F., 1930, Fifty-Two Years of Research, Observation and Publication 1877–1929: New York, Charles Scribner's Sons, 160 p.

Osborn, H.F., 1931, Lindsey Morris Sterling: Natural History, v. 31, no. 5, p. 563.

Osborn, H.F., 1936–1942, Proboscidea: A Monograph of the Discovery, Evolution, Migration and Extinction of the Mastodonts and Elephants of the World, Volumes 1 and 2: New York, American Museum Press, 1675 p., https://doi.org/10.5962/bhl.title.12097.

Paid Notice: Deaths, 1998, Buba, Margret Joy Flinsch: The New York Times, https://www.nytimes.com/1998/03/08/classified/paid-notice-deaths-buba-margret-joy-flinsch.html (accessed December 2019).

Panama-Pacific International Exposition, 1915, Official Catalogue of the Department of Fine Arts, Panama-Pacific International Exposition (with Awards), San Francisco, California, 1915: San Francisco, The Wahlgreen Company, 255 p.

Rainger, R., 1991, An Agenda for Antiquity: Henry Fairfield Osborn & Vertebrate Paleontology at the American Museum of Natural History, 1890–1935: Tuscaloosa, University of Alabama Press, 360 p.

Richards, A., 2003, Argument and authority in the visual representations of science: Technical Communication Quarterly, v. 12, no. 2, p. 183–206, https://doi.org/10.1207/s15427625tcq1202_3.

Rieppel, L., 2012, Bringing dinosaurs back to life: Exhibiting prehistory at the American Museum of Natural History: Isis, v. 103, p. 460–490, https://doi.org/10.1086/667969.

U.S. Department of the Treasury, 2015, WPA Art Collection: https://home.treasury.gov/about/history/collection/paintings/wpa-art-collection (accessed December 2019).

Witton, M., 2016, Trunk or no trunk, small or giant ears, long or short neck… What did the giant rhinocerotoid *Paraceratherium* really look like?: http://markwitton-com.blogspot.com/2016/08/trunk-or-no-trunk-short-or-giant-ears.html (accessed December 2019).

Manuscript Accepted by the Society 15 January 2021
Manuscript Published Online 22 September 2021

Printed in the USA

The Geological Society of America
Memoir 218

The Fritz Zerritsch/Erich Thenius suite of paleontological wall roll-ups and the pageant-of-life-through-time genre of paleontological art

Stephen M. Rowland
Department of Geoscience, University of Nevada Las Vegas, Las Vegas, Nevada 89154, USA

ABSTRACT

Here I rescue from obscurity a mid-twentieth-century sequence of ten paintings representing biotas and ecosystems present in different periods of geologic time. They were used to illustrate a 1955 book titled *The History of Life on Earth* by University of Vienna paleontologist Erich Thenius. The paintings were also mass produced as classroom teaching aids in the form of wall chart roll-ups. Thenius collaborated with Viennese landscape artist Fritz Zerritsch to produce these scenes from Deep Time. In terms of the selection and arrangement of animals in some of the scenes, Thenius and Zerritsch were probably influenced by well-known paleoartists Rudolph Zallinger and Charles R. Knight. I corresponded with Professor Thenius concerning his collaboration with Zerritsch, and his answers to my questions illuminate some of the choices he made. The Zerritsch/Thenius collection of paleo-scenes is a good example of the pageant-of-life-through-time genre of paleontological art. I use this sequence of prehistoric tableaux to examine artistic conventions within this genre.

INTRODUCTION

The pageant-of-life-through-time is a very common genre within paleoart. It is a form of visual storytelling in which paleontologists and their artist, sculptor, or museum-design collaborators tell their version of the story of life through geologic time. They create a sequence of scenes representing extinct species and past ecosystems that are usually arranged in chronological order. The goal is to provide a time-travel experience in which viewers are visually transported back through unimaginably long periods of geologic time and stop multiple times along the way for a glimpse of the animals and plants that were living at a particular time and the ecological settings in which they lived.

This study focuses on one particular example of this genre: an obscure collection of ten mid-twentieth-century wall chart roll-ups depicting a sequence of scenes from the history of life. A set of these wall charts adorned the walls of the geology lecture hall at the University of Nevada Las Vegas (UNLV) when I joined the faculty in 1978, and I'm sure they had already been hanging there for several years before I arrived. In more recent decades they gathered dust in storage. I finally dusted them off, examined them closely, and researched their origin.

The objective of this chapter is twofold. First, I seek to rescue from obscurity this fascinating, nearly forgotten, mid-twentieth-century suite of pageant-of-life-through-time images. Second, I briefly explore the artistic conventions of the pageant-of-life-through-time genre of paleontological iconography to which these ten paintings belong.

THE FRITZ ZERRITSCH/ERICH THENIUS PAGEANT-OF-LIFE-THROUGH-TIME WALL CHARTS

The scenes examined in this study were painted by a twentieth-century Austrian landscape artist named Fritz Zerritsch the

Rowland, S.M., 2022, The Fritz Zerritsch/Erich Thenius suite of paleontological wall roll-ups and the pageant-of-life-through-time genre of paleontological art, *in* Clary, R.M., Rosenberg, G.D., and Evans, D.C., eds., The Evolution of Paleontological Art: Geological Society of America Memoir 218, p. 181–189, https://doi.org/10.1130/2021.1218(20).

Younger (1888–1985) (Fig. 1), who was a professor at the Vienna Graphic Arts Education and Research Institute. His father, Fritz Zerritsch the Elder (1865–1938), was a sculptor and graphic artist. The younger Zerritsch's artistic output was diverse and included tapestries, posters, mosaics, frescos, and an image on the 1938 Austrian 1000 schilling banknote (Vollmer, 1961). He is best known for his landscapes and scenes depicting animals, some prints of which are available for purchase through internet sources today.

Prior to the mid-1950s, Zerritsch had not painted any paleolandscapes. But he was recruited by Austrian paleontologist Erich Thenius (b. 1924) (Fig. 2) to provide illustrations for a book on the history of life (Thenius, 1955). The book, *Die Geschichte des Lebens auf der Erde* (*The History of Life on Earth*), was written in German and published in 1955. Zerritsch died in 1985, but in 2016 I was able to contact Erich Thenius—then age 92—and ask him about his collaboration with Zerritsch.

The project, Thenius told me, had been initiated by himself in 1954, when he was a 30-year-old lecturer (i.e., assistant professor) in paleontology at the University of Vienna specializing in the evolution of mammals. Thenius describes the motivation as follows:

Der Verlag war auf mich als damals jüngsten Dozenten für Paläontologie durch meine Rekonstruktionen vorzeitlicher Säugetiere, aufmerksam geworden. Damit erfüllte der längst nicht mehr existierende Verlag einen langjährigen Wunsch der Mittelschul- (= -AHS-) Lehrer nach einer lebensgeschichtlichen Schulwandtafelserie v.a. für den deutschsprachigen Raum. Prof. Zerritsch wurde mir als Künstler vom Verlag vertraglich "empfohlen". (2016, written commun.)

[The publication was for me, at that time a young Lecturer in Paleontology, a way to achieve recognition through my reconstructions of prehistoric mammals. In addition, it fulfilled the long-standing desire of teachers for a high-school-level, school-wall poster series illustrating the history of life, for German speakers. Professor Zerritsch was kindly "recommended" to me by the publisher to be the artist for this project.]

Zerritsch's pageant-of-life-through-time suite consists of ten paintings, each of which depicts the animals and plants that lived during a specific time period in Earth history (Fig. 3). Black-and-white versions of the Zerritsch paintings were included as plates at the back of Thenius's book, and the text of the book frequently refers the reader to specific plates. Each colored poster image is 94 cm wide and 52 cm tall and mounted on a cloth backing that measures 100 cm × 65 cm. The set of prints was marketed as visual aids to be hung on the walls of classrooms and lecture halls. Each of the prints is attached at the top and bottom to 2-cm-diameter wooden rollers that are each 109 cm long. The images thus can be rolled up for storage. A metal ring in the center of the upper roller facilitates hanging the panel on a wall. Each print has two cloth ribbons attached to the upper roller, permitting the rolled-up print to be tied up and secured.

In German-speaking countries, the Thenius book and the Zerritsch wall charts were presumably marketed together. The

Figure 1. Sketch by Robert Fuchs shows Fritz Zerritsch at age 49 (1937). Used with permission of ÖNB/Vienna B00502.

Figure 2. Photograph of Erich Thenius; courtesy of Erich Thenius and Department of Paleontology, University of Vienna. Photograph taken by Rudolf Gold in 2005.

Figure 3. The ten paintings by Fritz Zerritsch that comprise the Zerritsch/Thenius wall-chart suite are shown. Courtesy of University of Nevada Las Vegas and (J) Alexander Stewart, St. Lawrence University.

title page of the book advertises illustrations from a school wall chart series (*Schulwandbildserie*) by Professor Fritz Zerritsch. Beneath each colored image is a series of black-and-white sketches, one of which is a miniature of the painting with an identification number on each animal and plant featured in the painting. The other black-and-white sketches are shaded drawings of various numbered taxa that lived during the time interval depicted, whether or not they are illustrated in the painting. Surprisingly, only two of the ten scrolls—numbers 1 (Silurian) and ten (Pleistocene)—contain in the lower right corner a list of

G. Cretaceous Marine

H. Tertiary Brown Coal Forest

I. Late Tertiary Marine

J. Ice Age

Figure 3. *Continued.*

the numbered fossils and a label indicating the age of the scene being represented; the other eight have a blank spot where such information would go. The result is that when the scrolls are displayed—except for the Silurian and Pleistocene scenes—the viewer is not informed about the age of the scene or the identity of the organisms. I presume that this information was intended to be included on each panel; for some reason it was apparently left off of eight of them, at least in the case of the UNLV set. A label on each upper dowel identifies the time period depicted, but these labels are not conspicuous when the panels are on display. The black-and-white versions of Zerritsch's images in Thenius's book include numbers identifying the taxa as well as a label indicating the period of time being depicted, thereby providing the classroom teacher with the requisite information.

The Zerritsch pageant-of-life-through-time roll-ups were printed by Hofmanndruck Wien, a Viennese printing company that is no longer in business. Their name is visible on the bottom of some of the scrolls; on others it is presumably obscured by the lower dowel. No copyright holder is indicated. In the United States, the series was distributed by Denoyer-Geppert Co., an American company specializing in maps, charts, models, and globes. An adhesive label identifying Denoyer-Geppert as the distributor is attached to each of the UNLV roll-ups. Denoyer-Geppert is still in business, but the representative with whom I communicated was unable to find any record of this item in their archives. So, I have no information concerning the number of wall-chart sets sold in the United States or the cost. Nor do I know how one set came to adorn the walls of the UNLV Geology Lecture Hall.

Content and Style of the Zerritsch Paintings

Thenius decided which geological periods to illustrate and the design of each painting. Translated from the German, the titles of the ten roll-ups are: 1, *Early Paleozoic (Silurian Sea)*; 2, *Late Paleozoic I (Devonian)*; 3, *Late Paleozoic II (Pennsylvanian Coal Swamp)*; 4, *Triassic (Lower Triassic Landscape)*; 5, *Jurassic I (Lias Sea)*; 6, *Jurassic II (Upper Jurassic Landscape)*; 7, *Cretaceous (Cretaceous Sea)*; 8, *Tertiary I (Brown Coal Forest)*; 9, *Tertiary II (Upper Tertiary Sea)*; and 10, *Quaternary (Ice Age*

Landscape). Four of the ten (*Silurian*, *Jurassic I*, *Cretaceous*, and *Tertiary II*) depict underwater marine scenes, while the other six depict terrestrial scenes (Fig. 3).

Zerritsch was clearly a talented artist, but—having had no experience with paleoart—he and Thenius must have used the work of other paleoartists to help them decide how to depict a particular prehistoric ecosystem. In that vein, it is interesting to compare the style and content of Zerritsch's images with those of other twentieth-century paleoartists such as Rudolph Zallinger (1919–1995) and Charles R. Knight (1874–1953).

In terms of content, Zerritsch's six terrestrial scenes share some similarities with the work of Zallinger. Zallinger is best known for his large, Pulitzer Prize–winning fresco mural, *The Age of Reptiles*, in the Yale Peabody Museum (Fig. 4). Zallinger's mural depicts a succession of tetrapods (mostly dinosaurs) and associated plant communities ranging from Devonian to Cretaceous (Volpe, 2007). In the pageant-of-life-through-time genre, Zallinger's mural is unusual in that he presented his succession of scenes in one grand mural with different segments representing different periods of geologic time. From right to left, the segments of the mural portray terrestrial life from the Devonian to the Cretaceous. Zallinger used trees as boundaries to separate adjacent time slices.

Zallinger painted *The Age of Reptiles* mural between 1943 and 1947 (Davidson, 2008). In response to my query, Erich Thenius told me that he had been familiar with the Zallinger mural (E. Thenius, 2016, personal commun.), and I suggest that the composition of Zerritsch's Jurassic landscape (Fig. 3F) was influenced by Zallinger's work. Zallinger placed the following five animal taxa in this section of his mural (Fig. 4): (1) *Stegosaurus* (dinosaur with plates on its back); (2) *Apatosaurus* (long-necked sauropod dinosaur with fern in its mouth), and another in the distance; (3) *Allosaurus* (dinosaur eating flesh, and another one standing on two legs in background on right); (4) the iconic early bird *Archaeopteryx* (lower right corner, and another one flying over pond in center); and (5) the long-tailed pterosaur *Rhamphorhynchus* (upper left, above neck of *Apatosaurus*).

Zerritsch's Jurassic landscape (Fig. 3F) displays a similar structure and fauna. As in the Zallinger mural, *Stegosaurus* was placed in the center of the scene, oriented exactly as in the Zallinger mural. As in the Zallinger mural, Zerritsch counterbalanced *Stegosaurus* with a bipedal theropod dinosaur in the background, although the genera are different; Zerritsch and Thenius used *Ceratosaurus* where Zallinger had used *Allosaurus*. Both of them are North American genera. There is no long-necked sauropod in Zerritsch's painting, but he included the same two flying genera: *Archaeopteryx* (upper left corner) and the long-tailed pterosaur *Rhamphorhynchus* (upper right corner).

The flora depicted in the Zerritsch painting is also very similar to Zallinger's Jurassic flora. The tall trees in the distance on the right in the Zerritsch landscape are *Araucaria*, as are the trees in the right background of the Zallinger scene. Cycads are placed

Figure 4. Jurassic portion of Rudolph Zallinger's fresco mural *The Age of Reptiles* in the Yale Peabody Museum. Compare with Figure 3F. Reproduced with permission of Peabody Museum of Natural History, Yale University.

in the foregrounds of both tableaux, and tree ferns are also prominent in both. Zallinger's paleoecosystem is more mesic and lush than Zerritsch's, but the taxa depicted and their arrangement in the scene are strikingly similar.

In terms of the use of color and light, however, Zerritsch's art is very different than Zallinger's. Zerritsch's terrestrial Jurassic tableau (Fig. 3F) is brightly lit with a blue sky; moderately low-angle light comes from the right, as indicated by shadows beneath the dinosaurs. In contrast, Zallinger's palette included a wider range of colors and shades. His scene is lit by diffuse light coming from a cloudy sky (Fig. 4). Zallinger's mural is more vibrant than Zerritsch's painting, although the vibrance of the Zerritsch roll-ups may have suffered due to many years of exposure.

Another of Zerritsch's terrestrial scenes for which I suggest a likely influence in terms of composition is his Pleistocene scene (Fig. 3J). In this image, two woolly mammoths are walking single-file across a snowy, boulder-strewn landscape with a herd of caribou in the distance. The arrangement and anatomical details of the mammoths are very similar to those in an early 1930s mural of marching mammoths painted by Charles R. Knight for the Field Museum in Chicago (illustrated in Milner, 2012, p. 162–163) (Fig. 5). Furthermore, another Knight painting, this one painted in 1916 for the American Museum of Natural History (illustrated in Milner, 2012, p. 160–161), shows a herd of woolly mammoths in close association with a herd of caribou; this is quite similar to the Zerritsch/Thenius arrangement of mammoths and caribou (Fig. 3J). I suggest that Zerritsch and Thenius were influenced by these two images of Knight's when they composed their Pleistocene scene (Fig. 3J).

A conspicuous difference between the Zerritsch-Thenius marching mammoths (Fig. 3J) and those painted by Knight (Fig. 5) is the curvature of the tusks. The Zerritsch painting depicts the tusks flared outward relative to the plane of bilateral symmetry of the animal, while the Knight painting shows the tusks deflected slightly inward. All modern reconstructions agree with Knight, but in the early- and mid-nineteenth century, when Knight and Zerritsch, respectively, were creating these images, the orientation of mammoth tusks was less certain.

The Zerritsch/Thenius Devonian scene (Fig. 3B) shows a "freshwater landscape" in which the featured organism is a lobe-finned fish with its forelimbs on dry land and its hind limbs still in the water. This scene symbolically represents the evolution of terrestrial, air-breathing quadrupeds from lobe-finned fish, but it is surprising that Thenius chose this particular genus of lobe-finned fish, *Tristichopterus*, for Zerritsch to cast in this pivotal evolutionary role. In the early 1930s, more than two decades before Thenius's book was published and Zerritsch's scenes were painted, the genus *Ichthyostega* was discovered and described from the Devonian of Greenland (Clack, 2002). *Ichthyostega* has a dorsoventrally flattened skull, dorsally placed eyes, and forelimbs that were more adapted for pushing the animal's head upward than are the generic, pectoral fin forelimbs in the fish illustrated by Zerritsch. After *Ichthyostega* was described in 1932, it quickly became the "poster fish" for the evolutionary transition from fish toward amphibians (Clack, 2002), so it is surprising not to see it in Zerritsh's Devonian scene. Nor is it mentioned in Thenius's book. The lobe-finned fish in Zerritsch's Devonian poster (Fig. 3B), in contrast to *Ichthyostega*, appears to be anatomically unprepared to survive more than a few minutes out of the water.

Four of Zerrtisch's scenes depict submarine scenes (Figs. 3A, 3E, 3G, and 3I). Collectively, these scenes illustrate a broad range of invertebrate and vertebrate marine taxa, including

Figure 5. Portion of a mural of marching woolly mammoths in the Field Museum that was painted by Charles R. Knight in the early 1930s. Compare with Figure 3J. Reproduced with permission of Field Museum.

sponges, cnidarians, mollusks, echinoderms, arthropods, graptolites, fish, reptiles, and mammals. The marine faunas chosen for these four panels range in age from the early Paleozoic through the Mesozoic to the Cenozoic. Thenius's selection of a manatee as the focal point of Zerritsch's Tertiary marine scene (Fig. 3I) is a surprise, as manatees are less familiar to the general public than are most other groups of marine mammals. As a mammal specialist, Thenius presumably chose to feature the manatee to emphasize mammalian diversity.

Which Period Should Be Used to Lead the Parade of Life Through Time?

Thenius and Zerritsch used the Silurian Period as their opening scene, which raises the question of why a particular author chooses one period or another as the beginning of his or her excursion through the history of life. Discussion of this question is complicated by the fact that the geologic time scale itself was evolving during the nineteenth and twentieth centuries (Berry, 1987). Throughout most of the twentieth century, when illustrating the history of life with a succession of images, the convention was to begin with a Cambrian seafloor scene (e.g., Knight, 1942, 1946, 2001; Augusta and Burian, 1958). However, Zerritsch and Thenius, in their 1955 succession of illustrations, broke with this convention and began their succession with the Silurian (Fig. 3A); no Cambrian scene was included.

Why would Thenius choose to not include a Cambrian seafloor scene among the ten roll-up posters that Zerritsch painted? I suggest two reasons. First, prior to the detailed study and description of many Burgess Shale taxa (which are Cambrian) in the 1970s and 1980s, and Stephen Jay Gould's widely read book *Wonderful Life*, about the fossils of the Burgess Shale, the Cambrian Period was less famous and less charismatic than it is today (Gould, 1989). Second, and most significantly, below the phylum level the Cambrian is less taxonomically diverse than the Silurian with fewer well-known fossil groups. In response to my questions about choice of subjects, Thenius explained the dilemma he faced in choosing which intervals of time to include:

Das Problem für mich war, auf 10 Tafeln keine „Menagerie"-Bilder, sondern nach Möglichkeit "Lebensbilder" zu entwerfen, die auch in stammesgeschichtlicher Hinsicht interessant waren. (E. Thenius, 2016, personal commun.)

[The problem for me was to design 10 scenes—not "menagerie" scenes but realistic "life" scenes—which were also interesting from a phylogenetic perspective.]

In view of these constraints, the choice was clear: the Silurian seafloor provided the opportunity to display a more diverse fauna of familiar fossil-forming groups than did the Cambrian seafloor, so the Silurian was more interesting to Thenius from a phylogenetic perspective. Knight (1942) and Augusta and Burian (1958) were not limited to such a small number of scenes, so they could include multiple scenes dominated by invertebrates early in the Paleozoic Era.

None of the successions of scenes that I encountered while researching this topic include an image representing the Ordovician Period, which lies between the Cambrian and Silurian. Within this genre it is the most neglected interval of the Phanerozoic Eon, in spite of the fact that a major diversification of multicellular animals occurred during the Ordovician Period. The reason for this neglect is that the Ordovician was not proposed as an interval of the geologic time scale until 1879, several decades after most of the other periods had become widely used (Berry, 1987). And even then, it was slow to be widely adopted. On the European continent the Ordovician was not recognized as a distinct period until quite late. On the geologic time scale included within Thenius's 1955 book, *The History of Life on Earth,* Ordovician is defined as the lower part of the Silurian Period.

Artistic Conventions and Biases of the Genre

Several artistic conventions are commonly employed by paleoartists, including those working in the pageant-of-life-through-time genre (Gould, 1993). Most of these are completely necessary and unavoidable. With a limited number of scenes to tell their story, it is a standard convention for the artist to pack more animals and a higher diversity of species into each image than would normally be observed in nature. Zallinger, for example, in his *Age of Reptiles* mural, presented his viewers with a scene of extraordinary zoological density and diversity (Fig. 4). Most adults viewing Zallinger's masterpiece on a visit to the Yale Peabody Museum understand this purposeful exaggeration, but many children probably do not.

Similarly, paleoartists want to show animals engaged in interesting behavior. Carnivores spend more time sleeping than hunting and fighting, but hunting and fighting scenes are more exciting to the viewer as well as to the artist; such scenes are certainly over-represented in paleoart, in comparison with how animals were behaving during any random moment of geologic time, but few viewers would fault the artist for displaying such a behavioral bias.

A more subtle, but equally understandable, bias that is especially common in the pageant-of-life-through-time genre is the emphasis on vertebrates at the expense of invertebrates and plants. The convention is to show a wide variety of invertebrates in the Cambrian through Devonian, but once vertebrates—especially tetrapods—become diverse in the fossil record, they become the dominant subjects in subsequent scenes. Post-Devonian diversification of invertebrates is often ignored, or at least not emphasized. We are, after all, vertebrate animals, so it is not a surprise that most of us find the evolutionary history of our own phylum more engaging than that of other clades. But it is important to acknowledge that such a bias is present in the way the history of life is usually presented visually. Thenius and Zerritsch, in fact, largely avoided this bias. In their Cretaceous marine scene, invertebrates are the featured animals (Fig. 3G), and their Tertiary marine scene also includes many invertebrate taxa (Fig. 3I). Their Carboniferous forest scene also includes several invertebrates; huge dragonflies and other arthropods are prominently on display (Fig. 3C).

There is one additional common bias that, from the viewpoint of mainstream biology and paleontology, is perceived as much more problematic and insidious than those discussed above. This is the teleological bias: the subtle—and sometimes not so subtle—impression or interpretation that the pageant-of-life-through-time had a predetermined direction or goal—that goal being *Homo sapiens*. This teleological, progressivist perspective was expressed astonishingly overtly by Czech paleontologist Josef Augusta, a professor of paleontology at Charles University in Prague. In the introduction to his 1958 book *Prehistoric Animals* (beautifully illustrated by Czech artist Zdeněk Burian), Augusta wrote:

> From the very beginning of the history of life on Earth we see how life constantly develops and progresses, how it is constantly being enriched by new, ever higher and more complex forms, how even man, the culmination of all living things on Earth, is tied to it by his life.

Charles R. Knight, probably the best-known twentieth-century paleoartist, embraced a similarly progressivist outlook (Gould, 2001). The way this perspective was often expressed in the work of Augusta/Burian and Knight was by ending their sequence of prehistoric tableaux with one or more images of humans, usually males, in a hunting scene, symbolizing the triumph of *Homo sapiens* over other species. In his 1942 *National Geographic Magazine* article "Parade of Life Through the Ages," Knight ended the parade with an image of Bronze Age hunters preparing to dispatch a terrified, swimming, Irish elk (Fig. 6). And in his 1946 book *Life Through the Ages*, Knight's final scene shows Ice Age hunters fighting a cave bear. This triumphalist view that humans are the culmination of the pageant-of-life-through-time—the glorious climax of a long evolutionary symphony—is, of course, a religiously inspired concept that has no support among modern biologists and paleontologists. An unbiased reading of the fossil record reveals no such directionality in the history of life. Thenius and Zerritsch, in fact, neatly avoided this teleological bias by ending their series with mammoths and caribou (Fig. 3J). No humans are included in the colored image; however, Thenius and Zerritsch included a Neandertal skull in the black-and-white panel below the painting. In this subtle way, they appropriately indicated that *Homo* was an important member of the Pleistocene fauna without implying that our genus represents the triumphant culmination of hundreds of millions of years of evolution.

Figure 6. Culminating image in Charles R. Knight's 1942 *National Geographic Magazine* article "Parade of Life Through the Ages." Image credit: Charles R. Knight/National Geographic Creative. Reproduced with permission.

ACKNOWLEDGMENTS

This study was originally stimulated by a topical session titled "Great Images in the History of Geology" at the Geological Society of America Annual Meeting in 2015. That session was organized by Renee Clary, of Mississippi State University, one of the editors of this volume. Encouragement by Renee to contribute to that topical session prompted me to unroll my department's collection of the Zerritsch/Thenius roll-ups and—for the first time—look at them closely. I am grateful to Renee for stimulating me to launch this study and for the encouragement by all of the editors of this volume to write the chapter. In the early stages of this study, I discussed the Zerritsch images with my colleague Jane P. Davidson, an art historian at the University of Nevada Reno; Jane discovered—and alerted me to—the presence of the Thenius book, to which the set of Zerritsch paintings was a companion. The UNLV collection of roll-ups is inexplicably missing the tenth one—the Pleistocene scene. Professor Alexander Stewart of St. Lawrence University informed me that he had one of the Pleistocene-scene roll-ups hanging on his office wall, and he kindly sent me a photograph of it. Lastly, I am very grateful to Professor Erich Thenius for corresponding with me and answering my questions about his collaboration with Fritz Zerritsch.

REFERENCES CITED

Augusta, J., and Burian, Z., 1958, Prehistoric Animals: London, Paul Hamlyn, 47 p. + 60 plates.

Berry, W.B.N., 1987, Growth of a Prehistoric Time Scale (revised ed.): Palo Alto, California, Blackwell Scientific, 202 p.

Clack, J.A., 2002, Gaining Ground: The Origin and Evolution of Tetrapods: Bloomington, Indiana University Press, 369 p.

Davidson, J.P., 2008, A History of Paleontological Illustration: Bloomington, Indiana University Press, 217 p.

Gould, S.J., 1989, Wonderful Life: The Burgess Shale and the Nature of History: New York, Norton, 347 p.

Gould, S.J., 1993, Reconstructing (and deconstructing) the past, *in* Gould, S.J., ed., The Book of Life: New York, Norton, p. 6–21.

Gould, S.J., 2001, Foreword, *in* Knight, C.R., Life Through the Ages: Commemorative Edition: Bloomington, Indiana University Press, p. vii–x.

Knight, C.R., 1942, Parade of life through the ages: National Geographic, v. 81, no. 2, p. 141–184.

Knight, C.R., 1946, Life Through the Ages: Bloomington, Indiana University Press, 69 p.

Knight, C.R., 2001, Life Through the Ages: A Commemorative Edition (new foreword by S.J. Gould; introduction by P.J. Currie): Bloomington, Indiana University Press, 66 p.

Milner, R., 2012, Charles R. Knight: The Artist Who Saw Through Time: New York, Abrams, 180 p.

Thenius, E., 1955, Die Geschichte des Lebens auf der Erde (The History of Life on Earth): Vienna, St. Pölten, and Munich, Hippolyt-Verlag, 96 p.

Vollmer, H., 1961, Allgemeines Lexicon der Bildenden Künstler des XX Jahrhunderts, Volumen 5: Leipzig, E. A. Seemann Verlag.

Volpe, R., ed., 2007, The Age of Reptiles: The Art and Science of Rudolph Zallinger's Great Dinosaur Mural at Yale (2nd edition): New Haven, Connecticut, Peabody Museum of Natural History, 76 p. with color fold-out.

Manuscript Accepted by the Society 14 January 2021
Manuscript Published Online 5 November 2021

Printed in the USA

The Geological Society of America
Memoir 218

Illustrating the unknowable: Women paleoartists who drew ancient vertebrates

Susan Turner*
Queensland Museum, Geosciences, 122 Gerler Road, Hendra, Queensland 4011, Australia

Annalisa Berta
Department of Biology, San Diego State University, San Diego, California 92182-4614, USA

ABSTRACT

Women have contributed to "paleoart" working in collaboration with scientists, using vertebrate fossils to reconstruct vanished worlds, and directly shaping the way humans imagine the distant past. "Backboned" animals of former times have been portrayed singly or in groups and were often set in landscape scenes. Women paleoartists in America and Europe began working in the nineteenth century often through family association, such as pioneers Orra White Hitchcock, Graceanna Lewis, and Mary Morland Buckland. Mainly using traditional two-dimensional styles, they portrayed ancient vertebrate fossils in graphite and ink drawings. Paleoartist Alice Bolingbroke Woodward introduced vibrant pen and watercolor reconstructions. Although female paleoartists were initially largely unrecognized, in the twentieth century they gained notice by illustrating important books on prehistoric vertebrate life. Paid employment and college and university training increased by the late nineteenth to early twentieth centuries, with larger institutions providing stable jobs. The "Dinosaur Renaissance" of the late 1960s gave a boost to new paleo-artistry. Women paleoartists became more prominent in the later twentieth to twenty-first centuries with the development of new art techniques, computer-based art, and use of the internet. Increasingly, there is encouragement and support for women paleoartists through the Science, Technology, Engineering, the Arts, and Mathematics (STEAM) movement.

INTRODUCTION

Humans have tried to restore prehistoric animals for millennia. With more traditional art styles we see attempts as early as the Middle Ages (e.g., Rudwick, 1972; Boucher, 2011). Women were active in the early development of geology and paleontology, bringing to life newly collected specimens through illustration (Aldrich, 1982; Rudwick, 1992; Turner et al., 2010; Kölbl-Ebert, 1997; Berta and Turner, 2020).

"Paleoart" is broadly defined as scientific or naturalistic rendering of paleontological subjects. The various forms of visualized past life, communities, and ecologies have engaged people since the science of paleontology began (e.g., Elbein, 2017). Artists come to paleoart through many different routes: self-taught; taught by tutor; or trained in natural, medical, or scientific

*paleodeadfish@yahoo.com

Turner, S., and Berta, A., 2022, Illustrating the unknowable: Women paleoartists who drew ancient vertebrates, *in* Clary, R.M., Rosenberg, G.D., and Evans, D.C., eds., The Evolution of Paleontological Art: Geological Society of America Memoir 218, p. 191–199, https://doi.org/10.1130/2021.1218(21).

illustration. Works of paleoart represent a synergy of scientific and artistic cooperation, and through time many women artists (and scientists) have contributed to this endeavor. The role of women in unfolding the paleoartistic expression of vertebrate evolutionary history has changed through time. The traditions of scientific illustration with classic drawing in graphite or pen, which became the standard in paleontological description, are not our main subject; we consider, rather, the process and styles of portraying fossil vertebrates as real animals. At the end of the last century, paleoartists began to illustrate fossil vertebrates using computer graphics.

Our research on the history of women in vertebrate paleontology has unearthed many artists who have complemented the science (Berta and Turner, 2020; see Supplemental Tables S1 and S2[1]). Paleoartists assist scientists in bringing the bones to life by placing extinct animals in context with reference to modern environments. The significant work by women paleoartists considered here has allowed the basic data of vertebrate paleontology to be disseminated, which has enhanced the educational component of the science. After all, a picture is worth a thousand words.

The history of paleoart also documents the evolution of paleontological knowledge from the earliest realization of the meaning of fossils. Several key women have taken part (Tables S1 and S2). Rudwick (1976, 1992, 2005) and Kölbl-Ebert (2012) emphasized the importance of visual expression in geology and paleontology, and women, particularly in the late eighteenth to nineteenth centuries, were encouraged to gain skills in drawing that brought many into the science. Kölbl-Ebert (2002) and Trusler et al. (2010) highlighted the importance of the integration of science and art in paleoart and the role of women in this process. Taylor and Torrens (1995), for example, recognized that Mary Anning (1799–1847), the first significant woman fossil collector, mastered the skill of artistically restoring her fossils without any special training. It was her friend, geologist Henry Thomas De la Beche (1796–1855), however, who used Anning's knowledge to bring those fossils to life in the first paleoenvironmental scenes in his ca. 1830 watercolor *Duria antiquior* (e.g., McCartney, 1977; Clary, 2003; Sharpe and Clary, this volume).

Art historian Jane P. Davidson (2008) made the first detailed study of the history of paleontological illustration with "bones," including scales and teeth, prominent. Nevertheless, she mentioned only a few women. Recent books on dinosaur art (e.g., White, 2012, 2017) include only one woman, twenty-first-century paleoartist Emily Willoughby (see below). Lescaze (2017) and Witton (2018) have also reviewed the history and styles of paleoart, but again women are few and exclusively from the modern era: Willoughby, Raven Amos, and Rebecca Groom (see Table S2).

[1]Supplemental Material. Tables S1 and S2: Women paleoartists in the nineteenth century and through the twentieth to twenty-first centuries. Please visit https://doi.org/10.1130/MWR.S.15079002 to access the supplemental material and contact editing@geosociety.org with any questions.

FOUNDATIONS OF PALEOART

Early Nineteenth Century

Fossil vertebrate reconstructions began to be depicted in prehistoric habitats that helped the public to imagine ecosystems in ancient times. During the early nineteenth century, women illustrated mainly for their geologist/paleontologist husbands or other relations (Kölbl-Ebert, 1997; Berta and Turner 2020), drawing with traditional graphite or pen. A rare few, such as Anning and Buckland, were more independent. Scientific illustration evolved from graphite, pen, and watercolor with printmaking techniques such as woodcuts to new print processes that converted drawings and paintings using lithography or engraving (Davidson, 2008; Allingham, 2017). Georges Cuvier (1769–1832) made realistic portrayals of fossil animals, some of which were published, and the significance of following his principles of comparative anatomy influenced the growing presence of paleoart. He fostered women in the burgeoning science of paleontology (Turner et al., 2010), and one—Mary Morland Buckland (1797–1857)—became a pioneer scientific illustrator. She was exceptional in being the first independent female fossil vertebrate artist, although she was not a paleoartist as such. She worked for Cuvier (e.g., Cuvier, 1836, plates 47 and 52, fossil rhinoceros bones) and for William Buckland (1784–1856) before she married him. Mary went on to foster Buckland's prominent role as a geologist (Kölbl-Ebert, 1997; Berta and Turner, 2020). Among her published drawings are those of a cave hyena (Buckland, 1823) and the jaw of dinosaur *Megalosaurus* (Buckland, 1824; Howlett et al., 2017). Mary Buckland's illustrations, as well as Anning's discoveries, were used by Benjamin Waterhouse Hawkins (1807–1894) for the mid-century Crystal Palace Exhibition (e.g., McCarthey and Gilbert, 1994; Freeman, 2004). His paintings and massive sculptured reconstructions of prehistoric vertebrates thrilled the Victorians, and they continue to captivate visitors (see also Peck and Rowland, this volume; Fig. 1A).

Fossil discoveries were revealed using visual aids in lectures. The first American female fossil illustrator was probably Orra White Hitchcock (1796–1863). Early in the 1840s, she worked with her husband, pioneer geologist Edward Hitchcock (1793–1864), at Amherst College, Massachusetts. She created large-scale art on canvas for his teaching (e.g., Hitchcock and Palatino Press, 2014; Fig. 1B). Hitchcock created an early restoration of an American mastodon and some of the first drawings of dinosaur footprints and fossil fish (Aldrich, 1982; Turner et al., 2010; Berta and Turner, 2020).

Mid- to Late-Nineteenth-Century Paleoartists (1851–1899)

The belief in a biblical flood and that fossils were remains created by that event were disavowed further with Charles Darwin's *On the Origin of Species* in 1859. Recognition of the importance of evolutionary ideas resulted in depictions of fossil

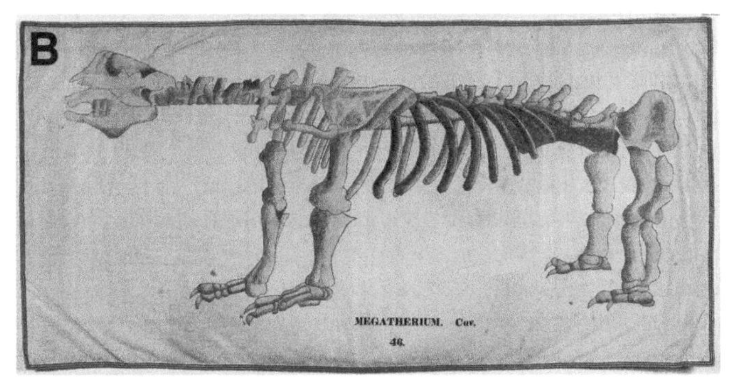

Figure 1. Nineteenth-century scientific illustration and early paleoart examples are shown. (A) Crystal Palace Exhibition three-dimensional models by Waterhouse Hawkins, based on Buckland and Anning examples; contemporary drawing by J.R. Hutchinson (relation/daughter? of H.N. Hutchinson) of Crystal Palace Sydenham (Public Commons). (B) "Pre-paleoart" example, *Megatherium* (59 cm × 121 cm), from Orra Hitchcock's visual charts at Amherst College, USA (courtesy of Amherst College Archives & Special Collections, Map Case 4, Drawer 13; view more charts at https://acdc.amherst.edu/view/asc:19891). (C) Alice B. Woodward's scene of South American giant ground sloth *Megatherium americanum* Cuvier, 1796, from a British Museum of Natural History postcard (courtesy of the Natural History Museum Archives).

animals showing changes through time, providing further evidence that fossils were once living organisms. The concept of evolution became an integral component of scientific illustration, with artwork reflecting Darwin's revolutionary theory (Rudwick, 1992). Both Ann Redfield (1800–1888) and Graceanna Lewis (1821–1912) developed ideas about the relationships of animal life. Redfield produced an 1857 wall chart titled a *General View of the Animal Kingdom* (Berta and Turner, 2020) and Lewis's sketch of a Permian reptile, *Dimetrodon*, which was displayed at the 1876 Centennial Exposition in Philadelphia (Post, 1976; Aldrich, 1982), was probably drawn when she trained at the Academy of Natural Sciences Philadelphia.

New books, especially for children, illustrating ancient life were appearing at this time. One important author was Arabella Buckley (1840–1929), who promoted Darwin's theory (Barber, 1980, p. 130–131). She employed artists to create paleoart for prehistoric animals. Buckley's (1882) *Winners in Life's Race* dealt with prehistoric fish to mammals with black-and-white representations in environmental scenes. Buckley employed one of Britain's earliest scientific artists, a "Miss Suft" (Buckley, 1882, p. vii; Turner et al., 2010), about whom we know little (Table S1).

INTO THE NEW ERA

The twentieth century saw a more mature "Paleoart Reformation" period (Debus and Debus, 2002). Britain and America were still the source of female paleoartists. In the late nineteenth century one of the young daughters of British Museum of Natural History (BMNH) Keeper of Geology Henry Woodward (1832–1921), Alice Bolingbroke Woodward (1862–1951), illustrated her father's lectures and his colleagues' papers (Turner et al., 2010). By the twentieth century, Alice became Britain's first female paleoartist and was well-known for her illustrations in books (Beare, 1999). Lescaze (2017) implied that she was inspired by the paleoart of Charles R. Knight (1874–1953). This seems unlikely both because she was already drawing fossils professionally in her teens and Alice and her siblings were probably brought up on contemporary British books such as Buckley's. Most likely her inspiration came from the Crystal Palace Exhibition (Fig. 1A) as well as visits to her father's place of work.

Alice Woodward's first restoration of dinosaur *Iguanodon* appeared in the *Illustrated London News* (*ILN*) in 1895 (Turner et al., 2010), a year before Knight's work for Osborne (Glut, 2001). Many of her artworks were used in or created for Henry

R. Knipe's *Nebula to Man* (Knipe, 1905) and *Evolution in the Past* (Knipe, 1912). Knipe (1854–1918) then shared them with the Reverend H.N. Hutchinson (1856–1927) for his 1910 edition of *Extinct Monsters and Creatures of Other Days*, which no doubt brought her additional acclaim. Further drawings (e.g., Hutchinson, 1910, fig. 105) were made based on her own admirable restorations. Woodward's reconstructions of Britain's earliest vertebrates, only then recently discovered and drawn for the first time for Hutchinson, are full of movement; this artwork inspired one of us (ST) to make her own thelodont restorations as a student. Alice worked for the weekly *ILN* for many decades until her death, often bringing the latest fossil "news" to the public, such as a restoration of *The Enormous Gigantosaurus* subtitled *As It Probably Appeared in Life* based on bones newly discovered at Tendaguru, Tanzania (Woodward, 1925; see Turner et al., 2010, fig. 9d). The BMNH turned her restorations of dinosaurs (see Turner et al., 2010) and mammals into collectible souvenir postcards (Fig. 1C), many of which are featured on the internet.

Alice Woodward's elder sisters Gertrude (1854–1939) and Ellen, "Nellie" (1860–1943), both became scientific illustrators employing traditional techniques for engravings. Gertrude became an excellent color wash illustrator and gained employment at the BMNH, working primarily with her father's successor, Arthur Smith Woodward (1864–1944). Her drawings and lithographs appear in journals such as her father's *Geological Magazine*. She worked alongside Arthur Smith Woodward making fish reconstructions as well as drawings of specimens for his classic four-volume (Woodward, 1889–1901) *Catalogue of Fossil Fishes* (Turner and Long, 2016). Ellen designed a delightful menu for the special knighthood dinner of Richard Owen (1804–1892; Rupke, 1994), with a range of life from invertebrate to human (Wellcome Library, 1884 lithograph no. 7553i; Wikimedia Commons V0004408.jpg; https://upload.wikimedia.org/wikipedia/commons/3/33/Sir_Richard_Owen._Lithograph_by_E._C._Woodward%2C_1884._Wellcome_V0004408.jpg).

The early twentieth century saw an increased fascination with the prehistoric, and fiction caught up with fact. Arthur Conan Doyle wrote *The Lost World* in 1912, and his 'beasts' captured the popular imagination and fostered a desire to know more about past worlds (e.g., Doyle, 1912; Batory and Sarjeant, 1989; Haste, 1993; Torrens, 1995). Interestingly, the 1977 Folio Society edition of that novel was illustrated by a woman: Elisabeth D. Trimby (Table S2). The real search for dinosaurs (especially) spread worldwide, and that spurred a new generation of expeditions, scientists, and the need for new artistic expression. During this time, government and philanthropic support for paleoart developed, and many women artists were employed in museums (e.g., BMNH, later Natural History Museum [NHM]; Yale Peabody Museum, New Haven, Connecticut; American Museum of Natural History, New York [AMNH]; U.S. National Museum of Natural History, Washington, D.C. [NMNH], as well as by state and national geological surveys. Women such as the Woodward sisters and others (see Table S2) benefitted by obtaining contract work and secure jobs.

Mass-Produced Paleoart (Post–World War II)

Soviet countries led the renewed search for prehistoric vertebrates with major Russian-Mongolian expeditions beginning in the 1940s. The Polish-Mongolian expeditions of the 1960s are considered to be some of the most important ventures ever undertaken. Copious new fossils were found, described, and illustrated (e.g., Berta and Turner, 2020). New museums and the first outdoor 'dinosaur parks' were created with life-sized, three-dimensional models (Lavas, 2016).

Growing Post–WWII Book Market

In the second half of the twentieth century, more women began to create books as well as illustrate those of others. English-born Helen Riviere Haywood (1908–1995) was a keen amateur naturalist and anthropologist. Her children's books on fossils were published from the 1950s to 1970s (e.g., Haywood, 1970). According to Connelly (2009), she conducted original comparative anatomical research into dinosaur skin colors for her illustrations. Haywood's works, as with Alice Woodward's paleoart, were based on contemporary ideas and, although scientific for their time, their dinosaurs especially were large and slow-moving in static poses in impressionistic landscapes, and these ideas were becoming scientifically out of date.

Interestingly, although mass-produced books on prehistoric life were available in the Soviet Union, we have found no prominent women paleoartists from that era. However, women scientists such as Elga Mark-Kurik (1928–2016) and Larissa Novitskaya later brought Paleozoic fish to life (e.g., Mark-Kurik, 1992; Novitskaya, 1971). Mark-Kurik's artistic flair is evident in her colorful reconstructions, models, and interpretations of fish behavior (Schultze et al., 2009).

Modern Paleoart (1970s–2000s)

Much of the fossil vertebrate paleoart of this era has been labeled "shrink wrap," where skin is tight against muscles—no flab, no hair, no feathers (Witton, 2018). New ideas appeared in the later twentieth century especially in dinosaur books. Many of these were produced by husband-and-wife teams: Colberts, Halsteads, Richs, and scientist–artist teams, e.g., Maisey–Rutzky, Trusler and Richs (e.g., Turner et al., 2010; Berta and Turner, 2020). Granddaughter of a paleontological dynasty, Margaret Matthew Colbert (1911–2007; Fig. 2A) had trained in the 1920s in art and sculpture at California College of Art, which gave her a great sense of three-dimensional style (e.g., Allmon, 2006). She began as an artist at the AMNH, where she drew fossil bones. She met her husband Edwin Colbert (1905–2001) there and produced paleo-artwork for his books (e.g., Colbert, 1983; Elliot, 2000; Berta and Turner, 2020). She was most productive artistically in retirement, producing sculptural models and museum murals (e.g., Elliot, 2000; Berta and Turner, 2020). Like other female artists, Colbert enjoyed bringing out the maternal side of vertebrates, and she illustrated a book on dinosaur babies (Elliot, 2000).

Figure 2. Twentieth-century women paleoartists: (A) Margaret Matthew Colbert when first at the American Museum of Natural History (photo courtesy of Matthew Colbert). (B) Jenny Halstead poster for the 150th anniversary of Richard Owen's 1841 coining of the word "dinosaur" (courtesy of Jenny Halstead). (C) Margaret Lambert's Quaternary ecological scene of Dart Bridge, Devon, representing the 100,000 k.y. Buckfastleigh Limestone Interglacial (modified from a 1960s Natural History Museum postcard; photo courtesy of S. Turner).

Jenny Middleton Halstead trained as a medical artist. She was working at the Royal Dental Hospital London when she joined forces with paleontologist L. Beverly Halstead (1933–1991) and illustrated his first book on fossil vertebrates (Halstead, 1968). After their marriage, they created many books together, mostly for children, which often featured a parental theme (e.g., Halstead and Lingham-Soliar, 1993; Berta and Turner, 2020; Fig. 2B). Haste (1993) claimed that the velociraptors of Michael Critchton's (1990) novel *Jurassic Park* were described just as Jenny Halstead had drawn them.

By the 1980s, book illustrators include Margaret "Maggie" Lambert, whose work was chosen by paleomammalogists Elaine Anderson (1936–2002; see Berta and Turner, 2020) and Bjorn Kúrten (1924–1988). Lambert executed numerous figures for their *Pleistocene Mammals of North America* (Kúrten and Anderson, 1980), which placed mammals within accurate landscapes. Some of her artwork was turned into NHM postcards (Fig. 2C).

The end of the twentieth century witnessed a major revolution in the Earth sciences with plate tectonics theory, a new paleobiological approach (see, e.g., Allmon, 2002), and a "Dinosaur Renaissance" influenced by new discoveries such as major dinosaur tracksites; nests with eggs, some of which had intact embryos; and evidence of parental behavior. Earlier ideas about dinosaur paleobiology were reignited (Desmond, 1975). Rather than depicting dinosaurs as sluggish, new interpretations strengthened the developing hypothesis of an evolutionary link between birds and dinosaurs and lent support to the portrayal of active and alert dinosaurs, which were postulated as warm-blooded and more similar to birds and mammals. Movies such as *Jurassic Park* (1993) and the British Broadcasting Company television series *Walking with Dinosaurs* (1999), which relied on computer-generated art, led to more dinosaur restorations with dynamic poses and colorful skin (e.g., Scotchmoor et al., 2003). New discoveries in the southern continents, such as Riversleigh in Australia (e.g., Quirk and Archer, 1983; Rich and Vickers-Rich, 2000), also led to a major rethinking of early fish to mammalian evolution, which again encouraged new paleoartists (Table S2).

One of the top paleoartists of this time, Eleanor "Ely" M. Kish (1924–2018), produced some of the new dynamic "look" for dinosaurs (Spears, 2014; Witton, 2018). She illustrated books with Canadian Dale Russell (1937–2019), such as *A Vanished World: The Dinosaurs of Western Canada* (Russell, 1977). One of her last paintings was a large mural that was formerly in the U.S. NMNH's "Life in the Ancient Seas" Hall (Berta and Turner, 2020). Another American, Sylvia Massey Czerkas, founded the Dinosaur Society and also served as illustrator, sculptor, editor, writer, and exhibition organizer (e.g., Glut, 2001). She is known for encouraging other women illustrators, including Colbert (Elliot, 2000). In 1982, Czerkas published *Dinosaurs, Mammoths and Cavemen* (Czerkas and Glut, 1982), which showcased Charles Knight's early paleoart. She has written about reconstruction and restoration (Czerkas, 1988; Currie and Padian, 1997). Working with her husband, Stephen, she has edited and illustrated more than 30 dinosaur books.

Mary Anning's bicentennial prompted a flourishing of new books and papers about her, many of which were for children (Berta and Turner, 2020, their table 2.2). Some are illustrated with impressions of Mary and also reconstructions of her finds. This spate of books for young readers, aimed at promoting enthusiasm for fossils and science (e.g., STEM-oriented *She Found Fossils* and *Daring to Dig*; see Berta and Turner, 2020) relied on the skills of several women paleoartists.

Twenty-First-Century Paleoart—Into the Cloud

Paleoart came of age with the use of computers and the prevailing influence of the internet (e.g., Broschinski and Kurth, 2000). However, it is still difficult to gauge the percentage of professional female versus male paleoartists. Although there is no professional society for paleoartists, the Wikipedia Paleoart website provides examples with ~14% being by women. Awards of recognition provide another source of data on recent women paleoartists. The Lanzendorf–National Geographic PaleoArt Prize, created by John J. Lanzendorf (1941–), was first awarded in 2000 at the annual meeting of the Society of Vertebrate Paleontology, which is the largest organization of vertebrate paleontologists. This prize recognizes outstanding achievement in paleontological two- and three-dimensional scientific illustration and naturalistic art. In the two decades since its inception, a small percentage (< 7%) of awards has gone to women (Berta and Turner, 2020).

In the twenty-first century, paleoartists made good use of new discoveries, e.g., by Jehol and Messel Lagerstätten, which have yielded evidence of feathered dinosaurs and furred mammals including some with color preserved (Ansón et al., 2016; Witton, 2018). Paleoartists showcase a greater range of form and behavior, which enhances habitat and community restoration. As examples, Danielle Dufault cooperates with scientists to make lively fish (e.g., Burrow and Rudkin, 2014; Fig. 3A). Illustrator Willoughby portrays dinosaurs and fossil birds using traditional and digital means inspired by her photography, which gives insight into color, behavior, and movement (White, 2017; Berta and Turner, 2020; Fig. 3B). Some, such as Willoughby, emphasize ultrarealism based on high-resolution photography and graphic detail (Fig. 3B). Using a stylus to draw and paint the images, they can replicate traditional oil paint and watercolor styles with software such as Painter 6 that mimics the canvases and media of traditional artists (e.g., Boucher, 2011). Digital painting gives the same freedom to layer and play with color without having to wait for paint to dry! These images can also be revised and modified and used to answer scientific queries, such as those involving postures, gaits, and locomotion. Nevertheless, as Antón and Sánchez (2004) reflected, innovative techniques such as computer modeling and animation of extinct vertebrates require as much research and knowledge of anatomy; the existence of adequate software does not always provide a shortcut to satisfactory results. They underscored the need for scientific accuracy, noting that a reconstruction is not a finished product—each has to be checked and revised to meet scientific understanding.

Figure 3. Twenty-first-century digital renditions are shown. (A) Dynamic reconstruction by Danielle Dufault of acanthodian *Nerepisacanthus denisoni* Burrow, 2011 in a lagoonal setting representing the Bertie Konservat-Lagerstätte (modified from Burrow and Rudkin, 2014). (B) Theropod *Serikornis* (adapted from Lefèvre et al., 2017) drawn in Photoshop CS4 (image by and courtesy of Emma Willoughby, https://emilywilloughby.com).

Sculptor Élisabeth Daynès has reinvigorated human evolution. Trained in the theatrical world, Daynès created masks and special effects in resins, silicone, and earthenware. Working with forensic anthropologist Jean-Noël Vignal in Paris, she perfected her knowledge of anatomy. She used computer modeling to estimate skull proportions and facial expressions that are largely artistically inspired to create a life-size reconstruction of a 17-member Neanderthal family. According to Daynès, her sculptures attempt to dispel stereotypes of violent, brutish, or "inhuman" early hominids (Daynès, 2020).

Prehistoric animals appear now in all shapes and sizes, and behind many is a woman paleoartist. Some employ their artistic skills to produce scientifically accurate merchandise such as games, jewelry, jigsaw puzzles, soft toys, stamps, and tee-shirts (Table S2).

CONCLUSION

Paleoart depends on an integration of both artistic and scientific training. Women have contributed to artistic representations of ancient vertebrates since their first scientific discoveries. They have become paleoartists through different routes. With few exceptions, the pioneers came into the genre in association with a paleontological family member, and this type of partnership continues to this day. Building upon recognized drawing and artistic skills, a few mid- to late-nineteenth-century women pursued a paleoart career, and the increase in formal art college and university education allowed more to do so in the twentieth century.

In the late twentieth to twenty-first centuries, paleoart has become more accessible and accurate. Paleoartists provide scientists with greater access to the public, thus supporting accountability for the basic research. Computers and the internet have had a fundamental effect in democratizing the genre, with digital art now predominating, which has allowed more women to embark on STEM careers via paleoart. Technical and theoretical information on anatomy and the behavior of fossil vertebrates is freely available so that anyone can contribute. The web, through social media image-hosting sites like "DeviantArt" (e.g., Elbein, 2017), serves the growing paleoart community by offering venues for the spread of data and merchandise. Researchers, professional artists, and amateurs can collaborate and critique across the world.

The future of paleoart will see breakthroughs in reconstructing fossil anatomies based on insight into areas such as soft tissue preservation, which will enable new predictions, for example, of color and behavior. As paleoartist Mark Witton (2018, p. 36) writes, "the days of paleoart being little more than fantastic interpretations of fossil specimens are long gone, and the future lies in an increasingly strong interplay between paleoartistry and scientific research."

ACKNOWLEDGMENTS

We thank many who helped us with information and illustrations, including Matt Colbert, Jenny Halstead, David Spalding, and Emily Willoughby. Comments from the editor and two reviewers helped to improve this chapter.

REFERENCES CITED

Aldrich, M.L., 1982, Women in paleontology in the United States 1840–1960: Earth Sciences History, v. 1, p. 14–22, https://doi.org/10.17704/eshi.1.1.18226u21t535x768.

Allingham, P., 2017, The technologies of nineteenth-century illustration: Woodblock engraving, steel engraving, and other processes: http://victorianweb.org/art/illustration/tech1.html (accessed April 2020).

Allmon, W.D., 2002, Stephen J. Gould (1941–2002): A personal reflection on his life and work: Journal of Paleontology, v. 76, p. 937–939, https://doi.org/10.1017/S0022336000057784.

Allmon, W.D., 2006, The pre-modern history of the post-modern dinosaur: Phases and causes in post-Darwinian dinosaur art: Earth Sciences History, v. 25, p. 5–35, https://doi.org/10.17704/eshi.25.1.g2687j050u3w1546.

Ansón, M., Pernas Hernández, M., Menéndez Muniz, R., and Saura Ramos, P.A., eds., 2016, Líneas Actuales de Investigación en Paleoarte: Madrid, Encuentro de Paleoarte, 146 p.

Antón, M., and Sánchez, I.M., 2004, Art and science: The methodology and relevance of the reconstruction of fossil vertebrates, *in* Baquedano Pérez, E., and Rubio Jara, S., eds., Miscelanea en homenaje a Emiliano Aguirre, Paleontología: Museo Arqueológico Regional, no. 2, Alcalá de Henares, Madrid, p. 3–22 and p. 74–94.

Barber, L., 1980, The Heyday of Natural History: London, Jonathan Cape, 320 p.

Batory, R.D., and Sarjeant, W.A.S., 1989, Sussex iguanodon footprints and the writing of *The Lost World*, *in* Gillette, D.D., and Lockley, M.G., eds., Dinosaur Tracks and Traces: Cambridge, UK, Cambridge University Press, p. 13–18.

Beare, G., 1999, The life and works of Alice Bolinbroke Woodward (1862–1951): The Imaginative Book Illustration Society Journal, v. 1, p. 70–144.

Berta, A., and Turner, S., 2020, Rebels, Scholars and Explorers: Women in Vertebrate Paleontology: Baltimore, Maryland, The Johns Hopkins University Press, 328 p.

Boucher, E.M., 2011, Digital paleoart: Reconstruction and restoration from laser-scanned fossils [M.Sc. thesis]: Philadelphia, Drexel University, x + 228 p.

Broschinski, A., and Kurth, O., 2000, Einführung der Computeranimation "Oberkreidezeitlicher Plesiosaurier" in einer geowissenschaftlichen Ausstellung [Hannover]: Der Präparator, v. 46, no. 2, p. 87–93.

Buckland, W., 1823, Reliquiae Diluvianae or, Observations on the Organic Remains Contained in the Caves, Fissures and Diluvial Gravel, and on Other Geological Phenomena, Attesting the Action of a Universal Deluge: London, John Murray, 303 p.

Buckland, W., 1824, Notice on the *Megalosaurus*, or great fossil lizard of Stonesfield: Transactions of the Geological Society of London, v. 2, p. 390–396, https://doi.org/10.1144/transgslb.1.2.390.

Buckley, A.B., 1882, Winners in Life's Race or the Great Backboned Family: London, Edward Stanford, 367 p.

Burrow, C.J., and Rudkin, D., 2014, Oldest near-complete acanthodian: The first vertebrate from the Silurian Bertie Formation Konservat-Lagerstätte, Ontario: PLoS One, v. 9, no. 8, e104171, https://doi.org/10.1371/journal.pone.0104171.

Clary, R.M., 2003, Uncovering strata: An investigation into the graphic innovations of geologist Henry T. De la Beche [Ph.D. thesis]: Baton Rouge, Louisiana State University, 467 p., https://pdfs.semanticscholar.org/a8ad/f4d7e9ccb30e520bf3ded7e6de9347a03ac7.pdf?_ga=2.31122495.1625837002.1577594072-1513208922.1561950708 (accessed October 2019).

Colbert, E.H., 1983, Dinosaurs: An Illustrated History: Maplewood, New Jersey, Hammond World Atlas Corporation, 224 p.

Connelly, W., 2009, The life and work of Helen Haywood (1907–1995), *in* Beard, G., ed., Diverse Talents: Imaginative Book Illustration Society Journal, v. 3, p. 98–143.

Critchton, M., 1990, Jurassic Park: New York, Alfred A. Knopf, 448 p.

Currie, P., and Padian, K., 1997, Encyclopedia of Dinosaurs: San Diego, California, Academic Press, 869 p.

Cuvier, G., 1836, Recherches sur les Ossemens Fossiles: Atlas I & II: Paris, D'Ocagne, 208 p.

Czerkas, S.M., 1988, Windows to the past: The combined views of art and science in images of Alberta dinosaurs: Alberta Studies in the Arts and Sciences, v. 1, p. 131–140.

Czerkas, S., and Glut, D., 1982, Dinosaurs, Mammoths and Cavemen: The Art of Charles R. Knight: New York, E.P. Dutton Inc., 119 p.

Davidson, J.P., 2008, A History of Paleontology Illustration: Bloomington and Indianapolis, Indiana University Press, 240 p.

Daynès, E., 2020, Biography: http://www.daynes.com/en/biography-elisabeth-daynes.html (accessed May 2019).

Debus, A.A., and Debus, D.E., 2002, Paleoimagery Evolution of Dinosaurs in Art: Boston, McFarland & Company, 293 p.

Desmond, A., 1975, The Hot-Blooded Dinosaurs: London, Blond & Briggs, 238 p.

Doyle, A.C., 1912, The Lost World: London, Hodder & Stoughton, 319 p.

Elbein, A., 2017 (28 Nov.), The surprising evolution of dinosaur drawings: The Atlantic, https://www.theatlantic.com/entertainment/archive/2017/11/paleoart-and-dinosaur-art-2/544505/ (accessed December 2019).

Elliot, A.B., 2000, Charming the Bones—A Portrait of Margaret Matthew Colbert: Kent, Ohio, Kent State University Press, 236 p.

Freeman, M., 2004 Victorians and the Prehistoric: Tracks to a Lost World: New Haven, Connecticut, and London, Yale University Press, 310 p.

Glut, D.F., 2001, Jurassic Classics: A Collection of Saurian Essays and Mesozoic Musings: London, McFarland Publishing, 282 p.

Halstead, J., and Lingham-Soliar, T., 1993, Art in science: Illustrating the world of Beverly Halstead [+ color plates II–VII.]: Modern Geology, v. 18, no. I, p. 141–155.

Halstead, L.B., 1968, The Pattern of Vertebrate Evolution: San Francisco, W.H. Freeman, xii + 209 p.

Haste, H., 1993, Dinosaurs as metaphor: Modern Geology, v. 18, no. III, p. 349–370.

Haywood, H., 1970, My Book of Prehistoric Creatures: London, Pied Piper Library, Purnell, unpaginated.

Hitchcock, O.W., and Palatino Press, 2014, The Classroom Drawings of Orra White Hitchcock: Scotts Valley, California, CreateSpace Independent Publishing Platform, 66 p.

Howlett, E.A., Kennedy, W.J., Powell, H.P., and Torrens, H.S., 2017, New light on the history of *Megalosaurus*, the great lizard of Stonesfield: Archives of Natural History, v. 44, p. 82–102, https://doi.org/10.3366/anh.2017.0416.

Hutchinson, H.N., 1910, Extinct Monsters and Creatures of Other Days: London, Chapman & Hall, 270 p.

Knipe, H.R., 1905, Nebula to Man: London, J.M. Dent, 251 p., https://doi.org/10.5962/bhl.title.150022.

Knipe, H.R., 1912, Evolution in the Past: London, Herbert and Daniel, 241 p.

Kölbl-Ebert, M., 1997, Mary Buckland (née Morland) 1797–1857: Earth Sciences History, v. 16, p. 33–38, https://doi.org/10.17704/eshi.16.1.yl20183310h53372.

Kölbl-Ebert, M., 2002, British geology in the early nineteenth century: A conglomerate with a female matrix: Earth Sciences History, v. 21, p. 3–25, https://doi.org/10.17704/eshi.21.1.b612040xg7316614.

Kölbl-Ebert, M., 2012, Sketching rocks and landscape: Drawing as a female accomplishment in the service of geology: Earth Sciences History, v. 31, p. 270–286, https://doi.org/10.17704/eshi.31.2.n436w6mx3g846803.

Kurtén, B., and Anderson, E., 1980, Pleistocene Mammals of North America: New York, Columbia University Press, 442 p.

Lavas, J.R., 2016, Zofia Kielan-Jaworowska and the Gobi palaeontological expeditions: Palaeontologica Polonica, v. 67, p. 13–24.

Lefèvre, U., Cau, A., Cincotta, A., Hu, D., Chinsamy, A., Escuillié, F., and Godefroit, P., 2017, A new Jurassic theropod from China documents a transitional step in the macrostructure of feathers: The Science of Nature, v. 104, p. 74, https://doi.org/10.1007/s00114-017-1496-y.

Lescaze, Z., 2017, Paleoart: Visions of the Prehistoric Past: Cologne, Germany, Taschen, 292 p.

Mark-Kurik, E., ed., 1992, Fossil Fishes as Living Animals: Academia, no. 1, Tallinn, 299 p.

McCarthey, S., and Gilbert, M., 1994, The Crystal Palace Dinosaurs. The Story of the World's First Prehistoric Sculptures: Croydon, UK, The Crystal Palace Foundation, 99 p.

McCartney, P.J., 1977, Henry de la Beche: Observations on an Observer: Cardiff, Friends of National Museum of Wales, xiii + 77 p.

Novitskaya, L., 1971, Les Amphiaspides (heterostraci) du dévonien de la Sibérie: Paris, Cahiers de Paléontologie, C.N.R.S. édition, 130 p.

Peck, R.M., and Rowland, S.M., 2022, this volume, Benjamin Waterhouse Hawkins and the early history of three-dimensional paleontological art, *in* Clary, R.M., Rosenberg, G.D., and Evans, D.C., eds., The Evolution of Paleontological Art: Geological Society of America Memoir 218, Chapter 17, https://doi.org/10.1130/2021.1218(17).

Post, R., 1976, 1876: A Centennial Exhibition: Washington, D.C., Smithsonian Institution, 223 p.

Quirk, S., and Archer, M., 1983, Prehistoric Animals of Australia: Sydney, Australian Museum, 80 p.

Rich, T.H., and Vickers-Rich, P., 2000, Dinosaurs of Darkness. Life of the Past: Bloomington, Indiana, Indiana University Press, 222 p.

Rudwick, M.J.S., 1972, The Meaning of Fossils. Episodes in the History of Palaeontology: New York, Neale Watson History of Science Library, 287 p.

Rudwick, M.J.S., 1976, The emergence of a visual language for geological science 1760–1840: History of Science, v. XIV, p. 149–195, https://doi.org/10.1177/007327537601400301.

Rudwick, M.J.S., 1992, Scenes from Deep Time: Early Pictorial Representations of the Prehistoric World: Chicago & London, University of Chicago Press, 280 p., https://doi.org/10.7208/chicago/9780226149035.001.0001.

Rudwick, M.J.S., 2005, Bursting the Limits of Time: The Reconstruction of Geohistory in the Age of Revolution: Chicago, University of Chicago Press, 708 p., https://doi.org/10.7208/chicago/9780226731148.001.0001.

Rupke, N., 1994, Richard Owen: Victorian Naturalist: New Haven, Connecticut, Yale University Press, 462 p.
Russell, D., 1977, A Vanished World: The Dinosaurs of Western Canada: Edmonton, Canada, National Museum of Natural Sciences, 142 p.
Schultze, H.-P., Turner, S., and Grigelis, A., 2009, Great northern researchers: Discoverers of the earliest Palaeozoic vertebrates: Acta Zoologica, v. 90, suppl. 1, p. 22–37.
Scotchmoor, J.G., Springer, D.A., Breithaupt, B.H., and Fiorillo, A.R., eds., 2003, Dinosaurs: The Science Behind the Stories: Alexandria, Virginia, American Geological Institute, 186 p.
Sharpe, T., and Clary, R.M., 2022, this volume, Henry De la Beche's pioneering paleoecological illustration, *Duria antiquior*, *in* Clary, R.M., Rosenberg, G.D., and Evans, D.C., eds., The Evolution of Paleontological Art: Geological Society of America Memoir 218, Chapter 6, https://doi.org/10.1130/2021.1218(06).
Spears, T., 2014, Ely Kish: Artist of the ancient Earth (1924–2014), Ottawa citizen: http://ottawacitizen.com/life/life-story/ely-kish-artist-of-the-ancient-earth-1924-2014 (accessed October 2017).
Taylor, M.A., and Torrens, H.S., 1995, Fossils by the sea: Natural History, v. 104, no. 10, p. 66–71.
Torrens, H., 1995, The dinosaurs and "Dinomania" over 150 years, *in* Sarjeant, W.A.S., ed., Vertebrate Fossils and the Evolution of Scientific Concepts. Writings in Tribute to Beverly Halstead, by Some of His Friends: Amsterdam, Gordon & Breach/OPA, p. 255–284.
Trusler, P., Vickers-Rich, P., and Rich, T.H., 2010, The Artist. The Scientist. Bringing Prehistory to Life: Cambridge, UK, Cambridge University Press, 308 p.
Turner, S., and Long, J.A., 2016, The Woodward Factor: Arthur Smith Woodward's legacy to geology in Australia and Antarctica, *in* Johansson, Z., Barrett, P.M., Richter, M., and Smith, M., eds., Arthur Smith Woodward: His Life and Influence on Modern Vertebrate Palaeontology: Geological Society, London, Special Publication 430, p. 261–288, https://doi.org/10.1144/SP430.15.
Turner, S., Burek, C.V., and Moody, R.T.J., 2010, Forgotten women in an extinct saurian (man's) world, *in* Moody, R.T.J., Buffetaut, E., Naish, D., and Martill, D.M., eds., Dinosaurs and Other Extinct Saurians: A Historical Perspective: Geological Society, London, Special Publication 343, p. 111–153.
White, S., ed., 2012, Dinosaur Art: The World's Greatest Paleoart: London, Titan Books, 188 p.
White, S., ed., 2017, Dinosaur Art II: The Cutting Edge of Paleoart: London, Titan Books, 188 p.
Witton, M.P., 2018, The Paleoartist's Handbook: Wiltshire, UK, Crowood Press, 224 p.
Woodward, A.B., 1925 (17 Jan.), "Larger than any known land animal": A fossil-hunter's vision: Illustrated London News, p. 21, 98–99.
Woodward, A.S., 1889–1901, Catalogue of Fossil Fishes in the British Museum (Natural History) Cromwell Road, S.W.: London, Trustees of the British Museum of Natural History, Parts I–IV.

Manuscript Accepted by the Society 15 January 2021
Manuscript Published Online 22 September 2021

The Geological Society of America
Memoir 218

Foraminiferal art through the ages

Jere H. Lipps
Museum of Paleontology and Department of Integrative Biology, University of California, Berkeley, California 94720-4780, USA

ABSTRACT

Foraminifera are single-celled organisms with and without shells (tests). They have an abundant fossil record over the past 545 million years and presence in modern oceans. The art of forams is dominated by hand-drawn scientific illustrations to scanning electron microscopic images done over the past 455 years, providing vital knowledge about shelled forams. From 1665 to 1835, forams were assigned to micro-invertebrates rather than single-celled forms. With more than 75,000 publications and nearly 50,000 described species of forams, illustrations must number more than 200,000. The illustrations include a range from simple line drawings through shaded ink and pencil renderings, sometimes even colored, to photographs and scanning electron micrographs. Forams also appear in other art forms: The Pyramids at Giza in Egypt, hand-sized models, jewelry, flooring, stamps, coins, sculptures, and a Chinese Foraminiferal Sculpture Park. Foraminiferal art, although very abundant in many forms, has not caught the attention of many people outside of foraminiferology.

INTRODUCTION

Foraminifera, or forams, are single-celled protists with an abundant fossil record that spans 545 million years ago to recent times (Lipps and Rozanov, 1996). Most are microscopic and characterized by shells known as tests, and they have been the subjects of scientific illustration ever since 1665. This chapter provides a brief historical summary of the development of foram art with examples of illustrations and other artistic renditions of forams. Names of species are omitted because the images reproduced herein are for art appreciation rather than scientific purposes.

Forams have a type of pseudopodia with granules that extend from the cell in an anastomosing and reticulating pattern; these are granuloreticulopodia (Fig. 1). No other organisms have granuloreticulopodia (Loeblich and Tappan, 1964; Lee, 1990; Sen Gupta, 1999; Richardson and Lipps, 2020). In addition to forams with tests (testate), many modern species have no tests (non-testate). For 455 years, forams were defined as having a test, but both testate and non-testate types share gene sequences, thus establishing their close, intertwined relationships (Pawlowski et al., 2013).

Foram tests have a wide variety of shapes ranging from simple spheres or tubes to trochospirals and the complex tests of larger forams. Tests are made of $CaCO_3$ in one of several morphologic and crystallographic arrangements or of particles picked from the environment and assembled by the organism (Loeblich and Tappan, 1964; Lipps, 1973). Most forams are a millimeter or smaller in diameter or length, but some, known as "larger foraminifera," can be up to 10 cm long and are easily observed without magnification.

Testate forms radiated in the Ordovician and became abundant and diverse in marine environments of all ages. Non-testate forams may have originated 800 million years ago and would have occurred in those same ancient marine environments but also live in freshwater and mosses (Siemensma et al., 2017); they are not preserved in the fossil record. Forams are among the most

Lipps, J.H., 2022, Foraminiferal art through the ages, *in* Clary, R.M., Rosenberg, G.D., and Evans, D.C., eds., The Evolution of Paleontological Art: Geological Society of America Memoir 218, p. 201–212, https://doi.org/10.1130/2021.1218(22).

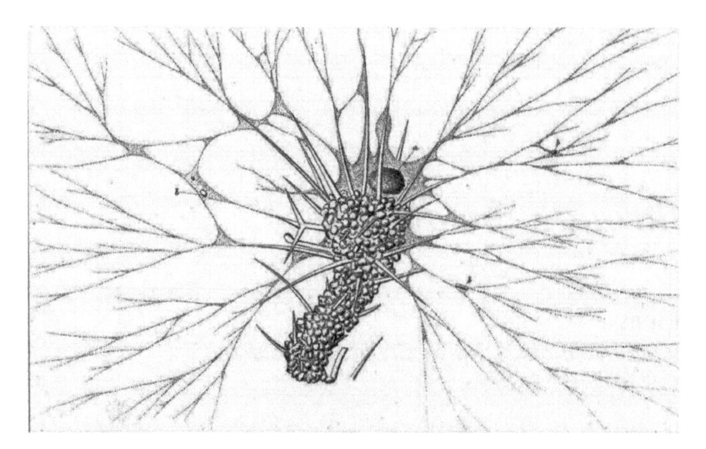

Figure 1. Line drawing of a living attached foram showing the agglutinated, single chambered test and granuloreticulopodia extending from the test to catch particulate food. From Kent (1878).

abundant eukaryotic organisms on Earth today and have likely been so since the early Paleozoic. Nearly 50,000 species, both fossil and living, have been validly described with illustrations (Hayward et al., 2020) based on test characteristics (Loeblich and Tappan, 1964, 1987; Culver, 1992). Over 75,000 geoscience publications since 1839 have mentioned forams (GeoRef, 2020/10). Many illustrations were of previously described forams as newer work documented their occurrences in studies other than those describing new species. Published foram illustrations now likely number in the 200,000–300,000 range due to the huge number of taxa identified in those publications.

Most forams are too small to be seen easily, and even when seen, they look unfamiliar to non-specialists. Many are strikingly beautiful in their living colors, forms, and symmetries. To show all aspects of forams, illustrations in scientific publications usually include three, four, or even more different views of a species. They have been hand drawn for over 350 years, but few people besides scientists were enamored with the illustrations; hence, foram illustrations have not become popular art objects. Foram art has an audience that is mostly limited to scientists, although they spectacularly appeared in Haeckel's (1904) *Art Forms in Nature*, which delighted readers with beautiful images of all sorts of organisms in both black and white and color (Fig. 2).

The need for accurate descriptions and recognition of species that range globally over a half a billion years resulted in remarkable and numerous illustrations of forams. From 1665 to ca. 1900, forams were described and illustrated to document their diversity, distribution, and stratigraphic occurrence as modern and fossil organisms. In the early 1900s, forams and their illustrations became critically important in the search for, and recovery of, petroleum throughout the world (Rauser-Chernousova and Fursenko, 1937; Finger, 2013; Bowden et al., 2013). Forams were used extensively in petroleum exploration because they provided stratigraphic control, age dating, and paleoenvironmental inferences, all of which are critically important in the search for oil. They could be retrieved in abundance from oil well cuttings and cores and examined microscopically in field and company laboratories for quick and accurate interpretations. As a result, foram illustrations expanded as foram scientists in the oil industry numbered in the thousands and academia provided specialized courses on forams. The number of oil company workers has declined as the industry developed other geophysical techniques, but the number of foram workers increased in biology, genetics, environmental analysis, paleoclimate, and paleoceanography.

Microscopy was required to illustrate the tiny forams; hence, they were drawn by observers using light microscopes beginning in 1665 and since the mid–twentieth century using electron microscopes. These technical drawings include several common illustration techniques: ink; stippled; shaded pencil; shaded drawings on textured paper; watercolors; charcoal; and pastels. A camera lucida was sometimes used, starting in the early 1800s, to make drawing proportions more precise. Photography through microscopes was done in the late nineteenth through the twenty-first centuries, but it could not easily provide adequate resolution of the small forams, so drawing continued to be a principal means of illustration. The advent of the scanning light microscope in 2003 resulted in clear photographs; a plane of light was scanned down a test with the exposure open, thus alleviating the problem of depth of focus (Javaux and Scott, 2003). Larger forams, such as the Paleozoic fusulinids, are studied and easily photographed in thin sections or by high-resolution X-ray computed tomography (CT) technique (Görög, et al., 2012; Shi et al., 2019). Electron microscopes with adequate resolving power using electron beams led to scanning electron microscopes (SEMs) that image a specimen's surface in detail (Hay and Sandberg, 1967).

FORAMINIFERAL ART

Foraminiferal art has been essential to basic and applied scientific work on forams over centuries. A few miscellaneous foram artistic applications have appeared, most of which developed recently. The history of discovery, description, and illustration is straightforward.

Foraminifera: Early Illustrations of Tiny Invertebrates

Forams were recognized as independent objects 2500 years ago by ancient Greeks and Romans at the Pyramids at Giza in Egypt: "One extraordinary thing which I saw at the pyramids must not be omitted. Heaps of stones from the quarries lie in front of the pyramids. Among these are found pieces which in shape and size resemble lentils. Some contain substances like grains half peeled. These, it is said, are the remnants of the workmen's food converted into stone; which is not improbable" (Strabo, 2020). These "pieces" were not recognized as fossils until Agricola (1558) showed they were once living organisms. In the Eocene, these forams grew in prolific numbers on the bottom of a shallow sea that later produced limestone that was quarried by the ancient Egyptians. The pyramids are thus the first use of forams in art, although they are not recognized as important in this regard.

Figure 2. Ernst Haeckel (1904, plate 2) illustrated forams on two of the 100 plates in his *Art Forms in Nature*, which demonstrates the art of organisms and evolution. Forams, drawn with ink and shading, were arranged symmetrically around a central spiney planktonic foram for artistic purposes.

In the sixteenth century, Agricola, Gesner, and Aldrovandi published simple descriptions and woodcut images of fossils, some of which could be forams, but these were vague, crude works that frustrate attempts to conclusively identify any of them. The first image of a foram was published in 1665 by Robert Hooke (Fig. 3), who called it a "pretty shell." Later, it was identified as a foram, "apparently of *Rotalia*" (Williamson, 1858, p. v), but that was never confirmed. Hooke did not understand how the shell got in the sand of an English beach, and because he had only one, he ranked it as "very rare" and speculated that it might be petrified. Antony Van Leeuwenhoek also illustrated a "snail-shell" from the gut of a shrimp in 1700 (Hoole, 1807; Dobell, 1932), but it too is a foram (Fig. 3).

Throughout the following century and more, forams from modern sediments and ancient rocks were illustrated but not as unique organisms (Carpenter et al., 1862). They were first classified by Beccari (1731; Vaiani et al., 2019) as invertebrates and included with snails, cephalopods, corals, or "worms." Other authors did likewise (Brünnich, 1772; Förskal, 1775; Soldani, 1789, 1798; Bosc, 1802; Lamarck, 1806; de Blainville, 1827). Their illustrations are generally well done and can be recognized today as particular foram species. Indeed, Linnaeus (1758), who set the rules for giving organisms binomial names, assigned, to cephalopods, worms, and a gastropod, 12 previously described taxa that are now recognized as forams (Hayward et al., 2020).

Perhaps the most influential foram worker of the nineteenth century was Alcide d'Orbigny (Carpenter et al., 1862; Heron-Allen, 1917; Le Calvez, 1974; Lipps, 2002; Vénec-Peyré, 2002, 2004, 2005). Born in Couëron, France, in 1802, he, at age 11 and with his father, studied, drew, and described forams from

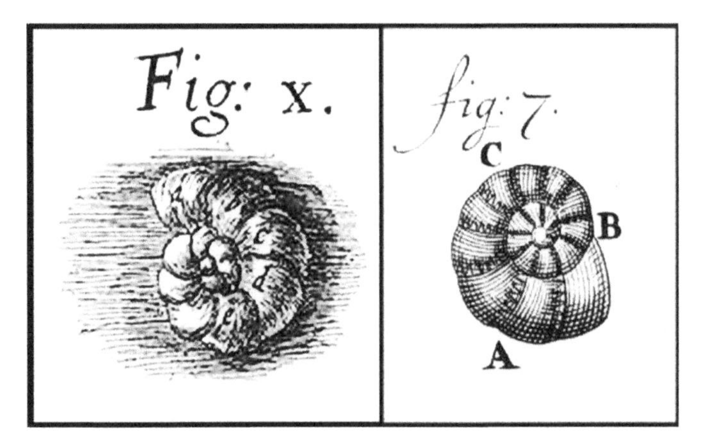

Figure 3. (Left) Hooke's (1665) foram, which was printed by woodcut. From *Micrographia* 1665 (scheme V, fig. X, p. 80). (Right) Leeuwenhoek's 1700 snail shell, which is obviously a foram but not shown in sufficient detail to assign a current name. Printed by woodcut. From Hoole (1807).

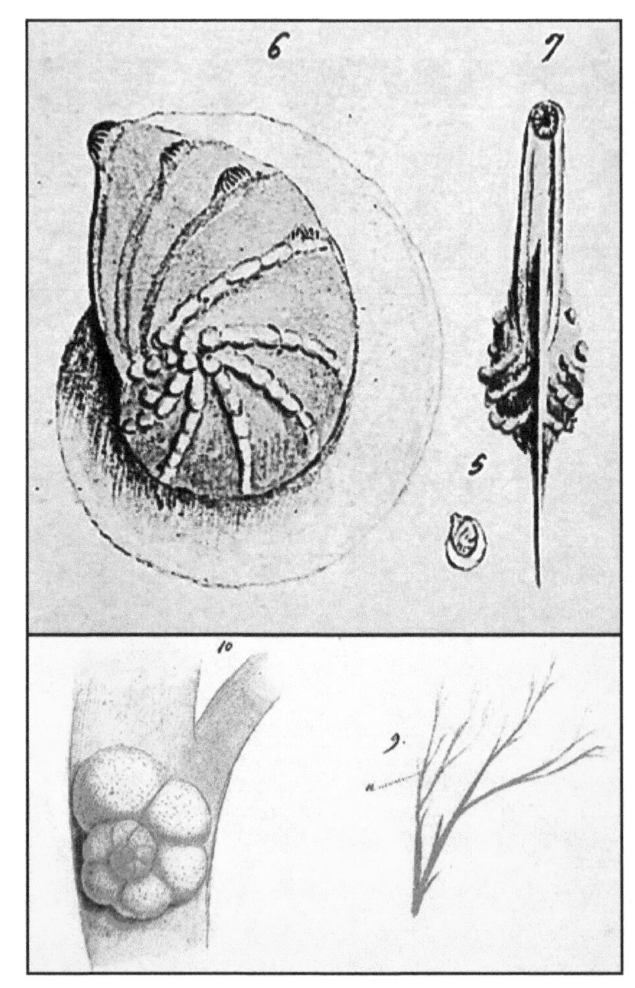

Figure 4. (Top) Unpublished drawings of d'Orbigny shaded with pencil and using color (Vénec-Peyré, 2005, p. 212–213, plate 34, figs. 5–7). Figure 5 in the original shows the specimen at natural size. ©Publications Scientifiques du Muséum national d'Histoire naturelle, Paris. Used with permission. (Bottom) D'Orbigny in the original drew and colored illustrations of an attached *Rosalina* and its granuloreticulopodia (Vénec-Peyré, 2005, p. 164–165, plate 20, figs. 9–10), which he thought were tentacles of the tiny cephalopods he believed these were. ©Publications Scientifiques du Muséum national d'Histoire naturelle, Paris. Used with permission of M.-T. Vénec-Peyré.

local sites and samples given to them and even made models of forams (d'Orbigny, 1843). After 13 years, he published *Tableau méthodique de la classe des Céphalopodes* (1826). In it, he named the Order Foraminifères and placed it in the Cephalopoda, thinking the foramina between their chambers were similar to the siphons in cephalopod shells. He listed 544 species of forams, illustrating only 31, and referred to his models to enhance their study (Vénec-Peyré, 2005). D'Orbigny prepared more illustrations, arranged on 73 plates, for later publication (Fig. 4). However, just after publication of the *Tableau*, he was appointed as naturalist on an expedition to South America (1826–1834) for the Muséum d'histoire naturelle, Paris; thus, those illustrations were never published by him. Many years later they were elegantly published by the Muséum d'histoire naturelle, Paris, along with historical and systematic discussions by Dr. Marie-Thérèse Vénec-Peyré (2005). D'Orbigny drew his own illustrations in pencil and wash, and they were sometimes lightly colored or in ink (Vénec-Peyré, 2005, p. 15, 33). After he returned from South America in 1834, he studied fossil collections including forams (d'Orbigny, 1839, 1846, 1849–1852), but he never finished his 1826 illustrations. He is now considered the "Father of Micropaleontology" (Galloway, 1933) for his careful descriptions and illustrations of forams.

Foraminifera: Single-Celled Organisms (1835–1900)

No one in the early 1800s knew what forams really were. D'Orbigny (1826) arranged them in groups within the Foraminifères, describing heads and tentacles on live forams. Dujardin (1835), however, determined that forams were not tiny cephalopods but rather single-celled protozoans whose pseudo-podia were mistaken as organs of cephalopods, a conclusion that d'Orbigny accepted when he returned from South America. Foram studies were important in Europe, but uncertainty about their relationships to other organisms remained until the 1850s (Murray, 2012). For example, in France, d'Orbigny (1839, 1846, 1849–1852) and D'Archiac and Haime (1853–1854) studied forams from fossil outcrops; in Great Britain, Carpenter (1850), Carpenter et al. (1862), Williamson (1858), and Parker et al. (1871) were influential in foram work (Fig. 5); in Germany, Ehrenberg's (1854) *Mikrogeologie* illustrated forams alone or with other microfossils or inorganic objects. Micropaleontologists in other countries also contributed illustrated papers on forams. The magnificent "Report on the Foraminifera dredged by *H.M.S. Challenger*" (Brady, 1884), with 115 plates of illustrations, is a classic in micropaleontology (Fig. 6). Brady created an organized classification that was used by others including J.A. Cushman in the United States 1900s.

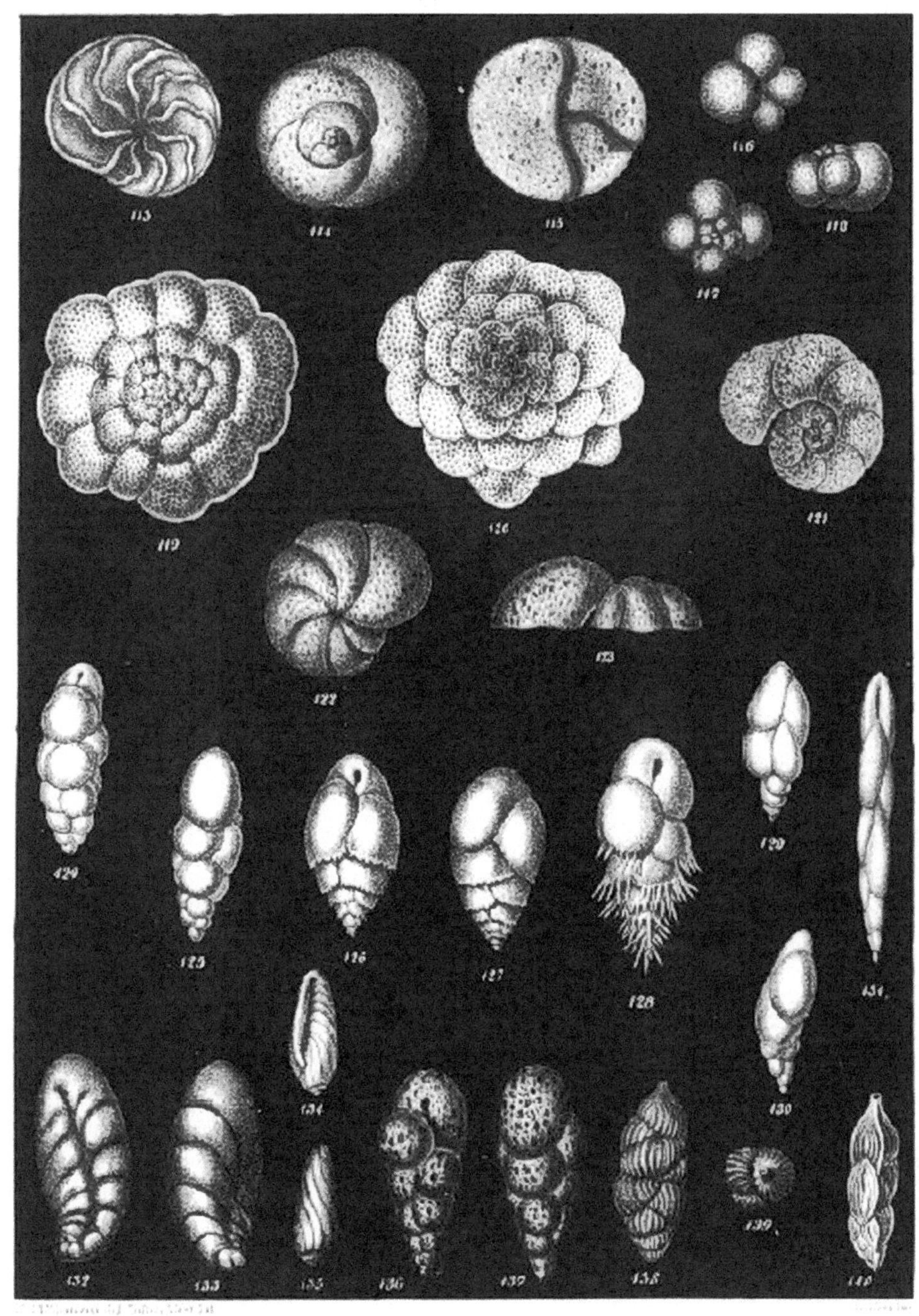

Figure 5. W.C. Williamson, a prominent British foram worker, published from 1847 to 1876. His greatest contribution was *On the Recent Foraminifera of Great Britain*, in which he illustrated forams using ink, pencil shading, and stipples (1858, plate 2, 27 figs.).

Foraminifera: Applications in Industry and Science (1900–2020)

Starting in 1910, the increasing utility of forams in oil exploration compelled work on the stratigraphic occurrence of species. Joseph A. Cushman led in the publication of foram descriptions, all of which were illustrated with hand drawings using shaded pencil, ink, or stipples. Cushman published works on forams starting in 1910, and in 1922 he took a position as a micropaleontologist with an oil company in Mexico. That work gave him the finances to establish his own laboratory and to publish his own journal; he thus became the dominant foraminiferalogist until his death in 1949, publishing over 700 papers and four textbook editions (Cushman, 1948) with more illustrations of forams than anyone else had produced (Figs. 7–8).

Many other micropaleontologists also contributed to the illustrations of forams during this time. J.J. Galloway, for one, published many papers and a textbook on forams (Galloway,

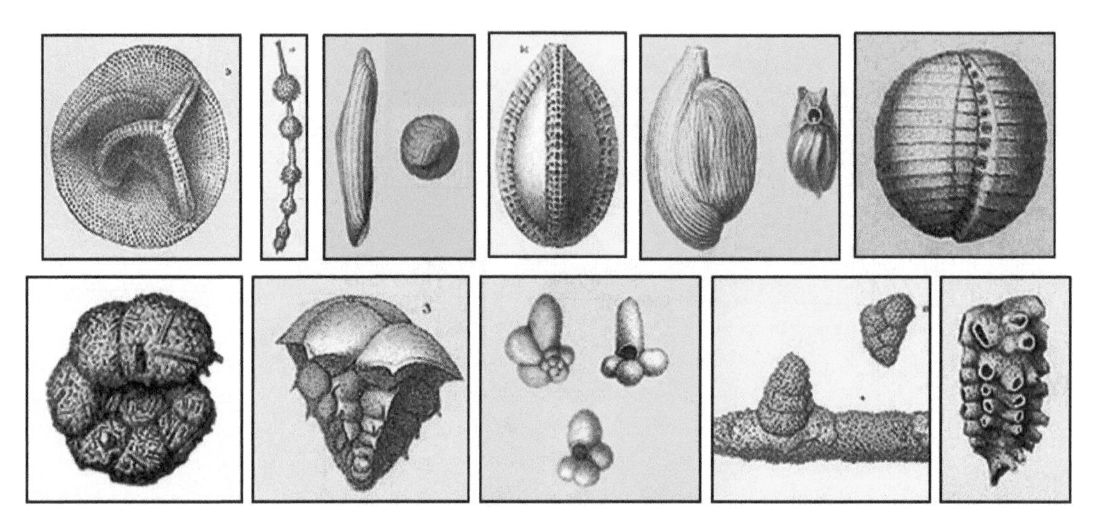

Figure 6. Eleven individual foram illustrations are shown selected from the 115 plates in "Report on the Foraminifera dredged by *H.M.S. Challenger*" (Brady, 1884).

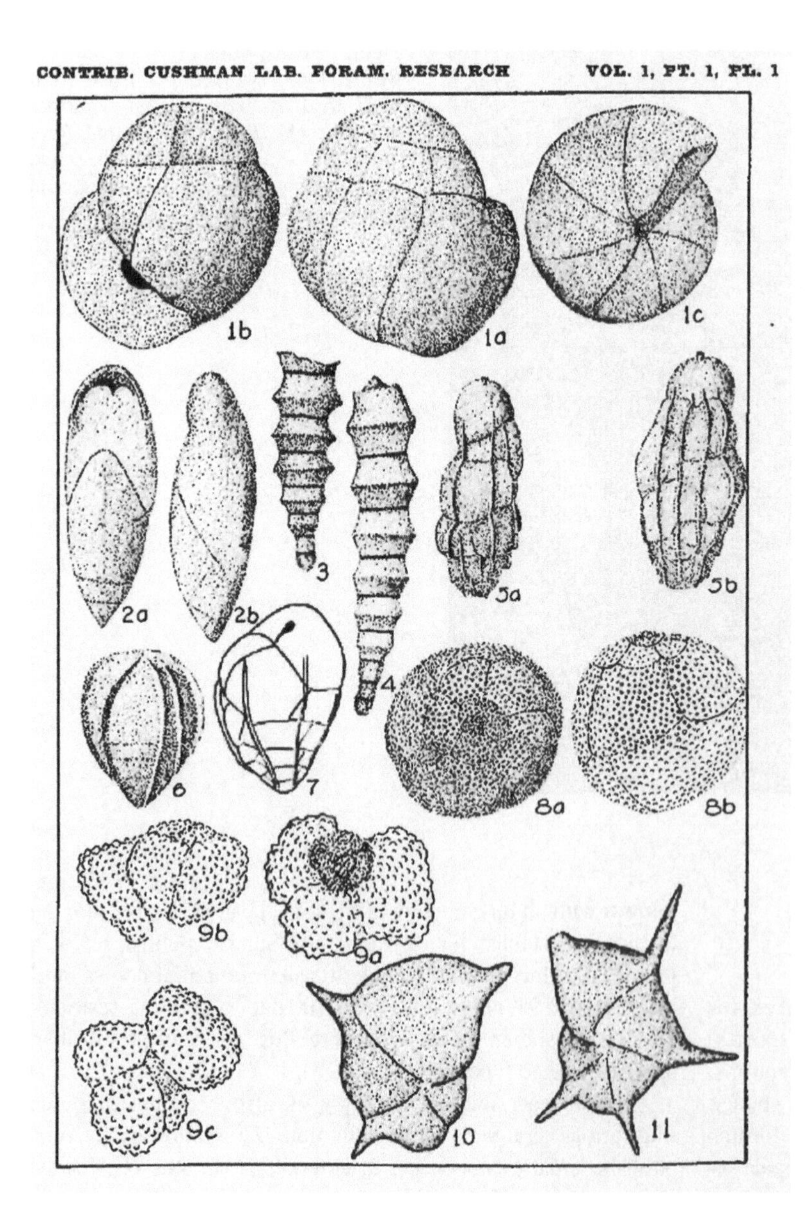

Figure 7. Joseph A. Cushman published his own journal, *Contributions from the Cushman Laboratory of Foraminiferal Research*, from 1925 to 1949. His first issue had one plate drawn with inked lines and stipples (Cushman, 1925, v. 1, plate 1); he used shaded ink and pencil drawings in later volumes. Courtesy of Cushman Foundation for Foraminiferal Research, Inc.; used with permission.

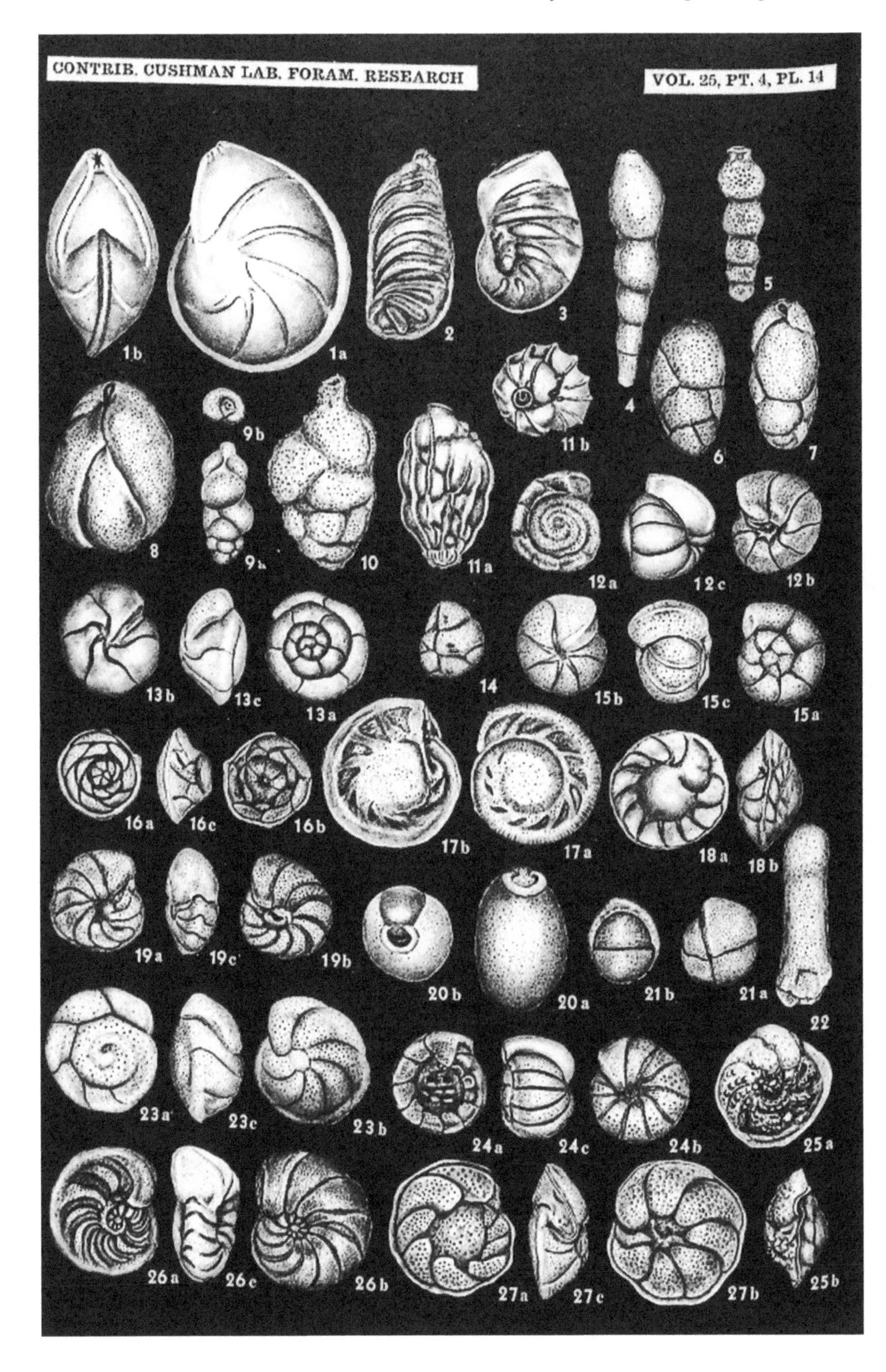

Figure 8. One of the last plates, a drawing shaded in pencil, published by Joseph A. Cushman (Cushman and Stone, 1949, v. 25, plate 14) appeared in the December 1949 issue of the *Contributions from the Cushman Laboratory of Foraminiferal Research* eight months after his death in April. Courtesy of Cushman Foundation for Foraminiferal Research, Inc.; used with permission.

1933) as did others around the world including Chinese, European, Japanese, Russian (Mikhalevich et al., 2020), Argentinian, and other micropaleontologists who collectively published thousands of illustrated papers. In 1964, the two-volume *Treatise on Invertebrate Paleontology* (Loeblich and Tappan, 1964) included every genus of forams published to 1963 and was illustrated with 650 figures showing up to two dozen images, many of which were drawn by Helen Tappan in pencil (Fig. 9). Forams continued to be hand drawn by international authors in the first seven decades of the twentieth century with the occasional use of other illustration techniques such as stippled images (Parker, 1962) and shading on textured paper (Lipps, 1967). Fusulinids, which are

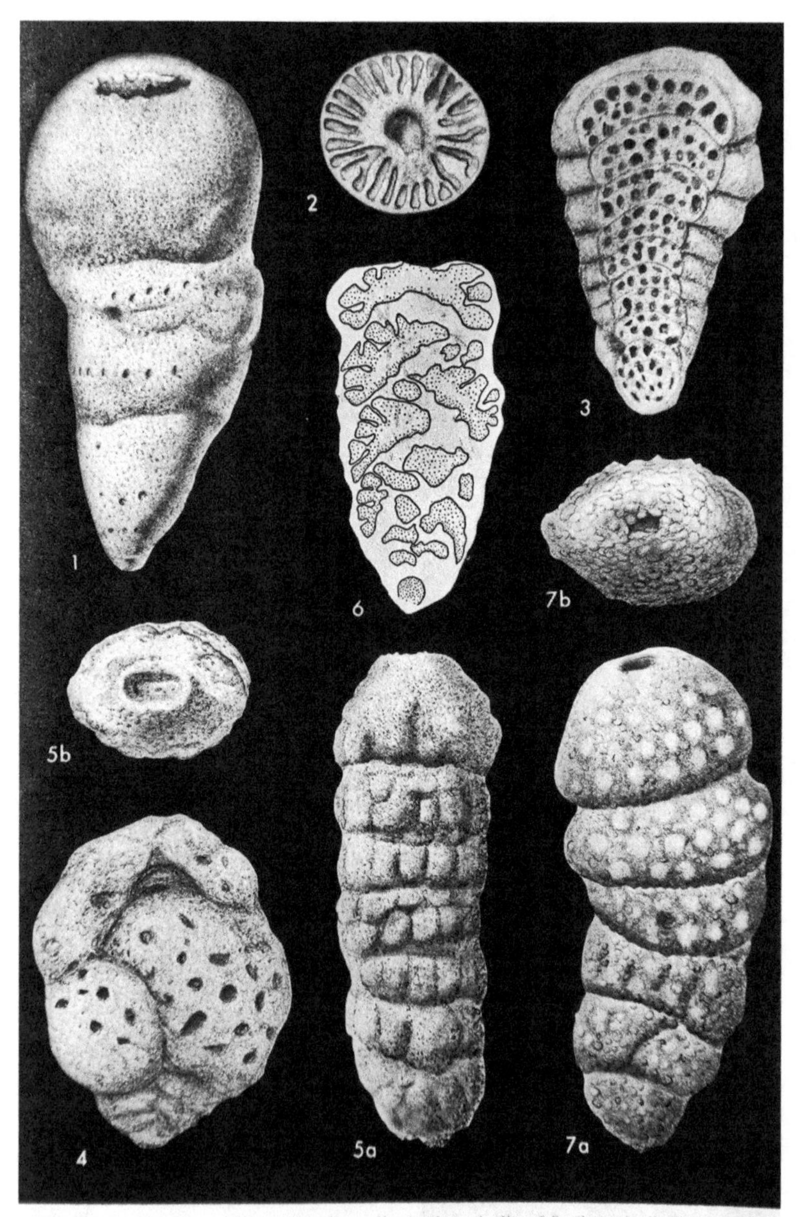

ɜ. 204. Pavonitinidae (Pavonitininae; *1-3, Guppyella; 4, Alveovalvulina; 5-7, Alveovalvulinella*) (p. C298).

Figure 9. Figure 204, drawn in shaded pencil by Helen Tappan, is one of the 650 figures from the *Treatise on Invertebrate Paleontology* (Loeblich and Tappan, 1964). Courtesy of University of Kansas Paleontological Institute.

best studied in thin sections, were illustrated by photographs and more recently by micro-CT scans (Görög et al., 2012).

While hand drawings continued to be published and still are, they were largely replaced by scanning electron micrographs (SEMs) starting in 1967 (Hay and Sandberg, 1967). Soon, most foram publications included SEM images (Fig. 10). They are made by electrons scattered off the surface of the specimen, which reveals detailed morphology with an enhanced depth of field. They do not provide information about the internal structures observed in light photographs of the tests or in thin sections, as light penetrates through the transparent tests revealing chamber, wall, pore, suture, other internal structures, and colors.

Other Forms of Foraminiferal Art

As appreciation of the unique nature and beauty of forams grew, other forms of art were undertaken, often at the urging of foram workers themselves, even though forams remained unknown to the public. Models of forams, first made by d'Orbigny (1826), included 100 models ~4 cm across, which were sold in four sets from 1823 to 1826 to be used to recognize and explain his species (see Vénec-Peyré, 2005, p. 37, for images of 29 models). Model sets were also made by others and sometimes sold from 1861 to 2007 (Miller, 2013) to complement the teaching and demonstration of forams. Foram art has appeared in other situations as well: in an advertisement for a bank in Louisiana, in

Figure 10. Scanning electron microscope images of deep-sea Eocene to modern forams are shown (Hayward et al., 2012, plate 18). Courtesy of Bruce Hayward; used with permission of Cushman Foundation for Foraminiferal Research, Inc.

the floor of the Miami International Airport (Fig. 11), as jewelry of silver or other metals (necklaces, earrings, and pins), necklaces made by Pacific Islanders, and on postage stamps (Lipps et al., this volume) and coins.

Perhaps the ultimate and a most impressive way to show forams to the public is as large-sized sculptures that are easily seen and understood. Such sculptures have appeared in at least one museum (Fig. 12) and in a Foraminiferal Sculpture Park in Zhongshan City, Guandong, China (Haq, 2009; Miller, 2013). This park was conceived by Dr. Zheng Shouyi (Haq, 2005), a member of the Chinese Academy of Sciences, who believed that everyone should know about forams, so she initiated and oversaw its construction, which was completed in December 2009 (Fig. 13).

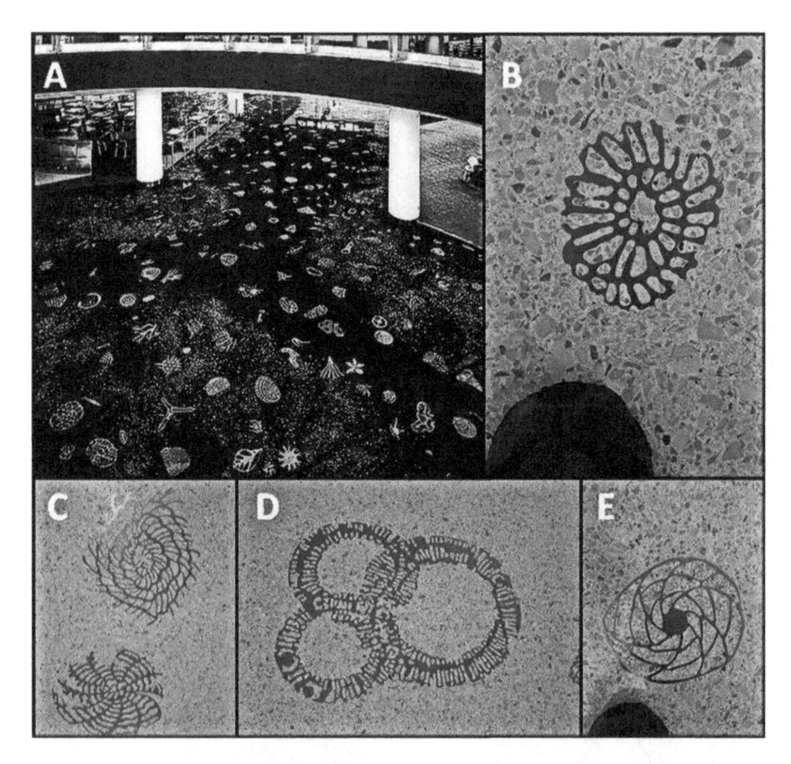

Figure 11. (A) Bronzes in the floor of the Miami International Airport, North Terminal D, Level 2; (B–E) bronzes in the floor as foram cross sections. Artist Michele Oka Doner included marine organisms in *A Walk on the Beach, 1995–1999*, in terrazzo, bronze, and mother-of-pearl (Doner and Dunlop, 2016). Tip of shoe in parts B and E is 8 cm wide. Photographs courtesy of Bruce Hayward.

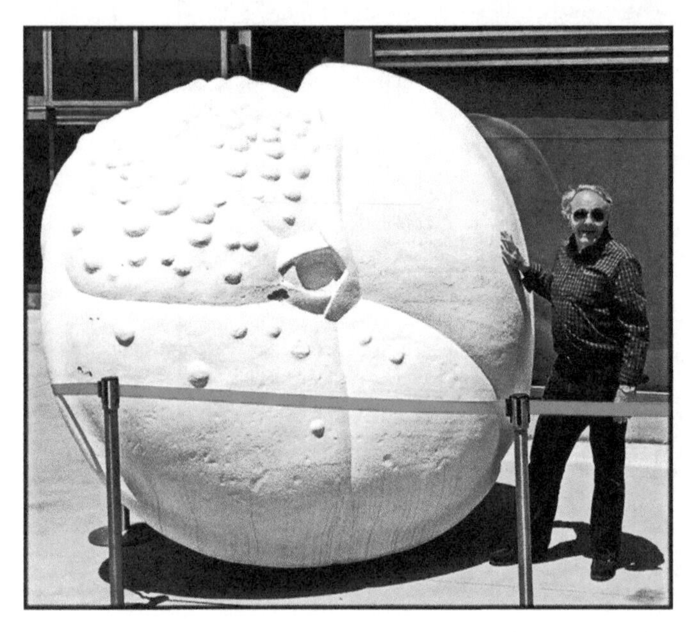

Figure 12. A large foram sculpture at the Ocean Institute, Dana Point, California, is used for educational purposes. Photograph taken by Meredith Riven.

CONCLUSIONS

Foraminiferal art has progressed slowly but significantly in its 450-year history. It has been essential to foram science and of practical use in the petroleum industry. Illustrations were chiefly pencil and ink shaded drawings of specimens over the past 455 years and later photographs, scanning electron microscopic images in the past 50 years, and micro-CT scanning images more recently. More than 200,000 foram pictures have been created in that time. Forams have also been featured in models, a poster, floors, stamps, coins, and sculptures. Indeed, a Foraminiferal Sculpture Park in China is the outstanding example of foram art outside of illustrations. But forams have not captured much of the general public's interest.

ACKNOWLEDGMENTS

Many people have helped me extensively in putting this paper together: Kenneth Finger, University of California, Berkeley; Bruce Hayward, GeoMarine, Auckland; Martin Langer, Bonn University; Alexei Rozanov, Paleontological Institute, Moscow; Barun Sen Gupta and Lorene Smith, Louisiana State University, Baton Rouge; Zheng Shouyi, Institute of Oceanography, Quindao, China; Marie-Thérèse Vénec-Peyré, Natural History Museum, Paris; and, long ago, Alfred R. Loeblich, Jr., and Helen Tappan, University of California at Los Angeles, stimulated my interest in foram art. Editors Professor Renee Clary, Mississippi State University, and Professor Emeritus Gary D. Rosenberg, Indiana University, Purdue University, Indianapolis, and Adjunct Curator of Geology, Milwaukee Public Museum, were patient, helpful, and kind in finishing this job in 2020–2021 under the difficult conditions of the COVID-19 pandemic. Professors Laurel Collins, Florida International University, and Sally Walker, University of Georgia, provided excellent, helpful reviews. This is publication number 3005, University of California Museum of Paleontology.

Figure 13. The Foraminiferal Sculpture Park in Zhongshan City, Guandong, China, is 7000 m^2 in size and exhibits 116 sculptures of 90 genera. (A–C) Parts of the park are shown. (D–E) Video frames show park construction; Professor Zheng Shouyi is wearing a white coat. Photographs and videos courtesy of Zheng Shouyi, 2018.

REFERENCES CITED

Agricola, G., 1558, De natura fossilium, lib. X: p. 166–380, *in* Georgii Agricolae De ortu & causis subterraneorum, lib. V; De natura eorum quæ effluunt ex terra, lib. IIII; De natura fossilium, lib. X; De ueteribus & nouis metallis, lib. II; Bergmann's, siue De re metallica dialogus, lib. I: Bailee, In Officina Frobeniana.

D'Archiac, A., and Haime, J., 1853–1854, Description des animanux fossiles de groupe nummulitique de l'Inde precede d'un résumé geologique et d'une monograph des Nummulites: Paris, Gide and J. Baudry, 2 volumes, 373 p.

Beccari, J.B., 1731, De bononiensi arena quadam: De Bononiensis Scientiarum et Artium Instituto atque Academia Commentarii, v. 1, p. 62–70.

de Blainville, H.M.D., 1827, Manuel de malacologie et de conchyliologie (1825): Paris, F.G. Levrault, 664 p.

Bosc, L.A.G., 1802, Sur deux nouvelles Alvéolites: Bulletin des Sciences par la Société Philomathique de Paris, v. 3, no. 61, p. 99.

Bowden, A.J., Gregory, F.J., and Henderson, A.S., eds, 2013, Landmarks in Foraminiferal Micropalaeontology: History and Development: Geological Society, London, Micropalaeontological Society Special Publications, v. 6, 368 p.

Brady, H.B., 1884, Report on the foraminifera dredged by H.M.S. *Challenger*, during the years 1873–1876, *in* Report on the Scientific Results of the Voyage of the H.M.S. *Challenger*: Zoology, v. 9, 814 p.

Brünnich, M.T., 1772, Brünnich Zoologiae fundamenta: Hafniae et Lipsiae, Grunde i Dyeloeren, 253 p.

Carpenter, W.B., 1850, On the microscopic structure of *Nummulina, Orbitolites,* and *Orbitoides*: Quarterly Journal of the Geological Society of London, v. 6, p. 21–39, https://doi.org/10.1144/GSL.JGS.1850.006.01-02.08.

Carpenter, W.P., Parker, W.K., and Jones, T.R., 1862, Introduction to the Study of the Foraminifera: London, The Ray Society, 319 p.

Culver, S.E., 1992, Foraminifera, *in* Lipps, J.H., ed., Fossil Prokaryotes and Protists: Boston and Oxford, UK, Blackwell Scientific Publishers, p. 203–247.

Cushman, J.A., 1925, New foraminifera from the Upper Eocene of Mexico: Contributions from the Cushman Laboratory for Foraminiferal Research, v. 1, p. 4–8, plate 1.

Cushman, J.A., 1948, Foraminifera, Their Classification and Economic Use (4th edition): Cambridge, Massachusetts, Harvard University Press, 605 p.

Cushman, J.A., and Stone, B., 1949, Foraminifera from the Eocene, Verdun formation, of Peru: Contributions from the Cushman Laboratory for Foraminiferal Research, v. 24, pt. 4, p. 73–84, plate 14.

Dobell, C., 1932, Antony van Leeuwenhoek and His 'Little Animals', Being Some Account of the Father of Protozoology and Bacteriology and His Multifarious Discoveries in the Disciplines: New York, Harcourt, Brace and Company, 435 p.

Doner, M.O., and Dunlop, B., 2016, A Walk on the Beach, Miami International Airport: New York, Andrea Monfried Editions LLC, 24 p.

Dujardin, F., 1835, Observations nouvelles sur les Céphalopodes microscopiques: Annales des Sciencies Naturelles, Zoologie, ser. 4, v. 6, p. 588–602.

Ehrenberg, C.G., 1854, Mikrogeologie: Leipzig, L. Voss, 374 p., 40 plates.

Finger, K.L., 2013, California foraminiferal micropaleontology, *in* Bowden, A.J., Gregory, F.J., and Henderson, A.S., eds., Landmarks in Foraminiferal Micropalaeontology: History and Development: Geological Society, London, Micropalaeontological Society Special Publications, v. 6, p. 125–144.

Förskal, P., 1775, Descriptiones animalium: Copenhagen, Hauniae, 164 p.

Galloway, J.J., 1933, A Manual of Foraminifera: Bloomington, Indiana, Principia Press, Inc., 483 p.

GeoRef, 2020/10, Database of geoscience literature of the world: Products - GeoRef (proquest.com).

Görög, Á., Szinger, B., Tóth, E., and Viszkok, J., 2012, Methodology of the micro-computer tomography on foraminifera: Palaeontologia Electronica, v. 15, no. 1, 3T, 15 p., https://doi.org/10.26879/261

Haeckel, E.H.P.A., 1904, Kunstformen der natur. Von prof. dr. Ernst Haeckel. [Hundert] illustrationstafeln mit beschreibendem text [allgemeine erläuterung und systematische übersicht]: Leipzig und Wien, Verlag des Bibliographischen Instituts, 100 plates.

Haq, B.U., 2005, Joseph A. Cushman Award: Journal of Foraminiferal Research, v. 35, p. 274–276, https://doi.org/10.2113/35.3.274.

Haq, B.U., 2009, Foraminifera Sculpture Park, Zhongshan, China: https://cushmanfoundation.allenpress.com/Resources/WorldsFirstForaminiferalSculpturePark (accessed March 2021).

Hay, W.W., and Sandberg, P.A., 1967, The scanning electron microscope, a major break-through for micropaleontology: Micropaleontology, v. 13, p. 407–418.

Hayward, B.W., Kawagata, S., Sabaa, A., Grenfell, H., Van Kerckhoven, L., Johnson, K., and Thomas, E., 2012, The Last Global Extinction (Mid-

Pleistocene) of Deep-sea Benthic Foraminifera (Chrysalogoniidae, Ellipsoidinidae, Glandulonodosariidae, Plectofrondiculariidae, Pleurostomellidae, Stilostomellidae), Their Late Cretaceous-Cenozoic History/Taxonomy: Cushman Foundation for Foraminiferal Research Special Publication 43, 408 p., 39 plates.

Hayward, B.W., Le Coze, F., Vachard, D., and Gross, O., 2020, World foraminifera database: http://www.Marinespecies.Org/Foraminifera (accessed March 2021).

Heron-Allen, E., 1917, Alcide d'Orbigny, his life and work: Journal of the Royal Microscopical Society, ser. 2, v. 37, p. 1–105, https://doi.org/10.1111/j.1365-2818.1917.tb05148.x.

Hooke, R., 1665, Micrographia: London, Royal Society.

Hoole, S., 1807, The Select Works of Antony van Leeuwenhoek Containing His Microscopical Discoveries in Many of the Works of Nature: London, G. Sydney, 314 p.

Javaux, E.J., and Scott, D.B., 2003, Illustration of recent benthic foraminifera in Bermuda and remarks on species distribution: Palaeontologica Electronica, v. 6, 29 p.

Kent, W.S., 1878, The Foraminiferal nature of Haliphysema Tumanowiczii, Bow (*Squamulina scopula*, Carter), demonstrated: Journal of Natural History, 2, no. 7, p. 68–78, https:/doi.org/10.1080/00222937808682382.

Lamarck, J.B., 1806, Explication des planches, relatives aux coquilles fossiles des environs de Paris: Annales du Muséum National d'Histoire Naturelle, v. 8, p. 383–387, plates 59–62.

Le Calvez, Y., 1974, Greatest names in micropaleontology. 1. Alcide d'Orbigny, *in* Hedley, R.H., and Adams, C.G., eds., Foraminifera: London, Academic Press, p. 261–264.

Lee, J.J., 1990, Phylum Granuloreticulosa (Foraminifera), *in* Margulis, L., et al., eds., Handbook of Protoctista: Boston, Jones and Bartlett Publishers, p. 524–528.

Linnaeus, C., 1758, Systema Naturae per regna tria naturae, secundum classes, ordines, genera, species, cum characteribus, differentiis, synonymis, locis. Editio decima, reformata (10th revised edition) Volume 1: Holmiae [Stockholm], Laurentius Salvius, 824 p.

Lipps, J.H., 1967, Age and environment of a marine terrace fauna, San Clemente Island, California: The Veliger, v. 9, p. 388–398.

Lipps, J.H., 1973, Test structure in foraminifera: Annual Review of Microbiology, v. 27, p. 471–486, https://doi.org/10.1146/annurev.mi.27.100173.002351.

Lipps, J.H., 2002, Alcide d'Orbigny and American micropaleontology: Comptes Rendus Palévol, v. 1, p. 461–469, https://doi.org/10.1016/S1631-0683(02)00069-6.

Lipps, J.H., and Rozanov, A.Yu., 1996, The Late Precambrian–Cambrian agglutinated fossil *Platysolenites*: Paleontological Journal, v. 30, p. 679–687.

Lipps, J.H., Vartak, A., Van Eijden, T., Rajshekhar, C., Vaddadi, S., and Vartak, R., 2022, this volume, Paleontological postage stamps in art and education, *in* Clary, R.M., Rosenberg, G.D., and Evans, D.C., eds., The Evolution of Paleontological Art: Geological Society of America Memoir 218, Chapter 25, https://doi.org/10.1130/2021.1218(25).

Loeblich, A.R., Jr., and Tappan, H., 1964, Sarcodina chiefly 'Thecamoebians' and Foraminiferida, *in* Moore, R.C., ed., Treatise on Invertebrate Paleontology, Volume C, Protista 2: Lawrence, Kansas, Geological Society of America and University of Kansas Press, 2 vols., v. 1, p. 1–510A; v. 2, p. 511–900.

Loeblich, A.R., Jr., and Tappan, H., 1987, Foraminiferal Genera and Their Classification: New York, Van Nostrand Reinhold Co., 2 vols., v. 1, 970 p.; v. 2, 847 p.

Mikhalevich, V., Bugrova, E., Basov, V., Zakrevskaya, E., Dmitrieva, V., and Barash, M., 2020, The Russian school of foraminiferology: Journal of Foraminiferal Research, v. 50, p. 97–107, https://doi.org/10.2113/gsjfr.50.1.97.

Miller, C.G., 2013, A brief history of modelling Foraminifera: From d'Orbigny to Zheng Shouyi, *in* Bowden, A.J., Gregory, F.J., and Henderson, A.S., eds., Landmarks in Foraminiferal Micropalaeontology, History and Development: Geological Society, London, Micropalaeontological Society Special Publications, v. 6, p. 337–349, https://doi.org/10.1144/TMS6.24.

Murray, J.W., 2012, Early British students of modern foraminifera: Carpenter and Williamson: Journal of Micropalaeontology, v. 31, p. 159–167, https://doi.org/10.1144/0262-821X11-035.

d'Orbigny, A.D., 1826, Tableau méthodique de la classe des Céphalopodes: Annales des Sciences Naturelles, v. 7, p. 96–169, 245–314.

d'Orbigny, A.D., 1839, Foraminifères, *in* de la Sagra, R., ed., Histoire physique, politique et naturelle de l'île de Cuba: Paris, Arthus Bertrand, p. 1–224.

d'Orbigny, A.D., 1843, Modéles de Foraminiféres vivans et fossils (2nd edition): Paris, Cosson, 24 p.

d'Orbigny, A.D., 1846, Foraminiféres fossiles du bassin tertiaire de Vienne (Autriche): Paris, Gide et Compe, 302 p., https://doi.org/10.5962/bhl.title.145432.

d'Orbigny, A.D., 1849–1852, Cours élémentaire de paléontologie et de géologie stratigraphiques: Paris, Victor Masson, 2 vols., v. 1, 299 p.; v. 2, 847 p.

Parker, F.L., 1962, Planktonic foraminiferal species in Pacific sediments: Micropaleontology, v. 8, p. 219–254, https://doi.org/10.2307/1484745.

Parker, W.K., Jones, T.R., and Brady, H.B., 1871, XVIII. On the nomenclature of the Foraminifera: Journal of Natural History, v. 8, no. 45, p. 145–179, https://doi.org/10.1080/00222937108696460.

Pawlowski, J., Holzmann, M., and Tyszka, J., 2013, New supraordinal classification of Foraminifera: Molecules meet morphology: Marine Micropaleontology, v. 100, p. 1–10, https://doi.org/10.1016/j.marmicro.2013.04.002.

Rauser-Chernousova, D.M., and Fursenko, AV., eds., 1937, Ключевая книга по фораминиферам нефтеносных районов СССР [The key book on foraminifera of the oil-bearing regions of the USSR]: Leningrad-Moscow, Glavnaya Redak. Gorno-Topliv. Lit., pt. 1, 319 p.

Richardson, S.L., and Lipps, J.H., 2020, Foraminifera C. E. Eichwald: p. 67–83, *in* de Queiroz, K., Cantino, P.D., and Gauthier, J.A., eds., Phylonyms: A Companion to the PhyloCode: Boca Raton, Florida, CRC Press, p, 67–83.

Sen Gupta, B.K., 1999, Systematics of modern foraminifera, *in* Sen Gupta, B.K., ed., Modern Foraminifera: Dordrecht, the Netherlands, Kluwer Academic Publishers, p. 7–36.

Shi, Y.-K., Huang, H., and Shen, Z.-H., 2019, New insights for ancient foraminifera through 3D visuals of fusulinids: Palaeoworld, v. 28, p. 478–486, https://doi.org/10.1016/j.palwor.2018.07.003.

Siemensma, F., Apotheosis-Perret-Gentil, L., Holzmann, M., Clauss, S., Völcker, E., and Pawlowski, J., 2017, Taxonomic revision of freshwater foraminifera with the description of two new agglutinated species and genera: European Journal of Protistology, v. 60, p. 28–44, https://doi.org/10.1016/j.ejop.2017.05.006.

Soldani, A., 1789; 1798, Testaceographiae ac zoophytographiae parvae et microscopiae: Tomus primus (1789), p. i–xxxii, 1–289; plates 1–179; Tomus secundus (1798), p. i–vii, 1–148; plates 1–26, and appendix plates I–XXIII [reproduced from *Saggio orittografico*, 1780]: Senis [Sienna], Francisco Rossi.

Strabo, 2020, Geography, Notice: http://www.perseus.tufts.edu/hopper/text?doc=Perseus:text:1999.01.0239, Book XVII, Chapter 1, Section 34 [English translations of Strabo's writings] (accessed March 2021).

Vaiani, S.C., Vai, G.B., Borsetti, A.M., and Sarti, C., 2019, From Ammonites to *Ammonia*, a tale on the early history of micropaleontology by Jacopo Bartolomeo Beccari (1682–1766): Micropaleontology, v. 65, p. 551–560.

Vénec-Peyré, M.-T., 2002, Les travaux micropaléontologiques d'Alcide d'Orbigny: Comptes Rendus Palévol, v. 1, p. 449–459, https://doi.org/10.1016/S1631-0683(02)00053-2.

Vénec-Peyré, M.-T., 2004, Beyond frontiers and time: The scientific and cultural heritage of Alcide d'Orbigny (1802–1857): Marine Micropaleontology, v. 50, p. 149–159, https://doi.org/10.1016/S0377-8398(03)00064-1.

Vénec-Peyré, M.-T., 2005, Les Planches inédites de Foraminifères Alcide d'Orbigny à l'aube de la Micropaléontologie [The unpublished plates of Foraminifera d'Alcide d'Orbigny—the dawn of micropaleontology]: Paris, Publications scientifiques du Muséum, 304 p., 62 plates.

Williamson, W.C., 1858, On the Recent Foraminifera of Great Britain: London, Ray Society, 107 p., https://doi.org/10.5962/bhl.title.139719.

Manuscript Accepted by the Society 20 January 2021
Manuscript Published Online 5 November 2021

Printed in the USA

The Geological Society of America
Memoir 218

"Extreme dinosaurs" and the continuing evolution of dinosaur paleoart

Warren D. Allmon
Paleontological Research Institution, 1259 Trumansburg Road, Ithaca, New York 14850, USA

ABSTRACT

Humans have made visual representations of what they think dinosaurs looked like since before the term and concept of "dinosaur" were first published in 1842. Over the next 175 years, these images have varied widely. The current era of dinosaur paleobiology began in the late 1960s and emphasized scientific and artistic conceptions of dinosaurs as more active and diverse in their metabolism, ecology, and behavior than previously thought. Over the past 25 years in particular, the rise of computer-generated images and the discovery of spectacularly preserved fossils from the Early Cretaceous of China and elsewhere have further revolutionized our understanding of the biology and external appearance (especially integument) of dinosaurs. Yet despite these innovations, dinosaur paleoart is still fundamentally shaped by the same basic set of influences that affected previous, now-discarded, images. These include (1) the fossils; (2) debates about which modern animals are the best bases for uniformitarian comparison with extinct taxa; (3) extrapolation (i.e., how far can we go from the known to the unknown); (4) the enabling effects of new artistic techniques; and (5) the ever-present pressures of the marketplace.

INTRODUCTION

Among the most conspicuous characteristics of paleontology in the late-twentieth and early-twenty-first centuries have been explosions of both new dinosaur fossils and new dinosaur art, which have in turn been aided by the explosion in artistic and electronic technology. An astonishing wealth of new dinosaur fossils, particularly from China, has combined with the continued sophistication and accessibility of computer-assisted imaging and the ubiquity and influence of the internet to produce a mind-boggling abundance of dinosaur images. This chapter surveys some of the most recent dinosaur art, especially that at the cutting edge of the discipline. I show that the challenges presented by new fossils are essentially the same as those presented by the first dinosaurs described in the 1820s, and the controversies associated with new dinosaur art are very similar to those that greeted nineteenth-century and early-twentieth-century dinosaur art.

The history of dinosaur art began before the word and concept of "dinosaur" were first published by Richard Owen in 1842 (Owen, 1842; Allmon, 2006). The first scientific description of what would eventually be called a dinosaur was of *Megalosaurus*, published in 1824 by William Buckland (1784–1856), but Buckland did not attempt either a skeletal reconstruction or life-restoration of the animal (Buckland, 1824).[1] The first published illustration of a life-restoration of a dinosaur was probably a tiny image of *Iguanodon* in Buckland's (1836) *Bridgewater Treatise*.

[1]The terms *restoration, reconstruction, model,* and *recreation* are frequently used synonymously in discussions of paleoart. Here I use *reconstruction* to refer to depiction of how the skeletal remains might have fit together in the living organism and *restoration* to depict the external appearance of the animal when it was alive, complete with soft tissues. This usage follows, among others, Swinton (1969), Debus and Debus (2002), and Taquet and Padian (2004).

Allmon, W.D., 2022, "Extreme dinosaurs" and the continuing evolution of dinosaur paleoart, *in* Clary, R.M., Rosenberg, G.D., and Evans, D.C., eds., The Evolution of Paleontological Art: Geological Society of America Memoir 218, p. 213–220, https://doi.org/10.1130/2021.1218(23).

Owen's proposal of dinosaurs as a previously undescribed taxon of extinct reptiles was an enormous leap of extrapolation, a spectacular example of the importance of true creativity and the ability of extraordinary science to "look beyond" what is immediately at hand (Desmond, 1982; Torrens, 2012). Again, no reconstructions or restorations of the newly defined dinosaurs accompanied Owen's revolutionary (1842) paper, but he was soon handed an extraordinary opportunity to create such illustrations for the Crystal Palace Park in South London, which opened in 1853 (McCarthy and Gilbert, 1994; Secord, 2004). Artist Benjamin Waterhouse Hawkins was hired to make life-sized models of ancient vertebrates for the park, and Owen was engaged to advise him. The famous models were not only reflections of what Owen and Hawkins thought dinosaurs looked like, but also conspicuous demonstrations of scientific ideas being built, at least in part, under strong non-scientific influences. It was in the popular guidebook for the Crystal Palace (Owen, 1854) that the first-ever image was published showing a reconstructed (partial) dinosaur skeleton with restored soft parts (whether this drawing originated with Owen or Hawkins we may never know; see, e.g., Secord, 2004; Dawson, 2016).

The half-century after the Crystal Palace was a period of prolific discovery and description of new dinosaurs, mostly from the American West, but very little dinosaur paleoart. This changed in the early twentieth century, as a new generation of scientists, authors, and museums sought to portray ancient life in as many ways as possible, both to general public and scientific audiences. Yet most of these depictions were focused on a relatively narrow conception of what dinosaurs looked like. Almost all paleontologists and artists viewed them as ponderous, slow, and dull-witted, and these images became self-reinforcing through the 1960s (Allmon, 2006).

This changed abruptly in 1969, when Yale paleontologist John Ostrom described a small, carnivorous dinosaur, *Deinonychus,* from the Cretaceous of Montana (Ostrom, 1969), which had multiple morphological features that cried out for a more energetic interpretation of dinosaur physiology. Ostrom worked with an undergraduate student, Robert Bakker, who was both paleontologist and artist, and who provided for Ostrom's paper a highly active restoration of *Deinonychus*, which became one of the most influential pieces of dinosaur paleoart of the second half of the twentieth century. The discovery, description, and interpretation of this one dinosaur ignited an almost total change in prevailing scientific views of dinosaurs.

Within a decade, most dinosaur paleontologists came to see dinosaurs as much more active and agile than they had before (Bakker, 1975, 1986; Desmond, 1975). This "dinosaur renaissance" (see below) included reconsideration of the earlier hypothesis of an evolutionary connection between birds and dinosaurs, which soon came to dominate paleontological thinking. The preferred modern analog was no longer reptilian but avian and mammalian, and these comparisons were taken more seriously (e.g., Paul, 1987).

At the same time that this paleontological revolution was happening, another was occurring in artistic technology in the form of computer-generated imagery (CGI), which allowed for previously unfathomable levels of realism in paleoart (Campbell, 2009). This was spectacularly brought to public attention with the 1993 film *Jurassic Park.* These two developments—one paleontological and one technological—led to a major change in how dinosaurs were depicted. Between the early 1970s and late 1990s, images of dinosaurs in popular books and other media gradually shifted to show more energetic postures of most dinosaurs (although other popular culture images were much slower to change; Ross et al., 2013).

THE JEHOL FOSSILS

In 1994, on a hillside near the village of Sihetun in Liaoning Province in northeastern China, a farmer named Li Yinfeng found the world's first known feathered, non-avian dinosaur, a creature that was later named *Sinosauropteryx* (Chen et al., 1998; Chang et al., 2003; Norell, 2005; Norell and Xu, 2005). This little dinosaur was part of the Jehol Biota, an extraordinary occurrence of fossils from the Yixian and Jiufotang Formations dating to the Early Cretaceous (ca. 130–120 m.y. ago). The biota includes dozens of dinosaur and bird species plus a diverse array of other organisms from turtles to mammals to insects (Chang et al., 2003; Coniff, 2018). The fossils are extraordinarily well-preserved, a situation attributed to a combination of the organisms being washed into lakes and then quickly covered with volcanic ash (Zhou et al., 2004).

The Jehol Lagerstätten revolutionized our understanding of the evolution of theropod dinosaurs and birds (e.g., Currie et al., 2004; Norell, 2005; Norell and Xu, 2005; Pickrell, 2014a; Chiappe and Qingjin, 2016). The Jehol fossils revealed that feathers were present in many taxa, not just a few, and ignited a new phase in the expansion of scientific and popular dinosaur art that continues today (e.g., Sloan, 2000; Paul, 2002; Long and Schouten, 2008; Terakado, 2017; Greshko, 2020).

FEATHERS

Integument—the skin and its excrescences—has always been the least known aspect of the outward appearance of dinosaurs. With the renewed attention to the evolutionary connection between birds and dinosaurs in the 1970s, this took on new urgency, since the integument of birds (especially feathers) can change their outward appearance more than that of reptiles such as lizards and crocodilians (Conway et al., 2013, p. 11, 13).

Prior to the early 1990s, feathers were known only on birds, although a few authors had speculated about feathers on non-avian dinosaurs. For example, the first illustration of a non-bird theropod dinosaur with feathers may have been a drawing by Sarah Landry in Bakker's 1975 *Scientific American* article influentially titled "Dinosaur Renaissance" (Fig. 1). Around the same

Figure 1. This is the earliest published illustration of a non-avian dinosaur with feathers: *Syntarsus* by Sarah Landry (from Bakker, 1975). Reproduced with permission from *Scientific American*.

Figure 2. Life-restoration of *Dilong* by Portia Sloan Rollings/National Geographic Creative is shown. Courtesy NG Image Collection.

time, paleoartist Greg Paul was producing his first speculative feathered dinosaur images and published them in the late 1980s.[2] Other early images of feathered dinosaurs appeared during this time in popular and semi-popular books (e.g., Glut, 1982, p. 269; Lambert, 1983, p. 43, 67; Lambert, 1990, p. 45, 120, 197; Bakker, 1986, p. 310; Preiss and Silverberg, 1992, p. 3, 27, 123) and on the cover of *Time* magazine (26 April 1993). But there were as yet no fossils that directly indicated the presence of feathers. This changed with the Jehol Biota, in which almost all of the small theropods had feathers. The first published life restoration of a Chinese "feathered dinosaur" was apparently a painting of *Sinosauropteryx* by paleoartist Michael Skrepnick, which was done for the cover of Currie and Padian (1997) and reproduced elsewhere (Unwin, 1998; Skrepnick, 2005). This illustration was followed by scores of others in a cascade of discoveries and announcements. It raised numerous questions with major artistic implications including, "did all dinosaurs have feathers?"

The discoveries among the Jehol fossils of feathers on two larger theropods—*Dilong*, a relative of *Tyrannosaurus rex*, and *Yutyrannus*, the largest feathered dinosaur (Xu et al., 2004, 2012)—as well as of attachments for feathers on *Velociraptor* from Mongolia (Turner et al., 2007) were particularly startling (Fig. 2) because they suggested that multiple large, well-known dinosaurs might also have had feathers. This set off a flood of feathered *T. rex* images (Fig. 3) and controversy about whether they were justified.[3] The discovery of feather-like integumentary structures in multiple ornithischians (Zheng et al., 2009; Clarke, 2013; Godefroit et al., 2014; Vinther et al., 2016) suggested that feathers might even have been a primitive feature of all dinosaurs. As paleoartist John Conway (in White, 2012, p. 137) put it, "… whether to feather a dinosaur or not … is now a standard question in restoring ancient life…."

Figure 3. Life-restoration of feathered adult *T. rex* by Luis V. Rey (2013) is shown. Reproduced with permission from the artist.

Popular culture responded to these discoveries with a torrent of books, toys, and online images. Feature film, however, has remained unfeathered, and the *Jurassic Park* franchise has been criticized for not putting feathers on its dinosaurs, for example, in its latest film, *Jurassic World* (2015) (e.g., Pickrell, 2014b, 2014c; Opfer, 2017; Gleason, 2018). The possible reasons suggested by

[2]See https://alchetron.com/Gregory-S-Paul and Paul (1987, 1988; accessed March 2021). Not everyone appreciated Paul's work. In a review of Paul (1988), Padian (1987, p. 283) wrote of the dinosaurs: "Gaping at each other like reptilian Muppets, they prance gaily through the pages in an elephantine scamper, festooned with conjectural stripes and spots, their starched tails trailing behind them."

[3]See, e.g., Sloan (1999); Xu and Norell (2006); Tudge (2009); and Switek (2013). A recent paper reporting on the discovery of an exceptionally well-preserved *T. rex* with feather-free integument makes a strong case that adults of the species did *not* have feathers (Bell et al., 2017).

critics include that the dinosaurs would be less interesting or scary if they were presented as "just birds instead of mysterious monsters." Not showing "dinosaurs as we now know them to have appeared is tantamount to spreading misinformation; and through toys, other merchandise and spin-off series (and no doubt *Jurassic World* sequels) it will have a cultural trickle effect that will last for many years" (Pickrell, 2014b).

COLOR

One of the most commonly asked questions by the general public about dinosaurs is, "what color were they?" The answer, until recently, was essentially that we had no idea (Ryan and Russell, 1997). For most of the history of dinosaur imagery, paleoartists chose dull colors—greens, grays, and browns—that characterize the largest living terrestrial vertebrates, such as elephants, rhinos, crocodilians, tortoises, and monitor lizards. In other words, they chose colors of what seemed like appropriate modern analogs.

With increased acceptance of a close relationship between birds and dinosaurs, however, some paleoartists began to put brighter colors and more striking color patterns on dinosaurs (Fig. 4). Associated with this change was increased explicit and detailed comparison with living analogs (Witton, 2018, p. 104). For example, integumentary color in terrestrial vertebrates shows a number of regular patterns (see Diamond and Bond, 2013, and references therein) that may apply to fossils. Feathers of many (although by no means all) living birds show a wide diversity of colors, and many are quite brilliant; if birds are living theropod dinosaurs, then nonavian dinosaurs might have had similar diversity of color (e.g., Walters and Kissinger, 2014, p. 17).

The Jehol fossils contributed to this debate in an utterly surprising way. Examination of the microstructure of the feathers of *Sinosauropteryx* revealed previously unsuspected details of the form and arrangement of melanosomes (tiny pigment-containing organelles in skin and feathers) (Zhang et al., 2010). Different types of melanosomes are associated with different kinds of pigments (Vinther, 2020). Zhang and colleagues identified melanosomes in the tail of *Sinosauropteryx* and inferred stripes along the tail in the fossil and "chestnut to rufous (reddish-brown) tones" on the filamentous crest along the back (Zhang et al., 2010, p. 1077; see also Smithwick et al., 2017) (Fig. 5). Li and colleagues (2010) described the coloration of another feathered theropod, *Anchiornis huxleyi*, and then (2012) suggested that the small "four-winged" theropod dinosaur *Microraptor* had iridescent black feathers[4] (iridescence results from physical structure rather than pigment; Prum, 2006) (Fig. 6). Hu et al. (2018) described an even more spectacular example of multi-colored iridescence in *Caihong juji*. Beyond China, Carney et al. (2012) also reported that *Archaeopteryx* had black wing feathers (see also Manning et al., 2013). Even skin color seems to have been revealed. Brown et al. (2017) described an exceptionally preserved armored dinosaur with preserved organic scales showing reddish-brown coloration interpreted as countershading camouflage. Vinther et al. (2016) described countershading of skin in a small ceratopsian dinosaur, which was also interpreted as potentially functioning for camouflage in a forested environment (Fig. 7).

These discoveries of preserved color in dinosaurs were truly surprising. They have established a genuine study of "paleo-

[4]Black is a pigment. Iridescence results in rainbow colors, often green, blue, or bronze.

Figure 4. This is one of the first life-restorations of a dinosaur with complex coloration: *Hypacrosaurus* by Eleanor Kish, 1974. © Canadian Museum of Nature; reproduced with permission.

color" in terrestrial vertebrates (Vinther, 2020) and have even been a subject of serious philosophical reflection (e.g., Turner, 2016). Empirical knowledge of dinosaur color is more than just an amazing curiosity; it can contribute to our understanding of past ecologies and behaviors (contra Turner, 2016, p. 60, who suggested it was "not too relevant to the big questions about evolutionary patterns and processes that many paleontologists care most about").

The number of dinosaur species for which color patterns are known directly from fossils is still tiny, but significantly these discoveries have contributed to a general sense among many paleoartists that "if you add additional colors [to a dinosaur restoration], be ready and able to explain your decision-making" (Nicholls *in* White, 2017, p. 15).

Figure 5. Life-restoration shows preserved color on *Sinosauropteryx*. From Smithwick et al. (2017); CC-BY 4.0.

Figure 6. Life-restoration shows preserved color on *Anchiornis*. From Li et al. (2010); reprinted with permission from the American Association for the Advancement of Science.

Figure 7. Life-restoration shows preserved color on *Psittacosaurus*. From Vinther et al. (2016); reproduced under CC-BY 4.0.

EXTREME DINOSAURS

Like most intellectual revolutions, the "dinosaur renaissance" of the 1970s featured enthusiastic advocates rushing far ahead of conventional wisdom, in this case in their interpretations of dinosaur behavior, posture, physiology, and appearance (e.g., Bakker, 1975, 1986; Desmond, 1975; Paul, 1987, 1988). Many of these interpretations featured dinosaurs with feathers and/or bright colors. The discoveries of the 1990s in China appeared to confirm many of these views, and this stimulated still more "extreme" dinosaur paleoart. One of the most unbridled among these paleoartists has been Luis Rey (e.g., Rey, 2001; Gee and Rey, 2003; Holtz and Rey, 2007; Bakker and Rey, 2013), whose work includes bold feathers, colors, and behaviors (Fig. 8).

Rey says he was strongly influenced by Bakker's work (White, 2012, p. 122). He admits that when he first started doing dinosaur paleoart, many of his reconstructions were "exaggerated—more provocation than anything else," and that he feels "somewhat responsible to the new wave of dinosaurs dressed as colorful clowns." He adds that this "was never my intention though. Colorful, yes, but believable please!" (White, 2012, p. 123, 124). Rey's work clearly walks a line between science fantasy and serious paleoart. One of his books he describes as "a work of fiction" (Gee and Rey, 2004, p. 6), but many of the images in that book are also reproduced in a serious-intentioned textbook (Holtz and Rey, 2007).

Evaluating the work of Rey and similar "extreme" modern dinosaur paleoartists involves considering several questions that are relevant to all paleoart. First, what is the purpose of paleoart? Second, how "extreme" is nature? And third, how much should a paleoartist extrapolate from the known to the unknown?

A main purpose of paleoart has historically been to display the current state of paleontological thinking (among professionals as well as others). Yet, paleoart also has served and continues

Figure 8. Deinonychus *Pack* by Luis V. Rey (2001). Reproduced with permission of the artist.

to serve other purposes, such as to be a platform for creativity, imagination, or self-expression. Paleoart can be "an arena to propose new hypotheses, rather than repetitively drawing proven theories. In the history of palaeontology, out-of-the-norm images have been crucial in popularizing new notions about the appearance and behavior of extinct animals" (Conway et al., 2013, p. 16). In this role, paleoart can frequently be "ahead" of the scientists of its time (Padian, 1987; Northcut, 2011). Paleoart may also, however, be mainly about copying and promulgating established ideas, in which case it may fall "behind" cutting-edge science (Ross et al., 2013).

Many of today's paleoartists believe that their profession was too conservative for too long and that the future belongs to those artists willing to take chances (see discussion in Conway et al. [2013] and Witton [2018]). For example, paleoartist Todd Marshall suggests that perhaps the scientific paleoart community has been too restrained in choosing color schemes for dinosaurs. "I think that for a long time, the scientific community has stuck to earth tones to play it safe," he says (quoted in Tan, 2016). Marshall says he does not "do anything that I believe is too fantastical, but I do like pushing the limits a little and pushing the viewer's imagination" (in White, 2012, p. 97, 100).

At first glance, it may be easy not to take some of the most extreme of "extreme dinosaurs" of Rey, Paul, and others seriously. They're just too bizarre and unfamiliar. On the other hand, we do in some sense live today in a world that includes many "extreme" creatures, including more than a few brightly colored birds, of which sparrows are not necessarily representative. It is not unreasonable that ancient biotas were similarly phenotypically diverse. The history of paleontology is replete with examples of the discovery of unexpected forms, from heteromorph ammonites to giant pterosaurs to Early Cambrian arthropods.

Paleontologist and paleoartist Mark Witton cogently describes the problem: "Arguments against 'dressing up' fossil animals are that it is distracting and scientifically questionable. While we cannot firmly falsify applications of modern colour schemes or specifics of integument to fossil taxa, 'dressing up' fossil species in this way implies near identical phylogenetic and adaptive factors shaping the anatomy of both species—which is demonstrably untrue in both cases." We need to be careful, he argues, that "our intention to add borrowed real-world authenticity to an artwork" does not undermine the available science (Witton, 2018, p. 139). On the other hand, "multiple lines of evidence show or strongly infer completely unexpected anatomies in prehistoric animals, and this invigorates our license to be adventurous with reconstructions" (Witton, 2018, p. 137). Indeed, recent discoveries of feathers and colors have led some paleoartists to suggest—or even to argue explicitly—that "extreme" is more likely to be true. As Witton notes, "It is clear that some speculative paleoartworks are created to break tropes and conventions instead of legitimately restoring an extinct animal..." (2018, p. 137–138). This, combined with the temptation to be provocative for commercial reasons, has clearly contributed to the modern "extreme" movement in dinosaur art.

UNIFORMITARIANISM AND BEYOND

The central approach of paleontology is comparison of past with present organisms. Despite its complex history (e.g., Shea, 1982, and references therein), this uniformitarian (aka actualistic) logic (at least in the form of taxonomic uniformitarianism—assuming a constant relationship between taxa and their environment and of preserved to unpreserved morphology, absent evidence to the contrary) remains our most important tool (e.g., Frey and Seilacher, 1980; Witmer, 1995; Alley, 2001; Allmon, 2017). But the method breaks down when there *is* adequate contrary evidence, or it is unclear which modern taxon should be used as an analog for an extinct taxon. Modern species are, at best, incomplete analogs, but they are where we must start.

Modern "extreme" paleoart highlights a tension that has been in paleoart from the beginning and remains highly relevant today. There is a spectrum from empirical observations (e.g., "*Sinosauropteryx* had feathers") to imaginative extrapolation from those observations (e.g., "all dinosaurs had feathers and they were brightly colored"), and from the standards of "rigor" (sensu Witton, 2018; being able to defend every artistic decision by specific reference to fossils) to the attractions of extrapolation as a tool to transcend "conservatism" that can hold back more daring restorations.

"Dinosaur" was itself a bold extrapolation and inference, as were the first restorations by Mantell, Buckland, Owen, and Hawkins. Modern dinosaur paleoart is continuous with this historical tradition. What is judged "realistic," "accurate," and "plausible" in paleoart, however, has changed through time. Indeed, one of the most fascinating aspects of paleoart is that the definition of what is judged "plausible" is not static either in time or across all audiences. Great paleoart both reflects and expands the plausible. Paleontology starts with extrapolation from a fragmentary fossil record based on comparison with modern organisms. We can never be certain that our conclusions are correct but can only add more evidence with the goal of getting closer to the truth. Paleoart reflects what we think, but it also can materialize our speculations and hypotheses and inspire us to think of new interpretations. Nature is both "dull" and "extreme," and the past is both similar to and different from the present. One is not inherently more likely to be correct. *Caveat emptor.*

ACKNOWLEDGMENTS

I am grateful to Chelsea Steffes and Catherine Matteson for editorial help, to Mark Norell and Michael Skrepnick for sharing information, and to Peter Dodson and two anonymous reviewers for comments on previous drafts of the manuscript.

REFERENCES CITED

Alley, R.B., 2001, The key to the past?: Nature, v. 409, p. 289, https://doi.org/10.1038/35053245.

Allmon, W.D., 2006, The pre-modern history of the post-modern dinosaur: Phases and causes in post-Darwinian dinosaur art: Earth Sciences History, v. 25, p. 5–35.

Allmon, W.D., 2017, Life-restorations of ammonites and the challenges of taxonomic uniformitarianism: Earth Sciences History, v. 36, no. 1, p. 1–29, https://doi.org/10.17704/1944-6178-36.1.1.

Bakker, R.T., 1975, Dinosaur renaissance: Scientific American, v. 232, no. 4, p. 58–79, https://doi.org/10.1038/scientificamerican0475-58.

Bakker, R.T., 1986, The Dinosaur Heresies: New York, William Morrow and Company, 481 p.

Bakker, R.T., and Rey, L.V., 2013, The Big Golden Book of Dinosaurs: New York, Golden Books, 61 p.

Bell, P.R., Campione, N.E., Persons, W.S.I.V., Currie, P.J., Larson, P.L., Tanke, D.H., and Bakker, R.T., 2017, Tyrannosauroid integument reveals conflicting patterns of gigantism and feather evolution: Biology Letters, v. 13, no. 6, p. 20170092, https://doi.org/10.1098/rsbl.2017.0092.

Brown, C.M., Henderson, D.M., Vinther, J., Fletcher, I., Sistiaga, A., Herrera, J., and Summons, R.E., 2017, An exceptionally preserved three-dimensional armored dinosaur reveals insights into coloration and Cretaceous predator-prey dynamics: Current Biology, v. 27, no. 16, https://doi.org/10.1016/j.cub.2017.06.071.

Buckland, W., 1824, Notice on the *Megalosaurus* or great fossil lizard of Stonesfield: Transactions of the Geological Society of London, v. 21, p. 390–396, plates 40–44.

Buckland, W., 1836, Geology and minerology considered with reference to natural theology: Bridgewater Treatise VI: London, William Pickering, 2 vols., v. I, 599 p.; v. II, 128 p., 69 plates.

Campbell, V., 2009, The extinct animal show: The paleoimagery tradition and computer generated imagery in factual television programs: Public Understanding of Science (Bristol, UK), v. 18, p. 199–213, https://doi.org/10.1177/0963662507081246.

Carney, R.M., Vinther, J., Shawkey, M.D., D'Alba, L., and Ackermann, J., 2012, New evidence on the colour and nature of the isolated *Archaeopteryx* feather: Nature Communications, v. 3, no. 1, p. 637, https://doi.org/10.1038/ncomms1642.

Chang, M.M., Chen, P.J., Wang, Y.Q., and Wang, Y., 2003, The Jehol Biota: Shanghai, China, Shanghai Scientific and Technical Publishers, 208 p.

Chen, P., Dong, Z., and Zhen, S., 1998, An exceptionally well-preserved theropod dinosaur from the Yixian Formation of China: Nature, v. 391, p. 147–152, https://doi.org/10.1038/34356.

Chiappe, L., and Qingjin, M., 2016, Birds of Stone: Chinese Avian Fossils from the Age of Dinosaurs: Baltimore, Maryland, Johns Hopkins University Press, 304 p.

Clarke, J., 2013, Feathers before flight: Science, v. 340, p. 690–692, https://doi.org/10.1126/science.1235463.

Coniff, R., 2018, The great Chinese dinosaur boom: Smithsonian Magazine, www.smithsonianmag.com/science-nature/great-chinese-dino-boom-180968745/ (accessed 13 July 2021).

Conway, J., Kosemen, C.M., and Naish, D., 2013, All Yesterdays: Unique and Speculative Views of Dinosaurs and Other Prehistoric Animals: Lexington, Kentucky, Irregular Books, 100 p.

Currie, P.J., and Padian, K., eds., 1997, Encyclopedia of Dinosaurs: San Diego, California, Academic Press, 869 p.

Currie, P.J., Koppelhus, E.B., Shugar, M.A., and Wright, J.L., 2004, Feathered Dragons: Studies on the Transition from Dinosaurs to Birds: Bloomington, Indiana University Press, 376 p.

Dawson, G., 2016, Show Me the Bone: Reconstructing Prehistoric Monsters in Nineteenth-Century Britain and America: Chicago, University of Chicago Press, 476 p., https://doi.org/10.7208/chicago/9780226332871.001.0001.

Debus, A.A., and Debus, D.E., 2002, Paleoimagery: The Evolution of Dinosaurs in Art: Jefferson, North Carolina, McFarland and Co., 293 p.

Desmond, A., 1975, The Hot-Blooded Dinosaurs: A Revolution in Palaeontology: New York, Dial Press, 238 p.

Desmond, A., 1982, Archetypes and Ancestors: Palaeontology in Victorian London 1850–1875: Chicago, University of Chicago Press, 287 p.

Diamond, J., and Bond, A.B., 2013, Concealing Coloration in Animals: Cambridge, Massachusetts, Harvard University Press, 271 p., https://doi.org/10.4159/harvard.9780674074200.

Frey, R.W., and Seilacher, A., 1980, Uniformity in marine invertebrate ichnology: Lethaia, v. 13, p. 183–207, https://doi.org/10.1111/j.1502-3931.1980.tb00632.x.

Gee, H., and Rey, L., 2003, A Field Guide to Dinosaurs: The Essential Handbook for Travelers in the Mesozoic: London, Quarto Publishing, 144 p.

Gleason, A., 2018 (22 June), The real reason feathered dinosaurs won't appear in Jurassic Park has nothing to do with science: The Federalist, https://thefederalist.com/2018/06/22/real-reason-feathered-dinosaurs-wont-appear-jurassic-park-nothing-science/ (accessed March 2021).

Glut, D., 1982, The New Dinosaur Dictionary: Secaucus, New Jersey, Citadel Press, 288 p.

Godefroit, P., Sinitsa, S.M., Dhouailly, D., Bolotsky, Y.L., Sizov, A.V., McNamara, M.E., Benton, M.J., and Spagna, P., 2014, A Jurassic ornithischian dinosaur from Siberia with both feathers and scales: Science, v. 345, p. 451–455, https://doi.org/10.1126/science.1253351.

Greshko, M., 2020, Reimagining dinosaurs: National Geographic, v. 238, no. 4, p. 38–89.

Holtz, T.R., Jr., and Rey, L.V. (illustrator), 2007, Dinosaurs: The Most Complete, Up-to-Date Encyclopedia for Dinosaur Lovers of All Ages: New York, Random House, 432 p.

Hu, D., Clarke, J.A., Eliason, C.M., Qiu, R., Li, Q., Shawkey, M.D., Zhao, C., D'Alba, L., Jiang, J., and Xu, X., 2018, A bony-crested Jurassic dinosaur with evidence of iridescent plumage highlights complexity in early paravian evolution: Nature Communications, v. 9, https://doi.org/10.1038/s41467-017-02515-y.

Lambert, D., 1983, A Field Guide to Dinosaurs. The First Complete Guide to Every Dinosaur now Known: New York, Diagram Group/Avon Books, 256 p.

Lambert, D., 1990, The Dinosaur Data Book. Facts and Fictions about the World's Largest Creatures: New York, Diagram Group/Avon Books, 320 p.

Li, Q., Gao, K.Q., Vinther, J., Shawkey, M.D., Clarke, J.A., D'Alba, L., Meng, Q., Briggs, D.E.G., and Prum, R.O., 2010, Plumage color patterns of an extinct dinosaur: Science, v. 327, p. 1369–1372, https://doi.org/10.1126/science.1186290.

Li, Q., Gao, K.Q., Meng, Q., Clarke, J.A., Shawkey, M.D., D'Alba, L., Pei, R., Ellison, M., Norell, M.A., and Vinther, J., 2012, Reconstruction of *Microraptor* and the evolution of iridescent plumage: Science, v. 335, p. 1215–1219, https://doi.org/10.1126/science.1213780.

Long, J., and Schouten, P., 2008, Feathered Dinosaurs: The Origin of Birds: Oxford, UK, Oxford University Press, 193 p.

Manning, P.L., Edwards, N.P., Wogelius, R.A., Bergmann, U., Barden, H.E., Larson, P.L., Schwarz-Wings, D., Egerton, V.M., Sokaras, D., Mori, R.A., and Sellers, W.I., 2013, Synchrotron-based chemical imaging reveals plumage patterns in a 150 million year old early bird: Journal of Analytical Atomic Spectrometry, v. 28, no. 7, p. 1024, https://doi.org/10.1039/c3ja50077b.

McCarthy, S., and Gilbert, M., 1994, The Crystal Palace Dinosaurs. The Story of the World's First Prehistoric Sculptures: London, The Crystal Palace Foundation, 99 p.

Norell, M., 2005, Unearthing the Dragon: The Great Feathered Dinosaur Discovery: New York, Pi Press, 254 p.

Norell, M.A., and Xu, X., 2005, Feathered dinosaurs: Annual Review of Earth and Planetary Sciences, v. 33, p. 277–299, https://doi.org/10.1146/annurev.earth.33.092203.122511.

Northcut, K.M., 2011, Insights from illustrators: The rhetorical invention of paleontology representations: Technical Communication Quarterly, v. 20, no. 3, p. 303–326, https://doi.org/10.1080/10572252.2011.578236.

Opfer, C., 2017, Why won't Hollywood depict dinosaurs with feathers?: How Stuff Works: https://animals.howstuffworks.com/dinosaurs/why-no-feathers-on-movie-dinosaurs.htm (accessed October 2019).

Ostrom, J.H., 1969, Osteology of *Deinonychus antirrhopus*, an unusual theropod from the Lower Cretaceous of Montana: Bulletin of the Peabody Museum of Natural History, Yale University, v. 30, p. 1–165.

Owen, R., 1842, Report on British fossil reptiles. Part II: Report of the British Association for the Advancement of Science (Plymouth Meeting), p. 60–204.

Owen, R., 1854, Geology and Inhabitants of the Ancient World: London, Bradbury and Evans, 39 p.

Padian, K., 1987, The case of the bat-winged pterosaur: Typological taxonomy and the influence of pictorial representation on scientific perception, *in* Czerkas, S.J., and Olson, E.C., eds., Dinosaurs Past and Present, Volume 2: Los Angeles and Seattle, Natural History Museum of Los Angeles County in association with University of Washington Press, p. 64–81.

Paul, G.S., 1987, The science and art of restoring the life appearance of dinosaurs and their relatives: A rigorous how-to guide, *in* Czerkas, S.J., and Olson, E.C., eds., Dinosaurs Past and Present, Volume 2: Los Angeles and

Seattle, Natural History Museum of Los Angeles County in association with University of Washington Press., p. 64–81, p. 4–49.

Paul, G.S., 1988, Predatory Dinosaurs of the World: New York, Simon & Schuster, 464 p.

Paul, G.S., 2002, Dinosaurs of the Air: The Evolution and Loss of Flight in Dinosaurs and Birds: Baltimore, Maryland, Johns Hopkins University Press, 472 p.

Pickrell, J., 2014a, Flying Dinosaurs: How Fearsome Reptiles Became Birds: New York, Columbia University Press, 215 p., https://doi.org/10.7312/pick17178.

Pickrell, J., 2014b (5 July), Why *Jurassic Park* had it all wrong: Australian Geographic: https://www.australiangeographic.com.au/blogs/austropalaeo/2014/07/why-jurassic-park-had-it-all-wrong/ (accessed October 2019).

Pickrell, J., 2014c (28 Nov.), *Jurassic World*'s dinosaurs lack feathers—and authenticity: Sydney Morning Herald: https://www.smh.com.au/opinion/jurassic-worlds-dinosaurs-lack-feathers--and-authenticity-20141127-11vjs1.html (accessed October 2019).

Preiss, B., and Silverberg, R., eds., 1992, The Ultimate Dinosaur: Past, Present, and Future: New York, Bantam Books, 336 p.

Prum, R.O., 2006, Anatomy, physics, and evolution of structural colors: Bird Coloration, v. 1, p. 295–353.

Rey, L., 2001, Extreme Dinosaurs: San Francisco, California, Chronicle Books, 62 p.

Ross, R.M., Duggan-Haas, D., and Allmon, W.D., 2013, The posture of *T. rex*: Why do student views lag behind the science?: Journal of Geoscience Education, v. 61, p. 145–160, https://doi.org/10.5408/11-259.1.

Ryan, M.J., and Russell, A.P., 1997, Color, *in* Currie, P.J., and Padian, K., eds., Encyclopedia of Dinosaurs: San Diego, California, Academic Press, p. 134–135.

Secord, J.A., 2004, Monsters at the Crystal Palace, *in* DeChardarevian, S., and Hopwood, N., eds., Models: The Third Dimension of Science: Stanford, California, Stanford University Press, p. 138–169.

Shea, J.H., 1982, Twelve fallacies of uniformitarianism: Geology, v. 10, p. 455–460, https://doi.org/10.1130/0091-7613(1982)10<455:TFOU>2.0.CO;2.

Skrepnick, M., 2005, *Sinosauropteryx*: Mysterious Feathered Dinosaur: New York, Enslow Elementary, 24 p.

Sloan, C.P., 1999, Feathers for *T. rex*?: National Geographic, v. 196, no. 5, p. 98–107.

Sloan, C.P., 2000, Feathered Dinosaurs: Washington, D.C., National Geographic Society, 64 p.

Smithwick, F.M., Nicholls, R., Cuthill, I.C., and Vinther, J., 2017, Countershading and stripes in the theropod dinosaur *Sinosauropteryx* reveal heterogeneous habitats in the Early Cretaceous Jehol Biota: Current Biology, v. 27, p. 3337–3343, https://doi.org/10.1016/j.cub.2017.09.032.

Swinton, W.E., 1969, Dinosaurs: London, British Museum (Natural History), 47 p.

Switek, B., 2013, The truth about *T. rex*: Nature, v. 502, p. 424–426, https://doi.org/10.1038/502424a.

Tan, A., 2016 (15 June), The art of deciding what color dinosaurs are is part paleontology, part palette-ontology: ABC News: https://abcnews.go.com/Technology/art-deciding-color-dinosaurs-part-paleontology-part-palette/story?id=39227262 (accessed October 2019).

Taquet, P., and Padian, K., 2004, The earliest known restoration of a pterosaur and the philosophical origins of Cuvier's *Ossemens Fossiles*: Comptes Rendus Palévol, v. 3, p. 157–175, https://doi.org/10.1016/j.crpv.2004.02.002.

Terakado, K., ed., 2017, The Art of the Dinosaur: Tokyo, PIE International, 199 p.

Torrens, H.S., 2012, Politics and paleontology: Richard Owen and the invention of dinosaurs, *in* Brett Surman, M.K., Holtz, T.R., Jr., and Farlow, J.O., eds., The Complete Dinosaur: Bloomington, Indiana University Press, p. 25–44.

Tudge, C., 2009, The Bird: A Natural History of Who Birds Are, Where They Came from, and How They Live: New York, Crown, 480 p.

Turner, A.H., Makovicky, P.J., and Norell, M.A., 2007, Feather quill knobs in the dinosaur *Velociraptor*: Science, v. 317, p. 1721, https://doi.org/10.1126/science.1145076.

Turner, D.D., 2016, A second look at the colors of the dinosaurs: Studies in History and Philosophy of Science Part A, v. 55, p. 60–68, https://doi.org/10.1016/j.shpsa.2015.08.012.

Unwin, D.M., 1998, Feathers, filaments and theropod dinosaurs: Nature, v. 391, p. 119–120, https://doi.org/10.1038/34279.

Vinther, J., 2020, Reconstructing vertebrate paleocolor: Annual Review of Earth and Planetary Sciences, v. 48, p. 345–375, https://doi.org/10.1146/annurev-earth-073019-045641.

Vinther, J., Nicholls, R., Lautenschlager, S., Pittman, M., Kaye, T.G., Rayfield, E., Mayr, G., and Cuthill, I.C., 2016, 3D camouflage in an ornithischian dinosaur: Current Biology, v. 26, no. 18, p. 2456–2462, https://doi.org/10.1016/j.cub.2016.06.065.

Walters, B., and Kissinger, T., 2014, Discovering Dinosaurs: Kennebunkport, Maine, Applesauce Press, 143 p.

White, S., ed., 2012, Dinosaur Art: The World's Greatest Paleoart: London, Titan Books, 188 p.

White, S., ed., 2017, Dinosaur Art II: The Cutting Edge of Paleoart: London, Titan Books, 188 p.

Witmer, L.M., 1995, The extant phylogenetic bracket and the importance of reconstructing soft tissues in fossils, *in* Thomason, J., ed., Functional Morphology in Vertebrate Paleontology: Cambridge, UK, Cambridge University Press, p. 19–33.

Witton, M.P., 2018, The Palaeoartist's Handbook: Recreating Prehistoric Animals in Art: Wiltshire, UK, Crowood Press, Ltd., 224 p.

Xu, X., and Norell, M.A., 2006, Non-avian dinosaur fossils from the Lower Cretaceous Jehol Group of western Liaoning, China: Geological Journal, v. 41, p. 419–437, https://doi.org/10.1002/gj.1044.

Xu, X., Norell, M.A., Kuang, X., Wang, X., Zhao, Q., and Jia, C., 2004, Basal tyrannosaurids from China and evidence for protofeathers in tyrannosaurids: Nature, v. 431, p. 680–684, https://doi.org/10.1038/nature02855.

Xu, X., Wang, K., Zhang, K., Ma, Q., Xing, L., Sullivan, C., Hu, D., Cheng, S., and Wang, S., 2012, A gigantic feathered dinosaur from the Lower Cretaceous of China: Nature, v. 484, p. 92–95, https://doi.org/10.1038/nature10906.

Zhang, F., Kearns, S.L., Orr, P.J., Benton, M.J., Zhou, Z., Johnson, D., Xu, X., and Wang, X., 2010, Fossilized melanosomes and the color of Cretaceous dinosaurs and birds: Nature, v. 463, p. 1075–1078, https://doi.org/10.1038/nature08740.

Zheng, X.T., You, H.L., Xu, X., and Dong, Z.M., 2009, An early Cretaceous heterodontosaurid dinosaur with filamentous integumentary structures: Nature, v. 458, p. 333–336, https://doi.org/10.1038/nature07856.

Zhou, Z., Barrett, P.M., and Hilton, J., 2004, An exceptionally preserved Lower Cretaceous ecosystem: Nature, v. 421, p. 807–814.

Manuscript Accepted by the Society 14 January 2021
Manuscript Published Online 5 November 2021

Printed in the USA

The Geological Society of America
Memoir 218

A quest for perfection in science and art: The paleontological legacy of Manfred Reichel (1896–1984)

Mario M.A. Wannier
Chemin des Vignes 5, 1806 St-Légier, Switzerland

ABSTRACT

Professor of paleontology at the University of Basel, Switzerland, Manfred Reichel was as much an accomplished scientist as a talented artist. Skilled in mental 3-D-visualization, aided by a sharp memory, and with a fine hand for illustration, he introduced comparative anatomy to the study of foraminifera, which is masterly illustrated in his analysis of Alveolinids, and used his knowledge of locomotion in modern birds as an actualistic method for portraying flying reptiles. Teaching was his motivation, and to aid his classes, beyond multiple drawings, he created a large number of scaled structural models of foraminifera and a life-size wooden replica of the *Pteranodon* with mobile articulations. Manfred Reichel was a perfectionist who left a large part of his studies and drawings unpublished.

INTRODUCTION

The link between scientific observations and artistic representations is especially strong in the branches of geology dealing with reconstructions of past environments and extinct creatures. The need to assemble puzzles from a fragmentary fossil record leads inevitably to an overlap between science and art. Reconstructions must account for all available datapoints and be displayed in an imaginary way to illustrate salient features. Here, we review the career and work of Manfred Reichel (1896–1984), an eminent paleontologist who excelled as a scientist as well as an artist.

MANFRED REICHEL'S LIFE AND CAREER

Manfred Reichel was born in 1896 and grew up in Montmirail, a boarding school near Neuchâtel, Switzerland, that was directed by his father. After losing his parents at the age of 11, Reichel was raised by his uncle, Alfred Richard, a keen ornithologist with whom he regularly observed birds in the surrounding lowlands, swamps, and lake shores. After completing his baccalaureate, he entered the Geneva School of Fine Arts (1916–1918), where he learned the skills necessary to achieve highly refined drawings. He later returned to pursue studies in zoology at the University of Neuchâtel (1918–1926). There, he also enrolled in the Geology Department (1923–1928) and worked as an assistant to Émile Argand. This professor, who was proficient in geometrical reconstructions and had a natural propensity for drawing, remained a role model for Reichel. Under his request, Reichel translated Alfred Wegener's *The Origin of Continents and Oceans* into French (Wegener, 1924), which provided first-time access of this seminal work to the French-speaking community of geologists; in Switzerland, Wegener's concepts were quickly accepted and tested on Alpine tectonics problems (Carozzi, 1985). Reichel's dissertation on the anatomy of a blind catfish from Brazil (Reichel, 1927) earned him the Léon DuPasquier Prize, which is bestowed by the University of Neuchâtel for outstanding scientific contribution.

In 1928, Reichel was hired by the University of Basel, where he would spend the rest of his career. His first job was assistant

Wannier, M.M.A, 2022, A quest for perfection in science and art: The paleontological legacy of Manfred Reichel (1896–1984), *in* Clary, R.M., Rosenberg, G.D., and Evans, D.C., eds., The Evolution of Paleontological Art: Geological Society of America Memoir 218, p. 221–228, https://doi.org/10.1130/2021.1218(24).

at the Geological-Paleontological Institute, and from 1933 on he served as a lecturer in micropaleontology. In 1940 he was promoted to professor and director of the Department of Paleontology, a position from which he retired in 1966 (Fig. 1).

During his tenure, the Department of Paleontology in Basel became famous and attracted visiting micropaleontologists from far and wide. Reichel's original approach to the study of foraminifera and his ability to interpret random cuts of skeletal elements from thin sections in three dimensions made him a recognized authority in the field of micropaleontology. Students of Reichel successfully entered the oil industry and the academic world; at the University of Basel, Professor L. Hottinger continued and diversified the fields of study pioneered by Reichel.

In the years 1956, 1958, and 1962, Reichel worked part-time as an expert for the United Nations to set up a laboratory for micropaleontology in Athens. The University of Dijon named him *Dr. honoris causa* in 1957. In 1966, at the end of his career, Reichel was honored with a dedicated issue of the *Swiss Journal of Geosciences* (*Eclogae Geologicae Helvetiae*, v. 59) and with the special publication *Benthos '83* following the Second International Symposium on Benthic Foraminifera (Pau, France, April 1983). Reichel married Lydia Buck in 1928 and had two daughters; he passed away in Basel in 1984 at the age of 88.

MANFRED REICHEL'S LEGACY

The Teacher's Skills

"If you have not drawn it, you have not seen it." That was what Reichel used to tell his students. Judging by the voluminous legacy papers conserved in his archives at the Basel Natural History Museum (NMB), Reichel must have been drawing every day, creating elaborate sketches and fine illustrations with graphite pencils. He used goose quills for ink drawings as he found the metal pen tips too hard to vary the width of the flowing ink. When the objects he drew were too tiny to be seen sharply under the microscope, he used a stippling technique.

Foraminifera, reptiles, and birds were the main subjects of his scientific studies. Every element, to its finest details, was studied and drawn multiple times, dissected, and reconstructed under various orientations, all done at scale with a *camera lucida*. His sense of perfection drove him to discard even the most complete drawings if he had the smallest doubt about this or that detail.

Reichel was extraordinarily gifted in the 3-D interpretation of the complex inner structures of foraminifera as seen in thin sections. This ability allowed him to reverse-engineer random geometric cuts through organisms into an organized spatial architecture (Leria-Morillo, 2015) and to reconstruct the entire body and inner skeleton of larger foraminifera found embedded within indurated limestones.

Reichel created plasticine models of the inner structure of the larger foraminifera he was studying (Fig. 2). In this process, he used to slice his prototypes along various orientations to verify if the figure of the cut matched what he observed in the thin sections, remodeling them as he progressed in his interpretation. His finalized models were made of plasticine, beeswax, wood, or earthenware. Reichel used his structural models of foraminifera as a teaching tool. Considering the depth of his research, he published relatively few accounts of his work. Reichel was a coauthor of the *Treatise on Invertebrate Paleontology*, which dealt with foraminifera (Loeblich et al., 1964).

Planktonic Foraminifera

Reichel was a pioneer in the study of fossil planktonic foraminifera. He used to prepare individual specimens by heating

Figure 1. Portrait of Manfred Reichel in 1965 (with permission by NMB Basel).

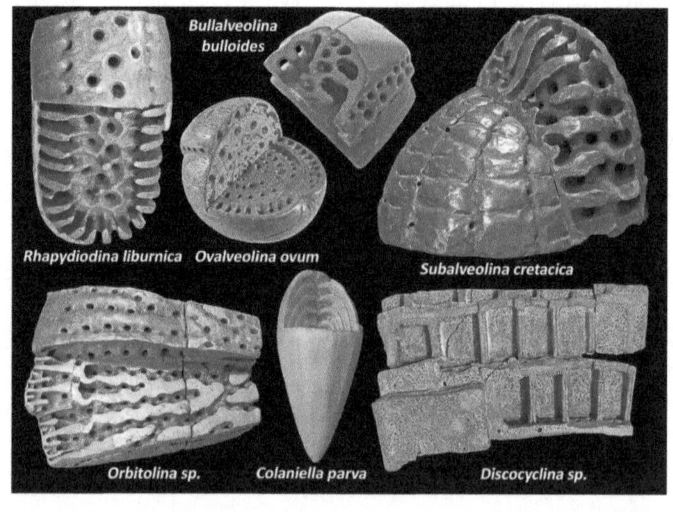

Figure 2. Plasticine models showing the internal structure of selected foraminifera (no scale; Manfred Reichel's teaching material; with permission by NMB Basel).

them, which rendered them opaque, and then observed them under a drop of water or clove oil (Reichel, 1948, 1953). To observe diagnostic features in their umbilical openings (at a scale of 50 μm), which were generally hidden under a sediment coating, Reichel cleaned his specimens under a binocular microscope; he first used a fine metal needle or a cactus spine and then, to reveal the finer details, he used bumblebee hair (Luterbacher, 1986) or a wasp stinger mounted on a wooden handle (Hottinger, 2013). In this way, he was able to demonstrate the complex chamber apertures that characterize the Albian-Cenomanian genera *Ticinella*, which he named, and *Rotalipora*. He was one of the first to describe the association of minute planktonic foraminifera present at the base of the Paleocene following the massive extinction event that marks the end of the Maastrichtian (Reichel, 1953).

Schakoina are minute planktonic foraminifera with a spinal extension of the chambers that appeared during the Albian. Reichel pioneered the study of their morphology and evolution, combining observations from loose specimens and specimens found in thin sections. He recognized three new species and two new subspecies and illustrated them with drawings (Reichel, 1948) and plasticine models enlarged 100 times. Various sketches and meticulous drawings of *Schakoina* demonstrate Reichel's precision in illustrating these foraminifera, which he drew and redrew in various orientations and under different light conditions with pencil shadings and stippling before submitting to print (Fig. 3).

Alveolinid Larger Foraminifera

Manfred Reichel made the greatest impact through his detailed analysis of the internal structure of Alveolinids, a group of larger foraminifera that lived in the Tethys seas. Despite being unicellular organisms, Alveolinids build shells that can be centimeters long and have a rounded to cigar shape with a complex inner architecture. Emerging during the Late Cretaceous, this group of extant larger foraminifera has a record of appearances and disappearances during the last 100 Ma; through the Paleogene, they could be locally abundant in sufficient numbers to form massive "*Alveolina* limestones."

These larger foraminifera are rarely found as loose specimens, and their study relies largely on the analysis of random thin sections, which yield only a partial 2-D view of a specimen. Reichel had the extraordinary ability to interpret the shape of the inner structures (walls, canals, apertures) as cut randomly by the thin section and then reconstruct the entire 3-D figure of the foraminifera (Fig. 4). Reichel's major achievement was in deciphering the internal architecture of Alveolinids, and by comparing details of their anatomy, showing how the structural elements were reorganized and modified through time. This allowed him to set up clear taxonomic criteria that tracked the group's evolution and made it a tool for biostratigraphic dating (Reichel, 1931, 1937). His drawings of Alveolinids, which show the entire skeleton with equatorial, axial, and oblique sections all in one,

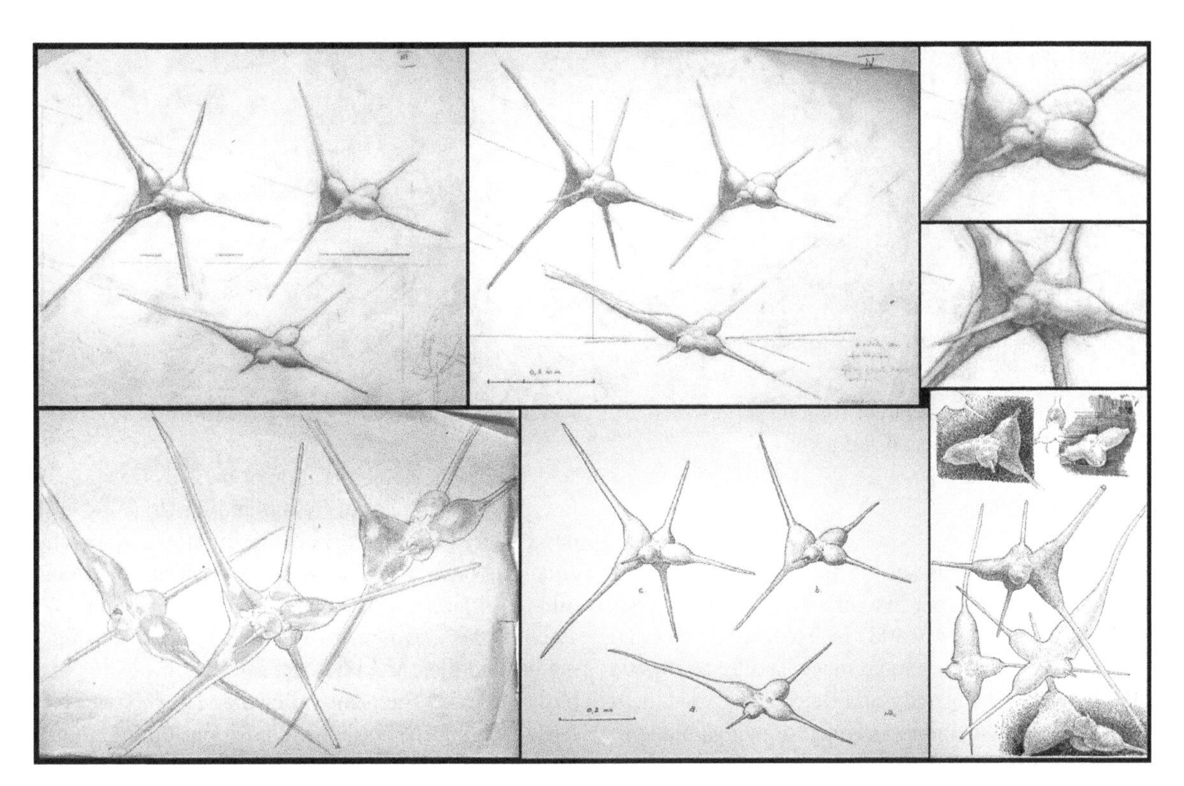

Figure 3. Pencil and ink drawings of planktonic foraminifer *Schakoina* (×125; Manfred Reichel, 1948; with permission by NMB Basel).

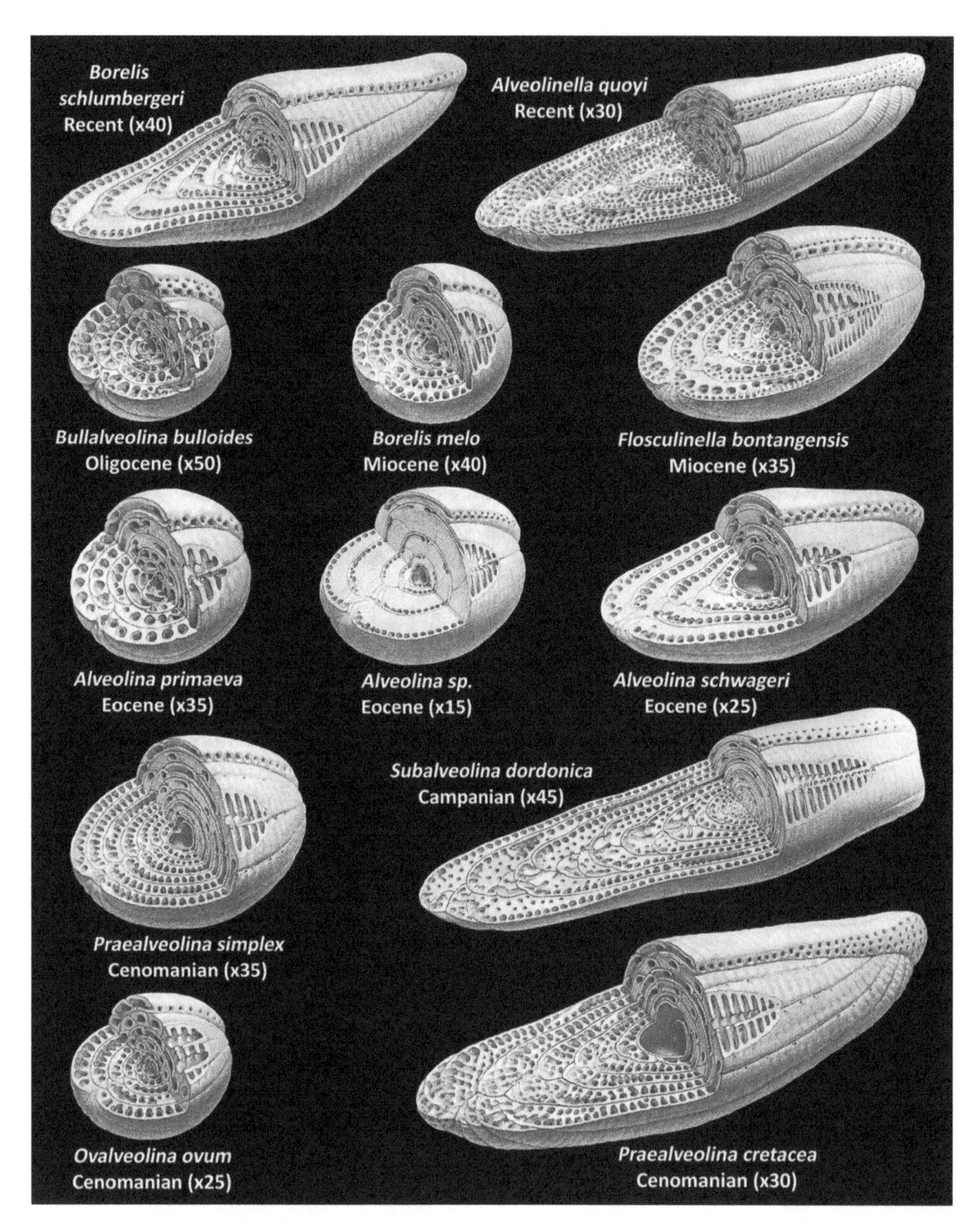

Figure 4. Pencil drawings showing the internal structure of Alveolinid foraminifera (modified from Manfred Reichel, 1937; with permission by the Commission for the *Swiss Journal of Palaeontology*).

are iconic representations of these larger foraminifera, which are found unaltered in all modern specialized textbooks.

Other Larger Foraminifera

When Reichel arrived in Basel, he found rich micropaleontological collections that were assembled by oil geologists practicing in many parts of the world. Isolated specimens and rock samples of all groups of larger and many smaller benthonic foraminifera were available for study, and Reichel analyzed them meticulously. Multiple plasticine models and drawings made to illustrate his lessons for the benefit of his students, but which were never published, attest to his careful attention to this group of unicellular fauna (Fig. 5).

Reichel's Interest in Aerial Locomotion

Trained in the observation of birds by his uncle, Reichel was fascinated by the act of flying, and his drawings of birds are as numerous as his drawings of foraminifera. His archives include countless drawings of birds in all positions but mainly in flight, often at a meter-scale, drawn on large wrapping paper. Reichel assembled a comprehensive collection of prepared wings that maintained their articulations, and he drew wings of all common birds at scale. Frequently illustrated in his archives are time-lapse drawings of bird's wing positions during flight; high-speed photography did not exist at the time, and he had to rely on his photographic memory to dissect the bird's movements in time-steps. For an ornithological congress held in Basel in 1954, he

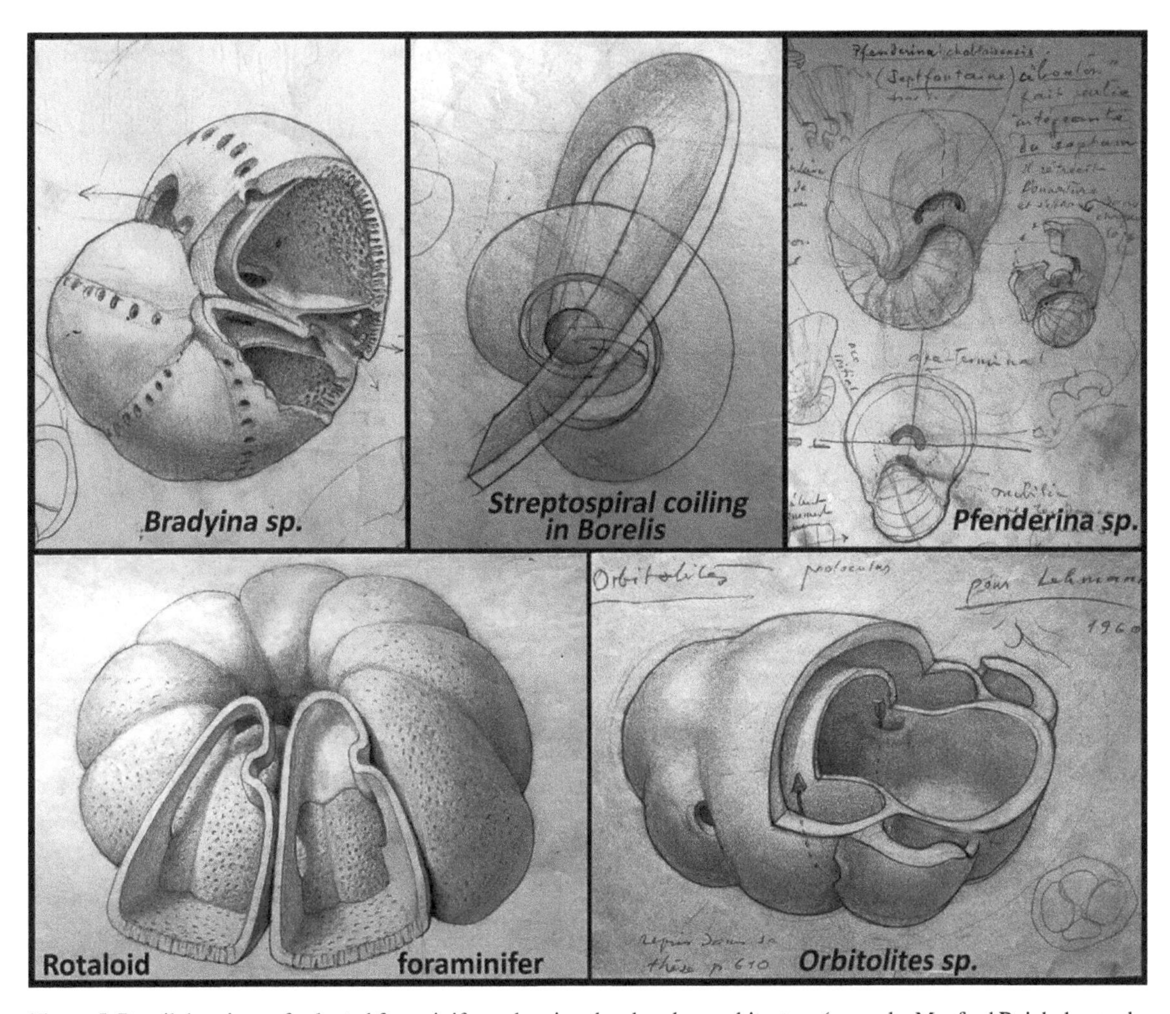

Figure 5. Pencil drawings of selected foraminifera, showing the chamber architecture (no scale; Manfred Reichel, unpublished drawings; with permission by NMB Basel).

prepared a mobile model representing one square millimeter of a pigeon wing flight feather (Luterbacher, 1986). His full-scale, mobile wooden model of a *Pteranodon* skeleton hung over the paleontological collections at the institute before it was moved to the Natural History Museum at Basel, where it is now exhibited in the right entrance hall.

Reichel's interest in aerial locomotion extended to Jurassic pterosaurs and *Archaeopteryx*, which he studied first-hand during an extended visit to Munich in 1935/1936 and which were central to his lectures in vertebrate paleontology. He combined his analysis of their skeleton parts and his knowledge of modern birds to create pictures of the prehistoric animals on the ground and in the sky, which were rendered in highly finished drawings (Reichel, 1941; Hottinger, 1985; Fig. 6). His reconstruction of the plumage of *Archaeopteryx* is confirmed by the discovery of new fossils in China that show the entire body covered in pennaceous feathers. In the later years of his life, Reichel came to use the electron microscope to observe details of bird feathers where he recognized minute hooks and loops on the barbs; he thought of them as a "Velcro-like" device that allowed barbs to reattach themselves for repair.

MEMORY AND OBSERVATIONS

Reichel used his photographic memory to draw, from memory, the portraits of scientists and visitors to the institute as well as those of casual encounters. For him it was an exercise of observation and memory that he maintained throughout his whole life. His fine sense of humor is revealed in some of his portraits, which he kept for his eyes only (Fig. 7).

CONCLUSIONS

Reichel was a pioneer in applying comparative anatomy to track the structural modifications of the endoskeleton of larger foraminifera through geological time. The presence or absence of structural elements of the test led him to define new genera. He was primarily a taxonomist who worked out the development of

Figure 6. Pencil and ink drawings of pterosaurs and *Archaeopteryx* are shown (no scale; Manfred Reichel, 1941; used with permission from the Geological-Paleontological Institute in Basel and © *Nos Oiseaux* [GPI]/[NO]).

Figure 7. Left to right: Pencil sketch of a *Sinanthropus* head and portraits of paleoanthropologist G.H.R von Koenigswald; Professor Ernst Staehelin, Basel; French micropaleontologist Pierre Marie (Manfred Reichel, unpublished drawings; with permission by NMB Basel)

foraminifera from the Carboniferous to the Recent. His drawings and models of foraminifera, executed in observance of measurements and proportions and composed with style and finesse, are as much scientific masterpieces as they are finished artworks.

Academic interest in the study of larger foraminifera, particularly their structure, largely subsided at the turn of the century, and few attempts have been made to revisit Reichel's interpretations. A recent study of an Alveolinid using computed tomography scan analysis (Kellner et al., 2019) concluded by fully upholding Reichel's published results and confirmed the durability of his work. Reichel's Alveolinid illustrations remain the standard in modern micropaleontology, which is a testimony to his lasting influence through paleontological illustration.

Reichel's main contribution to paleontological art and science in general is his insistence on scientific precision and particularly on the accuracy of paleontological illustrations. While his illustrations of Alveolinids are well known and remain relevant today, his studies on aerial locomotion include a large number of unpublished illustrations and diagrams. As nature is beautiful in the eyes of man, so it must be reflected in scientific illustrations; Reichel strived to achieve this aim and was aided by outstanding talent and intellect.

PERSONAL REFLECTIONS ON MANFRED REICHEL

Manfred Reichel was a retired professor at the Geological-Paleontological Institute in Basel when I was a student. I remember him as a true gentleman in every aspect of his personality; he was always affable and offering to help. Under his guidance, my wife created ceramic replicas of many of his plasticine models, as over time the original exemplars were drying up and becoming too brittle to be handled by students. Nearly all of these structural models of Alveolinids, a delicate reproduction of a *Globotruncana* made of beeswax, and his entire collection of bird wings went missing during the relocation to the Basel Natural History Museum early in this century.

Throughout his life, Reichel felt strongly bound to the great tradition of geology in Neuchâtel, where Louis Agassiz was a professor before moving to the United States; for him, visiting the city of his youth was almost a pilgrimage. On one occasion I accompanied Reichel to the dark chamber to print photographs of thin sections. He favored long exposure time with a narrow aperture opening, so we often waited a minute or more for the photographic paper to be properly exposed. As he never looked at his watch, I asked him how he measured time. He told me that he closed his eyes and followed the flight of seagulls as he saw them on Lake Neuchâtel, with a wing flapping rhythm of 1.3 seconds, until the exposure time was up! Perhaps in the horizon he also portrayed the snowy summits of the Alps, which he had studied with Émile Argand.

ACKNOWLEDGMENTS

Michael Knappertsbusch (Natural History Museum Basel) offered access to the archives of Manfred Reichel, provided copies of documents, and granted copyright clearance for Figures 1, 2, 3, 5, and 7. Please note that the original drawings are deposited in the geological archive of the Natural History Museum Basel. Hanspeter Luterbacher (Barcelona), Edith Müller-Merz (Basel), Pierre Reichel (Lausanne), Verena Scheuring (Basel), and Dominik A. Tröster (Magden) shared personal details about Reichel and commented on the text. Esmeralda Caus (Barcelona) provided access to the thesis of Maria Leria Morillo. Reviewers comments by Renee Clary (Mississippi State University), James O. Farlow (Purdue University), Christian Koeberl (GSA Books science editor), Liz Nesbitt (University of Washington), Dallas Evans (lead curator of Natural Science and Paleontology at The Children's Museum of Indianapolis), and Gary Rosenberg (Indiana University–Purdue University, Milwaukee Public Museum) are gratefully acknowledged. Copyright clearance to reproduce drawings published in the Swiss Paleontological Society, in the

Journal *Nos Oiseaux*, and in a publication by the Geological-Paleontological Institute in Basel were granted respectively by Daniel Marty (Zurich), Bertrand Posse (Martigny), and Dominik Fleitmann (Basel).

REFERENCES CITED

Carozzi, A., 1985, The reaction in continental Europe to Wegener's theory of continental drift: Earth Sciences History, v. 4, no. 2, p. 122–137, https://doi.org/10.17704/eshi.4.2.a747p657926x8j58.

Hottinger, L., 1985, Manfred Reichel 1896–1984, Dessins, Mit Curriculum und Bibliographie. Institut Géologie-Paléontologie de l'Université de Bâle: Riehen, Switzerland, Schudeldruck, 60 p.

Hottinger, L., 2013, Micropaleontology in Basel (Switzerland) during the twentieth century, rise and fall of one of the smaller fields of the life sciences, *in* Bowden, A.J., Gregory, F.J., and Henderson, A.S., eds., Landmarks in Foraminiferal Micropaleontology, History and Development: The Micropalaeontological Society Special Publication, v. 6, p. 317–335, https://doi.org/10.1144/TMS6.23.

Kellner, S.K., Knappertsbusch, M.W., Costeur, L., Müller, B., and Schulz, G., 2019, Imaging the internal structure of *Borelis schlumbergeri* Reichel (1937): Advances by high-resolution hard X-ray microtomography: Palaeontologia Electronica, article no. 22.1.17A 1–19, https://doi.org/10.26879/854.

Leria Morillo, M., 2015, Dibujo Científico en Micropaleontología, Proceso en la Representación de Foraminíferos Fósiles, Interacción entre Arte y Ciencia [Ph.D. thesis]: Barcelona, España, Universitat de Barcelona, 421 p.

Loeblich, A.R., Jr., Tappan, H., Barker, W.R., Cole, S.W., Douglass, R.C., Reichel, M., and Thompson, M.L., 1964, Sarcodina, chiefly "Thecamoebians" and Foraminiferida, *in* Moore, R.C., ed., Treatise on Invertebrate Paleontology, Part C, Protista 2: Lawrence, Kansas, The University of Kansas, vols. 1 & 2, 900 p.

Luterbacher, H.P., 1986, Manfred Reichel (1896–1984): Bulletin de la Société Neuchâteloise des Sciences Naturelles, v. 109, p. 175–178.

Reichel, M., 1927, Étude anatomique du *Phreatobius cisternarum* Goeldi, silure aveugle du Brésil: Revue Suisse de Zoologie, v. 34, p. 285–401.

Reichel, M., 1931, Sur la structure des Alvéolines: Eclogae Geologicae Helvetiae, v. 24, no. 2, p. 289–303.

Reichel, M., 1937, Étude sur les Alvéolines: Mémoires de la Société Paléontologique Suisse, v. 57–59, p. 1–147.

Reichel, M., 1941, L'Archaeopteryx, un ancêtre des Oiseaux: Nos Oiseaux: Bulletin Société romande pour l'étude et la protection des oiseaux, v. 159, p. 93–107.

Reichel, M., 1948, Les Hantkéninidés de la Scalia et des Couches Rouges (Crétacé supérieur): Eclogae Geologicae Helvetiae, v. 40, no. 2, p. 391–409.

Reichel, M., 1953, Remarques sur les globigérines du Danien de Faxe (Danmark) et sur celles des couches de passage du Crétacé au Tertiaire dans la Scaglia de l'Apennin: Eclogae Geologicae Helvetiae, v. 45, no. 2, p. 341–349.

Wegener, A., 1924, La Genèse des Continents et des Océans (Translation by Manfred Reichel based on the 3rd German edition): Paris, Albert Blanchard, 161 p.

Manuscript Accepted by the Society 13 January 2021
Manuscript Published Online 21 September 2021

The Geological Society of America
Memoir 218

Paleontological postage stamps in art and education

Jere H. Lipps
Museum of Paleontology, University of California, Berkeley, California 94720, USA

Ajit Vartak
Department of Geology and Petroleum Technology, Wadia College, Pune, India

Ton Van Eijden
De Sparren 85, Bussum, The Netherlands

C. Rajshekhar
Department of Geology and Petroleum Technology, Wadia College, Pune, India

Sudha Vaddadi
Centre for Education and Research in Geosciences, Pune, India

Rohit Vartak
Department of Geology and Petroleum Technology, Wadia College, Pune, India

ABSTRACT

Postage stamps are small works of art seen by people worldwide that can be used effectively in education. The first paleontological stamp was released by India in 1951. Since then, over 4000 stamps with fossils, paleontologists, museums, and collecting sites have been issued by almost 200 countries. Stamps that illustrate fossils or reconstructions are intrinsically interesting and popular with many of the millions of stamp collectors. All disciplines of paleontology are represented, but dinosaurs are by far the most common subject, although even bacteria appear on a few stamps. Most of the stamps were scientifically accurate at the time they were issued though some artists took artistic liberties to fashion unique stamps. Overall, the stamps are artistic and educational because their small sizes and low cost make them easily accessible for classroom activities, exhibits, and presentations. They cover topics such as biodiversity, geology, ecology, oceanography, and evolution, among others. Paleophilately has provided art, education, joy, and happiness to people worldwide.

INTRODUCTION

Postage items focused on paleontology are popular among collectors and philatelists. Stamps attract millions of collectors who seek a wide assortment of stamps including those showing fossils. Fossil stamps can also be used in education at all levels to inform the history of life, plate tectonics, climate change, evolution, among other topics. These stamps are readily available from many sources, especially countries seeking income and private purveyors. This chapter is an introduction to the art

Lipps, J.H., Vartak, A., Van Eijden, T., Rajshekhar, C., Vaddadi, S., and Vartak, R., 2022, Paleontological postage stamps in art and education, *in* Clary, R.M., Rosenberg, G.D., and Evans, D.C., eds., The Evolution of Paleontological Art: Geological Society of America Memoir 218, p. 229–235, https://doi.org/10.1130/2021.1218(25).

and educational values of paleontological postage stamps. For detailed information, see references herein and the Paleophilately and Stampedout websites.[1]

The first stamp was issued in 1840 by England with an image of Queen Victoria (DeYoung, 1986). Other countries followed, also with images of important or famous people. That was also true for paleontological stamps. Thomas Jefferson, the third President of the United States, is considered a founder of vertebrate paleontology in America because he had a fondness for fossils; debated the Frenchman Georges-Louis Leclerc, Comte de Buffon, about vertebrate paleontology; and presented a paper at the American Philosophical Society 1797 meeting on *Megalonyx* or "Giant Claw," which later turned out to be a giant ground sloth. So, philatelists include Jefferson stamps, starting in 1856 and now numbering 139 different stamps[2] (Figs. 1A, 1B), but none include his paleontological interests and are focused on his presidential service. In this sense, his stamps are not paleontological but rather political; nevertheless, they can play an important role in education about stamps, philately, fossils, and presidents. The USSR issued stamps in 1947 showing actual paleontologists (Fig. 1C), and the Germans printed one with Agricola in 1955 (Fig. 1D), as did a few other countries.

[1]For information on and images of paleontological stamps, including history, current issues, links, and other items, see Paleophilatelie, "The Place Where Paleontology and Paleoanthropology Meets Philately": http://www.paleophilatelie.eu/index.html (accessed January 2020). For a thorough fossil stamp site with history, species lists, errors, and more, see Stampedout, "Prehistoric Life on Stamps": http://www.stampedout.nl/ (accessed September 2020).

Figure 1. (A, B) U.S. President Thomas Jefferson was enthusiastic about paleontology, took part in it, and even published a paper on it, but these stamps celebrate him as a president. Philatelists consider the stamps as an indication that he was important in paleontology too. USA, 1870 and 1857 (public domain). (C) Aleksandr Karpinskiy (1847–1936), a geologist and paleontologist and president of the Soviet Academy of Science from 1917 to his death in 1936. He worked in the Ural Mountains describing Permian fossils including the unusual shark *Helicoprion* with a coil of teeth extending outside and below the mouth. USSR, 1947. (D) Georgius Agricola, geologist and mineralogist, believed fossils formed in the earth from organic matter, failing to recognize them as the remains of once-living organisms. German Democratic Republic, 1955. (E) The first stamp to show an image of an extinct animal. The stamp shows an image of an extinct bovine, *Bos primigenius,* drawn on the wall of Lascaux Cave. It celebrates the cave paintings, not the fossil. Monaco, 1949. (F) An early stamp showing an ammonite issued in a semi-postal set. It was issued in cooperation with the Swiss Pro Patria as a way to earn funds for that patriotic and charitable organization. Switzerland, 1958; copyright Post CH AG. (G) A German advertising postcard with a dinosaur, ~1912. (Courtesy of Jon Noad.)

Stamps with images of fossils first appeared 109 years after England's first stamp, although paleontological subjects were illustrated on a postcard in 1912 (Fig. 1G), on a mailing envelope in 1922 (Fig. 2A), and later on cancellations and metered mail. An extinct bovine, *Bos primigenius,* appeared as an image of a Lascaux Cave painting on the first stamp to bear an extinct animal; it was distributed by Monaco in 1949 to celebrate the cave paintings not the animal (Fig. 1E). India released a stamp in 1951 with two reconstructed fossil elephants to honor the 100th anniversary of the Geological Survey of India, and Algeria did the same in 1952 with an ammonite on a stamp to welcome the XIX Geological Congress to the country. Cuba, China, and Switzerland also honored people and fossils early in 1958 (Fig. 1F). Mary Anning (1799–1847), a famous English fossil collector and seller of ichthyosaurs, plesiosaurs, pterosaurs, fish, and other fossils she found at Lyme Regis, England (Berta and Turner, 2020), was honored by Mozambique on the 165th anniversary (2012) of her death (Fig. 2B).

Colorful and popular, stamps and stamp sets illustrating fossils were increasingly issued globally. Interest in fossil stamps increased, especially for those bearing dinosaurs. For example, after the release of the movie *Jurassic Park* in 1993, which was seen by over two billion people worldwide, the United States issued the "World of Dinosaurs" souvenir sheet on 1 May 1997 to coordinate with the release of *The Lost World: Jurassic Park.* First day covers with fossils were routinely issued by countries as well. So far, nearly 200 countries have issued over 4000 paleontological stamps.[2]

[2]For information on stamps worldwide, see the American Topical Association website, especially the "Animals–Dinosaurs / Prehistoric Animals / Fossil" page: https://americantopical.org/Checklist-Topics#ANIMALS (accessed September 2020). Note, membership is required to access some information.

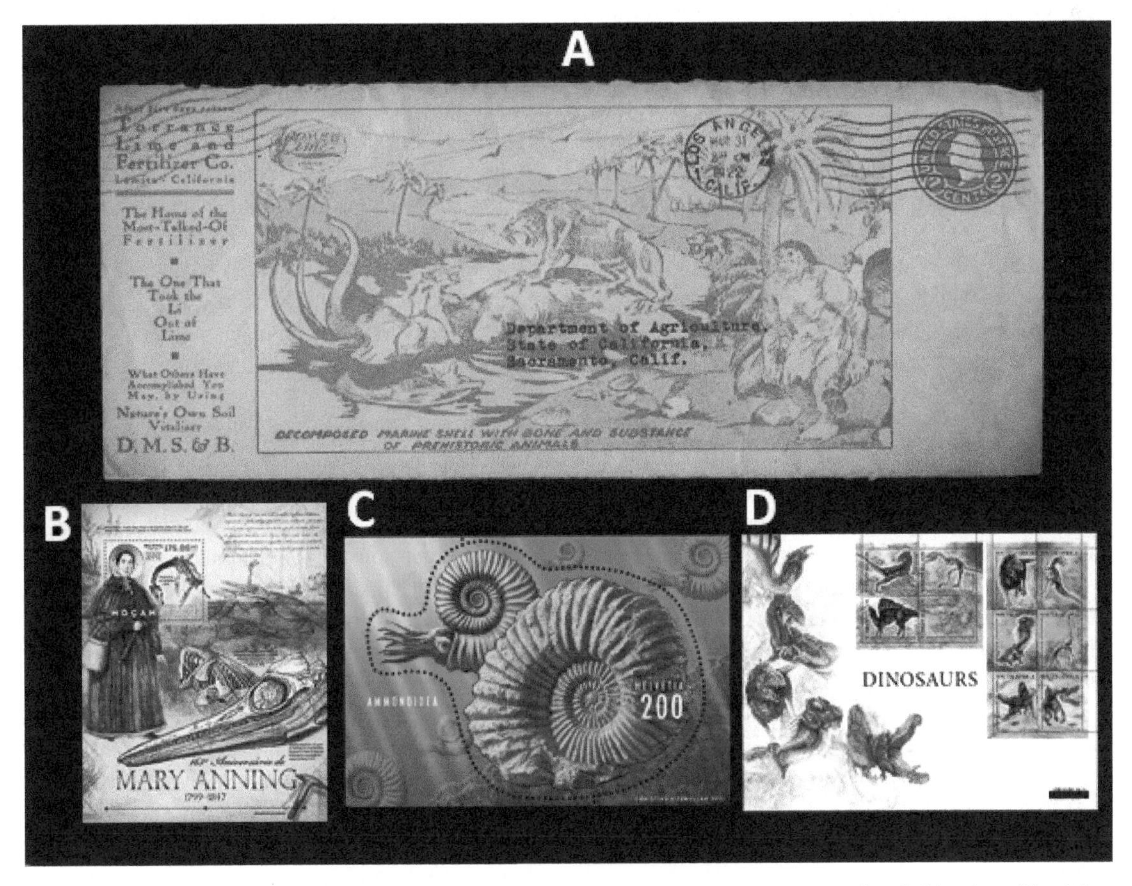

Figure 2. (A) A 1922 postal envelope by the Torrance Lime and Fertilizer Company, Lomita, California, utilized fossils in advertisements for mined marine shell bed material for fertilizer. Pleistocene sabretooth cats, dire wolves, and a Columbian mammoth, from the La Brea Tar Pits in nearby Los Angeles, were featured in a reconstructed environment of palm trees with a Neanderthal (only found in Europe) and a dinosaur (known only from rare fragments in the Los Angeles area). (Courtesy of Michael Kogan.) (B) Mary Anning (1799–1847) collected and sold fossils from the age of 10 at Lyme Regis, England. The fossils included Jurassic reptiles, fish, and other fossils. She was honored on the 165th anniversary of her death with this stamp. Mozambique, 2012; courtesy of Stamperija. (C) A sheet with irregular perforations outlining two ammonites, one a probable Cretaceous species and the other in the background its reconstruction as a living animal. Switzerland, 2015; copyright Post CH AG. (D) An international air mail postcard with a 3-D stamp set showing 10 different dinosaur reconstructions. Special 3-D glasses are required to see the dimensional effects. South Africa, 2009. Used with permission of the South African Post Office.

Useful books, articles, and websites by paleo-philatelists document the history and variety of fossils on stamps. Nichols (1971), Editors (1976), and Haile (1977a, 1977b) published early articles on paleophilately, and others followed (Ashby, 1986; Feldman, 2000) on dinosaur stamps (Scott, 1991; van Niekerk, 2009; Floyd, 2014) and on *Homo naledi* (Poo, 2017). Books concentrated on particular fossils like dinosaurs (Baldwin and Halstead, 1991; Benton, 2021); fishes, amphibia, and reptiles (Bearse et al., 1977); trilobites (Ernst and Rudolph, 2002); nautiloids and ammonites (Ernst and Klug, 2011); and fossil fishes (Ernst and Hampe, 2018). Websites, dedicated and specialized, provide a wealth of information about fossils, stamps, paleontologists, fossil sites, and history (see footnote 2).

PRODUCTION OF PALEONTOLOGICAL STAMPS

Fossil stamps became increasingly complex with multiple specimens or ancient habitats printed on sheets. The illustrations on these stamps were done in various artistic styles, including hand-produced color drawings of fossils and reconstructions. Some artists drew with little error at fossil sites while others drew from specimens or illustrations. Illustrators are not usually named on the stamps, but many are identified on the Paleophilatelie and Stampedout websites (see footnote 1). The American artist Charles R. Knight (1874–1953) is famous for paintings of extinct animals that were based on careful research (Knight, 2001, 2005). They are displayed in American natural history museums, in his articles (Knight, 1942), and in his 1946 book *Life through the Ages* (Knight, 2001). Knight's illustrations influenced stamp designers who followed his style or even used his illustrations. A large number of artists from many countries have created illustrations for stamps in the past 60 years.

Stamps are printed by government agencies or contracted companies[3] (Barden, 1989). The principal printing methods are intaglio and gravure or photogravure processes that create stamps of fine design and multiple colors. Stamps also come in different shapes—triangular, trapezoidal, oval, elongate rectangular, diamond-shaped, or irregular (Fig. 2C). 3-D stamps have been printed occasionally since the 1960s, for example, by South Africa in 2009 (Fig. 2D). Stamps have been printed on paper, cardboard (Fig. 3A), plastic, or metal. Technology has also enabled stamps to be designed and legally used by individuals[4] (Fig. 3B). Paleontological stamps occasionally have errors: transposed names, synonyms, wrong information or reconstructions, and impossible temporal, geographical, or ecological juxtapositions (see the Stampedout website [footnote 2]). Unofficial and unauthorized non-postage stamps have been printed, too (Fig. 3C), some long before the first official stamps appeared (Noad, 2018).

PALEONTOLOGICAL STAMPS AS ART

Whether or not postal stamps are "art" is debated, but they are creative and skilled products, and they differ little from other objects of art except in size, utility, and abundance. Postal contributions to art and education are important in popularizing subjects and educating people. Fossil art was created in various styles as the stamps evolved with new discoveries and revisions in science and paleontology, with special events, and with changing interests of countries. Scientific views of dinosaurs, for example, changed; at first, they were thought of as lumbering giants and then as agile, rapidly moving animals in the late 1960s (Brett-Surman, 1997; Allmon, 2006). Stamps soon followed with revised illustrations showing those changes.

Fossil stamps can be arranged in several ways: taxonomically, geographically by country, environmentally, and chronologically. Here we arrange them chiefly by subdisciplines of paleontology (DK Publishing, 2012): paleobotany (Taylor and Taylor, 1993), palynology (pollen; Saxena, 1993), micropaleontology (Lipps, 1981, 1993), invertebrate paleontology from sponges to chordates (Taylor and Lewis, 2007), vertebrate paleontology including fish to mammals (Carroll, 1997), human (pre-cultural species) paleontology, and ichnology (tracks, trails, and behavioral marks) (DK Publishing, 2012; Boardman et al., 1987). Dinosaurs, of course, dominate as stamp subjects and many books have been written about them (Scott, 1991; Benton, 2021).

Stamps show fossils of every kind and age, from Precambrian bacterial stromatolites to microfossils (Fig. 3D) through Pleistocene *Homo sapiens* (Fig. 3E). Invertebrate and microfossil images are among the most artistically appealing; for example, the Australian souvenir sheet on the first animals, which are 543 to ca. 600 m.y. old (Fig. 3F). Later invertebrates appear on stamps, including mollusks (especially ammonites), echinoids, and arthropods (especially trilobites) among many others. Tracks and trails (ichnology) appear on a few stamps. Few fossil plants have been on stamps, although India issued its second fossil stamp in a 1997 set of plant fossils. Vertebrate paleontology has dominated paleontological stamps ever since China's 1958 stamp showing a dinosaur was issued. Dinosaurs are favored on stamps; fewer reptiles, birds, and mammals appear on them.

Other paleontological stamps can be separated into different categories: history, paleontologists, excavation or occurrence sites, and natural history museums. Thus, paleontological stamps depict early paleontologists such as Steno, one of the founders of modern paleontology and geology, and Thomas Jefferson (Figs. 1A, 1B) who had an interest in fossils but was a politician. Other important paleontologists also appear on many stamps (Figs. 1C, 1D, 2B).

Over 1000 natural history museums exist in the world, and most have fossils on display (Lipps, 2018), commonly with

[3]For an explanation of the techniques used in stamp production, see the U.S. Postal Museum website, "Creating America's Stamps": https://postalmuseum.si.edu/exhibition/stamps-take-flight/creating-america%E2%80%99s-stamps (accessed September 2019).

[4]On www.stamps.com, individuals can submit their own illustrations to make legal, personalized stamps: https://www.stamps.com/welcome/getstamps/ (accessed February 2020).

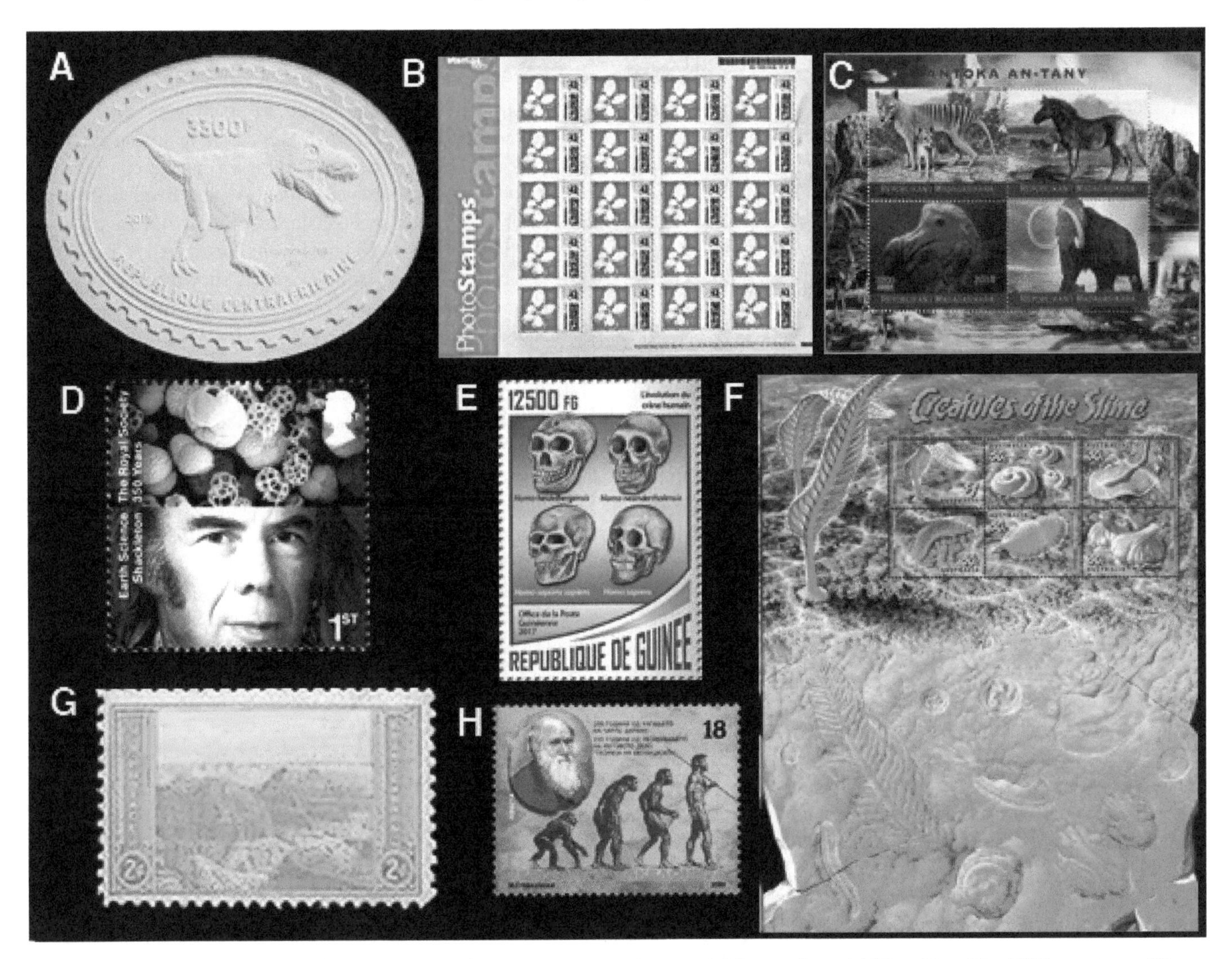

Figure 3. (A) A cardboard stamp with a reconstructed *Tyrannosaurus rex* in a special frame. Central African Republic, 2018, courtesy of Stamperija. (B) A personal stamp used an image of *Protentella,* a planktic foraminiferan from the Miocene of California (Lipps, 1964). Such stamps can be designed by individuals, printed online (Stamps.com 2020/02), and used legally. From collection of Jere H. Lipps. (C) Unauthorized dinosaur stamps, attributed to Madagascar, were published in 2019. Such stamps, usually with dinosaurs, are produced for sale to philatelists but cannot be used for postage. (D) Stamp showing fossil planktonic foraminifera and radiolarians used by Sir Nicholas John Shackleton, a member of the Royal Society, to determine ancient oceanography and climates. He led the way in this field for many years starting in the mid-1970s. Stamp design © Royal Mail Group Limited. (E) In two 2017 issues of the same stamp, the Republic of Guinea celebrated Charles Darwin's 80th anniversary, later correcting it to the 135th anniversary. One of the stamps in this Darwin celebration showed the evolution of the cranium of three fossil hominoid skulls leading to *Homo sapiens.* Republic of Guinea, 2017; courtesy of Stamperija. (F) The Ediacaran (543 to ca. 600 million years old) biota, including the first animals, on a slab of rock (lower) and as reconstructed animals (upper) on a souvenir sheet. Illustrations: Peter Trusler; stamp design: Belinda Marshall, Australia Post Design Studio; ©Australian Postal Corporation 2005. (G) The Grand Canyon of the United States exposes millions of years of Precambrian, Paleozoic, and Mesozoic sedimentary rocks, many of which contain fossils. USA, 1934 (public domain). (H) A stamp celebrating Charles Darwin's 200th birthday with his picture and that of an evolutionary scheme no longer accepted for humans. It provides an example of how stamps can be used in education, in this case tracking hypotheses through time. Macedonia, 2009.

dinosaurs as showpieces. Countries frequently issue stamps for their museums. Sites where fossils were found also appear on stamps, including Olduvai Gorge, where early hominins were found (Tanzania, 1965), the Eocene Messel deposit (Germany, 1978, 1998), the Dunarobba Miocene Forest Park (Italy, 2000), the Grand Canyon in the United States (Fig. 3G), and the famous Jurassic Solnhofen (Germany, 2011).

PALEOPHILATELY IN EDUCATION

Paleontology captures interest in science and inspires learning. Stamps provide educational materials for teaching science at any level (DeYoung, 1986). They are useful in biology courses (Calver et al., 2011) including animal classification, medicine (Pai, 2007), and the environment (Brunn, 2017). Commonly attractive, colorful, and visually appealing, fossil stamps are effective in lifelong learning because they cover topics in simple and interesting ways. Thus, students and laypeople may develop curiosity and interest in paleontology, geology, biology, and philately. The small size and availability of stamps allows students to simultaneously examine a number of different images and topics. They can exchange stamps, which provides broader coverage of paleontology and promotes discussion and interpretation of each stamp. Presentations of stamps can be integrated into lectures, written materials, and social media posts, thus increasing their educational potential.

Used in education, or simply as collections, these stamps convey information about the history, diversity, life functions, and the formation of fossils, as well as geology, ecology, paleoenvironment, paleoclimate, continental drift, evolutionary history, fossil fuels, and geoparks (Vartak et al., 2017). For example, Bolivia's 2012 stamp compares dinosaur footprints and those of a modern man. A Central African Republic stamp (1996) of a dinosaur and its eggs provides insight into the reproduction and biology of dinosaurs, which may spur further discussion. Likewise, evolutionary history is well documented on postal stamps. The Republic of Congo released a stamp (2003) set showing a history of elephants, and Peru issued a stamp (2010) depicting the evolution of a marine sloth, while Charles Darwin—along with an old, no longer valid but common view of human evolution—appeared on a Macedonian stamp in 2009 (Fig. 3H). Some countries issue a multitude of stamps showing fossils (Fig. 3E); this practice is discouraged by some collectors, but among those stamps are many that illustrate the art and educational aims of this paper.

Events in Earth history, from its origin to man's lunar landing, are recounted on stamps. A 1989 set of 15 stamps from Niuafo'ou illustrates those events as well as evolution on land and in the sea. Even more inclusive is the British Antarctic Territory six-stamp set (1982) on continental drift with three themes: continental paleogeography, paleoclimate, and a feature or fossil typical of each time period. These kinds of paleontological stamps provide a basis for understanding the relationship of tectonics and paleoclimate to the sequence of life types in the southern hemisphere over the past 280 million years.

New printing methods offer additional instructional value. A 3-D stamp set with viewing glasses issued by South Africa in 2009 depicted skeletons and reconstructions of dinosaurs. In 2015, Canada released a five-stamp set with an unusual 3-D design of dinosaurs that once roamed Canada. In the same year, Spain issued a four-stamp set of well-known dinosaurs that includes scale textures, augmented reality, phosphorescence, 3-D stamps, and glasses to view the special effects. In 2019, the United States used lenticular techniques on stamps featuring *Tyrannosaurus rex* to produce images on two that change as they rotate; one shows a skeleton that becomes covered in flesh and skin while the other shows a running *T. rex* that quickly turns toward the viewer with its toothy mouth wide open.

CONCLUSION

Paleontological stamps, which are small works of art, have changed over the 165 years since Thomas Jefferson appeared on a stamp or the 70 years since the fossils first appeared as simple, single images or reconstructed animals to sets of related fossils and complex souvenir sheets. Single stamps with fossils were issued initially in 1951, and sets were issued in 1965, advancing in the early 1990s to complex sheets showing fossils as live animals and plants in landscapes with individual illustrations perforated for use as stamps. Now, over 4000 different stamps have been issued by nearly 200 countries that celebrate fossils, reconstructions of fossils as living organisms, paleontologists including the amateur Jefferson, museums with fossils, and collecting sites. In general, stamps keep up with the science and new discoveries at the time of issue. Fossil stamps can be used in the classroom and for general education to demonstrate aspects of ancient life, evolution, and Earth history. Stamps show sufficient material for students to learn directly from them. Newer, 3-D stamps offer unique opportunities for learning. Stamps for a class can be purchased from philatelic websites and stores at affordable prices.

ACKNOWLEDGMENTS

We thank Renee Clary, Professor and Director of the Dunn-Seiler Museum, Department of Geosciences, Mississippi State University, Starkville, Mississippi, and Gary D. Rosenberg, Professor Emeritus, Department of Earth Sciences, Indiana University, Purdue University, Indianapolis, Indiana, and adjunct curator of geology, Milwaukee Public Museum, for organizing the art and paleontology symposium at the Geological Society of America 2018 annual meeting and this book. We thank Michael Kogan of Paleophilatelie, Ton van Eijden (coauthor) of Stampedout, and Jon Noad for permission to use the images in this chapter and for discussions about the use of stamps in publication. For their generosity in allowing use of images of their stamps, we appreciate and thank Australia, the Central African Republic, Macedonia, Monaco, Mozambique, South Africa, Switzerland, the United Kingdom (Royal Mail Group Limited), and Stamperija. This is University of California at Berkeley Museum of Paleontology publication 2096.

REFERENCES CITED

Allmon, W.D., 2006, The pre-modern history of the post-modern dinosaur: Phases and causes in post-Darwinian dinosaur art: Earth Sciences History, v. 25, no. 1, p. 5–35, https://doi.org/10.17704/eshi.25.1.g2687j050u3w1546.

Ashby, W., 1986, Fossils on stamps: The Ecphora: Quarterly Newsletter of the Calvert Marine Museum Fossil Club, v. 2, no. 1, p. 3–6.

Baldwin, S., and Halstead, B., 1991, Dinosaur Stamps of the World: Witham, UK, Baldwin's Books, 128 p., https://doi.org/10.1111/j.1365-2451.1991.tb00801.x.

Barden, M., 1989, How Royal Mail Special Stamps Are Produced: London, Royal Mail, 28 p.

Bearse, G.A., Stanley, W.F., Raasch, M.S., Stahl, U., Bookwalter, E.O., Gordon, R.E., and Skaroff, M.L., 1977, Lower Vertebrates: Fishes, Amphibia and Reptiles on Stamps of the World: American Topical Association Handbook, no. 91, 119 p.

Benton, M.J., 2021, The Dinosaurs: New Visions of a Lost World: London, Thames & Hudson, 256 p.

Berta, A., and Turner, S., 2020, Rebels, Scholars, Explorers: Women in Vertebrate Paleontology: Baltimore, Maryland, Johns Hopkins University Press, 320 p.

Boardman, R.S., Cheetham, A.H., and Rowell, A.J., eds., 1987, Fossil Invertebrates: Palo Alto, California, Blackwell Scientific Publications, 713 p.

Brett-Surman, M.K., 1997, Appendix: A chronological history of dinosaur paleontology, *in* Farlow, J.O., and Brett-Surman, M.K., eds., The Complete Dinosaur: Bloomington, Indiana, Indiana University Press, p. 707–720.

Brunn, S.D., 2017, A geopolitical and geovisualization challenge: Increasing the awareness of global environmental change through postage stamp issues: Natural Resources, v. 8, p. 130–158, http://www.scirp.org/journal/nr, https://doi.org/10.4236/nr.2017.83010.

Calver, M., Addison, K., and Annan, J., 2011, Postage stamps as teaching aids in biology: The American Biology Teacher, v. 73, no. 5, p. 289–290, https://doi.org/10.1525/abt.2011.73.5.10.

Carroll, R.L., 1997, Vertebrate Paleontology and Evolution: New York, W.H. Freeman and Company, 698 p.

DeYoung, G., 1986, Postage stamps and the popular iconography of science: Journal of American Culture, v. 9, no. 3, p. 1–14, https://doi.org/10.1111/j.1542-734X.1986.0903_1.x.

DK Publishing, 2012, Prehistoric Life: The Definitive Visual History of Life on Earth: New York, DK Publishing, 512 p.

Editors, 1976, Fossils on stamps: Fossils Magazine, v. 1, p. 68–74.

Ernst, H.U., and Hampe, O., 2018, Fossil Fishes Worldwide—The World of Prehistoric Fishes and Their Reflection in Philately: Munich, Germany, Verlag Dr. Friedrich Pfeil, 240 p.

Ernst, H.U., and Klug, C., 2011, Nautiloids and Ammonites World Wide: The World of Cephalopods and the Reflection in Philately: Munich, Germany, Verlag Dr. Friedrich Pfeil, 224 p.

Ernst, H.U., and Rudolph, F., 2002, Trilobites Worldwide: The World of Trilobites and Their Reflection in Philately: Munich, Germany, Verlag Dr. Friedrich Pfeil, 118 p.

Feldman, V.I., 2000, Philatelic Geology: Moscow, Ministry of the Natural Resources of Russia and Russian Geological Society, Ocean Picture Ltd., 492 p.

Floyd, B.N., 2014, Dinosaurs, majestic prehistoric creatures: The American Philatelist, December, p. 1126–1137.

Haile, N.S., 1977a, Geology on stamps 1. Extinct animals and minerals [The Newsletter of the Geological Society of Malaysia]: Warta Geologi, v. 3, no. 4, p. 47–50.

Haile, N.S., 1977b, Geology on stamps 2. More extinct animals, fossils and minerals [The Newsletter of the Geological Society of Malaysia]: Warta Geologi, v. 3, no. 4, p. 71–76.

Knight, C.R., 1942, Parade of life through the ages: National Geographic, v. 81, no. 2, p. 141–184.

Knight, C.R., 2001, Life through the Ages, A Commemorative Edition: Bloomington, Indiana, Indiana University Press, 96 p.

Knight, C.R., 2005, Autobiography of an artist: https://GT-Labs.com (accessed March 2021).

Lipps, J.H., 1964, Miocene planktonic foraminifera from Newport Bay, California: Tulane Studies in Geology, v. 2, p. 109–133.

Lipps, J.H., 1981, What, if anything, is micropaleontology? Paleobiology, v. 7, p. 167–199, https://doi.org/10.1017/S0094837300003973.

Lipps, J.H., ed., 1993, Fossil Prokaryotes and Protists: Boston and Oxford, Blackwell Scientific Publishers, 342 p.

Lipps, J.H., 2018, Natural history museums: Facilitating science literacy across the globe, *in* Rosenberg, G.D., and Clary, R.M., eds., Museums at the Forefront of the History and Philosophy of Geology: History Made, History in the Making: Geological Society of America Special Paper 535, p. 9–33, https://doi.org/10.1130/2018.2535(02).

Nichols, R.L., 1971, Philately and geology: Journal of Geological Education, v. 19, p. 176–181, https://doi.org/10.5408/0022-1368-XIX.4.176.

van Niekerk, L., 2009, Dinosaurs: SETEMPE [South African Stamp News], v. 14, no. 3, p. 8–11.

Noad, J., 2018, Diamond Dinoversary: Prehistoric Times, no. 125, p. 28–29.

Pai, S., 2007, Medical stamp collecting: BMJ, November, p. 395–396, http://archive.student.bmj.com/issues/07/11/life/395.php.

Poo, D., 2017, Meet *Homo naledi*: South African Stamp News, v. 22, no. 3, p. 4–5.

Saxena, M.R., 1993, Palynology, a Treatise: New Delhi, India, Oxford & IBH Pub. Co., 127 p.

Scott, A.C., 1991, Geology on stamps: 150 years of dinosaurs: Geology Today, September–October, p. 187–189.

Taylor, P.D., and Lewis, D.N., 2007, Fossil Invertebrates: Cambridge, Massachusetts, Harvard University Press, 208 p.

Taylor, T.N., and Taylor, E.L., 1993, The Biology and Evolution of Fossil Plants: Englewood Cliffs, New Jersey, Prentice-Hall, 981 p.

Vartak, R., Vartak, A., Rajshekhar, C., and Vaddadi, S., 2017, Geosciences and philately, *in* Proceedings of the Seminar on Philately: India Philately Bureau, Pune GPO, Pune 411001, India, p. 31–37.

Manuscript Accepted by the Society 20 January 2021
Manuscript Published Online 29 November 2021

Printed in the USA

The Geological Society of America
Memoir 218

Ancient creatures of Hungary: Bringing the animals to life

Tibor Pecsics
Department of Systematic Zoology and Ecology, Eötvös Loránd University, 1117 Budapest, Pázmány Péter sétány 1/C, Hungary

ABSTRACT

The first trace fossils in Hungary, dinosaur footprints, were found in the coal mines of the Mecsek Mountains. The footprints belonged to small theropod dinosaurs. The first fossil bones of vertebrate animals from present-day Hungary were found in 2000 in the mountainous region of Bakony. Numerous taxa have been collected from the locality of Iharkút. These fossils represent a diverse fauna (including fishes, amphibians, turtles, lizards, crocodilians, dinosaurs, birds, and pterosaurs) that lived between 85.8 and 83.5 m.y. ago in the Santonian Age during the Late Cretaceous period. Paleoart can depict these fossil remains in an engaging way to help inform the public about the ancient creatures of Hungary. This chapter provides an overview of how the Mesozoic vertebrates from Hungary have been reconstructed for scientists and the public.

INTRODUCTION

Fossil vertebrates are usually unique and rare in Central Europe (Kocsis et al., 2009). Remains from Mesozoic continental vertebrates from present-day Hungary were nearly unknown for a long time. Most of the findings were from marine sediments, and these were almost exclusively the remains of fishes and marine reptiles (Ősi et al., 2013). Serious research was begun by the famous paleobiologist Baron Ferenc Nopcsa, who discovered and studied the Transylvanian dinosaurs between the 1910s and 1930s and theorized insular dwarfism in dinosaurs (Benton et al., 2010). Early Hungarian and foreign researchers tried to understand why fossils of Mesozoic animals have not been found more frequently in Hungary (Ősi, 2004). Since the end of the nineteenth century, a rich assortment of Late Cretaceous continental vertebrate fossils has been unearthed from the Haţeg Basin in Transylvania (the eastern region of the historical Hungarian Kingdom) (Codrea et al., 2010).

The first trace fossils in Hungary, dinosaur footprints, were found in the coal mines of the Mecsek Mountains in 1966. However, the bones of a dinosaur that could have made those tracks, which was given the ichnogenus name *Komlosaurus carbonis,* have never been found.

In 2000, Hungarian researchers led by Attila Ősi turned their attention to some Upper Cretaceous fluvial sediments. This Csehbánya Formation was exposed in large bauxite open-pit mines located in the mountainous region of Bakony near the village of Németbánya in the Iharkút locality. The formation dates to the Late Santonian (around 85 m.y. ago) of the Late Cretaceous. During fieldwork in the northern part of the mine, the first vertebrate remains were found in a sandstone bed under the surface. This site produced the first body fossils of dinosaurs from present-day Hungary (Ősi, 2012).

As a prehistoric and extant wildlife illustrator working with Eötvös Loránd University, I have had the privilege during the past ten years of spending time in the company of local expedition researchers, visiting the fieldwork at the excavation site, working with local fossil material, and artistically depicting the newly discovered mysterious species.

*nobilis.equus@gmail.com

Pecsics, T., 2022, Ancient creatures of Hungary: Bringing the animals to life, *in* Clary, R.M., Rosenberg, G.D., and Evans, D.C., eds., The Evolution of Paleontological Art: Geological Society of America Memoir 218, p. 237–243, https://doi.org/10.1130/2021.1218(26).

BUILDING A PHANTOM FROM A COAL MINE

The first dinosaur footprints were found in 1966 and were later described by the paleontologist László Kordos in 1983 as *Komlosaurus carbonis* (Kordos, 1983). The type remains came from the Mecsek Coal Formation of the Early Jurassic (middle Hettangian to the Early Sinemurian). In 1988, geology students and their professors from Eötvös Loránd University of Budapest organized a field trip to the formation and found complete associated trackways of similar footprints (Hips et al., 1988). The trackmaker was originally classified as a fragile ornithopod dinosaur, but recent studies (Ősi et al., 2011) suggest that the footprints belonged to a pack of primitive theropods. The traces are tridactyle, with long and thin digits, and have a birdlike impression. The footprints are similar to those of *Grallator* and *Eubrontes,* and these early theropod dinosaurs possibly looked like *Coelophysis* and its relatives (Lockley et al., 2003). The traces of *Komlosaurus* revealed that these dinosaurs were ~2 m long and were fast and agile bipedal runners (Ősi et al., 2011) (Fig. 1).

In 2011, I received a request from the Hungarian Natural History Museum to create a life-size model of the mysterious dinosaur *Komlosaurus carbonis.* I found creating an accurate hypothetic model of a creature that left only footprints 200 m.y. ago to be a very difficult task. I began the restoration process by studying the original fossils at the local museum of Eötvös Loránd University. After consultations with Attila Ősi—the leader of the local research group—and Géza Zboray—the university's anatomy teacher—I created a few sketches and small clay and beeswax models (Fig. 2). We used other footprints (Gerliński, 1996) and the skeletal remains of the possible coelophysoid relatives (Rowe, 1989; Bristowe and Raath, 2004; Gay, 2005) to reconstruct our dinosaur.

The model was created in Zalaegerszeg (a small town in western Hungary) in the workshop of the sculptor György Fischer. Fischer provided the material and the accessories. We built a metal armature to support the weight of the wooden struts, wires, and clay. To create the negative form, we used a plaster mold. The final version was casted with polymer resin and hardened with fiberglass. After that first *Komlosaurus* reconstruction, I created a second model of polyurethane, metal, and polymer clay for an exhibit in Komló (Fig. 3).

LATE CRETACEOUS CONTINENTAL VERTEBRATES FROM WESTERN HUNGARY

Thousands of isolated and sometimes associated fossilized bones, teeth, and scales of numerous different taxa have been col-

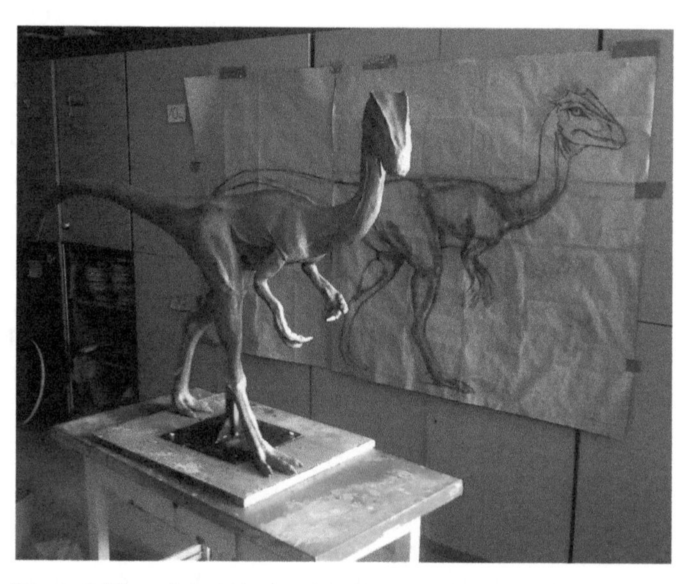

Figure 2. The original clay model (115 cm × 30 cm × 183 cm) of the mysterious dinosaur *Komlosaurus carbonis* is shown. The final fiberglass polyresin version is visible in the permanent exhibition of the Hungarian Natural History Museum. Image ©Tibor Pecsics, 2011.

Figure 1. Group of *Komlosaurus* from Hungary, which lived 200 m.y. ago (pencil, watercolor on paper, and digital; 29.7 cm × 42.0 cm). Client: Mining and Geological Survey of Hungary. Image ©Tibor Pecsics, 2014.

Figure 3. The second *Komlosaurus* model, exhibited in a reconstructed environment, was made of polyurethane, metal, and polymer clay (90 cm × 30 cm × 182 cm). Client: József Attila Town Library and Museum Collection of Komló, Hungary. Image ©Tibor Pecsics, 2017.

lected from the Iharkút locality since its discovery. The fossils represent a diverse fauna of fishes (Szabó et al., 2016), amphibians (Szentesi et al., 2013), turtles (Rabi et al., 2012), lizards (Makádi, 2013), crocodilians (Rabi and Sebők, 2015), theropod (Ősi et al., 2010a), ornithopod (Ősi et al., 2012b), and nodosaurid dinosaurs (Ősi and Prondvai, 2013), ancient enantiornithine birds (Dyke and Ősi, 2010), and pterosaurs (Ősi et al., 2005). The material is regarded as fragmentary because most of the bones show postmortem fractures. The breaks occurred after fossilization, which also suggests rapid burial and deposition shortly after the initiation of diagenetic processes. The animals lived between 85.8 and 83.5 m.y. ago during the Late Cretaceous on an island landmass in the western Tethyan archipelago—a series of island chains that sat between the African and Eurasian landmasses in what once was the Tethys Ocean (Ősi et al., 2012a).

My reconstruction portrays most of the species thought to live in the predicted forested wetland habitat. Reconstructed color patterns of dinosaurs were based on the pigmentation of present-day mammals and birds (Figs. 4–5). The base of the painting was made with watercolor on paper; I then used pencil and colored pencil for the details of the animals (scales, osteoderms, feathers) and foreground. Finally, I digitally drew the details of plants and background.

Figure 4. Some of the animals from Iharkút are shown (pencil, watercolor on paper, and digital; 29.7 cm × 42.0 cm). The fauna include *Pneumatoraptor*, a little paraves carnivore (on the left, hiding between the vegetation); *Hungarosaurus*, a nodosaurid dinosaur (in the middle); *Ajkaceratops*, a small ceratopsian (on the right); and other animals such as primitive Tetanurae theropod dinosaurs, azhdarchoid pterosaurs, pleurodiran turtles, and crocodilians. Image ©Tibor Pecsics, 2015.

An Unexpected Freshwater Monster

Because one creature's fossils were fragmentary, paleontologists believed that the bones belonged to large terrestrial lizards. A new fossilized creature discovered at Iharkút was at first considered by paleontologists to be a large terrestrial lizard (Ősi et al., 2016). Over several years, more remains were found at the site, which turned out to be from a freshwater mosasaur. In 2012, scientists named the discovery *Pannoniasaurus inexpectatus*, because it was unexpected to find a mosasaur in what used to be a freshwater environment. *Pannoniasaurus* was a medium-sized mosasaur and is estimated to have grown up to a maximum of 6 m in length. This size made it the largest known predator in the rivers of its paleoenvironment (Makádi et al., 2012). I based my first drawings and sketches on photographs and drawings of original specimens, and during the reconstruction process I also took photographs of monitor lizards and crocodiles at the local zoo. The remains suggested that *Pannoniasaurus* lived in a freshwater ecosystem; therefore, I used my photos to imagine how this creature could swim (Fig. 6).

Figure 5. A group of *Mochlodon vorosi* is pictured in the forests of Iharkút (pencil, watercolor on paper, and digital; 29.7 cm × 42.0 cm). Image ©Tibor Pecsics, 2012.

Small Crocodile with Unusual Teeth

Iharkutosuchus makadii was a small hylaeochampsid crocodile with a low skull and a short snout. The estimated body length was around 1 m. This crocodile developed heterodonty, wherein some of the teeth were similar to mammalian teeth (Ősi et al., 2007). The cranial structure suggested that this animal had a very complex jaw mechanism (Ősi and Weishampel, 2009). The feeding apparatus of extinct crocodylians is very similar to that of its extant relatives, which produces high measured bite forces, but crocodylians do not display the typical dorsally heightened skull of dinosaurs (Fig. 7). For this anatomical drawing I used my own sketches and photographs from anatomy lessons at the university. The dissection was performed on spectacled caiman (*Caiman crocodilus*). To construct a life-size model of *Iharkutosuchus makadii*, I used polyurethane, metal, and polymer clay, basing the color and the appearance on the broad-snouted caiman (*Caiman latirostris*) and the Chinese crocodile lizard (*Shinisaurus crocodilurus*) (Figs. 8–9).

Figure 6. Freshwater mosasaurs are pictured in an ancient river (pencil, watercolor on paper, and digital; 29.7 cm × 42.0 cm). Image ©Tibor Pecsics, 2012.

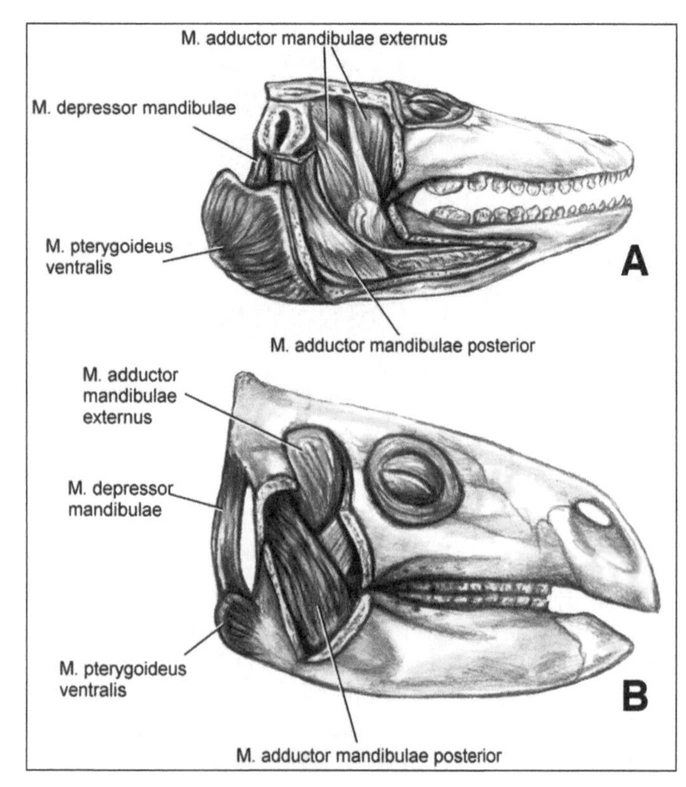

Figure 7. Comparative anatomy of the head is shown. (Top) *Iharkutosuchus makadii* and (bottom) *Mochlodon vorosi* (pencil and colored pencil on paper; 21.0 cm × 29.7 cm). Image ©Tibor Pecsics, 2012.

Figure 8. The crocodile *Iharkutosuchus makadii* is depicted in an ancient river with a juvenile *Foxemys trabanti* turtle (pencil, watercolor on paper, and digital; 21.0 cm × 29.7 cm). The turtle was named in honor of the cherished East German (former German Democratic Republic) automobile Trabant 601, which is frequently used by the Iharkút research group and serves as an indispensable field car and transporter vehicle during the excavations (Rabi et al., 2012). Image ©Tibor Pecsics, 2012.

Figure 9. Life-size model depicts *Iharkutosuchus makadii* (18 cm × 34 cm × 101 cm). Client: Ajka Coal Mine Museum. Image ©Tibor Pecsics, 2019.

Other Unique Animals from the Excavation Site

In 2005, the research group found the remains of pterosaurs, the first ever discovered in Hungary. The fossil material, named *Bakonydraco galaczi,* was based on a complete, well-preserved lower jaw, wing bones, and neck vertebrae (Ősi et al., 2005). The first publication described it as an azhdarchid, but other researchers proposed that it was related to tapejarid pterosaurs (Andres and Myers, 2013). During the life restoration of the animal, I used artificial fur to depict a fuzzy integument (similar to that of juvenile ostriches). The shape and the color pattern of the head crest were inspired by hornbills (Fig. 10).

Fossils of *Ajkaceratops kozmai,* a ceratopsian, were discovered in 2009 and described in 2010. The holotype is a skull fragment with a parrot-like upper beak. The fossil is very similar to Asian bagaceratopsid dinosaur remains. The fossils of ceratopsians are particularly rare in Late Cretaceous deposits of Europe (Ősi et al., 2010b). Despite the large heads of these dinosaurs, the hind limbs are more robust and bear most of the weight. The color pattern is based on study and investigation of the epidermal appearance of *Psittacosaurus* (Lingham-Soliar and Plodowski, 2010) and inspired by the extant sailfin lizard (*Hydrosaurus* sp.) species (Fig. 11).

Figure 11. Life-size model shows *Ajkaceratops kozmai* (polyurethane, metal, and polymer clay; 50 cm × 34 cm × 95 cm). Client: Ajka Coal Mine Museum. Image ©Tibor Pecsics, 2019.

CONCLUSION

Science and new findings are always molding our thoughts about species that once lived on our planet. The paleoartist tries to open windows to the extinct worlds to let people "see" the history of Earth. The Iharkút excavation site is still rich in fossils, and hopefully the researchers will find more extraordinary remains in the future. The synthesis of artist and scientist is essential in showing how extinct creatures looked and lived (Fig. 12). I'm looking forward to the opportunity to portray extraordinary animals and to continue the fascinating challenge of depicting prehistoric life forms and environments.

Figure 10. Life-size model depicts *Bakonydraco galaczi* restored as a tapejarid pterosaur (polyurethane, metal, polymer clay, artificial fur; 46 cm × 112 cm × 362 cm). Client: Ajka Coal Mine Museum. Image ©Tibor Pecsics, 2019.

ACKNOWLEDGMENTS

I am grateful to György Fischer, Géza Zboray, and Tibor Csörgő. Special thanks go to Péter Gulyás, Emese Abaházi, Martin Segesdi, Valentin Fejes, Tamás Henn, László Makádi, Edina Prondvai, Attila Ősi, and the members of the research group.

REFERENCES CITED

Andres, B., and Myers, T.S., 2013, Lone star pterosaurs: Earth and Environmental Science Transactions of the Royal Society of Edinburgh, v. 103, no. 3–4, p. 383–398, https://doi.org/10.1017/S1755691013000303.

Benton, M.J., Csiki, Z., Grigorescu, D., Redelstorff, R., Sander, P.M., Stein, K., and Weishampel, D.B., 2010, Dinosaurs and the island rule: The dwarfed dinosaurs from Haţeg Island: Palaeogeography, Palaeoclimatol-

Figure 12. A titanosaur sauropod walks along the seashore (acrylic on paper; 21.0 cm × 29.7 cm). A tooth represents the first European body fossil evidence of a sauropod from the Santonian of the European Late Cretaceous (Ősi et al., 2017). Image ©Tibor Pecsics, 2018.

ogy, Palaeoecology, v. 293, no. 3–4, p. 438–454, https://doi.org/10.1016/j.palaeo.2010.01.026.

Bristowe, A., and Raath, M.A., 2004, A juvenile coelophysoid skull from the Early Jurassic of Zimbabwe, and the synonymy of *Coelophysis* and *Syntarsus*: Palaeontologia Africana, v. 40, p. 31–41.

Codrea, V., Vremir, M., Jipa, C., Godefroit, P., Csiki, Z., Smith, T., and Fărcaş, C., 2010, More than just Nopcsa's Transylvanian dinosaurs: A look outside the Haţeg Basin: Palaeogeography, Palaeoclimatology, Palaeoecology, v. 293, no. 3–4, p. 391–405, https://doi.org/10.1016/j.palaeo.2009.10.027.

Dyke, G.J., and Ősi, A., 2010, A review of Late Cretaceous fossil birds from Hungary: Geological Journal, v. 45, no. 4, p. 434–444, https://doi.org/10.1002/gj.1209.

Gay, R., 2005, Sexual Dimorphism in the Early Jurassic Theropod Dinosaur *Dilophosaurus* and a Comparison with Other Related Forms: Bloomington, Indiana, Indiana University Press, 277 p.

Gierliński, G., 1996, Dinosaur ichnotaxa from the Lower Jurassic of Hungary: Geological Quarterly, v. 40, no. 1, p. 119–128.

Hips, K., Józsa, S., Nagy, Á., and Pataki, Zs., 1988, Őshüllők nyomában: Természet Világa, v. 120, p. 108–111.

Kocsis, L., Ősi, A., Vennemann, T., Trueman, C.N., and Palmer, M.R., 2009, Geochemical study of vertebrate fossils from the Upper Cretaceous (Santonian) Csehbánya Formation (Hungary): Evidence for a freshwater habitat of mosasaurs and pycnodont fish: Palaeogeography, Palaeoclimatology, Palaeoecology, v. 280, no. 3–4, p. 532–542, https://doi.org/10.1016/j.palaeo.2009.07.009.

Kordos, L., 1983, Fontosabb szórványleletek a MÁFI gerinces-gyűjteményében (8. közlemény). Dinosaurus lábnyomok *(Komlosaurus carbonis* n. g. n. sp.) a mecseki liászból: Annals of the Hungarian Geological Institute, 1981, p. 503–511.

Lingham-Soliar, T., and Plodowski, G., 2010, The integument of *Psittacosaurus* from Liaoning Province, China: Taphonomy, epidermal patterns and color of a ceratopsian dinosaur: Naturwissenschaften, v. 97, no. 5, p. 479–486, https://doi.org/10.1007/s00114-010-0661-3.

Lockley, M., Matsukawa, M., and Jianjun, L., 2003, Crouching theropods in taxonomic jungles: Ichnological and ichnotaxonomic investigations of footprints with metatarsal and ischial impressions: Ichnos, v. 10, no. 2–4, p. 169–177, https://doi.org/10.1080/10420940390256249.

Makádi, L., 2013, A new polyglyphanodontine lizard (Squamata: Borioteiioidea) from the Late Cretaceous Iharkút locality (Santonian, Hungary): Cretaceous Research, v. 46, p. 166–176, https://doi.org/10.1016/j.cretres.2013.08.001.

Makádi, L., Caldwell, M.W., and Ősi, A., 2012, The first freshwater mosasauroid (Upper Cretaceous, Hungary) and a new clade of basal mosasauroids: PLoS One, v. 7, no. 12, https://doi.org/10.1371/journal.pone.0051781.

Ősi, A., 2004, The first dinosaur remains from the Upper Cretaceous of Hungary (Csehbánya Formation, Bakony Mts): Geobios, v. 37, no. 6, p. 749–753, https://doi.org/10.1016/j.geobios.2003.06.005.

Ősi, A., 2012, Dinoszauruszok Magyarországon: Szeged, GeoLitera Kiadó, p. 1–168.

Ősi, A., and Prondvai, E., 2013, Sympatry of two ankylosaurs (*Hungarosaurus* and cf. *Struthiosaurus*) in the Santonian of Hungary: Cretaceous Research, v. 44, p. 58–63, https://doi.org/10.1016/j.cretres.2013.03.006.

Ősi, A., and Weishampel, D.B., 2009, Jaw mechanism and dental function in the Late Cretaceous basal eusuchian *Iharkutosuchus*: Journal of Morphology, v. 270, no. 8, p. 903–920, https://doi.org/10.1002/jmor.10726.

Ősi, A., Weishampel, D.B., and Jianu, C.M., 2005, First evidence of azhdarchid pterosaurus from the Late Cretaceous of Hungary: Acta Palaeontologica Polonica, v. 50, no. 4, p. 777–787.

Ősi, A., Clark, J.M., and Weishampel, D.B., 2007, First report on a new basal eusuchian crocodyliform with multicusped teeth from the Upper Cretaceous (Santonian) of Hungary: Neues Jahrbuch für Geologie und Paläontologie. Abhandlungen, v. 243, no. 2, p. 169–177, https://doi.org/10.1127/0077-7749/2007/0243-0169.

Ősi, A., Apesteguía, S., and Kowalewski, M., 2010a, Non-avian theropod dinosaurs from the early Late Cretaceous of Central Europe: Cretaceous Research, v. 31, no. 3, p. 304–320, https://doi.org/10.1016/j.cretres.2010.01.001.

Ősi, A., Butler, R.J., and Weishampel, D.B., 2010b, A Late Cretaceous ceratopsian dinosaur from Europe with Asian affinities: Nature, v. 465, no. 7297, p. 466–468, https://doi.org/10.1038/nature09019.

Ősi, A., Pálfy, J., Makádi, L., Szentesi, Z., Gulyás, P., Rabi, M., and Hips, K., 2011, Hettangian (Early Jurassic) dinosaur tracksites from the Mecsek Mountains, Hungary: Ichnos, v. 18, no. 2, p. 79–94, https://doi.org/10.1080/10420940.2011.573603.

Ősi, A., Rabi, M., Makádi, L., Szentesi, Z., Botfalvai, G., Gulyás, P., and Godefroit, P., 2012a, The Late Cretaceous Continental Vertebrate Fauna from Iharkút (Western Hungary): A Review. Bernissart Dinosaurs and Early Cretaceous Terrestrial Ecosystems: Bloomington, Indiana, University of Indiana Press, p. 532–569.

Ősi, A., Prondvai, E., Butler, R., and Weishampel, D.B., 2012b, Phylogeny, histology and inferred body size evolution in a new rhabdodontid dinosaur from the Late Cretaceous of Hungary: PLoS One, v. 7, no. 9, p. e44318.

Ősi, A., Botfalvai, G., Prondvai, E., Hajdu, Z., Czirják, G., Szentesi, Z., Pozsgai, E., Götz, A.E., Makádi, L., Csengődi, D., and Sebe, K., 2013, First report of Triassic vertebrate assemblages from the Villány Hills (Southern Hungary): Central European Geology, v. 56, no. 4, p. 297–335, https://doi.org/10.1556/CEuGeol.56.2013.4.2.

Ősi, A., Bodor, E.R., Makádi, L., and Rabi, M., 2016, Vertebrate remains from the Upper Cretaceous (Santonian) Ajka Coal formation, western Hungary: Cretaceous Research, v. 57, p. 228–238, https://doi.org/10.1016/j.cretres.2015.04.014.

Ősi, A., Csiki-Sava, Z., and Prondvai, E., 2017, A sauropod tooth from the Santonian of Hungary and the European Late Cretaceous 'Sauropod Hiatus': Scientific Reports, v. 7, no. 1, p. 3261, https://doi.org/10.1038/s41598-017-03602-2.

Rabi, M., and Sebők, N., 2015, A revised Eurogondwana model: Late Cretaceous notosuchian crocodyliforms and other vertebrate taxa suggest the retention of episodic faunal links between Europe and Gondwana during most of the Cretaceous: Gondwana Research, v. 28, no. 3, p. 1197–1211, https://doi.org/10.1016/j.gr.2014.09.015.

Rabi, M., Tong, H., and Botfalvai, G., 2012, A new species of the side-necked turtle *Foxemys* (Pelomedusoides: Bothremydidae) from the Late Cretaceous of Hungary and the historical biogeography of the Bothremydini: Geological Magazine, v. 149, no. 4, p. 662–674, https://doi.org/10.1017/S0016756811000756.

Rowe, T., 1989, A new species of the theropod dinosaur *Syntarsus* from the Early Jurassic Kayenta Formation of Arizona: Journal of Vertebrate Paleontology, v. 9, no. 2, p. 125–136, https://doi.org/10.1080/02724634.1989.10011748.

Szabó, M., Gulyás, P., and Ősi, A., 2016, Late Cretaceous (Santonian) pycnodontid (Actinopterygii, Pycnodontidae) remains from the freshwater deposits of the Csehbánya Formation, (Iharkút, Bakony Mountains, Hungary): Annales de Paléontologie, v. 102, no. 2, p. 123–134, https://doi.org/10.1016/j.annpal.2016.04.001.

Szentesi, Z., Gardner, J.D., and Venczel, M., 2013, Albanerpetontid amphibians from the Late Cretaceous (Santonian) of Iharkút, Hungary, with remarks on regional differences in Late Cretaceous Laurasian amphibian assemblages: Canadian Journal of Earth Sciences, v. 50, no. 3, p. 268–281, https://doi.org/10.1139/e2012-024.

Manuscript Accepted by the Society 8 February 2021
Manuscript Published Online 9 December 2021

The Geological Society of America
Memoir 218

"But why paint a dinosaur blue?": Envisioning the Cretaceous—A vitalizing, multidisciplinary project in a university museum

Todd M. Rowan
2942 Pat Station Road, Starkville, Mississippi 39759, USA

Thomas Brent Funderburk
W.L. Giles Distinguished Professor Emeritus, Department of Art, College of Architecture, Art, and Design, Mississippi State University, 105 Freeman Hall, 415 Barr Avenue, Mississippi State, Mississippi 39762, USA

Renee M. Clary
Department of Geosciences, Mississippi State University, Box 5448, Mississippi State, Mississippi 39762, USA

ABSTRACT

In 2017–2018, two fine arts undergraduate students, Todd Rowan and Moesha Wright, conceived and created a mural for the Dunn-Seiler Museum at Mississippi State University, Mississippi, USA, under the supervision of art professor emeritus Brent Funderburk. Students researched, conceptualized, and painted *Mississippi Cretaceous Panorama*, which interpreted the Late Cretaceous landscape that once surrounded the university and the momentous extinction event that brought the Mesozoic Era to its close. The project necessitated creativity to address several challenges, including funding, space constraints, and a local population with Young Earth views. The completed mural engages museum visitors with a mosasaur, ceratopsian dinosaur, and a meteorite impact—illustrating the local, terminal Mesozoic geologic history in a nonthreatening venue that can improve community geoliteracy.

INTRODUCTION

The Dunn-Seiler Museum of Geosciences on the Mississippi State University (MSU), Mississippi, USA, campus is currently undergoing renovation to make its collections and programs more relevant, interactive, and accessible to its university, professional, and public constituents. As conversation among these groups broadened, a design plan of more engaging visual exhibits, information graphics, and didactics enabled the initiation of an MSU 2017–2018 undergraduate research grant for two senior fine arts students to study museum design, historic mural painting processes, and archival materials, as well as the Late Cretaceous geohistory of Mississippi with the outcome of a permanent mural in the museum.

Brent Funderburk, a William L. Giles Distinguished Professor Emeritus at MSU, guided four mural projects dealing with health, childhood, Indigenous music, and paleontology in public areas on campus and in the community. Under his direction, MSU senior fine arts students Todd M. Rowan (artist/principal investigator) and Moesha Wright (artist/researcher) initiated design proposals and presentations in Spring 2018. With Renee Clary, MSU geosciences professor and museum director, and Amy Moe-Hoffman, museum collections manager, students discussed, researched, and developed a panoramic depiction of a segment

Rowan, T.M., Funderburk, T.B., and Clary, R.M., 2022, "But why paint a dinosaur blue?": Envisioning the Cretaceous—A vitalizing, multidisciplinary project in a university museum, *in* Clary, R.M., Rosenberg, G.D., and Evans, D.C., eds., The Evolution of Paleontological Art: Geological Society of America Memoir 218, p. 245–254, https://doi.org/10.1130/2021.1218(27).

of local paleo-geologic history of the local Black Belt Prairie[1] area involving Upper Cretaceous flora and fauna of marine and land environments at the end of the Mesozoic Era, which climaxed with the meteorite impact at Chicxulub. The Cretaceous-Paleogene (K-Pg) extinction is not only a significant event in Earth history, but its boundary is exposed within the immediate region. The K-Pg contact and biodiversity changes across the extinction horizon in the county have recently received renewed research attention (Broussard et al., 2019).

The mural, *Mississippi Cretaceous Panorama* (Fig. 1), serves as a bridge between science and art in its collaborative development and as a focal point for museum visitors who can now better envision life in Mississippi millions of years ago. The large-scale acrylic/enamel painting brings relevance to the geologic story by putting "flesh on the bones" of the state's unique Mesozoic past, thus enhancing the meaning and vitality of this university geosciences museum. We recount the realization of that mission, through the concerted work of scientists, artists, and museum experts, as well as the challenges the mural had to overcome with space constraints and the local population's personal beliefs.

[1]The original Black Belt Prairie, named for its dark soil, was a disjointed group of treeless prairies that coursed from Alabama, through Mississippi, and into Tennessee and roughly aligns with the outcropping Cretaceous limestone. Home to endemic and disjunct plant and insect species, the prairie remnants are small and face encroachment from human activity and invasive junipers.

BACKGROUND: THE DUNN-SEILER MUSEUM

Founded in 1946, MSU's Dunn-Seiler Museum serves a largely rural population in Mississippi and its adjacent states. It is situated in one of the more income disparate counties in the United States (Sutter, 2013) and is the only natural history museum within a 2+ hour driving distance; the other nearby museums are in Birmingham, Alabama; Jackson, Mississippi; and Memphis, Tennessee.

After Hilbun Hall was remodeled at the end of the twentieth century, the Dunn-Seiler Museum reopened in 2003 as a small public gallery that displayed rocks, minerals, and fossils behind locked glass cabinets and often with very little signage (Clary and Moe-Hoffman, 2018). During the last decade, Dunn-Seiler Museum Director Renee Clary and Collections Manager Amy Moe-Hoffman spearheaded multiple low-cost improvements in the museum's displays and outreach to engage visitors and improve the geoliteracy of the general population (Clary and Moe-Hoffman, 2018).

Figure 1. The *Mississippi Cretaceous Panorama* color composite, which was painted with acrylic and spray paint (photo credit: Todd M. Rowan). The three large panels are mounted along the tops of display cabinets in the Dunn-Seiler Museum. (Top) The asteroid approaches the planet, with the scene transitioning into a stylized Mississippi map with modern exposed Cretaceous strata in orangey-red hues. (Middle) The mosasaur, in the center, transitions into a terrestrial environment. (Bottom) The ceratopsian dinosaur glances at the meteorite right before impact; the scene transitions to the final view of the meteorite's impact.

In addition to financial obstacles (the museum has no independent budget), the Dunn-Seiler is challenged by a small space, and many within the local population self-identify as creationists (Clary and Moe-Hoffman, 2018). In the first decade of the twenty-first century, visitors challenged faculty and students staffing the museum when they encountered fossils labeled older than 6000 years. As a result, the museum's website was edited to explicitly state the 4.6 b.y. history of the planet, while museum programs—such as National Fossil Day Fossil Extravaganza, Darwin Day, and MSU Science Night at the Museum—engaged the public in geologic discussions, using scientifically accurate but non-confrontational language that is respectful of the community's personal beliefs (Clary and Moe-Hoffman, 2018).

The university is situated on top of Cretaceous strata, and the Dunn-Seiler Museum offers fossil-collecting tours at the local campus outcrop in addition to museum tours and events. The area is part of the Black Belt Prairie with some prairie remnants preserved near campus. For example, Osborn Prairie has been named a Mississippi Nature Conservancy site and contains Cretaceous fossils weathering from limestone chalk "moonscapes" and several endemic and disjunct faunal and floral species unique to the area (Brown, 2003; Wiygul et al., 2003).

Art professor Brent Funderburk was well acquainted with the Dunn-Seiler Museum on MSU's campus. As an amateur paleontologist since childhood, he extensively collected local Cretaceous fossils exposed in the Black Belt Prairie and worked with the state's paleontologists; Funderburk exchanged location information about unique collecting sites he uncovered, donated specimens, and participated in field excursions with George Phillips, paleontology curator at the Mississippi Museum of Natural Science in Jackson. Funderburk approached the museum staff to propose a science and art collaborative project that would illustrate the local Cretaceous strata. Through an MSU undergraduate research grant, Funderburk directed and supervised two students, Todd Rowan (artist/principal investigator) and Moesha Wright (artist/researcher)[2] (Fig. 2) in the construction of a mural that envisioned the Cretaceous paleoecosystem of Mississippi. After the first semester, Rowan became the sole researcher and artist of the mural.

PROJECT CONSTRAINTS

The Dunn-Seiler Museum is lined with glass-fronted cabinets along both side walls, under the windows in the front of the museum, and along either side of the entrance. The mural had to utilize the existing space above cabinets or require a substantial reorganization of the displays. The *Mississippi's Geological Timeline* exhibit showcases the fossils found within the state, with much of the display dedicated to the Cretaceous organisms exposed in Mississippi's northeast corner.

Figure 2. Brent Funderburk (top), William L. Giles Distinguished Professor Emeritus at Mississippi State University, directed B.F.A students Todd M. Rowan (middle, artist and principal investigator) and Moesha Wright (bottom, artist/researcher) in the development of the *Mississippi Cretaceous Panorama* mural.

[2]Moesha Wright assisted with the project throughout the spring 2018 semester. Todd Rowan, principal investigator for the mural, completed and installed the mural through summer 2018 and fall 2018.

Although Dunn-Seiler Museum staff and Funderburk were familiar with Cretaceous fossils, the undergraduate artists were not. The mural also had to take into consideration the students, faculty, and general public who visit and who may have alternative conceptions of the planet's history that are in direct opposition to geologic time. The artists and scientists determined that a creative depiction of the local Cretaceous organisms meeting their demise at the end of the Mesozoic Era would draw visitors into the extinction story in a non-threatening manner. Regardless of religious affiliations, younger visitors show great interest in the *Triceratops* cast in the museum. However, even some of the youngest visitors become unresponsive when evolution or geologic time is mentioned.

Upon the mural's completion, Funderburk and Rowan discussed the timeline, barriers, and project accomplishments. Rowan reflected on his first perceptions of designing and painting the Cretaceous mural:

First, the shape of the space was strange. It was huge—almost 15 meters (50 feet) wide, but it's only like a little over a meter vertically (3.5 feet), and it was to be above eye level in that museum. How to make that work? You [Funderburk] got me thinking "Oh my gosh, how will it be lit; what colors can we use?" And some thinking about, "Alright, so which dinosaurs were here; how much information?" Obviously, Dr. Clary and everybody at the Dunn-Seiler Museum would say, here are the bones; these were here. Then it became, "Okay, so now I've got to make it something that people want to look at," not just, "Oh, there're some dinosaurs up on the wall."

BACKGROUND RESEARCH

As part of their introduction to Cretaceous Mississippi, Funderburk brought Rowan and Wright to the Dunn-Seiler Museum for a full tour of the fossils, rocks, and minerals in the first of several visits that student artists made during the project. On several occasions, Funderburk brought along his personal Cretaceous fossil specimens as well as photographic presentations on his laptop computer. The student artists' education did not end in the Dunn-Seiler Museum, either. They investigated the Cretaceous Mississippi environment through the classic Mississippi State Geological Survey report *Cretaceous Shelf Sediments of Mississippi* (Mellen, 1958), the Mississippi State Geological Survey of Upper Cretaceous deposits (Stephenson and Monroe, 1940), and books on Mississippi's geology (Dockery and Thompson, 2016; Galicki and Schmitz, 2016). The Cretaceous moment was brought full circle when Funderburk brought the student artists to some of his local fossil collecting spots. Cretaceous fossil identification book (Stinchcomb, 2009) in hand, Rowan collected oysters and shark teeth and internalized the Cretaceous seas that covered the state. Rowan described how he shared that watery realization with a colleague:

I remember walking out here on campus with a fellow art student, Sam, telling him, "Dude! Imagine this 70 million years ago. There was water where we are standing now; you know, this sea of water way up there," I pointed over his head, "and these huge mega-beasts are swimming around us," and we both kind of looked up, in stunned silence, and he says, "Let's go indoors."

Funderburk directed Rowan and Wright in their research into Cretaceous creatures. Bakker's *Dinosaur Heresies* provided inspiration on dinosaurs as active, intelligent creatures that were also responsible parents (Bakker, 1986), further demonstrating that a scientist's creativity and imagination could advance the state of dinosaur science. The Dinosaur Revolution meant that dinosaurs were no longer depicted as dull, gray, or brown sluggish lizards. To study how to translate the Cretaceous research and fossils into artwork, the artists reviewed Lescaze et al. (2017) as a paleoart reference and learned how paleoart evolved and visually documented contemporary scientific understanding. The students researched the art history of mural painting through Mexican muralists (Charlot, 1963; Rochfort, 1998). They grasped how the Mexican muralists, such as Diego Rivera, David Alfaro Siqueiros, and Jose Clemente Orozco, boldly carried forth application of Renaissance linear perspective (especially three-point), the further exaggeration of space/scale relational illusion of deep (concave) and close (convex) architectonic forms in dynamic motion (by using diagonals, varied atmospheric edges and color, and attenuated modeling), in human and animal representations as well as architecture. The student artists would then design the museum mural to feature exaggeration of foreshortening and the use of organic (rather than geometric) three-point perspective in their structure and in modeling the Mesozoic creatures featured. With Funderburk's guidance, the students recognized that the use of super-proportioning in large public works influences the mural painting, super-graphics, and communication of art and design. Super-proportioning, a perspective device often used by the Mexican mural artists and American art educators, brings strong, spatial illusion to the viewer through dynamic scale changes within and between forms, as applied to a limited, two-dimensional space, such as a wall fresco or mural.

Further, Rowan studied specific subjects and topographical habitats as a matter of creating visitor engagement via the specificity of each episode. He observed various Black Belt Prairie fossil sites in the Ripley, Prairie Bluff, and Selma-Demopolis Chalk Formations of Oktibbeha County, as well as specimens of related fossil fauna of the region in the collection of the Dunn-Seiler Museum on the Mississippi State University campus. The artists studied the *Triceratops*, mosasaur, and other vertebrate specimens. Rowan's background in studio art education involved a curriculum of life drawing courses with both human and animal skeletal form subjects as well as drawing and painting from life. In his research on the morphology of Cretaceous subjects, he applied this training to Dunn-Seiler Museum specimens, renderings by other artists/illustrators, and extensive sketching. Rowan's knowledge of optical/mimetic coloration as well as psychological color was informed by his art history and studio coursework, which identified and encouraged expressive color as a theatrical means of emotional theming and storytelling.

THE DESIGN PROCESS

In the early stages of conception of the project, Wright helped Rowan develop the graphic design and compositional sequencing of the overall image. Their combined research on mural impact and continuity was integral to the unifying experience of a widespread panorama. From the initial collaboration, Rowan developed a full value range and color key in the composition, created specific scenes with central characters, and joined episodes with transitions.

Subjective Imagination

When designing artistic representations of scientific knowledge, artists' creative process requires subjective imagination and balance of risk and play. Although the Dunn-Seiler Museum's paleoart mural was intended for a scientific museum, the artists needed to look beyond local fossils, paleo-artwork, and the published science to capture the imagination of young visitors through *Mississippi Cretaceous Panorama.* Rowan had to return to the mindset of childhood, where imaginative free-flow is encouraged. Young children comfortably ask, "What if," and design creative solutions that are untested, and more importantly, unevaluated. "What if"—the imaginative and endless creative flow of possibilities (Csikszentmihalyi, 1990)—is essential to artists, though play and risk cannot be given too much weight because judgement will come, and failure is inevitable.

During his 2018 Geological Society of America Annual Meeting presentation (Rowan et al., 2018), Rowan showed a slide collage of multiple Bill Watterson's (2012) *Calvin and Hobbes* cartoon strips. Watterson rendered hyper-realistic dinosaurs amid flat cartoon characters with ironic punchlines that imply there's always the contrast of his imagination portrayed through illustrative realism versus a kind of daily, timely reality. Watterson said, "The challenge of drawing is that there is no one right way to visually describe something. It's a good thing to confront your limitations and preconceptions every so often" (Martell, 2010, p. 82). He noted that he was not in denial but selective in the reality he accepted. And as Rowan's research into paleoart revealed, even scientists disagree on the correct way to visualize and represent extinct life forms (e.g., see Allmon, this volume).

Rowan reflected that Bill Watterson found a way with *Calvin and Hobbes* to live in perpetual, childlike exploration. Watterson studied nature and drew a world that was real; then, through Calvin, he drew the world as he *wished* it were—the world inside the imagination of a child. When Watterson presented that abstraction on the printed page, no matter which world he drew, it became "real" as it existed in its image generation.

The artists recognized that in the daily grind of adulthood, we start to move past the childhood wonderment of Calvin's dinosaurs and extinct reptiles. They are pushed back into something that happened somewhere else long ago, a once-glowing reality that has become some nostalgic reality. This is especially true in Mississippi, because the concept of extinct Mesozoic organisms that existed in the realm of geologic time is not a bullet point of the local taught culture.

However, as the student artists experienced and came to realize, Mesozoic fossil evidence nonetheless still exists in the state, in the local dirt, under the grass. Rowan brought his children to wander the chalk badlands of the Black Belt Prairie less than 2 mi (2 km) from the university campus and found shark teeth strewn on the ground. He and his children talked about the coastal water being easily 200+ mi (300+ km) away. The receded waters now are now long gone and far out of sight, and residents do not usually think about that when they encounter fossils from ancient seas within the prairie.

Within his subjective imagination, Rowan identified the target audience for the mural and knew its consideration had to be "kids first." Whereas adults may view a mural and see the artistry of it, kids are not going to look up and say, "That's a well-painted mural." For children, it doesn't matter how the mural arrived on the museum walls; they are seeking an image that makes the unreal real. Or makes the real unreal.

The museum staff agreed that engaging the younger visitor with movement and color was the best approach for the mural. Most outside groups that tour the museum consist of elementary through middle school students, and these young visitors seem willing to connect with extinct organisms unless there is an explicit use of evolutionary theory and progression of life forms (Clary and Moe-Hoffman, 2018; Clary, 2017). With vibrant mosasaurs and dinosaurs portrayed within an extinction event, the mural excites museum visitors with a locally relevant story, translated to a "real scene" from the fossils that visitors collect at the campus outcrop—and from the mosasaur bones and *Triceratops* skull that they see in the museum. Visitors' interest in local Mesozoic fossils increases, and they willingly hear tales of geologically long-ago Mississippi, a meteorite impact, and critters long deceased.

Creatively Envisioning the Cretaceous Climax

In the case of paleontological art, the artist and the scientist could not exist without each other. The artist needs the scientist to describe what extinct beasts looked like, and the scientist needs the artist to realize the vision. With the Dunn-Seiler Museum mural, the scientists trusted the artists and the fine arts professor to come up with a shared vision. Professor Funderburk noted that the team worked together to come closer to the truth: "Beethoven listened to birds in the morning and wrote symphonies in the afternoon. I think we'll find that most artists and scientists live lives like that—full of fact and poetry."

We often uncover the best things when we are not looking for them. Colbert (1995, p. 21) described one such serendipitous moment at Ghost Ranch:

> The discovery of *Coelophysis* at Ghost Ranch (New Mexico) is a good example of the role of serendipity in paleontological research. According to the *Oxford English Dictionary* serendipity is a word "coined by Horace Walpole upon the title of the fairy-tale The Three Princes of

Serendip, the heroes of which were always making new discoveries, by accidents and sagacity, of things they were not in quest of." Exactly so, at Ghost Ranch.

Just as Colbert, Bakker, and other scientists acknowledge the role of accident in many successful outcomes, Funderburk revealed that artists carry "What if?" as a tool for broadening their periphery to include the landscape of the imagined as experiential:

As such, the eye, both inner and outer, is always open. To the child, this is the realm of play. To the artist, and I believe to the scientist as well, serious play—adult or professional play; if it is risky enough to be heroic (implied by Colbert), engages possibility as much as probability. Rowan noted that the mural began with a dilemma: how to create a work that maintains the artist's first function, which is that of documentarian, and then storyteller, or more appropriately, an *illustrator*. He pushed realistic boundaries and moderated the internal tug-of-war that is aesthetic versus journalistic and scientific integrity.

The mosasaur became one focal point, and then the artists' attention turned to dinosaurs. The Dunn-Seiler Museum displays hadrosaur vertebrae, a femur, and part of a foot that were found locally within a marine deposit, suggesting the carcass of the deceased animal was transported by "bloat and float." Rowan, however, looked to another dinosaur for inspiration: *Triceratops*. The museum displays a donated *Triceratops* cast, and recently a ceratopsian fossil was found in Mississippi. George Phillips, the Mississippi Museum of Natural Science paleontologist, discovered the first horned dinosaur evidence—a single fossil tooth—in eastern North America in the Owl Creek Formation near New Albany, Mississippi (Farke and Phillips, 2017). The discovery indicated that horned dinosaurs actually trekked in the Mississippi area as the Western Interior Seaway was retreating during the Late Cretaceous before the K-Pg impact. The artists wanted to incorporate this amazing, recent evidence in the mural, and in so doing, to honor MSU alumnus George Phillips. At the same time, Rowan was able to express his own personal preference for the ceratopsian, a prehistoric animal that everyone recognizes.

Throughout the mural design and construction process, the dialogue with the scientists continued. The scientists and artists navigated the presentation of ceratopsian horns and their relative positions for scientific accuracy while permitting creativity. In addition to the dinosaur, Clary and Moe-Hoffman questioned the design of the other large creature featured, the mosasaur, when it began to resemble the Mississippi state fossil, *Basilosaurus* (Eocene whale), more than a Mesozoic marine reptile.

From the beginning of the mural to its end, the artists considered the passage in the space of the room. Rowan questioned what event could move the visitor through the museum space. The K-Pg extinction was an obvious choice. While informed visitors already knew the ending of the story, Rowan wanted to stretch out the drama and hold back the final moment. Used to working with vertical arrangements, he found the mural's horizontal composition, with scenes of extinct organisms transitioning across the two walls of the museum, challenging. If the back of the mural—near the museum entrance—showcased the meteorite impact, could the artists still make the mural interesting toward its origin at the back corner of the room?

Rowan also knew that he didn't want to paint a standard, lateral, static picture of a diagram of a "dot, dot, dot." He was determined that the mural be dynamic:

It's got to have movement, you know, you have these thrashing, mega-reptiles dominating the Late Cretaceous—*T. rex* of the sea—the mosasaur; those big, swimmy, huge, crazy, evil-looking, crocodile-shark-whale things—dominating not just the wall, but ruling the room! How do I make this look like it just happened, a kind of virtual reality, while also looking super cool; an original and unprecedented creation to inspire kids to imagine them in long-ago Mississippi?

The result was intended dynamism, evidenced by the implied motion in every "scene," as well as in the sweeping movement of related color harmonies (powered by a limited thematic palette); broad, connective tonal gradients; and focal moments of strong contrast points repeated across the image. In the end, Rowan and Funderburk laughed that they ran out of wall with all of the content they wanted to cover. Both acknowledged they had spent a lot of time talking about the design aspect and its changing perspective of the incoming asteroid as it approached Earth, moving across the area that would become Mississippi, and back to an extraplanetary impact view (Fig. 3).

Why Paint a Dinosaur Blue?

The mosasaur and ceratopsian dinosaur serve as focal points in the mural's geological saga of impending Cretaceous doom. In the recognizable Mesozoic creatures, Rowan wanted to include an artistic interpretation that made visitors exclaim, "Wow!" Because the dinosaur was familiar, Rowan felt he could play with the design a little more. He could throw in color designs and new choices without negating the believability of the animal.

Funderburk acknowledges that his favorite subject is coloration, and he educated the student artists about different kinds of color. The artist should consider the innate color, the local color of the creature, contained in the skin cells; the chemical color; and the structural color caused by diffraction and prismatic cells or scales. Projected color arises from the color of external light and shadow. One of the other focal points of this mural, beyond the creatures, was the meteorite impact at Chicxulub, ca. 66 m.y. ago in the Gulf of Mexico, and its hot-colored, flaming explosion of orange has a complement in the shadow world of blue. As a result, Rowan had creatures in shadows of this super nova of a sunset for the doomed fauna turning toward orange and then back to blue.

When asked if most of the mural is thematically blue for impact, Rowan responded that first came the drama of values—light and dark—Japanese *notan* (Dow, 1899). Based on Japanese design, "notan" is not merely the presentation of light and dark values (tones) in a composition; it is the dramatic arrangement of a few differently sized, differently valued shapes of different

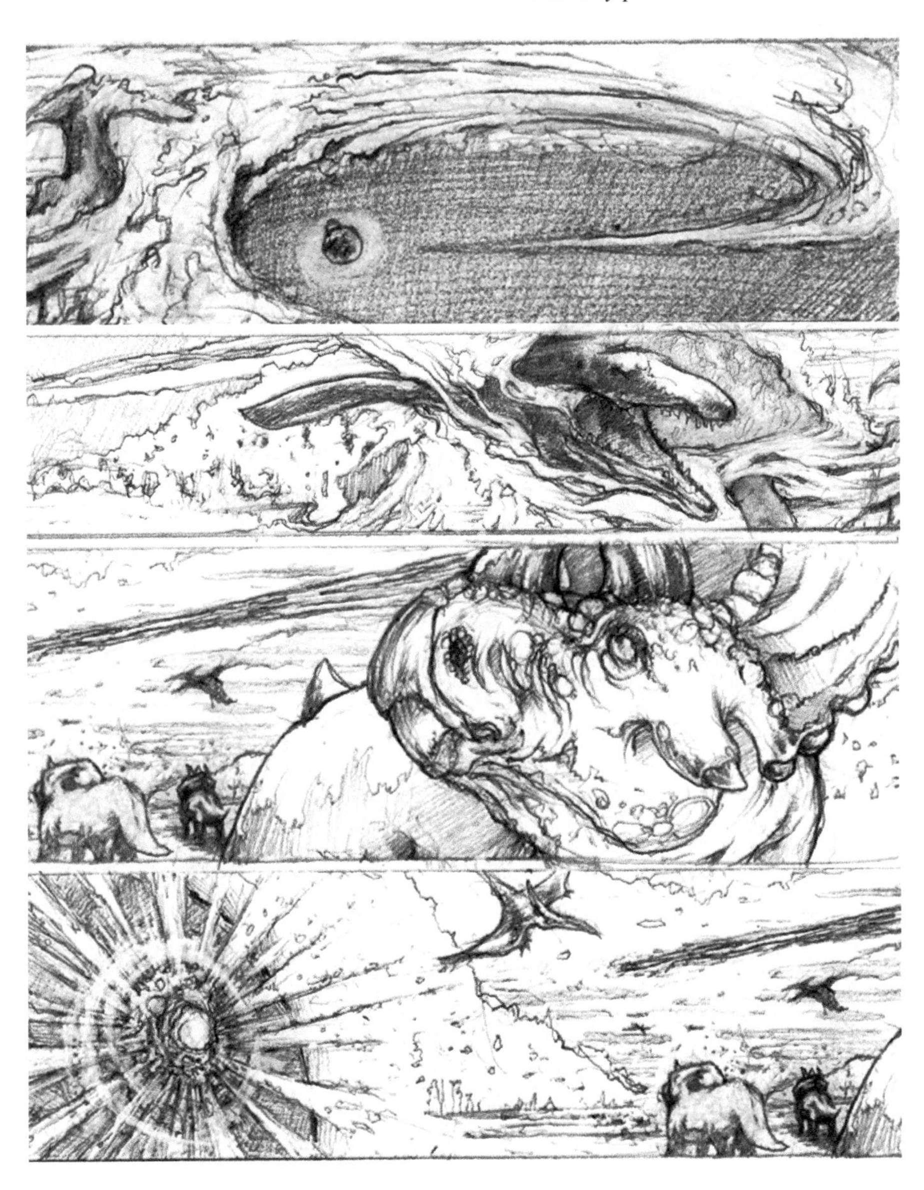

Figure 3. Early black-and-white concept sketches of the *Mississippi Cretaceous Panorama* are shown (photo credit: Todd M. Rowan).

kinds in a hierarchical balance, which creates strong impact as well as a meditative sense of infinity through the implication of progressive repetition within (but never to disturb) the larger simplicity. Funderburk instructed the student artists to study Arthur Wesley Dow's theories and examples and to apply these principles to the form of the mural painting's design and execution. Dow popularized the use of "notan" and its methodologies as relevant to applied art and decorative design. Rowan reflected:

> The starker contrast creating that Baroque idea of tenebrism, really jarring and dramatic chiaroscuro, when those dark darks set in, and then you see the light lights. When I was working on the mosasaur, obviously, he was underwater, blue [Fig. 4]. And then you had this dinosaur. We knew that the environment on top of them was this orangey craziness, right? So, you [Funderburk] suggested bringing those in as the highlights on the locally colored maroon-ish purple mosasaur and not making the highlight at the widest point of that tint of red, but making the highlight the actual color of the light that's going to be shining on them.

This served as a premonition of the asteroid on its way. Rowan remarked,

> Immediately made me want to jump back over to start working on a canvas with the ceratopsian on it because I knew that it had to fit into this hierarchy of impending color. And the ceratopsid dinosaur, in pictorial space, was in the left panel closest to the asteroid. Because even as this wasn't a timeline, there was a sense of chronology. The progression of light from orange to blue created gradual movement in time and space, but still respected that sense of a single moment of impact dominating the mural. Again, the "suite" of motion.

The notanic hierarchy is exemplified in the sense of optical movement formally presented by sweeping, gradated values in opposite colors (orange and blue as the thematic palette) and their concordance and complementary clash at juncture, and, in terms of content (story) in the illusion of coming or fading (or, impending or descending) natural light. The artists' intention was that

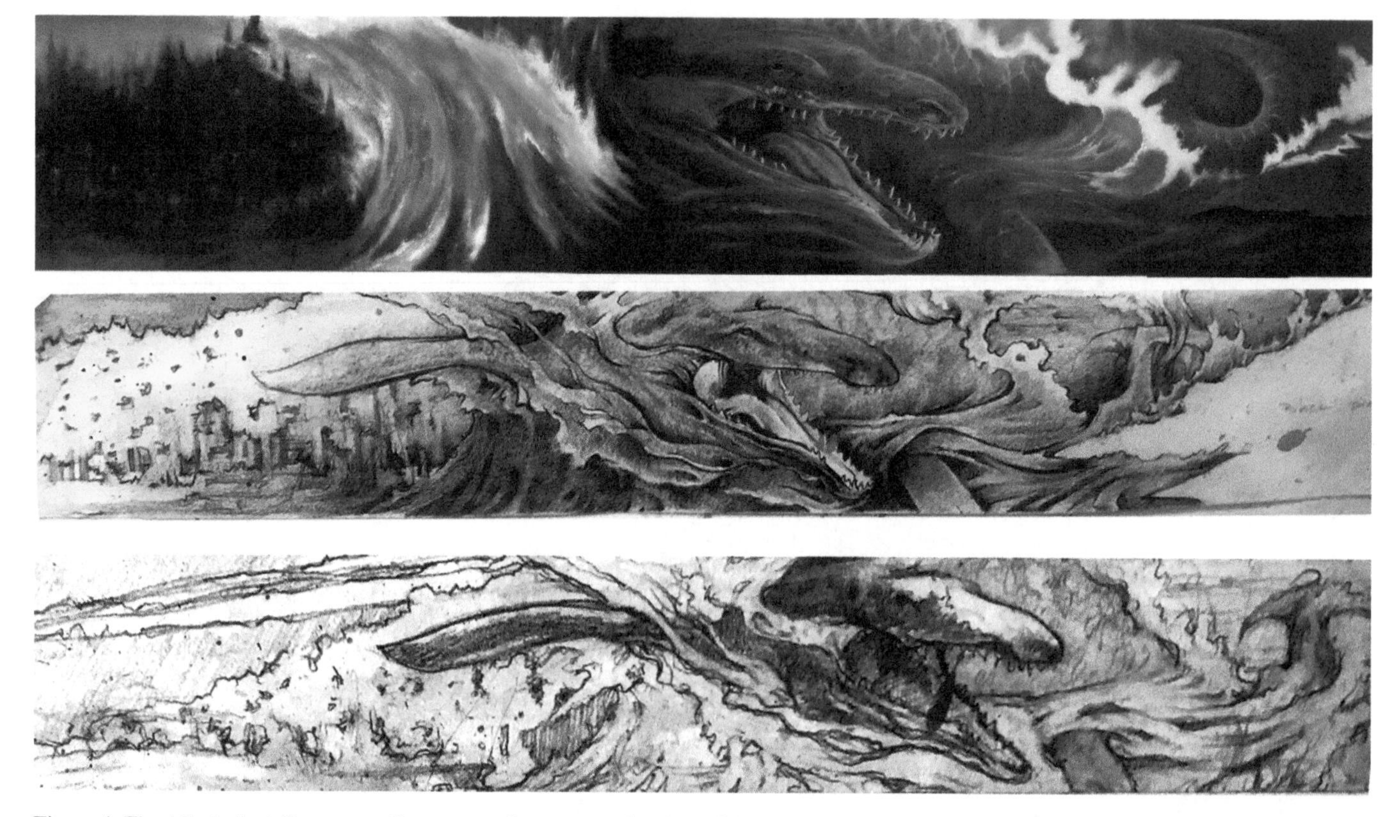

Figure 4. The *Mississippi Cretaceous Panorama* color concept sketches of the mosasaur section are shown (photo credit: Todd M. Rowan).

intensity transformation of rapidly changing color and luminosity at dawn or dusk (cool to warm/warm to cool) might serve to represent change at a larger scale of time/space as well. Finally, the hope was that the psychological impact of this color at peak luminance (i.e., Purkinje effect) might evoke and provoke emotion in the visitor.

The *Triceratops* ("Sarah") is depicted as turning to suddenly see that bombastic sunset on the whole world that shone for a good, long time. So then, that light and its color resonate through all of these creatures. Rowan observed:

> The other way the blue speaks to me is deep time in a way, represented by the deep water and space. From the blue-blackness of space with the brightest apex of the drama, from a ceratopsian's point of view. It's one creature representing all. From the corner of her eye, maybe, momentarily distracted by our little tiny blue rock floating through the universe, soon to be hit by, you know, a celestial spark—no big deal. I think the Chicxulub asteroid was 14 kilometers across; a rock the size of Starkville, Mississippi! [our town] bypass to bypass! But not the impact; the millisecond before.

DOES IT MATTER?

When Rowan accepted the task of creating and painting a mural for the Dunn-Seiler Museum, he knew he had to immerse himself in the scientific culture and speak scientists' language. The mural project necessitated dynamic conversations between scientists and artists about scientific research, design, and paleoart that converged in the vibrant mural of Cretaceous life on Earth at the verge of the K-Pg extinction event.

At the end of his 2018 presentation at the Geological Society of America (GSA) Annual Meeting in Indianapolis (Rowan et al., 2018), an audience member asked Rowan, "How do you make the decision about how to portray these animals when we don't really know what they looked like?" In the background, Rowan's big blue dinosaur spanned the room on the screen. Rowan looked and paused, and that was the answer. He responded, "There's a shared integrity between the art and science of it, we have a commitment to fact, to ego, and to interpretation." But it was the image, he thought, that went, "BING!"

So, that moment at GSA before the projected great blue ceratopsian mystery, Rowan found the moment he had worked for in his year of work and questioning. If artists could not get the wonder and the mystery as an emotional confrontation to the viewer in that museum, then what is the point of doing it? Rowan acknowledged that throughout the process, he asked himself that question most: "Does it matter?" He knew the result must excite museum visitors and inspire them to learn more. He had creatively returned to his imagined childhood, and asked:

> Can you dance to it? That is, what is your take, as a new question. My drawings were scientific up to a certain point. I studied morphology, color and pattern, but in them, I hope you can see that I also danced.

Figure 5. The *Mississippi Cretaceous Panorama* mural as displayed in the Dunn-Seiler Museum, Mississippi State University.

I got to be able to do a ceratopsian dance. We need more ceratopsian breakdancing in our museums!

Since the mural's installation, young visitors have confirmed the mural's dance directive. Visiting children point to the mural's mosasaur and the dinosaur, ask questions of their tour guides, and rush from cabinet display to cabinet display to see real dinosaur and mosasaur bones and examples of the fossils they can find in the campus outcrop. Their enthusiasm is contagious—and on more than one occasion, Clary reenacted a mosasaur's movements in a true follow-the-leader Cretaceous dance party.

For the young visitors to the Dunn-Seiler Museum, the mural does matter.

THE FINISHED PRODUCT

The *Mississippi Cretaceous Panorama* is a 1 m × 15 m mural depiction of a segment of paleo-geologic history of the local Black Belt Prairie area involving Upper Cretaceous flora and fauna of marine and land environments at the end of the Mesozoic Era, climaxing with the impact of a meteorite at Chicxulub (Fig. 5). The mural is an immediate focus of visitors entering the museum and has resulted in more dynamic interactions between younger visitors and the museum collections.

ACKNOWLEDGMENTS

We thank our reviewers Andrew A. Farke and James Starnes, and volume editor Gary Rosenberg, for insightful comments and suggestions that greatly improved the presentation of this chapter.

REFERENCES CITED

Allmon, W.D., 2022, this volume, "Extreme dinosaurs" and the continuing evolution of dinosaur paleoart, *in* Clary, R.M., Rosenberg, G.D., and Evans, D.C., eds., The Evolution of Paleontological Art: Geological Society of America Memoir 218, https://doi.org/10.1130/2021.1218(23).

Bakker, R.T., 1986, The Dinosaur Heresies: New Theories Unlocking the Mystery of the Dinosaurs and Their Extinction: New York, William Morrow, 481 p.

Broussard, J., Clary, R.M., and Phillips, G.E., 2019, Faunal composition and diversity across the K-Pg boundary in northeastern Mississippi: Geological Society of America Abstracts with Programs, v. 51, no. 5, https://doi.org/10.1130/abs/2019AM-338124.

Brown, R., 2003, Paleoenvironment and the biogeography of the Mississippi Black Belt, *in* Peacock, E., and Schauwecker, T., eds., Blackland Prairies of the Gulf Coastal Plain: Nature, Culture, and Sustainability: Tuscaloosa, Alabama, University of Alabama Press, p. 11–26.

Charlot, J., 1963, The Mexican Mural Renaissance, 1920–1925: New Haven, Connecticut, Yale University Press, 329 p.

Clary, R.M., 2017, Defusing discomfort: Bridging philosophical and religious conflicts through reflective writing: Science Teacher, v. 84, no. 2, p. 26–30.

Clary, R.M., and Moe-Hoffman, A., 2018, The role of the Dunn-Seiler Museum, Mississippi State University, in promoting public geoliteracy, *in* Rosenberg, G., and Clary, R., eds., Museums at the Forefront of the History and Philosophy of Geology: History Made, History in the Making: Geological Society of America Special Paper 535, p. 237–248, https://doi.org/10.1130/2018.2535(15).

Colbert, E.H., 1995, The Little Dinosaurs of Ghost Ranch: New York, Columbia University Press, 250 p.

Csikszentmihalyi, M., 1990, Flow: The Psychology of Optimal Experience: New York, Harper Perennial, 303 p.

Dockery, D.T., and Thompson, D.E., 2016, The Geology of Mississippi: Jackson, Mississippi, University Press of Mississippi, co-published with Mississippi Department of Environmental Quality, 692 p.

Dow, A.W., 1899, Composition: Understanding Line, Notan, and Color (E-book): Mineola, New York, Dover Publications.

Farke, A., and Phillips, G., 2017, The first reported ceratopsid dinosaur tooth from eastern North America (Owl Creek Formation, Upper Cretaceous,

Mississippi, USA): PeerJ, v. 5, p. e3342, https://doi.org/10.7717/peerj.3342.
Galicki, S., and Schmitz, D.W., 2016, Roadside Geology of Mississippi: Missoula, Montana, Mountain Press Publishing Company, 288 p.
Lescaze, Z., Ford, W., Taschen, B., and Wiener, N., 2017, Paleoart: Visions of the Prehistoric Past: Cologne, Germany, Taschen, 292 p.
Martell, N., 2010, Looking for Calvin and Hobbes: The Unconventional Story of Bill Watterson and His Revolutionary Comic Strip: New York, Continuum, 272 p.
Mellen, F.F., 1958, Cretaceous Shelf Sediments of Mississippi: Mississippi State Geological Survey Bulletin 85, 112 p.
Rochfort, D., 1998, Mexican Muralists: Orozco, Rivera, Siqueiros: San Francisco, Chronicle Books, 240 p.
Rowan, T.M., Wright, M., and Funderburk, B.T., 2018, Painting the Cretaceous; a vitalizing, multidisciplinary project in a university museum: Geological Society of America Abstracts with Programs, v. 50, no. 6, https://doi.org/10.1130/abs/2018AM-322300.
Stephenson, L.W., and Monroe, W.H., 1940, The Upper Cretaceous Deposits: Mississippi State Geological Survey Bulletin 40.
Stinchcomb, B.L., 2009, Mesozoic Fossils II: The Cretaceous Period: Atglen, Pennsylvania, Schiffer, 176 p.
Sutter, J., 2013, Change the list: The most unequal counties in America: http://www.cnn.com/2013/10/29/opinion/sutter-list-income-inequality/index.html (accessed May 2020).
Watterson, B., 2012, The Complete Calvin and Hobbes Paperback: Kansas City, Missouri, Andrews McMeel Publishing, 1456 p.
Wiygul, S., Krans, K., Brown, R., and Maddox, V., 2003, Restoration of a prairie remnant in the Black Belt of Mississippi, *in* Peacock, E., and Schauwecker, T., eds., Blackland Prairies of the Gulf Coastal Plain: Nature, Culture, and Sustainability: Tuscaloosa, Alabama, University of Alabama Press, 365 p.

Manuscript Accepted by the Society 20 January 2021
Manuscript Published Online 2 August 2021

Printed in the USA

The Geological Society of America
Memoir 218

Fossilarium: Paintings inspired by micropaleontological thin sections

Giles Ford*
University of the Creative Arts, Falkner Road, Farnham, GU9 7DS, UK

ABSTRACT

Inspired by his late father's thin section micropaleontology, artist Giles Ford created the Fossilarium, a series of large-scale paintings that investigates the nature of time and space through investigation of the miniature. Ford reflects on the influences of his work and how he developed a visual language inspired by repeating patterns of his father's microfossil thin sections. The Fossilarium presents abstract landscapes of interwoven time explored through layered images that intertwine the geological, industrial, societal, and personal spectrums. The Fossilarium thereby seeks to create timeless patterns that probe different subject areas from pure aesthetics through the Anthropocene and climate change provocations to more intimate multigenerational explorations of the thread of family history, loss, and the future. Through his paintings, Ford seeks to bring the micropaleontological view to a wider audience by posing questions about the role of industry, fossil fuels, the artist, and climate change.

INTRODUCTION

As an English fine artist, I am inspired and informed by the artistic and aesthetic properties of the oil industry through thin section micropaleontology. My large-scale paintings reside in several public, private, and corporate collections, including the Museum of Modern Art (MOMA), Wales, and Lambert Energy Advisory. In this chapter, I reflect on creating my recent Fossilarium series based on the investigation of my father's field research that was captured in the 1963 book, *The MicroFacies of the Cretaceous of Western Venezuela* (Ford, 1963). In the process, I address cross-disciplinary questions in my painting practice: Can micropaleontology be experienced and "read" as art? What are the similarities between geologic processes creating micropaleontological thin sections and the process of painting? What connections do paintings and microfossils have physically and philosophically as visual languages? What art movements and artists might have been affected by micropaleontological imagery? I probe whether there is a role for artists to play in honoring the beauty of micropaleontology and the constructive role of the oil industry in shaping the evolution of human society, while also asking visual questions about fossil fuel strategies and their impact on climate change (Arenas and Thackeray, 2003).

BACKGROUND AND HISTORY OF THE FOSSILARIUM PAINTING SERIES

When my father, Aubrey Ford, first saw a microfossil while studying at Oxford University just after World War II, he said he had found the beauty that he knew he wanted to look at for the rest of his life. He became a micropaleontologist with Shell, Maersk, and Polargas, traveling the globe for the next 40 years from Venezuela, Brazil, Tunisia, Iran, and Yemen through Sweden, the Netherlands, Denmark, Sweden, and Norway to the realm of the polar bear, where he lived in the Arctic at Spitsbergen.

Having largely, and quite unfairly, ignored my father's microscopic world during his lifetime, his death incited me to

*www.gilesford.com

Ford, G., 2022, Fossilarium: Paintings inspired by micropaleontological thin sections, *in* Clary, R.M., Rosenberg, G.D., and Evans, D.C., eds., The Evolution of Paleontological Art: Geological Society of America Memoir 218, p. 255–261, https://doi.org/10.1130/2021.1218(28).

discover what exactly my father had meant by "beauty" and why he had invested four decades of his life intensely examining minuscule fossilized organisms and creatures for hours, days, and weeks at a time.

I sought to learn what definition of beauty he was using and whether micropaleontology can be "artistic." On some level I realized there must indeed be secrets and images worth seeing and understanding, not just as his son with a desire to honor and connect with his father after his departure, but as a painter. What was so interesting to him? What was so compelling? How on Earth could there be anything really of such beauty in minute science as to warrant such a noble obsession?

I began by digging out a book from the attic that my father had co-written in the 1960s, with the niche title *The Micro-Facies of the Cretaceous of Western Venezuela* (Ford and Houbolt, 1963), opening the dusty covers to reveal a series of black-and-white plates with electron microscope and thin section images. I was utterly amazed.

The experience was as mind-blowing to me as when I had first seen the full-scale abstract expressionist painting *Corinthian II* (1961) by the artist Franz Kline in the Museum of Fine Arts in Houston a few years previously. Two paradigms collided: that of my father's micropaleontology universe and mine as an artist and painter. It was, in layman's terms, seismic. I was stunned by the shapes, patterns, harmonies, interactions, tones, values, and synchronicities with art that I saw in the images of, what I was to learn, were oolites.

Looking at these thin section photographs was for me like looking at an exhibition of unique paintings by an unknown artist storming the contemporary art scene. It was like looking at an entirely new, original visual language. I read the thin sections from an aesthetic perspective as paintings, be they paintings that had existed tens of millions of years before humans had even evolved.

These paintings were created not by paintbrush, palette knife, and oils but by numerous Earth forces and time. They were paintings that until recently had not been seen by the human eye. They had possibly been viewed up until this moment only through a scientific or geological lens, though they could clearly be understood immediately as "beautiful" by those with any artistic sensibility as my father had seen all those decades ago as a geology student.

On studying the thin sections, I was stimulated by the idea that there may be many similarities between the practice and experience of a micropaleontologist and that of a painter. I wondered if I could enter the world of micropaleontology, and if I did, what would I discover? Could I transport and translate what I experienced, felt, saw, learned, and understood into a painting practice?

Could I create a body of work that would stand on its own as paintings, that could be read as paintings, that had messages around time, history, humanity, contemporary society, and the future? Could I find a wider audience for micropaleontology's extraordinary world (Carnie, 2002; Fig. 1)?

Figure 1. This mixed media painting, *Oolite* (200 cm × 150 cm), was selected for the 2019 Micropaleontology Society Calendar. Image © 2019 Giles Ford.

AN ARTIST EXPLORES MICROPALEONTOLOGY

Questions began to pose themselves about art and micropaleontology. How is the nature and layering of time understood?

Micropaleontology records life forms, traces of the past, through geologic processes that can be seen and investigated (Bjonerud, 2006; Ellis, 2018; Zalasiewicz, 2012). Similarly, art captures life and thought forms, traces of the past, in an analogous process that can be seen and investigated. Both involve the layering down of time through images.

Micropaleontology presents in thin section a two-dimensional representation of inter-related shapes and forms, creating harmonies, conflicts, and patterns of different aesthetic interest and "beauty" as paintings do. Micropaleontological thin section images and paintings each have unique languages since thin sections are produced by nature while paintings are human-constructed. I was excited to explore how looking at and understanding microfossil symmetry and asymmetry might lead to the creation of a new signature artistic language.

What kind of intellectual pattern making could I experiment with, based on my father's thin section oil industry research, to create a kind of visual poetics that might be of interest to an audience in addition to micropaleontologists? What relationship would the paintings have to contemporary society and the debates of the morality of the oil industry, climate change, and the controversial Anthropocene Epoch?

I began a series of experimental explorations, initially purely drawing, then using charcoal and oils, which seemed to be appropriate materially as they visually mimicked the black and white of my father's thin sections (Fig. 2).

As I learnt more, I used different materials in the process of creation, incorporating painting, printing, plastics, photography, poetry, and sculptural forms, all informed by the thin section

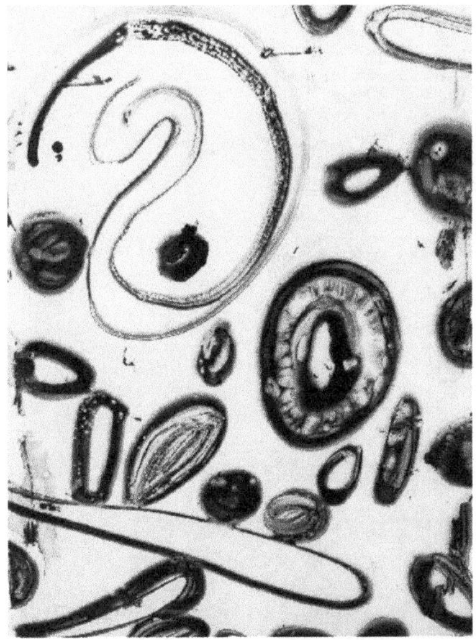

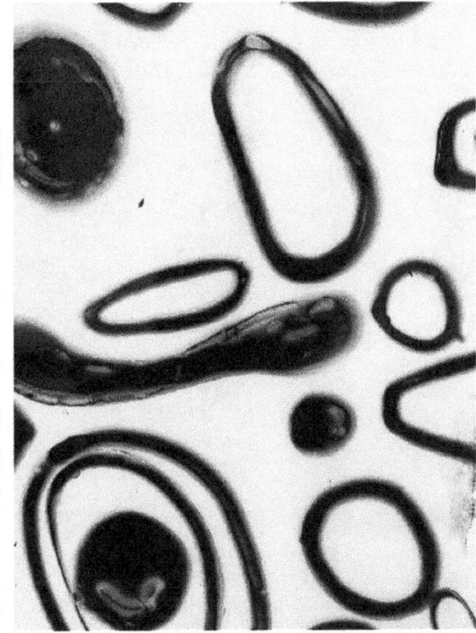

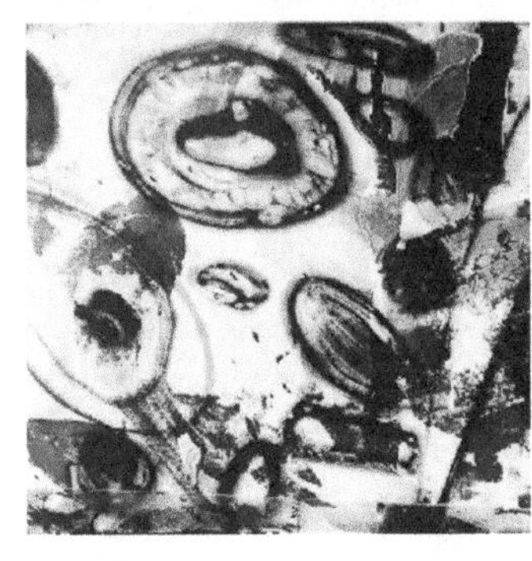

Figure 2. India ink on acetate was used to create exploratory drawings of various sizes to understand thin section fossil visual language. Image © 2018 Giles Ford.

plates and emanating from them. I began to wonder if painting itself might be considered as a life form of its own. As an artist, I viewed painting as an organism that propagates images, ideas, and traces of existence through its human hosts in a kind of historical and aesthetic evolution. Painters and artists serve as hosts for the information that needs to be captured and passed on, with paintings being similar to human thin sections.

With the ideas of propagation, the passage of time, and evolution swirling in my mind, I decided to explore including both my father's geological work and the drawings and art actions of my children—Arthur, then 7, and Poppy, 4—into my art practice so that we began creating multigenerational layered works (like the layering in the Earth of different organisms across time). These works included my father's thin section photographs, fossil images, his seismic graphs, my brush strokes, collage work, contemporary societal oil industry news coverage alongside art historical references, and the colorful fossil inventions and commentaries of my son and daughter (Fig. 3).

I feel that the processes of painting and micropaleontology, or more precisely thin section images from drilling bit petrology cores, reveal themselves to be remarkably similar. Both involve the layering of sedimentations, one on the sea floor and the other on the canvas. Both capture and encase life in fossilized form, one in the form of often single-cell organisms and the other in the form of more complex creatures and their activities in photographs or mixed media life fossil compilations.

The two worlds seemed to meld in the paintings themselves which, though often large scale, began to appear sometimes physically and at other times metaphorically like thin sections themselves—thin sections of my life at the moment of creation, curation, and compilation.

INFLUENCES ON THE FOSSILARIUM

In the series of paintings that I made on the micropaleontological theme, The Fossilarium, I experimented with interweaving different timescales from hundreds of millions of years ago to the present day.

I also began to investigate other art influences and movements that I feel are in some way connected to micropaleontology. My thin section paintings were directly and viscerally influenced, inspired, and informed by both abstract expressionist artists (including Franz Kline, Robert Motherwell, and Lee Krasner as well as, more recently, Brice Marden and Terry Winters [Handwerker, 2005]) and the more painterly, complex, and ambiguous paintings of Thérèse Oulton, who is seen by some as a landscape painter and by others as an abstractionist, but whom I see and know is deeply resonant of micropaleontology (Fig. 4).

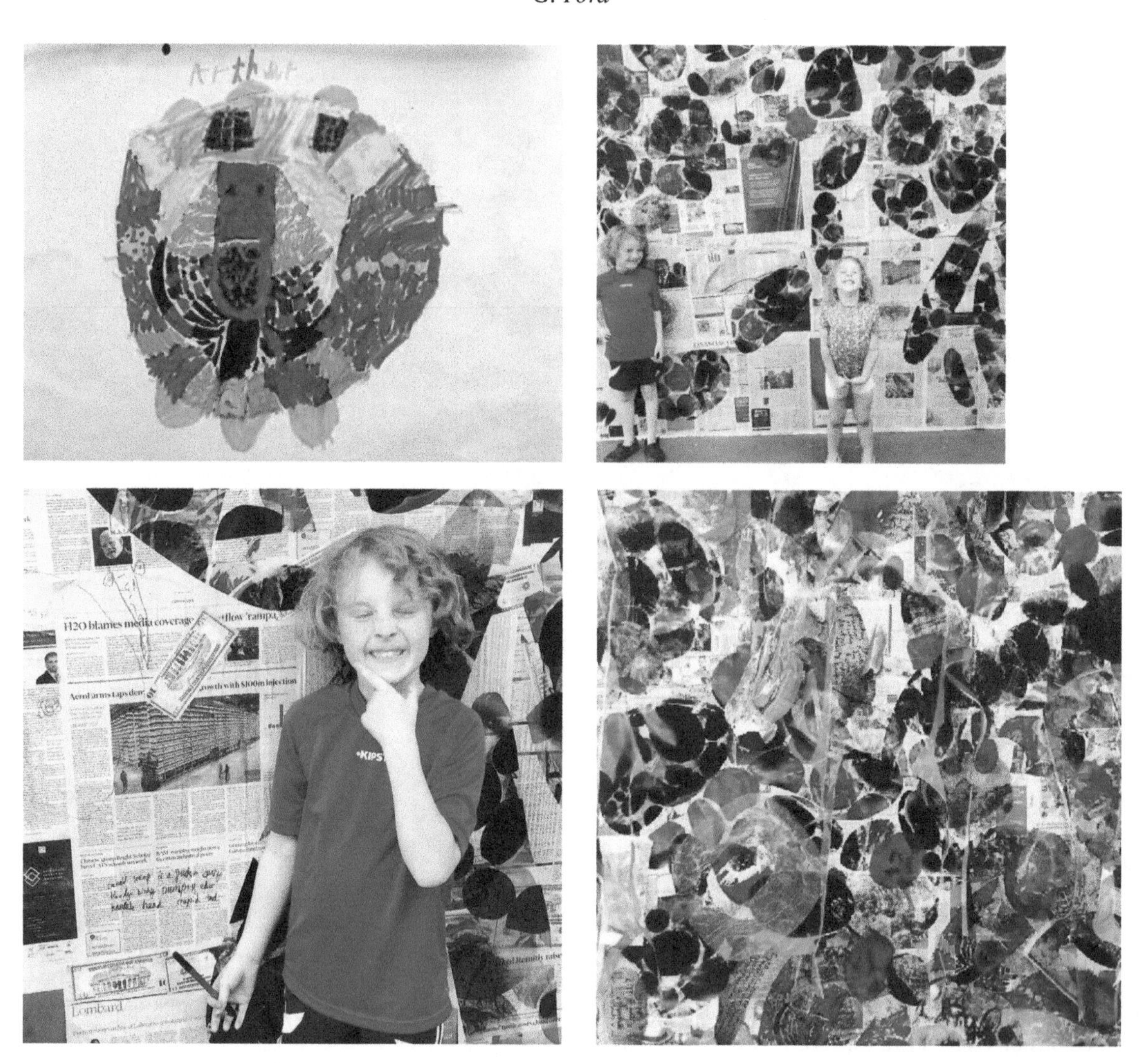

Figure 3. Fossil formations invented by Arthur Ford were developed with the help of Poppy Ford into a 7 m × 6 m wall-mounted, mixed media installation, *Graffiti*, shown at the University for the Creative Arts, Farnham, Surrey, UK, in 2019. Image © 2019 Giles Ford.

In this micropaleontology series of paintings, I took both thin section images and my connection to abstract expressionism as a foundation and starting point. I noticed works with surprising connections, resonances, and sometimes striking similarities in the shapes, forms, tones, mark making, and spatial relationships found between abstract expressionism and micropaleontological thin sections—specifically between Motherwell (*View Painting No. 3*, 1953) and Victor Pasmore's paintings (*The Paradox of Harmony*, 1988) and oolite microfossils found in the Venezuelan La Puma Formation, for instance (Fig. 5).

Alongside abstract expressionism and images of micropaleontological thin section fossils taken under an electron microscope, Thérèse Oulton (a brilliant painter who was shortlisted for the Turner Prize) is perhaps my deepest influence, inspiration, and artistic aspiration. As an acquaintance of my father, she was in my life when I was a child in the 1970s and was fascinated by the photographs of thin section fossils my father shared with her during a very formative time in her development just before and during her studies at the Royal College of Art. I was often present during these moments, looking on in wonder, slight bewilderment, and feeling a deep desire to join in. I believe now, that as with Oulton, my fundamental painting formations began at that time, though for both of us they began in different ways.

I am sure that the impact of micropaleontological images on Oulton went straight into her painting and has developed over time in an evolution of its own to become part of her visual intellectual, philosophical, material, and spiritual language.

Oulton has been described as a type of landscape painter influenced by geology, but my hypothesis is that she was much more specifically and indeed identifiably influenced by micropaleontology. In the last six months I have traced, compared, and contrasted Oulton's paintings over the past 40 years and matched them to my father's research book and found intriguing resonances. For me, Oulton's *Undoings*, *Coastline 2011*, and

Figure 4. *Financial Time.* This mixed media work (120 cm × 150 cm) mimics, in both its process and form, geological stratigraphy, sedimentary layering, and the perception of looking at a partially hidden oolite nanofossil through an electron microscope by using India ink acetate overlays on photographic transfer canvases. It includes copies of the *Financial Times* and stock market indexes, which touch on the role micropaleontology and microfossil expertise have had in driving the industrial and technological revolutions over the past 200 years and the incipient demise of capitalism in a post-fossil-fuel world—fossilized *Financial Times*. These themes are embedded in a meta-concept of time in the paintings, which reduces the importance of the *Financial Times*, companies, markets, shares, and "homo-sapient" activity to infinitesimally small microorganisms, alongside which they exist in the paintings. Image © 2019 Giles Ford.

Figure 5. *Anthropocene Blossom.* Working to the soundtrack to Bach's *Cello Suites* by Yo Ma and with A.E. Houseman's poem "Lovliest of Trees" in mind, I attempted in this painting—which uses layered and interwoven images of microfossils, cherry blossoms, and Victor Pasmore painting an outdoor shaman installation at the London South Bank—to portray the delicate interplay of time, transience, and longevity in a repeated rhythmic pattern that I hoped would create a feeling of timelessness. This mixed media work measures 120 cm × 150 cm. Image © 2019 Giles Ford, in Museum of Modern Art, Wales, permanent collection.

Hermetic Definitions were more than a little influenced by deep memory of microscopic fossils informing her consciousness.

Time as well as space is a central theme in micropaleontology as it is in my painting, and I seek to investigate and then condense time (geologic time, historical time, anthropocentric human time, art historical time, emotional/psychological and spiritual time) by interweaving different eras into often dense and intense paintings that present time in more than a linear way by incorporating simultaneously a sense of cyclical and parallel time. My paintings hint at a cartography of time and sometimes a song of time, with repeated patterns almost like refrains or verses (Fig. 6).

Over the two years it took to create the series, I began to see a visual language developing in the painting informed by the repeated images, rhythms, and refrains in the thin sections. I saw a kind of poetical aesthetics emerge that is resonant of memory, loss, inter-generational connections, and the pure beauty of the shapes and forms of micropaleontology.

THE EVOLUTION OF THE FOSSILARIUM

In Figure 7, my painting journey took a further step toward imitating the object of my investigation and interrogation. Moving from a two-dimensional, visible artistic representation of microfossils I turned to a three-dimensional, almost sculptural form that mimicked its subject matter. Taking two large-scale

Figure 6. *Time Out.* This mixed media work (120 cm × 150 cm) departs from the major microscopic fossil theme and focuses more on contemporary time, on the present, on creating, collating, and curating a series of images that encapsulates my own life during a specific period (October 2018) as if it is itself a thin section, a slice through my consciousness, mind, situation, and realities. Different coexisting worlds are merged and compressed together in a layer of time. One can see previous drawings appearing as if they were fossils, images of fossils drawn by my children, previous exhibition assemblage pieces depicting disintegration, and the last photograph of my family together. I liken this painting to Tracey Emin's *My Bed* installation thematically—raw entropy, chaos, and the unedited life. Image © 2019 Giles Ford.

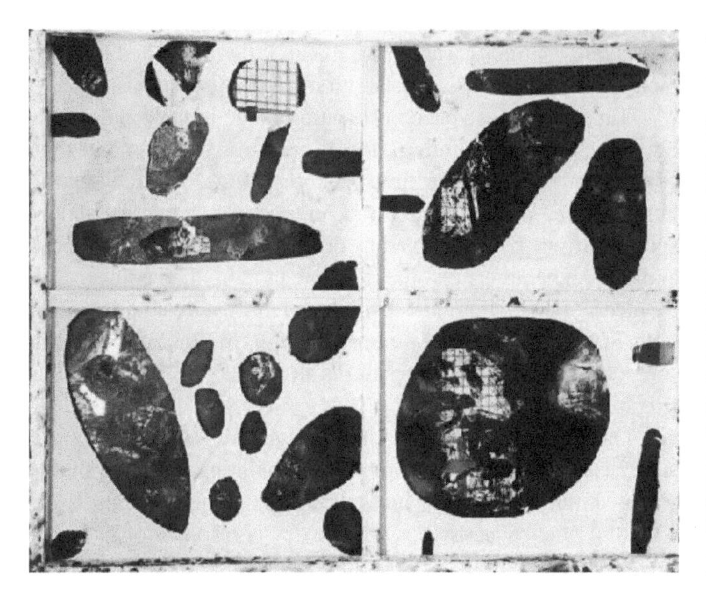

Figure 7. *Hidden.* This mixed media work, measuring 120 cm × 150 cm, physically reconstructs a three-dimensional sculptural form to mimic the microfossils in the thin sections. Image © 2019 Giles Ford.

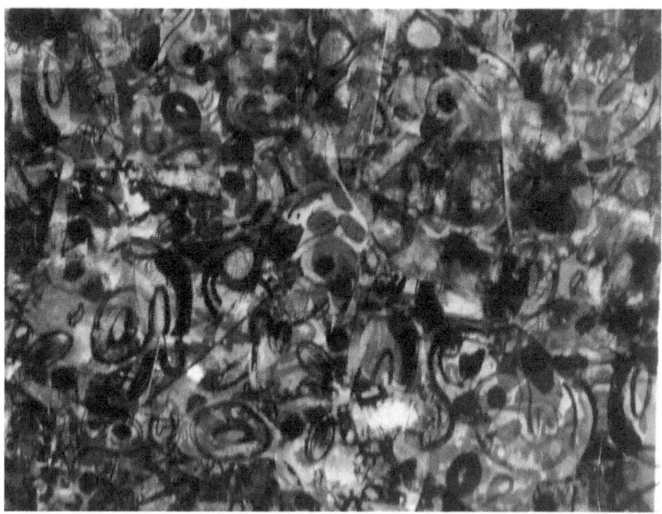

Figure 8. *Symphony.* This mixed media work, measuring 120 cm × 150 cm, brings disparate components to the canvas simultaneously, analogous to a time fossil. Image © 2019 Giles Ford, private collection.

paintings, I bolted them together after they were painted (face to face) so that the canvases themselves became strata and the "fossil images" and "images as fossils" were literally encapsulated and rendered invisible between the paintings. All images were embedded in the strata of the canvases so they could not be seen or reached unless there was some sort of mining, cutting away, or erosive destruction of the frames or canvases themselves. I then cut out oolite canvas shapes to randomly reveal what was imprisoned between the canvases and pasted some of the fossil shapes back onto the outside of the canvases to create new layering. The resultant interrelationship of shapes and forms became rather reminiscent of Pasmore's *Points of Contact* prints.

The overarching and more important element of all the paintings is the aesthetic dynamic of synchronous and asynchronous elements in a deeply integrated, intersecting, interlaced, complex, intricate, interrelated web of disparate components (like echoes of time itself or the resonance of music in a symphony simultaneously seen and played out all at once—time past, present, and future all existing in at once—an encapsulation—a time fossil) (Fig. 8).

The final art "action" performance and parallel in the process of painting and paleontology has been for me to encase and inter the paintings *Time Out, Detritus, Hidden,* and the microorganisms and other life forms they depict back into the ground, where the images first came from, hopefully to be found one day by an inquisitive seeker (perhaps by a young paleontologist on a dig).

WHAT QUESTIONS CAN ART HELP TO ADDRESS?

My investigations have raised a myriad of research questions about the relationship and intersections of art and science as well as the possibilities there are for artists (of many hues, approaches, and variations) to contribute meaningfully and significantly to important questions facing society and the human race today (Davis and Turpin, 2015; McKimm, 2013, 2015; Vince, 2014). I questioned how painting can understand, read, encapsulate, and communicate the science, geology, complexities, and implications of climate change for the human race, life on Earth, and the planet itself (Bjornerud, 2018). What will the sixth mass extinction look like if we don't act, and can painting, art, and visual communication contribute to solving the current challenges, existential threats, and conundrums? What is the role of art, in all of its forms, in the articulation, visualization, dissemination, education, and prevention of climate change disasters, if any at all? What is art's role in society (Fig. 9)?

I continue to constantly experiment with the use of both plastics and detritus from my painting process by recycling the leftover parts of cutouts used in the paintings back into previous paintings to create a juxtaposition of refuse deposit layering, recycling, and life sedimentation, highlighting the relationship of oil to plastics and the continuing anthropocentric effects of any industry, including painting (Fig. 10).

CONCLUSION

The investigative exploration, discovery, and translation of microfossil images into paintings has given me insight into the world of my father as a micropaleontologist. It has given me the insight that within the miniature there lies the universal; that in the scientific there lies the aesthetic; that thin sections and paintings are more alike than different in their unique visual languages and poetic rhythms; that both capture time and space in their own ways; that in the cut of a thin section moment in time there lies the epic story of evolution and possibly its demise. The Fossilarium paintings aim, through their repeating shapes and patterns,

Figure 9. *Spill.* This mixed media work, measuring 120 cm × 150 cm, changes the lens and focus from the personal to the external world with a concentration on the Anthropocene. The painting is made up of repeated images of aesthetically pleasing oil spills; dying, oil-covered birds; Andreas Gursky's Arctic land mass photograph of oil rigs burning; and toxic-suited, alien-like figures attempting to clean up the devastating mess. Image © 2019 Giles Ford.

Figure 10. *Detritus* (recycled), upper image, and *Detritus II* (recycled), lower image, are mixed media paintings measuring 120 cm × 150 cm that highlight the relationship of oil to plastics and the effects of industry. Both use plastics and detritus from my painting process to create layering. Image © 2019 Giles Ford.

to explore, record, and interweave different epochs of time and space, including that of the Anthropocene, into a rhythmic timelessness. Some of the paintings reveal the environmental consequences of our fossil fuel use while simultaneously, through their image content and aesthetics, honoring the fundamental and beautiful life-giving role they play in our lives. The Fossilarium explorations of art and fossil fuel micropaleontology, through the interplay of their various languages, pose more questions of each other than they provide answers, but it is my hope that those questions catalyze deeper and more nuanced insights into the relationship from a wider audience. As science has revealed itself in artistic shapes within thin sections, now I hope art will reveal a contemporary message for society.

REFERENCES CITED

Arenas, B., and Thackeray, D., 2003, Experiment: Conversations in Art and Science: London, The Welcome Trust/Cornerhouse Publishing, 359 p.

Bjonerud, M., 2006, Reading the Rocks: The Autobiography of the Earth: New York, Basic Books, 256 p.

Bjornerud, M., 2018, Timefulness—How Thinking Like a Geologist Can Help Save the World: Princeton, New Jersey, Princeton University Press, 221 p., https://doi.org/10.2307/j.ctvc772cs.

Carnie, A., 2002, Scientists and artists must rub shoulders: The Guardian, 17 March, https://www.theguardian.com/education/2002/mar/17/arts.highereducation (accessed March 2021).

Davis, H., and Turpin, E., 2015, Art in the Anthropocene: London, Open Humanities Press, 416 p.

Ellis, C., 2018, The Pebbles on the Beach—A Spotters Guide: London, Faber & Faber, 240 p.

Ford, A., and Houbolt, J.J., 1963, The MicroFacies of the Cretaceous of Western Venezuela: Leiden, The Netherlands, E.J. Brill, 55 p.

Handwerker, M., 2005, Terry Winters: Paintings, drawings, prints 1994–2004, 24 April, http://fnewsmagazine.com/2005/04/terry-winters-paintings-drawings-prints-1994-2004/ (accessed March 2021).

McKimm, M., 2013, Fossil Sunshine: Tonbridge, Kent, UK, Worple Press, 36 p.

McKimm. M., 2015, MAP Poems After William Smith's Geological Map of 1815: Tonbridge, Kent, UK, Worple Press, 88 p.

Vince, G., 2014, Adventures in the Anthropocene: A Journey to the Heart of the Planet We Made: London, Chatto & Windus, 438 p.

Zalasiewicz, J., 2012, The Planet in a Pebble: A Journey into Earth's Deep History: New York, Oxford University Press, 251 p.

Manuscript Accepted by the Society 14 January 2021
Manuscript Published Online 2 August 2021

The Geological Society of America
Memoir 218

Art about ancient life as a chronicle for the human condition

Gary D. Rosenberg*
Geology Department, Milwaukee Public Museum, 800 W. Wells Street, Milwaukee, Wisconsin 53233, USA, and *Earth Sciences Department, Indiana University–Purdue University, Indianapolis, Indiana 46202, USA*

Patricia Coorough Burke*
Geology Department, Milwaukee Public Museum, 800 W. Wells Street, Milwaukee, Wisconsin 53233, USA

ABSTRACT

Art about ancient life chronicles the human condition, less evidently but potentially as significantly, as it depicts life through geologic time. Selected examples surveyed here reveal human aspirations, values, conceits, sensibilities, and foibles and suggest that further in-depth study would be warranted. Greek bronzes embellished with griffins (625–575 B.C.E.) may represent ceratopsian fossils mythologized and commodified for their proximity to gold deposits. Encelius' anthropomorphized drawing (1557) of a fossil bivalve exemplifies a conservative deference to outdated paradigms about nature; inversely, Nicolaus Steno prized geometry—then offering a new perspective on nature—and realized in 1667 that a drawing of "tongue stones" depicted not, as commonly held, simulacra of snake tongues molded by vital forces within the Earth but fossilized teeth of a once living shark; Beringer's "lying stones" (1726) show how human conceit can bias the interpretation of "fossils." Artworks since the mid-twentieth century record a growing recognition that ancient life and its habitats evolved together and therefore that art about ancient life has lessons for contemporary environmentalism: Rudolph Zallinger's diachronous murals (mid-1940s) and the Milwaukee Public Museum's diachronous dioramas (installed in 2001) display progressions of ancient and contemporary habitats; Alexis Rockman's dystopian landscapes use ancient and extant life to critique human responsibility for degrading environments and endangering species. We conclude that studies of art about ancient life can deepen our understanding of the human condition and the cultural context in which it is created.

INTRODUCTION

Paleontological art conveys a vivid picture of life on Earth long ago. Yet, paleontological art historically has communicated and still expresses other, culturally informed and idiosyncratic aspects of the human condition. They will be exemplified here, and we will show that such connections have potential to serve the greater good; for example, stewardship of the planet.

SCYTHIAN GRIFFINS

Protomes, or embellishments, here in bronze with bone and ivory inlays on cauldrons created by Greek artisans (Fig. 1, 625–575 B.C.E.) may be early renditions of dinosaurs. These depict griffins, mythical creatures with an avian head, feline body, and horse-like ears. Classical folklorist Adrienne Mayor (1994, 2000) suggested that griffins were Greek interpretations of ceratopsian fossils that Scythians valued because they were found in the Gobi

*Emails: grosenbe@iu.edu; coorough@mpm.edu

Rosenberg, G.D., and Burke, P.C., 2022, Art about ancient life as a chronicle for the human condition, *in* Clary, R.M., Rosenberg, G.D., and Evans, D.C., eds., The Evolution of Paleontological Art: Geological Society of America Memoir 218, p. 263–275, https://doi.org/10.1130/2021.1218(29).

Figure 1. Two 8-in.-high (~20-cm-high) protomes (bronze embellishments with bone or ivory inlay, from cauldrons) depicting griffins from Greece, 625–575 B.C.E., are shown. Photo © Chicago Art Institute, Katherine K. Adler Memorial Fund. Ref. 1994.38.1–2. Creative Commons public domain.

Desert near deposits of gold. They believed living griffins dug for and protected the ore with their ferocious talons and beaks.

If Mayor is correct, Scythian and Greek valuation of the fossils in light of their proximity to nearby gold deposits confers upon them an aura of commodification, an issue that focuses debate about fossil collecting for profit even today. Additionally, reports of ceratopsian skeletons with beaked mouths and horned heads were transmitted orally and so could morph whenever stories of them were retold. Although the hybridization of a bird, lion, and horse was a stretch given the modern species concept, it took paleontologists decades to accept that some dinosaurs had features of both birds and reptiles even though the suggestion was first made in the mid-1800s (Cadbury, 2001).

CHRISTOPHER ENCELIUS' BIVALVE MOLLUSC

The earliest known published image of a fossil (Fig. 2) was a bivalve shell drawn by Christopher Encelius in 1557 (Gould, 2002). He classified it as a "tortoise," as defined by Pliny during the first century C.E. in his encyclopedic *Natural History*. The Renaissance (fifteenth to sixteenth century) was a time of rediscovery of classical knowledge when many naturalists accepted that the Greeks and Romans knew everything there was to know about nature. Progress meant fitting observations into classical paradigms which, for Encelius, was Pliny's taxonomy. We suggest that Encelius may have added the face to the umbo to portray a shelled animal with a head so he could shoehorn it into Pliny's "tortoises."

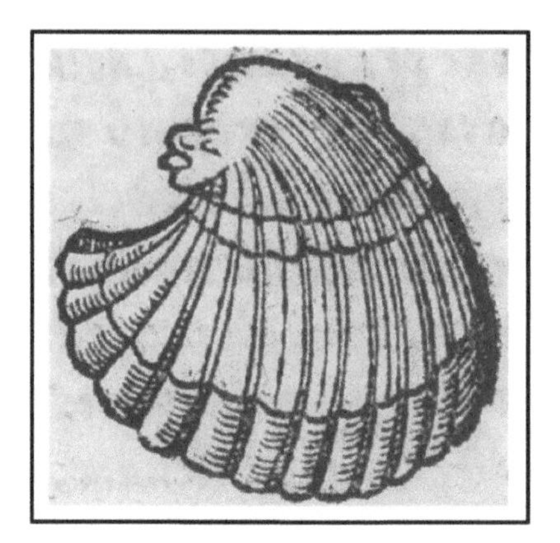

Figure 2. C. Encelius, 1557, created the earliest known published drawing of a fossil invertebrate. From Gould (2002, p. 2); used with permission of Cambridge University Press.

Swiss naturalist Konrad Gesner (1516–1565) compared Encelius' conception with Rondelet's drawing of a living clam, which had been published earlier (Gould, 2002). The comparison led to the realization that the fossil was not tortoise-like and, more generally, that new knowledge about nature was a worthy pursuit warranting new taxonomies. This sea change in philosophy was the harbinger of the Scientific Revolution (1543 C.E. to eighteenth century).

NICOLAUS STENO AND SHARK TEETH

In 1667, anatomist Nicolaus Steno (1638–1686) published a drawing of objects then called glossopetrae ("tongue stones") along with a drawing of a dissected shark head with teeth still in its jaw (Fig. 3). The drawings were by Michele Mercati, ca. 1580–1590, and engraved by Anton Eisenhout. They were in an unpublished book owned by Carlo Dati, a member of the Accademia del Cimento, who showed them to Steno. Steno then used them in his *Canis Carchariae* in 1667 (Steno, 1667). What we now know to be fossil shark teeth were then thought to have been simulacra of snake tongues shaped by plastic forces within the Earth. Steno, unlike Encelius, did not adhere to conservative academic paradigms and instead valued geometry, which offered him a new way to reveal the structure and spatial organization (anatomy) of animals and of landscape (Rosenberg, 2009). The visual context of "dug up teeth next to anatomy of jaw with teeth" in Steno's publication made the correct explanation of the fossil's origin evident to him and was a first step in conceptualizing the life of the past.

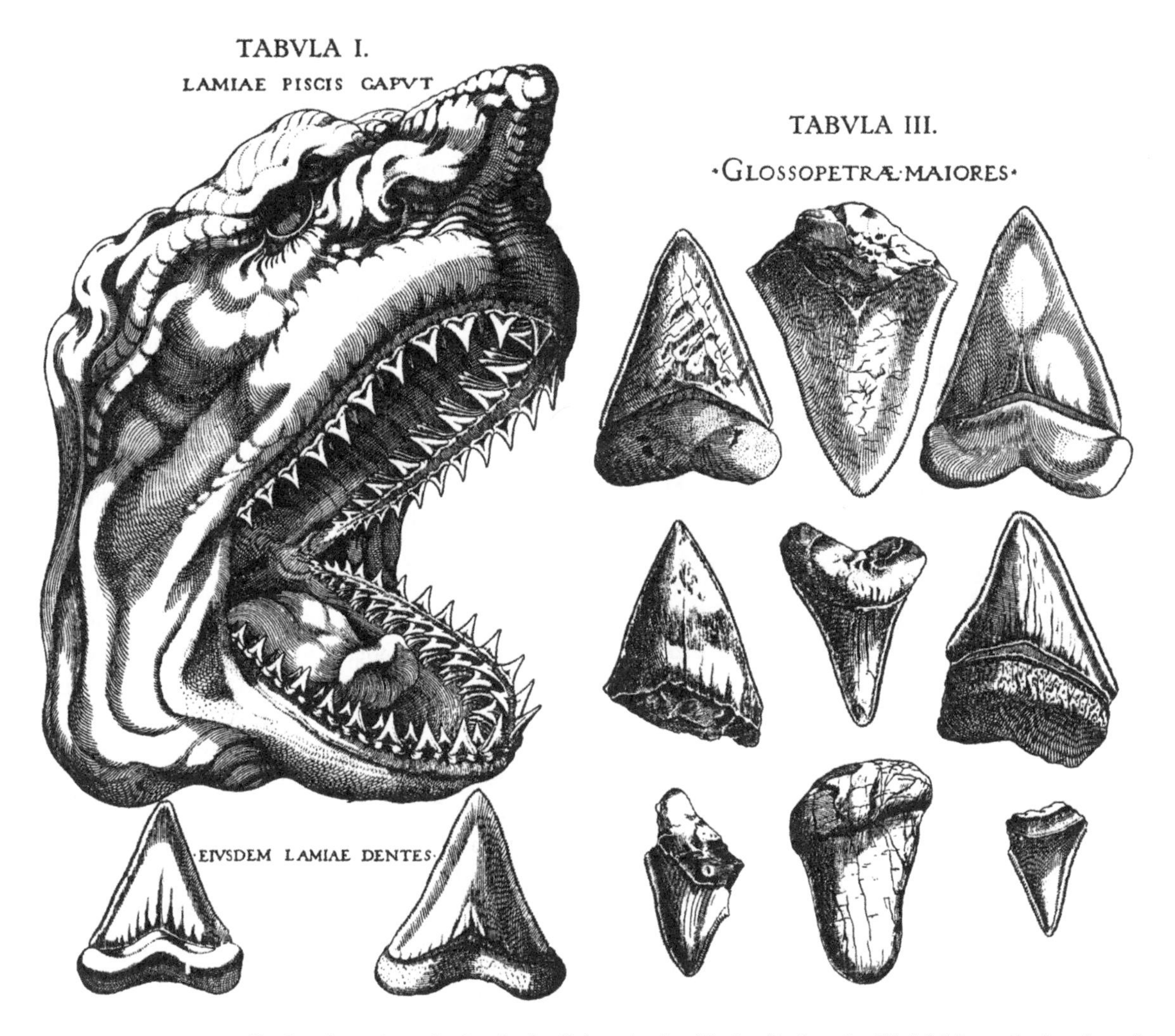

Figure 3. (Left) Mercati's drawings show the head of a living shark with detail of teeth. (Right) Mercati's drawing of "tongue stones." Both drawings are from Steno's *Canis Carchariae Dissectum Caput* (1667). From Hansen (2009, p. 171; used with permission from the Geological Society of America).

JOHANN BERINGER'S LYING STONES[1]

University of Würtzburg professor Johann Beringer (1667–1740) found clay tablets on outcrops in Germany with figures of birds in flight and at rest (some with eggs), frogs, worms, butterflies, beetles, comets, a sun with rays of light, bunches of grapes, his own initials, and even "Jehova" inscribed in Hebrew (Fig. 4). He claimed that tablets inscribed with "the ineffable name of Jehova" proved that his fossils "[commanded] the reverent admiration of myself…" Beringer created lithographs of this evidence using the Bavarian Solnhofen Limestone and published them in a monograph, *Lithographiae Wirceburgensis*, dated 1726. Only too late did he learn that J. Ignatz Roderick (professor at the University of Würzburg) and Georg von Eckhart (privy councilor and university librarian) had salted local outcrops with fabricated fossils to ruin him because of his arrogance and contempt for others. Subsequently, both pranksters were tried for conspiracy, and Beringer was exonerated. He attempted to retrieve all volumes of the monograph but failed. Beringer's conceit now is recorded history.

RUDOLPH ZALLINGER'S DIACHRONOUS MURALS

Many examples of art about ancient life from this volume and elsewhere would reveal other cultural contexts upon study, but paleoecological interpretations lead to the most explicit application of art to the benefit of the human condition. Paleontology participated in the emergence of ecological awareness in the

[1]We thank Professor J. William Schopf, University of California at Los Angeles Earth and Space Sciences Department, for permission to use the images in Figure 4 and for his unpublished PowerPoint presentation about Beringer's *Lithographiae Wirceburgensis*, from which the quotes in this section were obtained. The lithographs are from one of the few surviving first editions of Beringer's monograph (Codex Schopf). The clay tablets are at Würzburg University, the Tyler Museum, and the Berlin Museum of Natural History. For further information see Schopf (1999) and https://www.biodiversitylibrary.org/item/252852 (last accessed June 2020).

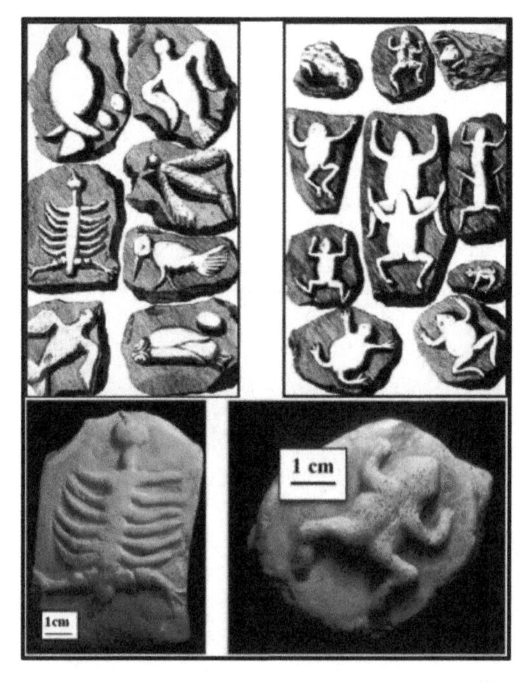

Figure 4. Lithographs of (top left) bird-like and (top right) frog-like "fossils" that Johann Beringer found as (bottom) tablets on German outcrops and published in a 1726 monograph are shown. Courtesy of J. William Schopf, University of California at Los Angeles Department of Earth and Space Sciences.

Figure 5. Rudolph F. Zallinger, 1943–1947, created *The Age of Reptiles* mural (detail shown here); 192 in. × 1320 in. (488 cm × 3353 cm)

early to mid-1800s with the publication of *Duria antiquior*, the first rendition of ancient life in its habitat (Sharpe and Clary, this volume).

Whereas *Duria antiquior* is a collage of organisms at a snapshot in time, Rudolph Zallinger's mural *The Age of Reptiles* (1943–1947; Fig. 5), and its companion, *The Age of Mammals*, depict a succession of reptiles and mammals in their habitats progressing toward the more distant past to the right. That is, the murals are diachronous: life of the past is not an object on one canvas and more recent life a separate and unrelated object on another. Instead, past life and its habitat are interdependent and evolve together to the present. The past becomes key to the present.

MILWAUKEE PUBLIC MUSEUM'S DIACHRONOUS DIORAMAS

The Milwaukee Public Museum (MPM) was one of the first museums to create diachronous dioramas when in 2001 it displayed three, two of which are depicted here. The two featherless dromaeosaurs prowling through a Cretaceous forest in Figure 6 (left) are early conceptions of these dinosaurs that now are regarded as having had feathers.[2] Not seen in this image are small mammals hiding on the forest floor.

At right, paleontologists excavate fossils at an outcrop of the iridium-rich termination of the Cretaceous in the Hell Creek Formation in Montana. The iridium-rich layer and the bolide impact that caused it are noted in the diorama labels. The viewer becomes engaged in the drama of the catastrophic demise of dinosaurs 66.1 m.y. ago and the subsequent rise of mammals, prompting the viewer to wonder if a future impact could produce another catastrophe. Although the consequent demise of the human species is not raised in the interpretive materials, contemporary news reports of asteroid-Earth near misses would facilitate the addition of an easily grasped, riveting lesson.

Figure 7 is a diorama that shows the habitat along the Menomonee River Valley in what is now the Milwaukee area. At left is the area 1000 years or so before European settlement and at right is a rendition of the modern-day environment transformed by urbanization. Nesting and walking herons, a stag, frogs, turtles, fish, and associated vegetation represent the aerial, land, and, in cutaway view at bottom, subaqueous habitats during the pre-European period. The freeway overpass and the floodwall barricading the riverbank at right signify the modern landscape and artifacts of human activity, which accelerated in Milwaukee beginning in the 1800s. Native animals are depleted from the area, and labels direct viewers instead to find invasive animals and plants that have replaced native species, among them rats hiding in litter, zebra mussels, starlings, and purple loosestrife. Interpretive materials reinforce the lesson that humans caused the environmental disruption. Such dioramas (and Rockman's dystopian visions, discussed next) extend the idea that organisms play a role in changing the Earth to include anthropogenic influence.

ALEXIS ROCKMAN'S DYSTOPIAN VISIONS

Few contemporary artists depict ancient life in the service of environmentalism as bluntly as Alexis Rockman (*b.* 1962; Figs. 8–10). His work hangs in fine art museums as well as in natural history museums such as the Smithsonian Institution. It shows a collision between humans, who presume themselves to be the epitome of evolutionary success, and "lesser" forms of life.

His work is informed by Zallinger's murals as well as the panoramas of the mid-nineteenth-century Hudson River School

[2]Feathered dromaeosaurs are shown elsewhere in the museum.

Figure 6. Diachronous diorama of the Hell Creek Formation, Montana, shows the area (left) 66 m.y. ago and (right) today. Milwaukee Public Museum. Installed 2001. Photo courtesy of Jon Haas, Milwaukee Public Museum.

Figure 7. Diachronous diorama of the Menomonee River Valley near Milwaukee, Wisconsin, USA, shows the area (left) 1000 years before European settlement and (right) in the present-day; the area has been transformed by urbanization. Photo courtesy of Jon Haas, Milwaukee Public Museum.

of artists (Friis-Hansen, 2018a, 2018b), whose idyllic pastorals are symbolic: the untapped potential of the American wilderness versus the worn European terrain; the frontier as daunting barrier to westward expansion; as elegiac for loss of wilderness due to intrusion of industry (e.g., railroads); or as a metaphor for the impending American Civil War (Howat, 1987; Hughes, 1997; Wilton and Barringer, 2002).

Rockman is knowledgeable about evolutionary theory and biodiversity, much of which he gained from visits to the American Museum of Natural History during his youth in New York City and from association with paleontologists such as Steve Gould. He grew up in New York and experienced urban environmental issues firsthand, and he does field studies across the country to inform his work.

Although Rockman sometimes appends keys listing the scientific names of the animals and plants he depicts, he veers away from representing biota in its natural habitat. His most explicit landscapes are dystopian, featuring rats, which are culturally regarded as vermin for their history as vectors of disease and pillagers of crops; invasive species that supplanted native species;

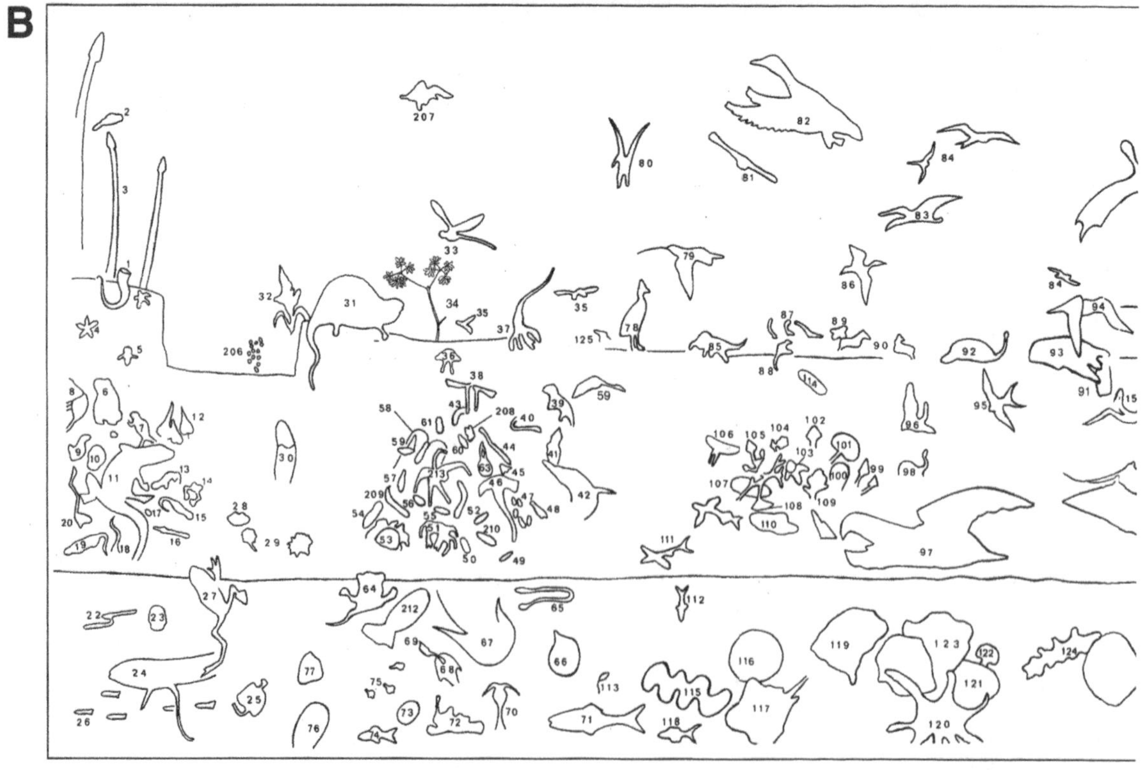

Figure 8. *Evolution* (A) Alexis Rockman, 1992, created *Evolution*; oil and wood, 96 in. × 288 in. (244 cm × 731.5 cm). Photo courtesy of Alexis Rockman. © Alexis Rockman. Collection of George R. Strimple. (B) Alexis Rockman, 1992, included this key to organisms depicted in *Evolution*. Image courtesy of Alexis Rockman. © Alexis Rockman. (*Continued on following two pages.*)

127
172
173
174
175
126
128
134
179
171
178
181
180
182
133
177
129
130
176
187
131
132
135
143
186
188
137
136
185
196
193
138
148
142
183
192
195
149
146
144
145
139
141
214
147
184
194
152
140
191
197
190
150
153
154
151
189
159
156
198
158
161
205
160
199
157
163
200
162
155
167
165
168
169
170
203
202
166
201
164
204

B

1. *Wepenthes sanguinea*
2. Cooper's Hawk
3. Horsetails
4. *Trichoglottis smithii*
5. *Paphiopedilum primulinum*
6. Cane Toad
7. New South Wales Tree Frog
8. Goliath Frog
9. Green Tree Frog
10. Mudpuppy eggs
11. *Hylonomus*
12. Arrowroot
13. Rough-skinned Newt
14. Red-eyed Tree Frog
15. Spotted Salamander
16. Texas Blind Salamander
17. Strawberry Poison Dart Frog
18. Kentucky Spring Salamander
19. Blotched Tiger Salamander
20. Grey Tree Frog
21. Poison Dart Frog
22. Mudpuppy
23. Amphibian eggs
24. African Lungfish
25. *Hallucigenia*
26. Ladyfish
27. *Rana dragtonii*
28. Bullfrog
29. Water Lilies
30. Coelacanth
31. Dimetrodon
32. Heliconia
33. Dragonfly
34. *Cecropia*
35. Army ant
36. Luna Moth
37. *Velociraptor*
38. Dragonflies
39. Marine Iguana
40. Emerald Tree Boa
41. Mata-Mata Turtle
42. *Tylosaurus*
43. Imperial Moth larvae
44. Mantis
45. Hoverfly
46. Hammerhead Shark juv.
47. Red ants
48. Katydid
49. Water Scorpion
50. Death's Head Cockroach
51. Purple Ghost Crab
52. Ten-lined Giant Chafer
53. Sally Light-foot Crab
54. *Cicada*
55. Plant Bug
56. Stink Bug
57. Red Cucujid
58. Banded Alderborer
59. Blue Morpho
60. Western Spotted Cucumber Beetle
61. Goldman's Leaf Beetle
62. Pseudo-sphinx Caterpillar
63. Giant Horned Beetle
64. Mudskipper
65. Coronet Fish
66. Spider Crab
67. Trilobite
68. Horseshoe Crab
69. *Hymenocaris*
70. Cyclopoid Copepod
71. Chum Salmon
72. Black Devil
73. Carpoid
74. Clown Loach
75. Brine Shrimp
76. Sea Scorpion
77. Trilobite
78. Cassowary
79. Whimbrel
80. *Gnathosaurus*
81. California Condor
82. Mallard
83. *Tropeognathus*
84. Magnificent Frigate Bird
85. *Cynognathus*
86. *Ichthyornis*
87. Plesiosaur
88. Shrew
89. Bright Tropic Bee
90. *Eohippus*
91. Komodo Monitor
92. *Glyptodon*
93. Polar Bear
94. Three-eyed Caspian Tern
95. Barn Swallow
96. Chinese Saltwater Crocodile
97. *Archelon*
98. Sphincter Crab
99. Ravenel's Stinkhorn
100. Netted *Rhodotus*
101. Destroying Angel
102. Felt-ringed *Agaricus*
103. Barometer Earth Star
104. Alcohol Inky
105. Scarlet Waxy-cup
106. Oedipoda Grasshopper
107. Yellow-red Gill Polypore
108. White fungus
109. Menstral Oysterfan
110. Red-belted Polypore
111. Atlantic Flying Fish
112. Striped Headstander
113. Copepod
114. Vertebrate remains
115. *Tridacna*
116. Coral sp.
117. Angel Shark
118. Lyre-tailed Coralfish
119. Fan Coral
120. Giant Octopus
121. Brain Coral
122. *Cerianthus viridius*
123. Shelf coral
124. Nudibranch
125. Icthyosaur
126. "Dragonslayer" dragon
127. *Pteranodon ingens*
128. *Eudimorphodon*
129. Roseate Spoonbill
130. Brown Pelican
131. *Aracuri x rodentra*
132. Black-necked Red Cotinga
133. Flying Lizard
134. Eastern Yellow Bat
135. Daubenton's Bat
136. Yellow Lady's Slipper
137. Honey Possum
138. Collared Peccary
139. Tank Bromilliad
140. Hyacinth Macaw
141. English Pouter
142. Holstein Cow
143. Chameleon
144. Red Colobus Monkey
145. White Rhinoceros
146. *Titanotylopus*
147. Striped Skunk
148. Bandicoot
149. River Otter
150. *Laysan Albatross juv.*
151. Tiger Shark
152. Urinator
153. Wolpertinger
154. Parasite Larval case
155. Arum
156. *Planorbis sp.*
157. Rosy Boa
158. Garbage Freak
159. *Heliconius hewittsoni*
160. *Brontotherium*
161. Ephemeropterid
162. Common Mosquito
163. *Limax*
164. *Dinichthys*
165. *Daphnia*
166. *Gonionemus murbachi*
167. *Hydra*
168. *Amoeba*
169. Silicon bodies
170. Procaryotic cells
171. Greater Glider
172. Anhinga
173. *Dimorphodon*
174. *Archaeopteryx*
175. Hoatzin juv.
176. Century Plant
177. Banana Tree
178. *Araucaria*
179. Flying Frog
180. Common Paradise Kingfisher
181. *Proavis*
182. Homo sapiens
183. Ring-tailed Lemur
184. *Paphiopedilum*
185. Nest Parasite
186. Bat-rat Spider
187. *Cladonia cristatella*
188. Hemopterid
189. *Vandopsis parishii*
190. Parasite egg sack
191. Ghost Orchid
192. Spider Bromilliad
193. *Chiasograthus granti*
194. *Paphiopedilum*
195. Golden-olive Woodpecker
196. *Ginkgo*
197. Proto-Chestburster
198. Toothed Kingfisher
199. *Alien* Facehugger x Robber Crab
200. Prairie Smoke
201. Rattlesnake skeleton
202. *Rhamphoryncus* femur
203. *Megaloceros* antler
204. *Homo sapiens* pelvis
205. Malaysian Tapir
206. *Drosophila*
207. *Teratornis*
208. Eastern-tailed Blue
209. *Scolopendra heros*
210. Agave Weevil
211. *Anabaena circinalis*
212. Giant Sea Scorpion
213. Wolf Spider
214. Arrowhead

Figure 8B (*Continued*).

unrelated species engaging together in intercourse[3]; sometimes mingling fabrications of alien and grotesquely mutated organisms lurking in cryptic habitats or scurrying about post-apocalyptic cities smoldering with pollution.

His mural *Evolution* (Fig. 8A, keyed in Fig. 8B) is stratified to show aerial, terrestrial, aquatic, and subaquatic habitats much like MPM's Menomonee River diorama. At first glance, the scene seems to celebrate the diversity of life from the Precambrian to the Recent. But the more than 200 extinct and extant organisms depicted are not in an orderly chronological progression in the manner of Zallinger's murals. Biota of all geologic ages cavort together along with bizarre mutants in frenetic

[3]This has been chronicled in living animals, and it superficially appears to defy the species concept, generating a sense of chaos in Rockman's oeuvre, see Rockman and Dion (1996).

activity.[4] Yet none of this is a creationist trope that flattens deep time to portray the co-existence of dinosaurs with humans or humans as the epitome of evolutionary success lording over every other animal that appeared on Earth. It is no peaceable kingdom; it displaces humans from favored status and holds us accountable for environmental degradation.

Rockman presents a post-apocalyptic environment contaminated by sewer outflows juxtaposed with a natural disaster wrought by a distant volcanic eruption. The eruption is a reference to Hudson River School artist Frederick Church's monumental painting, *Cotopaxi* (1862), which Church may have used as a parable for the American Civil War (Roberts, 1995; Hughes, 1997), suggesting that the environmental catastrophe amounts to a war humans have waged against nature.

One brave but lonely Eve, Fig. 8B, #182, a "deformed hermaphrodite" (Roberts, 1995, p. 63), surveys the deranged new world from the bluff at right. Yet there is no vestige of factories, sewage plants, or other sources of the pollution nor, apparently, any prospect of salvation from them. Rather, it asserts that humans have a history of irredeemably contaminating vast areas of the planet.

It also critiques the presumption of two separate cultures, the objective sciences and subjective, "inferior" humanities: "No prejudices are more pervasive than those arising from our failure to recognize our taxonomies are socioculturally embedded and therefore not ineluctably given as natural truth…" (Gould, 1995, p. 29). Gould added that phylogenetic trees beginning with Ernst Haeckel's "founding" tree of 1866 are commonly misinterpreted as "progressive directionality towards 'man'…" (Gould, 1995, p. 29). Rockman takes his cue from Gould. *Evolution* mocks that misconception by embedding combined sewer outflows in trees and expelling humans from the highest branches.

Rockman's Great Lakes Cycle (Fig. 9, keyed in Fig. 10) is an assemblage of five large murals and ancillary works that critique the increasing degradation of the Great Lakes and their watersheds.

Although ancient and mutated organisms are not as evident in *Cascade* as in other murals in the series, the entire series, like MPM's Menomonee River diorama, illuminates the dictum that biology makes no sense without evolution, notably lessons learned from ancient life about adaptation, competition, survival of the fittest, and extinction. In brief, Rockman shows that human folly is producing what will become known as ancient life of the twenty-first century.

Egan (2017) documented the cultural history. The watershed was a resource for Native Americans starting before the European advent and remains so for all Americans yet today. The lakes facilitated westward expansion of the young United States, and they remain resources for industry, agriculture, and transport of manufactured goods and raw materials between the continental interior and Atlantic seaways. A quantum jump in degradation began in the industrial era: pollution from households, manufacturing, and agricultural runoff. Since the St. Lawrence Seaway opened, the lakes facilitated the invasion of foreign species that have decimated many natural populations of wildlife throughout the watershed.

The growing population of the semi-arid western states is pressuring freshwater resources west of the Mississippi River just as geologist and anthropologist John Wesley Powell predicted in his 1878 "Report on the Lands of the Arid Region" (Stegner, 1992). The western states have begun to covet the Great Lakes for their water. States and Canadian provinces bordering the Great Lakes responded with treaties, agreements, and ultimately the Great Lakes Compact of 2008[5] to mitigate pollution and forestall depletion of the lakes by communities that were not part of the Great Lakes watershed.

Rockman plays on variations of this history in each mural of the Great Lakes Cycle. Each portrays a seamless chronologic continuity from relatively pristine[6] at left to human-induced disharmony among aquatic, terrestrial, and atmospheric biomes at right. The first mural, *Cascade* (Fig. 9, key in Fig. 10), begins with the waning of Pleistocene glaciers, proceeds to habitation by Native Americans, the advent of European trappers and pioneers, and on to clearcutting of forests, mining, and shipping toward the right. Other murals include extinct and mutant animals and chartreuse algal blooms of eutrophication caused by nutrients released from industrial farms and urban sewer outflows.

Cascade exemplifies lessons from evolution: a reminder that extinction is forever (the passenger pigeon, Fig. 9, keyed in Fig. 10 as #54 in top center); successful adaptation is never assured and unlikely when humans meddle with the environment (overfished lake sturgeon, salmon, and blue pike (#26, #27, #28, respectively, lower right). In other murals, invasive species including zebra and quagga mussels and lamprey have out-competed and displaced native species.

The Native American in a canoe (Fig. 10, #51) is Iron Eyes Cody from the Ad Council's 1971, "Keep America Beautiful" campaign. His "[shedding] a tear at the sight of a littered American landscape" is said to have helped define the beginning of the environmental movement (Friis-Hansen, 2018b, p. 70).

---

[4]Examples (Fig. 8A) include a Mallard (keyed in Fig. 8B, #82) flying along with a Pterosaur (#127, etc.) and a mythical dragon (#126); a lemur having intercourse with a hyacinth macaw (respectively #183 and #140); a two-headed boa (#157); Eocambrian *Hallucigenia* (#25) out of scale floating near an African lungfish (#24) and common frog (#25); *Eohippus* (#89) and *Glyptodon* (#92) straddling the edge of the pond with a Holstein cow (#142); fantasy animals include a Wolpertinger (#153—combination rabbit, wolf, reindeer from German myth), and a facehugger crab (#199) and Proto chestburster (#197) from the *Alien* franchise; a juvenile hammerhead shark (#46) clings impossibly to the side of a rock; and animals out of scale include a banded alderborer beetle (#58) the size of a hammerhead shark (#46) and a Nudibranch (#124) the size of *Dinichthys* (#164).

[5]Antecedents included the Great Lakes Charter signed in 1985, an Annex signed in 2001, and an additional Great Lakes–St. Lawrence River Basin Sustainable Water Resources Agreement in 2005. For a summary, see https://en.wikipedia.org/wiki/Great_Lakes_Compact (accessed June 2020).

[6]Whether there ever was an ideal wilderness is considered by Schama (1995).

Figure 9. Alexis Rockman, 2015, created *Cascade*; oil and alkyd on wood panel, 72 in. × 144 in. (183 cm × 366 cm). Commissioned by Grand Rapids Art Museum with funds provided by Peter Wege, Jim and Mary Nelson, John and Muriel Halick, Mary B. Loupee, and Karl and Patricia Betz. Photo courtesy of Alexis Rockman © Alexis Rockman. (*Continued on facing page.*)

SPEARS GERLI

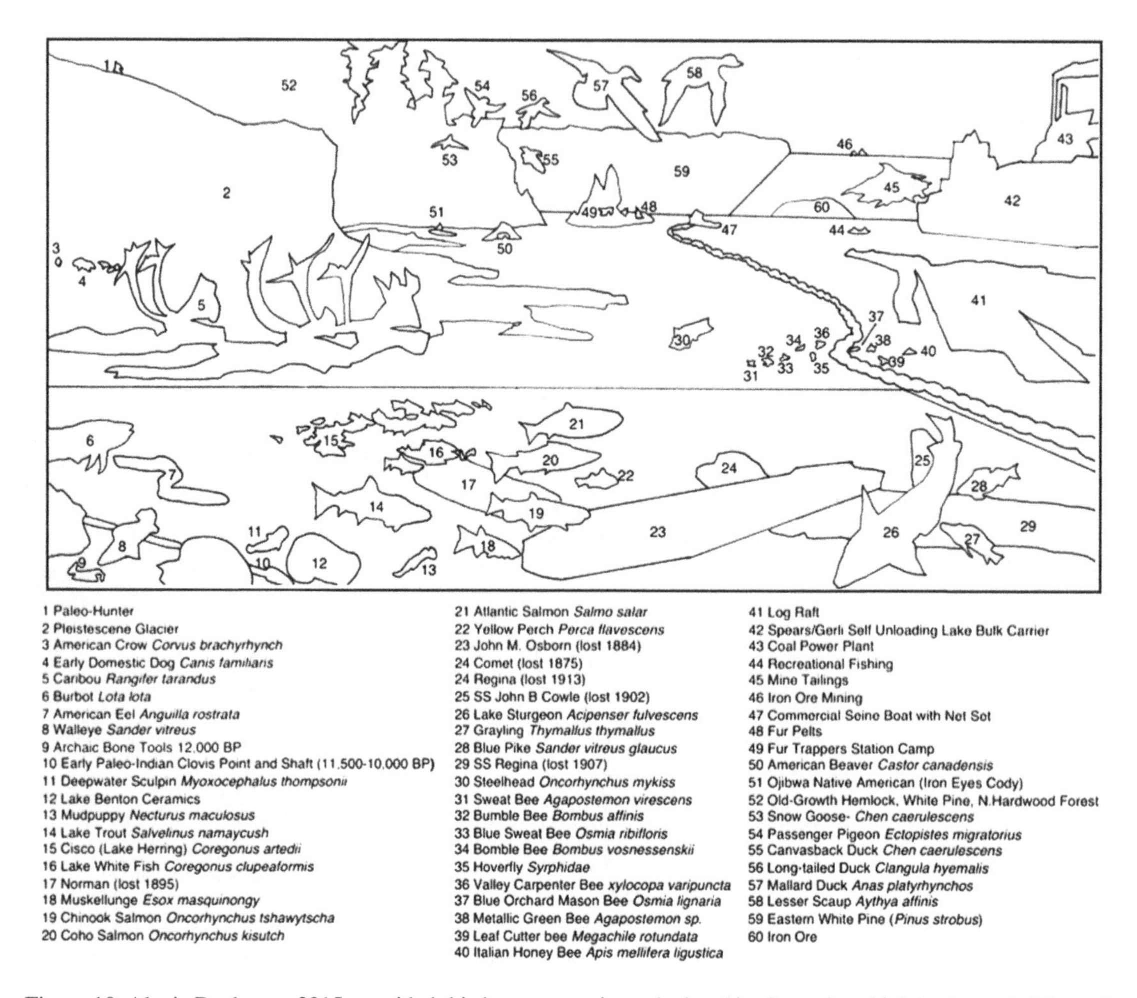

Figure 10. Alexis Rockman, 2015, provided this key to organisms depicted in *Cascade*, which is shown in Figure 9. Photo courtesy of Alexis Rockman. © Alexis Rockman.

Regardless, humans will have a hard time restoring the web of bioenvironmental relationships that evolved over millennia. Game fish such as salmon and steelhead trout (#19, #20, #21, #30) depleted by overfishing, pollution, and invasive species have been restocked but with only mixed success. Art about ancient life shows that evolution proceeds in one direction only. It doesn't repeat. *Cascade* warns of the consequences if that lesson continues to be disregarded.

CONCLUSIONS

Our scientific minds may suppose that art about ancient life conveyed messages about the human condition—conceit, resistance to new knowledge, commodification of nature, and other mores—once upon a time but no longer. However, these are indelible characteristics of the human condition, and as we humans become increasingly sensitive to our place on Earth and our role in Earth dynamics, we can hope (another characteristic of the human condition) that altruism (yet another) will help us further visualize ancient life for our benefit. The task is to discern how the entire historical oeuvre of art about ancient life—not only contemporary works such as MPM's and Rockman's—can enhance the human condition. This requires wise guidance whether the venue is a classroom, museum, or fossil park (Clary and Wandersee, 2014).

ACKNOWLEDGMENTS

We thank Susan Longhenry, director and chief curator, The Haggerty Museum of Art, Marquette University, Milwaukee, Wisconsin, for facilitating communication with Alexis Rockman; Alexis Rockman for permission to use images of his artwork; J. William Schopf, University of California at Los Angeles Department of Earth and Space Sciences, for images of Beringer's "lying stones"; Cambridge University Press for the image of Encelius' bivalve; Troels Kardel, Copenhagen; Stefano Dominici, Florence Museum of Natural History; Robert Truitt, docent, Milwaukee Public Museum; Brian Burke for discussion; and our reviewers and volume editors Renee Clary and Dallas Evans for valuable comments.

REFERENCES CITED

Cadbury, D., 2001, The Dinosaur Hunters: A True Story of Scientific Rivalry and the Discovery of the Prehistoric World: New York, HarperCollins, 384 p.

Clary, R.M., and Wandersee, J.H., 2014, Lessons from US fossil parks for effective informal science education: Geoheritage, v. 6, p. 241–256, https://doi.org/10.1007/s12371-014-0116-x.

Egan, D., 2017, The Death and Life of the Great Lakes: New York, W.W. Norton & Co., 347 p.

Friis-Hansen, D., 2018a, Alexis Rockman: The Great Lakes Cycle: Grand Rapids, Michigan, Grand Rapids Art Museum, 128 p.

Friis-Hansen, D., 2018b, Reflections and refractions: Alexis Rockman and the Great Lakes, *in* Friis-Hansen, D., Alexis Rockman: 2018. The Great Lakes Cycle: Grand Rapids, Michigan, Grand Rapids Art Museum, p. 42–61.

Gould, S.J., 1995, Boundaries and categories, *in* Rockman, A., Second Nature: Normal, Illinois, University Galleries of Illinois State University, p. 26–51.

Gould, S.J., 2002, Both neonate and elder: The first fossil of 1557: Paleobiology, v. 28, no. 1, p. 1–8, https://doi.org/10.1666/0094-8373(2002)028<0001:BNAETF>2.0.CO;2.

Hansen, J.M., 2009, On the origin of natural history: Steno's modern, but forgotten philosophy of science, *in* Rosenberg, G.D., ed., The Revolution in Geology from the Renaissance to the Enlightenment: Geological Society of America Memoir 203, p. 159–178, https://doi.org/10.1130/978-0-8137-1203-1-203.0.159.

Howat, J.K., 1987, American Paradise: The World of the Hudson River School: New York, The Metropolitan Museum of Art, 336 p.

Hughes, R., 1997, American Visions: The Epic History of Art in America: New York, Alfred A. Knopf, 620 p.

Mayor, A., 1994, Guardians of the gold: Archaeology, v. 47, p. 52–59.

Mayor, A., 2000, The First Fossil Hunters: Paleontology in Greek and Roman Times: Princeton, New Jersey, Princeton University Press, 349 p.

Roberts, P., 1995, Rockman's *Evolution* and the "Great Picture," *in* Alexis Rockman: Second Nature: Normal, Illinois, University Galleries of Illinois State University, p. 52–63.

Rockman, A., and Dion, M., eds., 1996, Concrete Jungle: New York, Juno Books, 219 p.

Rosenberg, G.D., 2009, The measure of man and landscape in the Renaissance and Scientific Revolution, *in* Rosenberg, G.D., ed., The Revolution in Geology from the Renaissance to the Enlightenment: Geological Society of America Memoir 203, p. 13–40, https://doi.org/10.1130/978-0-8137-1203-1-203.0.13.

Schama, S., 1995, Landscape and Memory: New York, Vintage Books, 624 p.

Schopf, J.W., 1999, Cradle of Life: The Discovery of Earth's Earliest Fossils: Princeton, New Jersey, Princeton University Press, 367 p.

Sharpe, T., and Clary, R.M., 2022, this volume, Henry de la Beche's pioneering paleoecological illustration, *Duria antiquior, in* Clary, R.M., Rosenberg, G.D., and Evans, D.C., eds., The Evolution of Paleontological Art: Geological Society of America Memoir 218, Chapter 6, https://doi.org/10.1130/2021.1218(06).

Stegner, W., 1992, Beyond the 100th Meridian: John Wesley Powell and the Second Opening of the West: New York, Penguin Books, 496 p.

Steno, N., 1667, *Canis Carchariae dissectum caput*, *in* Steno, N., Elementorum Myologiae Specimen: Florence, Italy, Stella, p. 90–110.

Wilton, A., and Barringer, T., 2002, American Sublime: Landscape Painting in the United States, 1820–1880: Princeton, New Jersey, Princeton University Press, 278 p.

MANUSCRIPT ACCEPTED BY THE SOCIETY 13 JANUARY 2021
MANUSCRIPT PUBLISHED ONLINE 29 NOVEMBER 2021

Printed in the USA